The New York Times

SUPERSIZED BOOK OF DAILY CROSSWORDS

Edited by Will Shortz and Eugene T. Maleska

ST. MARTIN'S GRIFFIN ☙ NEW YORK

ISBN 0-312-32836-2

First St. Martin's Griffin Edition: September 2003

10 9 8 7 6 5 4 3

The New York Times

SUPERSIZED BOOK OF DAILY CROSSWORDS

ACROSS

1. Homophone for a digit
4. "__ your lips . . .": Shak.
10. "Bonanza" character
14. Winery property
15. Undivided
16. Cry where Bacchus reigned
17. Kind of agent
19. Give up
20. Stronghold
21. Petty prince
23. Hounds' quarry
25. Egyptian goddess of fertility
26. Collected
29. Onetime P.M.
33. Have __ to pick
34. Lopez of Dallas
35. State west of Ga.
36. Baseball's Schoolboy __
37. Haley bestseller
38. Mine access
39. Blyth or Sheridan
40. Military force
41. Struck
42. Purplish blue or vice versa
44. Placed in storage
45. French department
46. To be, below the Border
48. Cite as an example
50. Double-deck card game
54. One of a Moslem people
55. Proletariat
58. Stigma
59. Exhibit
60. Daisy __ of Dogpatch
61. Glut
62. Sacred Jewish scrolls
63. Historic period

DOWN

1. ". . . three men in __"
2. Food usually tinned
3. Word attached to book
4. Arranged in rows
5. Call for repetition
6. __ with (agreeing)
7. Ullmann
8. Suffix denoting process
9. Iranians of the past
10. Feverish
11. Make less significant by comparison
12. Pop
13. Ooze out
18. A refrigerant
22. City on the Tanaro
24. Stanza
26. Miles or Bernhardt
27. Piano-key material
28. Destitute
30. Successes in show biz
31. Favored people
32. Estimated the worth of
34. Civil wrong
37. Short lyrical poem
38. Indifferent to right or wrong
40. Plane geom. figure
41. Attitudes
43. Curriculum unit
44. Laundry item
47. Part of a La Scala presentation
48. Hebrew prophet
49. Lady of Madrid
51. Identical
52. Absolute ruler
53. On the Yellow
56. Ab __ (from the start)
57. Personal pronoun in Köln

2

ACROSS
1. Masefield's "The ___ Wind"
5. Sixth-month heroes
9. Bankrolls, informally
13. Prefix with tank
14. Homeric work
16. Where to see tigers
17. U. of Maryland athlete
18. A DiMaggio
19. Romeo's last act
20. Calchas's daughter
22. She wrote "The Women's Room"
24. Cub reporter's brash question to a dowager
26. Life, in Lyon
27. Like Gable's chin
31. Pope John XXIII's "___ in Terris"
34. Hippodrome
36. English Channel feeder
37. Scent
38. Victimized by a con man
39. "Our Lady of ___": Swinburne
40. Beaked warship
41. Cliques
42. ___ Harry, Eastwood role
43. Muddle
45. Stat for Gossage
46. Dowager's reply to 24 Across
52. Porter
55. One who sits shivah
56. Ballet's Bruhn
57. Chew the scenery
59. She wrote "I'll Never Smile Again"

60. Sightless trio
61. Triangular letter
62. With: Fr.
63. Atramentous
64. Trotsky
65. Painter José Maria

DOWN
1. Usual gift for a retiree
2. Febrero follows it
3. Spread around
4. Cants
5. Great ___ (Rockies watershed)
6. Actress Valli
7. Money in Kuwait
8. Fox's relative
9. Rousing words
10. A ___ apple
11. Studio spinner
12. Frame for panes
15. Rebel's activity
21. Singer Whitman
23. "Tosca" locale
25. Noble English family
28. Role for Arnold Moss
29. Sartre's "No ___"
30. Gainsay
31. Hit the books
32. A first mate
33. What Brynner didn't need
34. In any way
35. Smuggle
38. Lost footing

39. Automatic music makers
41. Best seller by Robin Cook
42. Smith's opponents in 1928
44. Gin drink
45. Adjective for Vulcan's forge
47. St.-Cyr-l' ___
48. "Theirs ___ reason why": Tennyson
49. "___ Lucy"
50. More recent
51. Not slouching
52. Allies of Caesar in 57 B.C.
53. A Walton
54. Tess's bridegroom
58. Actor Ferrer

ACROSS
1. Service org.
4. Indian corn
9. Some of this is punk
13. Neutral color
14. Flâneur
15. Second Israeli ambassador to U.S.
16. Lyricist Asaf's advice in a 1915 song
19. Mayhew's "It's a Sin to __": 1936
20. Duke, for one
21. Harte
22. Trading center
24. A Ford who was born a King
27. Hari
28. Rudiments
31. Fish sauce
32. Carved shoe
33. "Bei __ Bist Du Schön"
34. Please with savory cuisine
38. Giants great Mel
39. "Let's Make __" (TV show)
40. Thousand Islands, e.g.
41. Model T contemporary
42. Lode or mood
43. Beribboned hat
45. West of Wis.
46. "The __ shall scorn pedantic laws": Scott
47. City known for its tapestries
50. Spar nearest the bow
54. Lewis-Young advice in a 1928 song
57. Taxman's claim
58. Nest found on a crag
59. Anatomical network
60. Alan or Robert
61. Stir
62. Former Estonian coins: Abbr.

DOWN
1. Zenith
2. Seed cover
3. Army's Doc Blanchard was one
4. Deceived
5. Own up
6. Nastase of tennis
7. Oriental cymbal
8. Homophone for heir
9. Send, as money
10. Item in a daily
11. Phone
12. Joint
13. Sum, es, __
17. Campbell or Sande
18. Layers
22. Normand of early films
23. At the summit
24. Jacksonville's Bowl
25. Type size
26. Opposed to verso
27. Noted U.S. naval historian
28. With strength
29. "Yes, please" in Bonn
30. Cockscomb
32. Seidel's relative
35. Extravagant
36. London hero
37. Kind of decision
43. Google of old comics
44. City on the Oka
45. Carta
46. He fell at the Alamo
47. Nazimova
48. ". . . I'll __ and brawl": Petruchio
49. Felt remorse
50. Spot encountered on a road
51. Mischa or Leopold
52. Ranks above cpl.
53. A brew in Calais
55. Surpass
56. August 1 baby, e.g.

4

ACROSS

1. Anagram for Elba
5. Cart
9. Bright fish
13. Heart's companion
14. Composure
15. Beverage ingredient
16. Rugby, in a Hughes book
19. Looked
20. Van Gogh lived here
21. Semirigid colloid
22. "__ like it hot . . ."
24. Adapted or adjusted
28. Clothes
31. Senate employee
32. __-propre
33. Tease
35. Toast accompaniment
39. Pro __
40. Proverb
41. Town on the IJsselmeer
42. Dietrich
44. Vessel groups
46. Adjunct for over or cover
47. Mauna __
48. "There Is Nothin' Like __," 1949 song
51. Ingress
56. Eddie Cantor hit: 1926
59. Organic compound
60. Sir Toby of "Twelfth Night"
61. __ Bator, Mongolian capital
62. British sandhill

63. Neb
64. Tanoan Indian

DOWN

1. Detective's pet in "The Thin Man"
2. Animated cartoon figure Betty
3. Portion of sugar
4. North Sea feeder
5. Wooden pin
6. Peel
7. Onager
8. "__, my darling daughter"
9. Pigments for Gainsborough
10. Certain stakes
11. Lily relative

12. "Laughing Cavalier" creator
14. Gazed earnestly
17. Fad
18. Judge's private room
22. Night sound
23. Egg-shaped ornament
24. Locality
25. Oda site
26. Iguana's relative
27. Shoat's home
28. Figure of speech
29. Word with wind or union
30. Memorable Mideastern leader
32. "For __ house is his castle": Coke

34. Spinel and peridot
36. Kind of proof or slave
37. Biographer Leon
38. Golf's Trevino
43. Meander
44. "To __ a pail of water"
45. Bird celebrated in "Cymbeline"
47. Aptitude
48. Not up
49. Unit of force
50. Ages untold
51. Fitzgerald
52. Touch upon
53. Shade of green
54. Crop
55. Ferber
57. Flow's partner
58. Nectar collector

ACROSS

1. Largest of seven
5. Role for Liz
9. Restraint
13. Al Hirt's companion
14. Its capital is Port-au-Prince
15. Blue dye
16. Sled dog
19. "— voyage!"
20. Not appropriate
21. Assail; plague
22. Phlegmatic fellow
23. One that deals in: Suffix
24. Part of the 49th state
32. Young horse
33. Diana's sister-in-law
34. Self: Comb. form
35. Garment for Mrs. O'Connor
36. Conduct a program: Colloq.
38. Brownish purple
39. Inner: Prefix
40. Tower in Genesis
41. Spoken
42. Westernmost North America
47. Time of the "darling buds"
48. A woodwind
49. Resource
52. Postsummer bloomer
54. "— Rhinestone Cowboy"
57. Feathered symbol at Juneau
60. Jai —
61. "— of vagabonds...": Shak.
62. Zip or area follower
63. System of exercise
64. Moist, as blossoms
65. Queeg's hands

DOWN

1. Melville's white-whale hunter
2. Alone
3. Qum's land
4. What a ques. expects
5. Eastern neighbor of the 49th state
6. Slack; soft
7. Coup d' —
8. Kind of field or man
9. Funt's source of fun
10. Ringling star who balanced on one finger
11. Bar mitzvah, e.g.
12. Disease of overripe fruit
14. Capital of Vietnam
17. Pleated wraparound tartan skirt
18. White poplar
22. Clever
23. Anglo-Saxon laborer
24. Lands; estate
25. Detached
26. Arm joint
27. Mother-of-pearl
28. Suffix with elephant
29. Pacific island republic
30. Princely
31. Monument pillar
36. Whirlpool
37. Chart
38. Do modeling
40. Muse of love poetry
43. Earhart
44. Public certifier
45. "Divertissement" composer
46. Standard
49. Not at home
50. Cylindrical bin
51. Dross of a metal
52. Basilica feature
53. Pack
54. Stravinsky
55. — in U.S.A.
56. Turn over — leaf
58. Soft plug
59. Fed. agency

6

ACROSS

1. Actor Sharif
5. Caesar, e.g.
10. Preacher's sign-off
14. Yield
15. Something to recite
16. Banker's advice
17. With 52 Across, epitaph for a smart aleck
20. Took a leisurely walk
21. Most exsuccous
22. Electrical units
23. Greek letters
24. "The __ a bucket of ashes": Sandburg
27. Rialto places
31. Peregrine
32. The staff of life
33. Fabulous bird
34. Feral
35. Like many a tasty cake
36. Hindu music
37. Mount __, Australia
38. Attachments on snells
39. He put his wife in a shell
40. Scatter
42. Toothsome
43. Future M.D.'s course
44. Noxious weed
45. Part of the Bahamas
48. Ruthian clouts
52. See 17 Across
54. "Let George __!"
55. Provide
56. Famed patentee's middle name
57. These may be loose or tight

58. Shipment from Bethlehem
59. Incline

DOWN

1. Memorable newspaper publisher
2. An assembling of huntsmen
3. Purim month
4. Had recourse (to)
5. Relieves
6. White House group
7. Lascivious
8. "Alas!" in Austria
9. Tie
10. Basketball statistic
11. This appears on a horse's neck
12. "__ Diary": Twain
13. Triton
18. U.S. designer
19. Musical chord
23. In which a queen is most powerful
24. Handled roughly
25. Point in a defendant's favor
26. Lapham or Marner
27. Three-wheeled vehicle
28. Sappho's inspirer
29. Jolly name
30. Like a fee-faw-fum
32. Give a leg up
35. Glacial deposits

36. Setback
38. Beautician's purchase
39. Porter's "You Don't Know __"
41. Body-shop supply
42. Anointer of Saul and David
44. Woman's small, round hat
45. __ one's time
46. Privy to
47. Marian of Sherwood Forest
48. Stash away
49. Top A.L. pitcher in 1926
50. PBS program
51. Nine inches
53. Powerful explosive

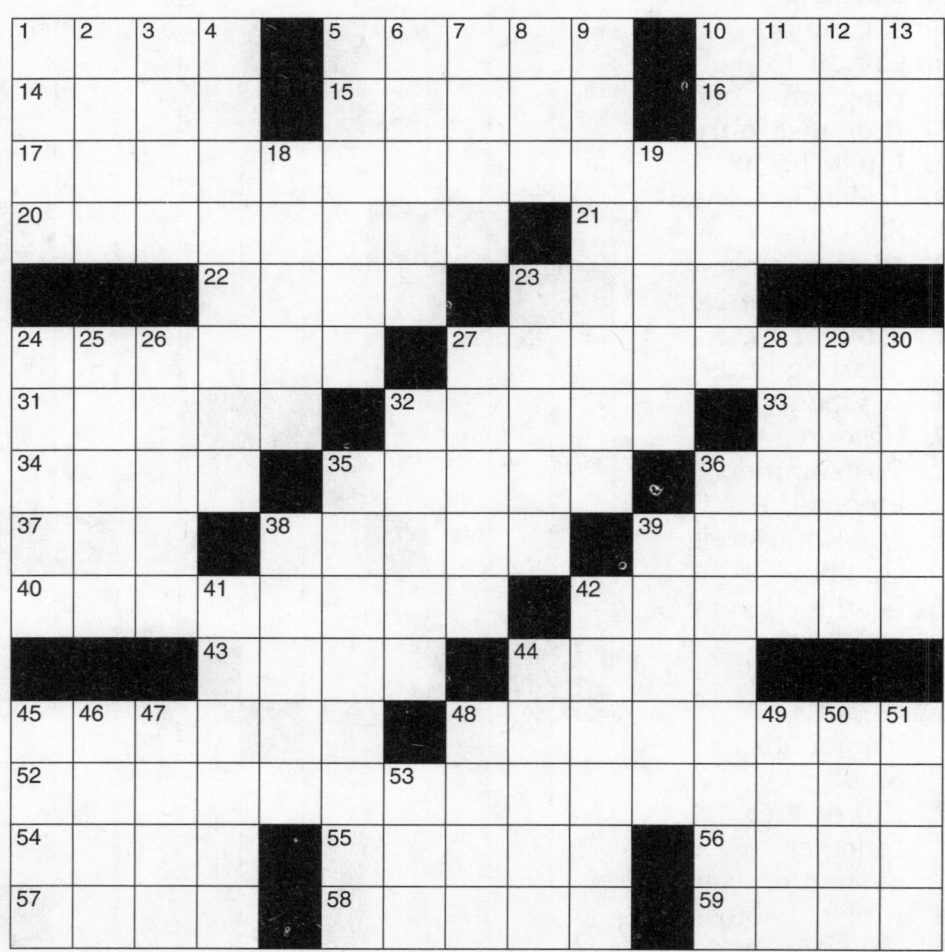

ACROSS

1. Hang about
6. Tub rub
10. Five-time Presidential candidate
14. Be devoted to
15. Medicinal plant
16. Quod __ demonstrandum
17. Assail
18. Old salt's tale
19. Author Gardner
20. "All the __ Men"
22. Pretense
23. Color of a fez
24. Group of four
26. Surprise for a bride-to-be
30. Mecca in summer
32. Doc and Hemingway
33. Museum workers
37. A son of Hera
38. Beat
39. Shortening
40. Shakespearean protagonist
42. Daughter of David
43. __ France
44. Comeback
45. Glistens
48. Bryant's "__ Waterfowl"
49. Engine knock
50. Cornfield figures
57. In __ (on a dull course)
58. Tom, Dick or Harry
59. Tumbledown shack
60. Game fish
61. Environs
62. Scottish capital, to poets
63. Paradise
64. Barber's question
65. Aussie songbird

DOWN

1. Luggage fastener
2. Frankfurt's river
3. Ballot
4. Historical periods
5. Calls it a day
6. Reacted to a full moon
7. Comedian King
8. Civil-suit basis
9. Blue __ (Delaware)
10. Informer, in 20 Across
11. Muffed fly, e.g.
12. Kon-Tiki material
13. War-horse
21. "__ Bingle" (Crosby)
25. Habitat: Prefix
26. Wrangle
27. Mata __
28. Oil cartel
29. Beat for Bernstein and Woodward
30. Misrepresent
31. They, in Torino
33. European fish
34. Sailors' patron
35. Hindmost
36. Type
38. Printer
41. Falstaff's drink
42. Plato, to Aristotle
44. Sterlet delicacy
45. Modern frontier
46. Took on hands
47. Habituate
48. Wine and dine
51. Solicitude
52. Author Comfort
53. Followed the hounds
54. "Amores" poet
55. Pursue one's way
56. Do in

8

ACROSS

1. Expunges
6. Well-known uncle
9. __ ben Adhem
13. Start of a Dickens title
14. Biblical prophet
16. Aaron or Raymond
17. Ice
18. Scarlett's place
19. Of the dawn
20. Berlioz work
23. Connective
24. Sin
25. Partner of tuck
26. Lerner-Loewe subject
32. Jump
36. Youth org.
37. Chopin specialty
38. Misbehave
40. Spasm
42. Drawing room
43. Glittered
44. Ethiopian prince
46. Robust
47. Rimsky-Korsakov aria in "Sadko"
51. Writer Anais __
52. Attention
53. Short swim
56. Copland score
60. Street sight
62. Powder
63. "__ say die"
64. Gelling agent
65. Dirk of yore
66. Concerning
67. Respighi's "Pini di __"
68. __ Passos
69. Ilks

DOWN

1. Russian villa
2. Allen of Ticonderoga
3. Scottish landowner
4. It, in Toledo
5. Dispenser of goods
6. Swift, for one
7. "End As __": Willingham
8. Violinist Erika
9. Cain's victim
10. Float
11. Handel opus: Abbr.
12. Coffeemaker
15. Bright fabric
21. Dull
22. Church parts
27. Scottish county
28. Deity featured in "Aida"
29. Large hall
30. Matinee __
31. Hawaiian goose
32. Maiden
33. Reverberate
34. Like __ of bricks
35. Sled
39. Hacienda hands
41. Chord sequences
45. Thailand's former name
48. Decrees
49. Opposite of maritime
50. Where the action is
53. Underwater man
54. Kind of sale
55. Boston and New York, e.g.
56. Student's concern
57. Syrian pound
58. Table spread
59. Foreign: Prefix
60. Sailor
61. Past

ACROSS

1. Did some carpentry
6. Actors' concerns
10. "__ She Sweet"
14. Star like Sills
16. Attic promenade
17. Army no-no
19. Kind of kick
20. Westminster judge's concern
21. Catches
22. Cry "Wolf!"
23. Tumult
24. Setting
27. Sharif
29. Corded fabric
31. Neighbor of R.I.
32. Islamic sect
34. "Eureka!"
35. Naive
38. Divinity-school deg.
39. Pay attention
40. Kind of duck
41. Gielgud's title
42. Unoriginal one
43. Warbucks
44. Some are common
46. Latin roll-call answer
49. W.W. I battle site
50. Bikini, for one
51. Wind dir.
54. Like many slum children
57. Wine bucket
58. Habitual
59. Cincinnati sluggers
60. Earl or duke
61. Runabout's relative

DOWN

1. Patio gear
2. River through Pisa
3. Mere handful
4. Bird that can't fly
5. What dilettantes do
6. Kitchen utensil
7. Reserved
8. Oklahoma city
9. __ Diego
10. Take __ at (try)
11. Traveled about
12. Fool
13. Hosiery shades
15. Copperfield's first wife
18. He took Rome: A.D. 410
22. Part of A.D.
23. "__ Street Blues"
24. Runs before the wind
25. Self-restraint
26. Concealed
28. Tone down
30. Rice field
32. Exports
33. Ease, in Paris
36. Carpenter, at times
37. Bede, of literature
43. He advocated "brinkmanship"
45. Customers
47. White-cliff territory
48. Skirt feature
49. Alaskan glacier
50. English composer
51. Old oath
52. __ precedent
53. British statesman
55. Domino spot
56. Prior to

10

ACROSS

1. Haberdashery stock
8. Gauchos' milieu
14. Native environment
15. Trattoria dish
16. Copy
17. Human being
18. Walter __ Mare (British poet)
19. Pairs or bridges
21. Biblical oldster
22. Supplement (with 23 Across)
23. See above
24. Add up
25. Bacon part
27. Feudal bigwigs
29. Napoleon won here in 1806
30. Show scorn toward
32. Sharks' fellow travelers
34. Chicle
35. It may move you
36. Clergymen
40. Island near Borneo
44. Woeful word
45. She wrote "A Certain Smile"
47. Ending with tire or irk
48. Dentist's rotary tool
49. Splash against
50. Capek classic
51. Came to rest
53. Spicy fruit
55. Ford's running mate in '76
56. Tapping sound
58. Virginia river
60. Cotton fabric
61. Hard rubber
62. Past, future et al.
63. Testified

DOWN

1. Faultfinders; nags
2. Baking dish
3. Where young Ike lived
4. "Ars longa, __ brevis"
5. __ loss for words
6. Makes lace
7. Do the town
8. Hippie apartments
9. Hollywood name
10. M. Marceau, for one
11. Hunting dog
12. City in Pennsylvania
13. Shut-eye sessions
15. One of the "harangue gang"
20. Sea bird
26. Manet's portraitist
27. Titled women
28. Most common dice throw
29. Naval hero: 1747–92
31. Motoring hazard
33. __ de mer
36. Broadway musical
37. Howl
38. River, town or bay in N.J.
39. Greet
40. Frolicked
41. Russian composer of "Prince Igor"
42. Rival
43. Tranquilized
46. Chatter
52. Headwear
53. Containers
54. Ruth or Zaharias
55. Nickname for singer Martin
57. Stalemate
59. Beverage

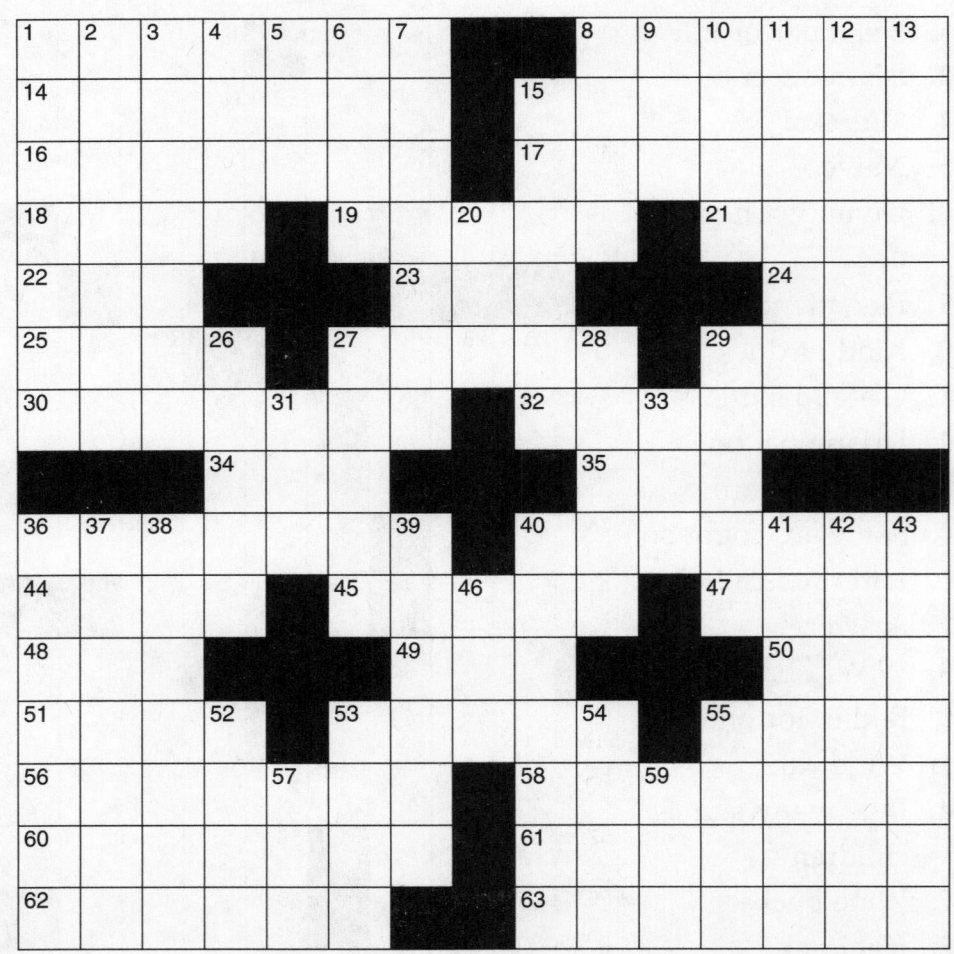

ACROSS

1. Kind of closet
6. Branch
10. Lucille's costar
14. Once upon —
15. Potentate in Arabia
16. Absorbed
17. Pilfer
18. Kind of rifle or pistol
20. Caesar's words re Cassius
22. First to draw the Democrats' mule
23. Covering on a Bernini creation
24. Eden
28. America or Liberty
29. Shun
30. Sound of a bullet or brat
32. Damage
35. Bird with a natural necklace
36. Snowshoe strap
37. Type size
38. Football player
39. Destroy by degrees
40. Popular garb
41. Sector
42. Pastor's people
43. Calorie
45. Please
47. Anthony's words re Brutus
53. Forbidding
54. Preach with passion
55. Canine star
56. Facility
57. Listings in a directory
58. Legumes
59. Ran
60. Ugly-weather factor

DOWN

1. Bills and coins
2. Feminine ending
3. Regimen
4. Asian nurse
5. Did an "inside job"
6. Some news sources
7. "— down to the seas again"
8. Baseball gear
9. In a moody mood
10. Shakespearean fare
11. Words to a dawdling diner
12. Variety, to life
13. Yen
19. Famed name in Oregon
21. Anagram for Ann
24. Hurricane's little sister
25. Bard of —
26. Cross
27. Clamor
28. Golconda
30. "Stop, steed!"
31. Bricklayer's burden
32. Kind of skirt
33. Performances
34. Heedless
36. Shakes
37. Golf score
39. Flynn of film fame
40. Clientele
41. Classic wanderer
42. Place for an orchestra
43. "— Foolish Things"
44. Seven: Comb. form
45. Horse or common
46. "Cómo está —?"
47. Snare
48. Ballet movement
49. Kind of test
50. Role for Russell and Lansbury
51. Fits to —
52. Cozy abode

12

ACROSS

1. Late Italian statesman
5. Wings for Amor
9. Hugh Capet, Louis XV et al.
13. Mighty mite
14. Stuffs
15. — Rubik, inventor of a cube
16. With 36 and 59 Across, parody on an adage
19. Famed astronomer: 1571–1630
20. Turkey in Asia
21. Let forth
23. Menilite
24. Some cocktails
28. Beloved of Verdi's Ernani
32. U.N. labor arm
33. Of birth
35. Place west of Nod
36. See 16 Across
40. Ancient strongbox
41. Singer John
42. A modern Caesar
43. Troutlike fish
46. Nondrafted soldier
48. Yegg's take
50. Famed round-the-world flier
51. Marginal note
55. "When I was —-twenty": Housman
59. See 16 Across
61. Fourth of HOMES
62. He wrote "The Hollow Men"
63. Director Clair
64. News
65. Cancel
66. Procyon, e.g.

DOWN

1. Lone Ranger's disguise
2. County in Neb.
3. Frolic
4. Short-order dish
5. Kennedy abbr.
6. Refrain strains
7. — acids
8. Emulate Harriet Tubman
9. Handgun
10. Russian grain center
11. Crucifix letters
12. Far East export to England
14. Resembling a keel
17. Child born on June 1
18. Catchall abbr.
22. What Ali held thrice
24. He had a golden touch
25. Clock adjunct
26. Philosopher Josiah: 1855–1916
27. One of the furs
29. That is, to Tiberius
30. Make new knots
31. Battery terminal
34. ". . . — dog bark!": Shak.
37. Defeated decisively
38. Retailer's jubilant sign
39. Marriages
44. "Welcome —," Altman film
45. No longer immaculate
47. Makeup mishaps
49. Tutu material
51. Twist
52. King mackerel
53. — apparent
54. Drudge
56. Mad as — hen
57. Barrie dog
58. He's a hue man
60. Darius III, to Alexander

ACROSS

1. Chem room
4. Steel-plow entrepreneur
9. Learning methods
14. Garb for Omar
15. Lumberjack
16. Super Bowl or World Series
17. Coiffure items
19. Aussie songbird
20. Promised the moon
21. Muffet morsel
22. Change from E.S.T. to D.S.T.
23. Like Warbucks
26. Apocalypse omen
28. Levy
29. G.I.'s first letter
30. Direction for Drake
33. Take ten
35. Blue-winged quacker
36. Jumbled mass
38. Cartesian graph line
40. Appease fully
41. Mute actor
42. Kitchen gadget
44. Type of herring
45. Bombeck
46. Some sighs
47. 18th Amendment foe
49. Model builder's material
51. City named "The Peace"
55. Away
56. Put into words
59. Fight a knight
61. Copper's persuader
62. Word with tube
63. Imbue
64. Postulate a flat world
65. Like Oscar Madison
66. Given medicine
67. Celebes, for one

DOWN

1. Dig trenches
2. Word with ground or board
3. Creatures in arms or woods
4. Sun, to Shelley
5. Montreal ballplayer
6. Author Ludwig
7. Cape Town dollar
8. Printers' measures
9. Network déjà vu
10. Yields to esurience
11. Plaything named for the 26th President
12. Sometimes it's bitter
13. Junior's room, often
18. Steep
21. Tricia or Archibald
23. Proverb
24. Bring glad tidings
25. Struck out
27. "Oedipus —"
28. Yellow streakers in Gotham
30. High points
31. She toys with the boys
32. Heaters' kin
34. Shaping machine
37. Hybrid garden flowers
39. Put in stitches
43. Passed the baton
46. Chemical ending
48. Apply a powder
50. Ingress
52. Dock supports
53. Cerulean shade
54. Savanna sight
56. Asti export
57. Auto pioneer
58. Inkling
59. Conrad's "Lord —"
60. "— man's meat . . ."
61. Pallet

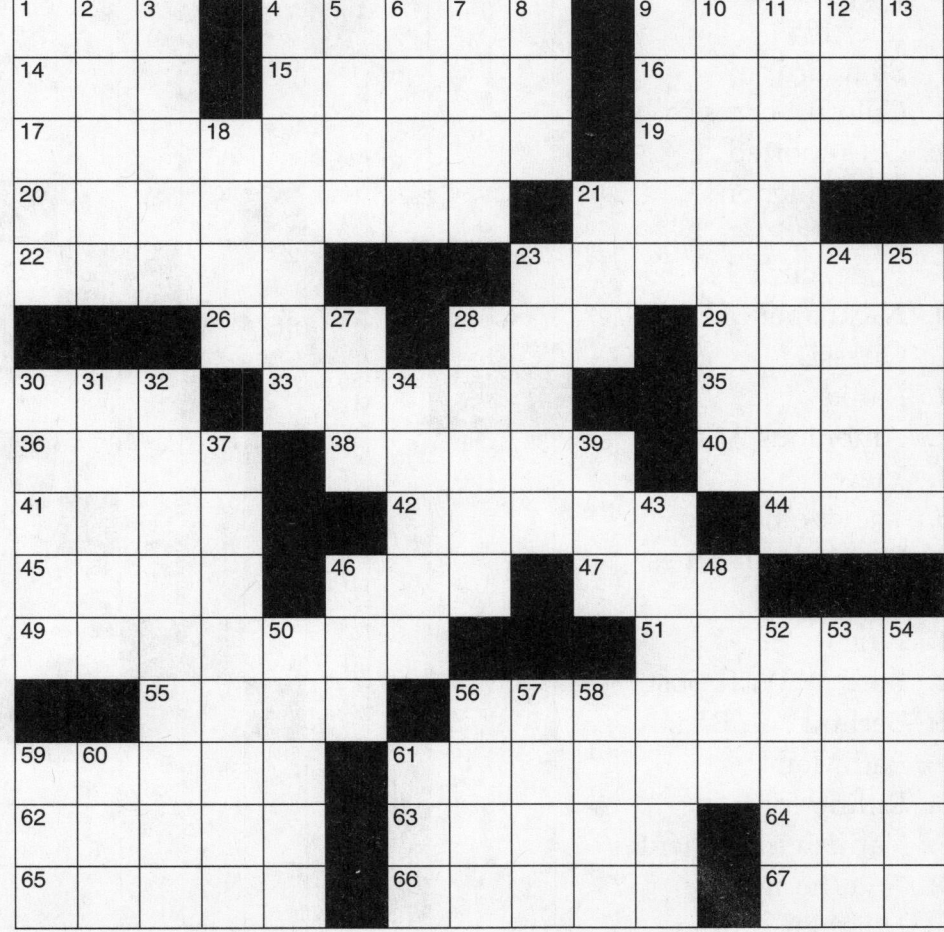

14

ACROSS

1. Aglets
5. Recipient of a McKinley message
11. ___ stump (perplexed)
14. Resuming activities
16. Pet's hold-out
17. Succeed, as plans
18. Word with type or horn
19. Drift along
20. Devilkin
21. Fumes
23. Page's "In ___ Virginia"
24. Mazel ___ (Hebrew congratulations)
26. Stowe's "dismal" tale: 1856
27. Standard
29. Colorful brassica
34. Oft-reported phenomenon
36. Revealed
37. Pope, circa 140–55
40. Nickname of Onassis
41. Ranks
42. Ambitious
44. View
45. They've been up
47. Steady with ropes at sea
51. Plugs
52. Ike's W.W. II post
54. Berlin's "___ Bad, Bad Man"
55. Riding for ___
57. Varnish ingredient
59. "Wuthering Heights" setting

61. ___ alai
62. Hard pressed
65. Summit: Comb. form
66. Causes
67. Crosses out
68. Partner of fits
69. Jewish month

DOWN

1. Home of some Wildcats
2. ___ Belvedere, Vatican statue
3. More risqué
4. Lop off, in Lanark
5. Lacuna
6. Disembark
7. Woolf's "Jacob's ___"
8. Moon's horn
9. Ending for Paul
10. Substance taken up in a lab
11. Like the late news
12. Similar set
13. Wheat "whiskers"
15. A tuneful twosome
22. Confer officially with a returned astronaut
25. Spanish gold
26. Cast a fly
28. "Annie" or "Evita"
30. Lament
31. Half of MDCCCII
32. Eur. land
33. Asner and Ames
35. Hydrants
37. Cushion
38. Japanese bay
39. To which some are kicked
40. Ampersand
43. Electees
44. Fast plane
46. Provide new actors
48. Ran amok
49. Hindu's ambrosial drink
50. A shepherd, originally
53. Prefix for potent
55. Greek hero
56. Confront
57. Etnean output
58. Dyer's device
60. Pelion's support
63. Cherry core
64. Collectors in Apr.

ACROSS

1. Town NE of Paris
5. Cures
10. __ of tears
14. Pisa's river
15. Islamic God
16. Rainbow
17. Old __ Village, Mass.
19. Refuge
20. Company's procedures expert
22. Owns
23. Citizen of Genoa: Abbr.
24. Fiery particle
27. Former rulers of Iran
29. What ff. means
32. River out of Pittsburgh
33. Ear bone
34. Muhammad __
35. Coded instructions for a modern machine
38. Like: Suffix
39. These fall in the fall
40. Passage
41. Above, to M. Arnold
42. Subdues
43. Pop
44. Poilu's weapon
45. Nourished
46. Electronic machines
53. Lawful
54. Absurd
55. Think-tank creation
56. Boys of old Rome
57. Bird that talks
58. Support
59. Urged, with "on"
60. Way out

DOWN

1. Girl
2. Like some mannerisms
3. Responsibility
4. Co-Nobelist in Chemistry: 1946
5. Damages
6. Site of ancient Olympic games
7. Director of "The Four Seasons": 1981
8. Gratuities
9. Scabbard makers
10. Kind of plastic
11. Atalanta's beloved
12. Tilt
13. Superlative ending
18. Bill
21. Rope
24. Kind of drama
25. "E.T. __ home"
26. To love, in Toulouse
27. Cover on a cruise
28. Nickname for Elwood P. Dowd's rabbit
29. Electrical unit
30. Swedish island
31. British tar
33. Boiler attachment
36. Extreme
37. Joyful
43. Arnaz
44. Perfume from roses
45. Smelly
46. Certain Easterner in the West
47. On the Marmora
48. Neighbor of Wash.
49. Part of t.l.c.
50. Cameo stone
51. Gypsy's wife
52. Blind part
53. Triangular sail

16

ACROSS

1. Job
6. Thesis
11. __ Gandolfo, Italy
12. Ready
14. Spendthrift
15. Young pig or chicken
17. Cuckoo
18. Food
20. Anger
21. Dog in "Peter Pan"
23. Backbone
24. Cousin of a beluga
25. One's pledged word
27. Explosive
28. Concorde's asset
29. Affecting the body generally
31. Hardens
32. Area above an earthquake's origin
34. Average
37. Facial décor
41. Take up and use
42. Allow
43. Mme. de __
44. Rampage
45. "... idle __": Tennyson
47. To be, in Orléans
48. Aurora, to Agamemnon
49. Ciceronian activity
51. Ad __ committee
52. Surgeons' threads
54. Einsteinium, e.g.

56. Moon goddess
57. Christeners
58. Music symbols
59. Jogs

DOWN

1. Las Vegas meccas
2. D.D.E.'s predecessor
3. Norwegian river
4. Hoedowns' kin
5. Ovate
6. Sire or dam
7. Solo
8. Map of a city
9. Curve shape

10. Pensioner, perhaps
11. Singer or color
13. __ gentle (trained male falcon)
14. Needs
16. Peruses
19. Pie filling
22. Try
24. Work
26. Liver: Comb. form
28. Cancels a deletion
30. One-thousandth of an inch
31. Abbrs. on 8 Down
33. Nourishing
34. Nostrils

35. Hateful
36. Morning "announcer"
38. Author Willa and family
39. Long-necked waders
40. Choose
42. Rental contracts
45. Council of __: 1545–63
46. Type of energy
49. Minerals
50. Verne captain
53. Diminutive suffix
55. Encountered

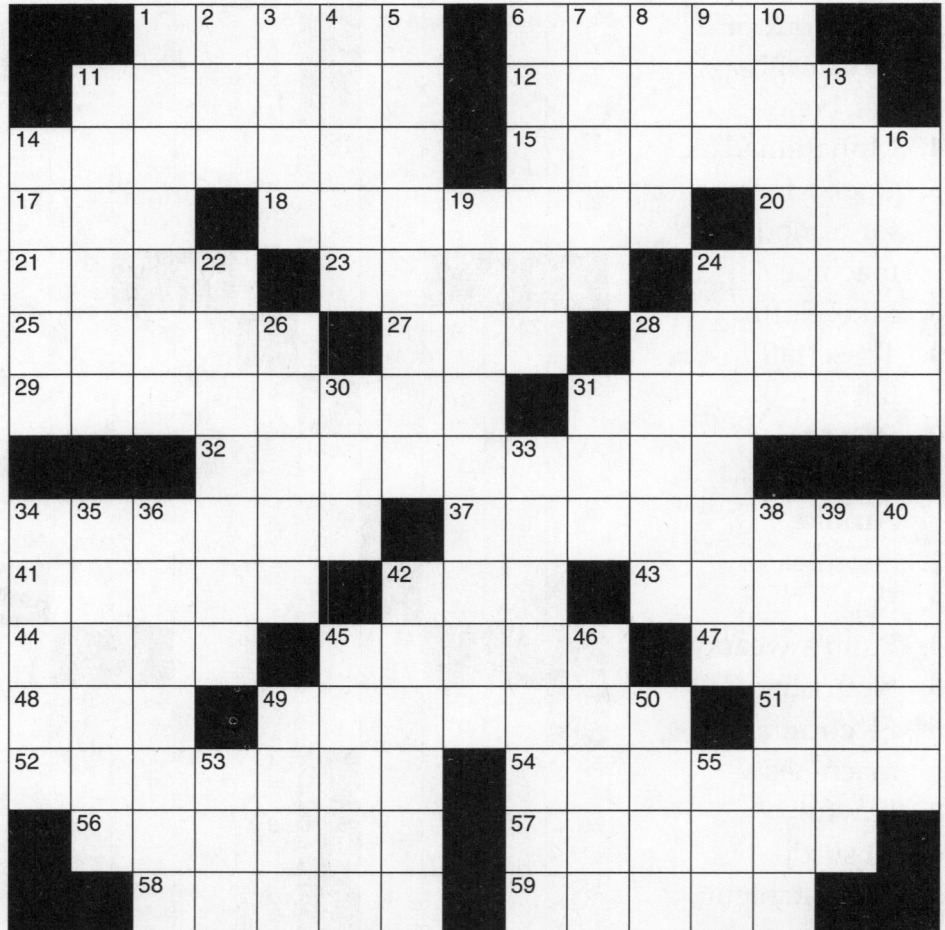

ACROSS

1. Colleen
5. Minor Moslem magistrate
9. "Hamlet" is one
13. Suffix with citron
14. Frank
15. Buenos __
17. Mine access
18. Olympic queen
19. Unsoiled
20. "De Rerum __": Lucretius
22. Pasteur portrayer
24. Start of an erudite barfly's lament at curfew
25. Hijack
26. Columbus, e.g.
28. Lament: Part II
33. Terminus
34. Some perfumes
35. Speedy
39. Clairvoyants
41. Happy __ clam
42. Nitrite is one
43. Lament: Part III
44. Cut out sweets
46. Field role
47. End of lament
50. Homer, the artist
53. Suffix for cash
54. "Fables in Slang" author
55. Out of port
57. Marketplaces
61. Alice the Goon's creator
63. K–P connection
65. Commotion
66. Gay city
67. Leo's home
68. Mrs. Battle's creator
69. Shopper's aid
70. "Auld Lang __"
71. File's partner

DOWN

1. Like Cassius
2. Caryl Chessman's portrayer
3. Skirt feature
4. Second-largest planet
5. Live together
6. Parrot
7. Skin: Comb.form
8. Begin
9. "Scarface" actor
10. West role
11. Alpine crest
12. Slangy assents
16. Koko's weapon
21. Rosters
23. N.J. five
27. Switch positions
28. Witty bit
29. "The __ Love," 1933 song
30. The same, to Seneca
31. Certain compartments in buildings
32. Caravan stopovers
36. Literary bell town
37. S.R.O. show prize
38. Tupelo or bay
40. Nash rivals
42. One of the Fords
44. Pairs
45. Leoncavallo's last opera
48. A Bordeaux wine
49. Babbler
50. Hornet
51. Perfect
52. Pola of silents
56. "More matter for _ morning": Shak.
58. "Nana" author
59. Tennis term
60. Drench
62. Loser to H.C.H.
64. She wrote "This Hunger"

18

ACROSS

1. Commanded
5. Haleakala's output
9. __ decision, bout outcome
14. Came to rest
15. "__ the Mood for Love"
16. Dryad, Muse or Nereid
17. Cleanse
18. Willfully destroyed
20. Activate
22. Prying device
23. Central point
24. Swift current of water
25. Kipling, to a Hindu
28. Thrilling moment at Belmont
32. Rare violin
33. Tackles Theismann
34. San Francisco's __ Hill
35. Like swamps
36. Winter jacket
37. Hair style
38. Ace
39. Heckles
40. "The Corn Is __"
41. In a sad way
43. "__ to bed . . ."
44. Moose relatives
45. Belgradian
47. Pang
49. Of a floral organ
53. Railroad dispatcher's record-keeping paper
55. Air: Comb. form
56. Repenter's activity
57. Buck or stag
58. Zola novel
59. Second-story men
60. Arm for Tommy Atkins
61. Movie or North follower

DOWN

1. Large bundle of hay
2. Arkin or King
3. Greg Louganis feat
4. Infinite time
5. Grayish-blue
6. Astound
7. Climber at Harvard
8. Tea __ crumpets
9. Chooses
10. Type of hedge
11. Be idle
12. Journey for Justinian
13. Bushy clump
19. Neighbor of Siberia
21. Much of Mongolia
24. Barkeep's ice
25. Greek isle
26. Kind of acid
27. Certain Moslem household
28. Bash
29. Construe
30. Edible mushroom
31. "__ and Ivory," 1982 hit song
33. Jibs, mizzens, etc.
36. Noted Australian statesman: 1815–96
37. Yemenis or Saudis
39. "My Heart __ to Daddy"
40. Microbe
42. Sea or strait near 19 Down
45. Commemorative slab
46. Devoured
47. Factual
48. Ex-Secretary of State
49. Do some ushering
50. Orderly
51. Writer Bontemps
52. Taradiddler
53. Strive
54. "__ Pinafore"

ACROSS

1. Very high mountains
5. Cancel, NASA-style
10. Below the __ (foul)
14. Dupe
15. Widow's inheritance
16. __ code
17. Medicinal plant
18. Former queen of Italy
19. Perjurer
20. Fast vehicle
23. Kitties
24. Large parrot
25. Per
28. Lickety-split
33. Toots __, memorable restaurateur
34. Large wading bird
35. Balmoral Castle's river
36. School of whales
37. Maude Adams was one
39. Eggs for Terence
40. Daughter of Cadmus
41. Gripper under Guidry
42. Dingle
43. Swiftness
45. Stanzas
47. Zip
48. "Utopia" author
49. Out-of-this-world tour
57. In the thick of
58. Uplift
59. Locale
60. Liturgy
61. Allude (to)
62. College in N.C.
63. Greek letters
64. Predictors
65. Depression

DOWN

1. Eastern rulers
2. Dilly
3. Fall clumsily
4. Surprising success
5. "__ Fideles"
6. Kin of machetes
7. Antiwar writer killed in action: 1918
8. "Madonna della Pietà" painter
9. Bounty hunters, e.g.
10. Song for Sinatra
11. Silkworm
12. Rawboned
13. Darnel
21. Mythical bird
22. Takes a sly look
25. A relish
26. Ring
27. An antiseptic
28. Get sidetracked
29. See 7 Down
30. Pagan gods
31. Embankment
32. Gives birth to a lamb
34. Let it stand
37. Land measures
38. Fast sailing vessels
42. Like __ lightning
44. Horatian creations
45. They're enrolled at polls
46. Do wrong
48. Rhythm
49. Swiss river
50. Discharge
51. Moreno or Gam
52. Skipper's command
53. Night spot
54. Anagram for "evil"
55. Collar for a scholar
56. Springtime event

20

ACROSS

1. S.A. snake
6. Seethe
10. Poison
14. Country byways
15. Division word
16. Wild goat
17. Whisper words of love
19. Mr. Strauss
20. Furtive
21. Went on horseback
22. BB, e.g.
24. Like a hive
25. Siamese
26. Roman magistrate
29. Leader of a singing group
33. Banishment
34. Court jester
35. Rambler or sweetbrier
36. Kittiwake
37. Thackeray's forte
38. Result of a gap in a tap
39. How otiose people spend time
40. Function
41. Aroma
42. Uneasy
44. Reasons; motives
45. Recipe verb
46. Fence picket
47. Respect
50. Where Callao is
51. Kentucky bluegrass
54. Castle for Fischer
55. Abélard-to-Héloise message
58. Body of Kaffir warriors
59. Sack; rifle
60. Tidal bore
61. Aforementioned
62. Finishes
63. Refuse

DOWN

1. Ecclesiastical garments
2. Bucket handle
3. Just
4. Country singer Tillis
5. Usually
6. Chicken
7. Single instance
8. Dancer Michio __
9. Means of evasion
10. Game accessory
11. First shepherd
12. Granular snow
13. Sign in a hospital
18. Word with cone or dive
23. Cob's locale
24. Copland ballet
25. Huxley's "__ Barren Leaves"
26. Norse god of the sea
27. Emit
28. Certain pickles
29. Loses ardor
30. Triangular insets
31. French factory
32. Clans
34. Jack the nipper
37. Introduction
41. Greeted
43. Sheltered side
44. Be concerned
46. Hides
47. Goddess of discord
48. Body, as opposed to soul
49. African antelope
50. Trudge
51. __ stick
52. Cather's "One of __"
53. Cutting tools
56. Charged atom
57. Women's org.

ACROSS

1. Camel's backbreaker
6. Traditional knowledge
10. Stimulate
13. Fragrance
14. High point
15. Auctioneer's word
16. Full
17. Instrument played by Clinton
19. Architectural space
21. Implanted
22. Winged
23. Deeds
24. Expose to public scorn
27. Unspoiled
31. Ills
32. __ Ventre, river in Wyo.
33. Receptacle
34. Facial feature
35. Refractor
36. Bee colony
37. Tail: Prefix
38. Frost
39. Astronomer, at times
40. Pattern of symptoms
43. Metallic element
44. Cowboy's item
45. Sugar island
46. Relaxed
49. Was contrite
53. Sunk
55. Sierra __
56. Portico for Plato
57. Actress Olin
58. Actor Jeremy
59. Mother Seton was one
60. Old Norse giant
61. First Sikh

DOWN

1. Pert talk
2. Rattle follower
3. Roster
4. Responsive
5. Duck walks
6. Kind of beam
7. October birthstone
8. Harrison or Stout
9. Action in a Blatty best seller
10. Metrical unit
11. Country singer Murray
12. Requirement
15. Revenant
18. Soup holders
20. Squeal or squealer
23. Sprang from
24. Class
25. Dentine of tuskers
26. Hoofed animal
27. Coach
28. Balearic island
29. New and strange
30. Make an effort
32. Sooty dirt
35. In the correct way
36. Tango's kin
39. A tapestry
41. Harold Pinter product
42. "Second Hand __," 1921 song
43. Chalice
45. Coniferous tree
46. A.A.A., for one
47. Ballerina's skirt
48. Black
49. "Myth of Hercules" painter
50. Elmer Fudd, e.g.
51. Sicilian resort
52. Escritoire
54. Jewel

22

ACROSS

1. Bridge wins
6. Wide-spouted pitcher
10. Realtors: Abbr.
14. Jeopardy
15. Pier support
16. "The cat's __!"
17. Hersey town
18. News report
19. Study closely, with "over"
20. Outdoor-advertising insider
23. Kind of session
24. Chimney, in Cottbus
25. Cipher
27. Valjean's escape routes
31. Made over
33. Writer Emily
34. Major or Minor predecessor
36. Rope fiber
39. Part of Ethiopia
41. "__ of King Arthur"
43. Houston athlete
44. __-majesté
46. Within: Comb. form
47. Island or festival
49. Flush
51. Wyo. city
53. Familiar with
55. Parseghian
56. Post-Martin Pan
62. Let out
64. To see, in Sedan
65. Itinerary
66. Partner of odds
67. Ending for kitchen

68. Jostle
69. W.W. II aircraft carrier
70. Wine leavings
71. Daytime TV dramas

DOWN

1. Marienbad et al.
2. Mother of Helen of Troy
3. Locale of a Flaherty film classic
4. Behave
5. More leisurely
6. "Beowulf" and "El Cid," e.g.
7. Loses freshness

8. Kind of sch.
9. Send back
10. Meas. of current
11. She wrote "Indiana"
12. Law, in Judaism
13. Won without one loss
21. Edition
22. End of a lasso
26. As one
27. Stadium for Mets
28. "I'm all __!"
29. N.M. missile range
30. Inveigle
32. Hash-house sign
35. Harsh chest sound
37. Der __ (Adenauer)
38. Boxer Spinks

40. Neckpiece for a Derby winner
42. King in Wilde's "Salomé"
45. Learned
48. It's said to broaden one
50. Accustoms
51. Rod feared by pitchers
52. Corrida site
54. Ganges sights
57. Dollar bill
58. __ contendere
59. Part of the Greater Antilles
60. Perched on
61. Network division
63. Recipe abbr.

ACROSS

1. Booth
6. __ Gatos, city in Calif.
9. TV's "The __ of Life"
14. Mushroom caps
15. High mountain
16. Type of committee
17. Up to the time of
18. Yellow-flowered plant
20. Interlinked series
22. British gun
23. __ et quarante, gambling game
24. Concorde, e.g.
25. Unfeeling
29. Luzon volcano
32. Hymns
33. __ non grata
36. Of the ear
37. Distant
38. Area
40. Barry of songdom
42. Tars
43. Unusual person
44. Sincere
45. Nourished
48. Graduates
50. Rainbowlike play of colors
52. What a pop song "never promised"
57. Scott hero
59. Cotton fabric
60. Organic compound
61. Lay an __ (bomb)
62. Lab burners
63. Guy
64. Observe
65. Acheson and Rusk

DOWN

1. Tater
2. Louise or Turner
3. High: Prefix
4. Flowery neckpieces
5. Emmy-winning comedienne
6. Negligence, to a judge
7. City in N.Y.
8. Abe at the rails
9. Devotee
10. Totals
11. Vouchers
12. Stereo owners' concerns
13. Fragrance
19. Close, to poets
21. Shank
25. Tax man: Abbr.
26. "Life is . . . not doing __": O. W. Holmes Jr.
27. Zhivago's love
28. Cousin of a campo
30. Star-shaped, as crystals
31. Navigational system
33. Huge hand
34. Title
35. Unreturned serves
37. "Except __ sake only": E. B. Browning
39. Explosive
41. Acquire knowledge
42. Emulated Roberta Flack
44. Finish a dive
45. __ mignon
46. Like some leaves
47. Pronouncements
49. Habit
51. Females
53. Surf sound
54. Actress Merrill
55. Dash
56. Loch __
58. Anger

ACROSS

1. Tea urn
8. Front foot of a dog
15. Characterized by strong feelings
16. Mother-of-pearl source
17. Moves quickly to and fro
18. Some compositions
19. Engage in: Suffix
20. Built
22. __ up (agitated)
23. Graceful movement
25. Some accounts
26. "__ In," Frost poem
27. Ria
29. Salt
30. Bobwhite
31. Struggled
33. Interweave
34. Rosebud, e.g.
35. Chirp
36. Glossy cloth
39. Coining fee
43. Improper
44. Football gadget
45. Large baskets, in Bilbao
46. Christian equivalent of Ramadan
47. Mangle
49. Some ships: Abbr.
50. S.A. nation
51. Embellishes
53. Gelderland city
54. "Fifty __ Frenchmen . . ."
56. Adjective for a Martian
58. Former Danish colony
59. Rut
60. Imposes, as a burden
61. Hemingway et al.

DOWN

1. South-side pews
2. "__ Grace," Anita Bryant book
3. Type of cherry
4. Mel of the Hall of Fame
5. Depraved
6. Prevent
7. Played musical chairs
8. Jet setter's cry?
9. Kin of English horns
10. South African coin
11. Note of note in crosswords
12. Pit
13. Lifelessness
14. Section of London
21. Attired
24. Most uptight
26. Four sights as "Hamlet" ends
28. Mah-jongg counters
30. Board game
32. Buddhist sect
33. Oolong, e.g.
35. Urgency
36. Deli purchases
37. "Beautiful" place
38. Felt excitement
39. Honey bunch
40. Moon goddess
41. Like some heraldic animals
42. Ancient ascetics
44. Current styles
47. Having a natural bent
48. Mister in Jaén
51. Radio tuner
52. Avoid
55. Deg. given to Betty Ford
57. Ouray was one

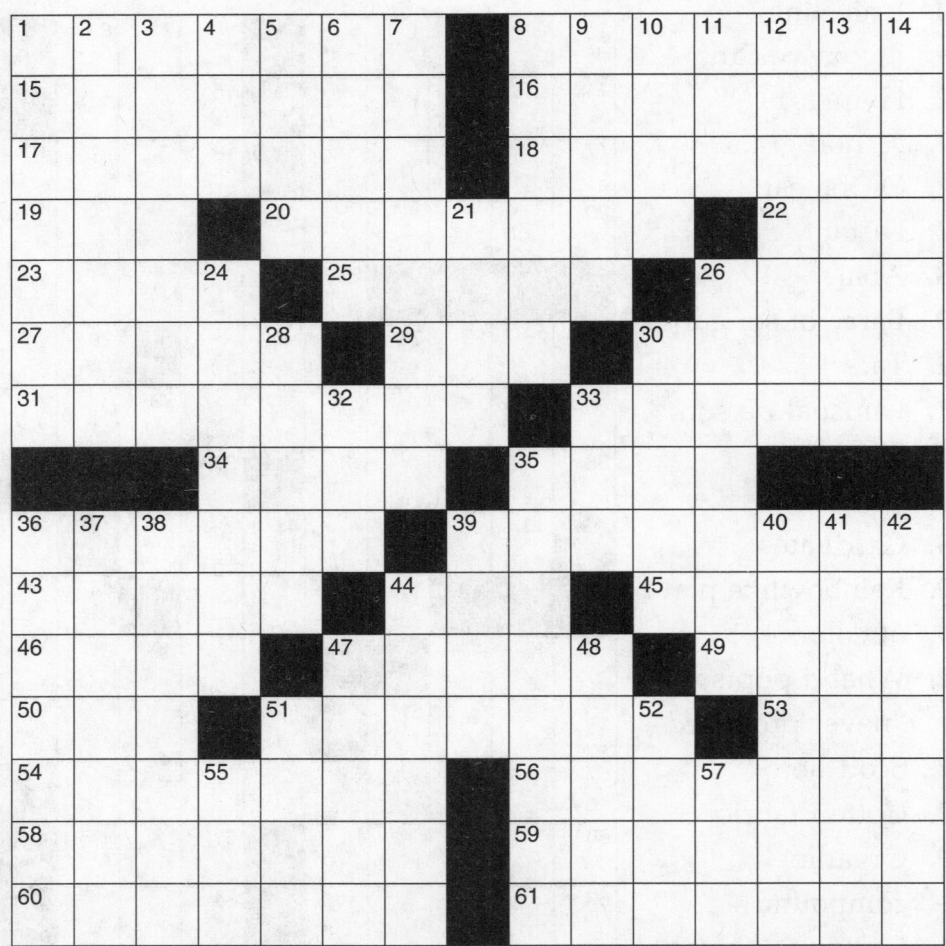

ACROSS

1. Obscures
5. Won
8. N.D.'s largest city
13. Plant of the lily family
14. Southern constellation
16. Marketplace
17. Bairn
18. Beatles' meter maid
19. Pardon or slacken
20. "Leave __," variation on 37 Across
23. Concept, to Camus
24. Stowe book
25. Fraud
28. Dutch city
29. Open a bit
33. "__ Give You Anything . . ."
34. Stocky person
36. Darling stat.
37. "Leave __," Delphic advice to Polycrates
40. Carol __, cover girl
41. Type of croquet
42. __ hand (helped out)
43. Dame Myra: 1890–1965
45. Swine genus
46. Golfer Gary
47. Canal for Sal
49. Kind of pearl
50. "Leave __," variation on 37 Across
56. Trunk vessel
57. Coagulate
58. Overlay
59. One of a laundry duo
60. Organic compound
61. __ bien
62. Roofers' tools
63. Pongid
64. Went under

DOWN

1. Bambi, e.g.
2. Dieter's spread
3. Small antelopes
4. Conscious
5. Attic
6. Suppose
7. Costume for Coppélia
8. Denmark's __ Islands
9. Committee's program
10. "Tony __," Sinatra film
11. Grating
12. Pilcorn
15. Saharan sight
21. Type of computer program
22. Negotiate
25. Alice's cat
26. Place for un maître
27. Trouters' specialties
28. Shaffer hit play
30. Jackass's mate
31. Alpine feature
32. Detection device
34. Continuous series
35. Kind of pass
38. Polite refusal
39. Espouses again
44. Small sofa
46. Mortar's partner
48. Builds
49. Pry
50. Ibsen's "doll"
51. Gemsbok
52. Radius's companion
53. City E of Osaka
54. 50-50
55. Lectern
56. Carpenter's tool

26

ACROSS
1. Easy fly ball
6. Tiff
10. Battle
14. Rub out
15. A first name in whodunits
16. Midler film, with "The"
17. Carl Lewis is one
18. "__ creature was . . ."
19. "Belvedere of Sicily"
20. Generous
22. German dam
23. Jerk-test joint
24. Escorts
26. Docked, as hair
30. __ magna, prelate's vestment
32. Heraldic band
33. Poufs' kin
35. "What's in __?"
39. Amble
41. Edwin Moses is one
43. Show contempt
44. Unsettled
46. Zest
47. Not so many
49. Until this time
51. Folly
54. Pathological suffix
56. With, in Paris
57. Generous
63. Mechanical repetition
64. Adriatic wind
65. Musical-scale inventor

66. Moon crater
67. Catchall abbr.
68. Join
69. Grouse house
70. Spouse of a knight
71. Pitiless

DOWN
1. Pisan's pear
2. Nuncupative
3. Covenant
4. Addict
5. Wig of yore
6. Sound judgment
7. Screen or shield
8. Choir voices
9. Spode item
10. Generous

11. Heavy-stroked script
12. Actor from Kansas City
13. "The __ at the spring": Browning
21. French department or river
25. Bandy words
26. Office bigwig
27. Algerian seaport
28. Cerulean
29. Generous
31. Court star in the 70's
34. Indonesian island group
36. Actress Nazimova

37. Gist
38. Petrel's cousin
40. __ bien
42. Free
45. Plan
48. Like a water shrew's feet
50. Orange and Indian
51. Rank below viscount
52. Call forth
53. Huguenots' heads
55. Cleavable rock
58. Smallest Greek letter
59. Peewee
60. Yugoslav hero
61. Original sin site
62. Sturdy boat

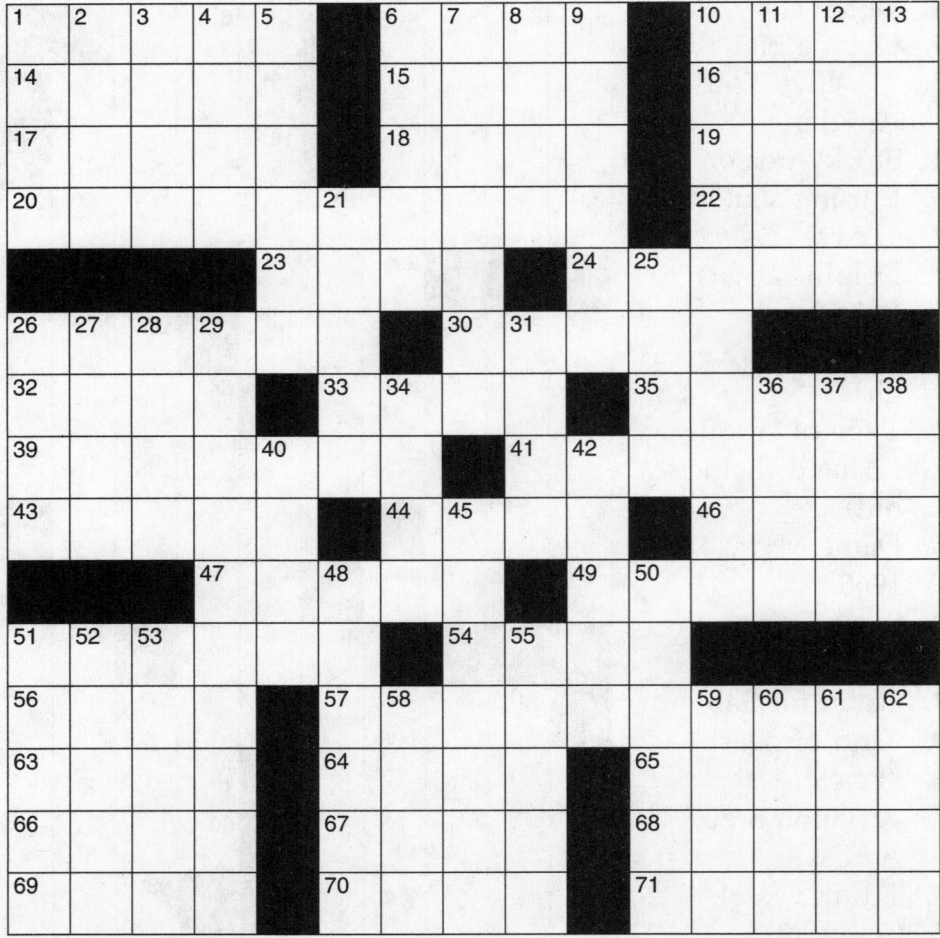

ACROSS

1. Counterpart of fraternal
8. Idle chatter
15. Run-of-the-mill
16. Raise
17. Threatens
18. Guided
19. Blab
20. Purvey
22. Anger
23. Kind of duck
24. Candle
25. More than some
26. Opposite of hiver
27. Hen
28. Curriculum __
29. Renovates
31. Highway havens
32. Exclamation of disgust
33. Quote
34. Treats a violin bow
37. Live with
41. A constellation
42. Fathered
43. Word with power or handle
44. Tend
45. Certain sports events
46. Ste. Jeanne __
47. Kind of salad
48. Bjorn Borg, for one
49. __ voce
50. Cracker
52. Tire type
54. Edited critically
55. Mistake indication
56. Antigone and Ismene
57. Wishes

DOWN

1. Wall ornament
2. Yielded to esurience
3. Appoints anew
4. Speak pompously
5. Dash
6. Mature
7. Haitian seaport
8. Badger
9. Tailor
10. Salacious look
11. Map abbr.
12. Statistics term
13. "Love is __," I. Stone book
14. Rock bass and rudd
21. Imitates
24. Bakery items
25. Liturgical headdress
27. Advances made by bankers
28. Performed a civic duty
30. True's partner
31. What an odometer measures
33. At bay
34. Abu Simbel figure
35. Oriental art
36. Kind of bar
37. What some are fit to be
38. Olympics competitor
39. Steak order
40. Does a cryptographer's job
42. Exceeds 55
45. One of the English gentry
46. Back: Comb. form
48. Kind of walk or wall
49. Stops on a RR
51. Trinitrotoluene, for short
53. Poetic palindrome

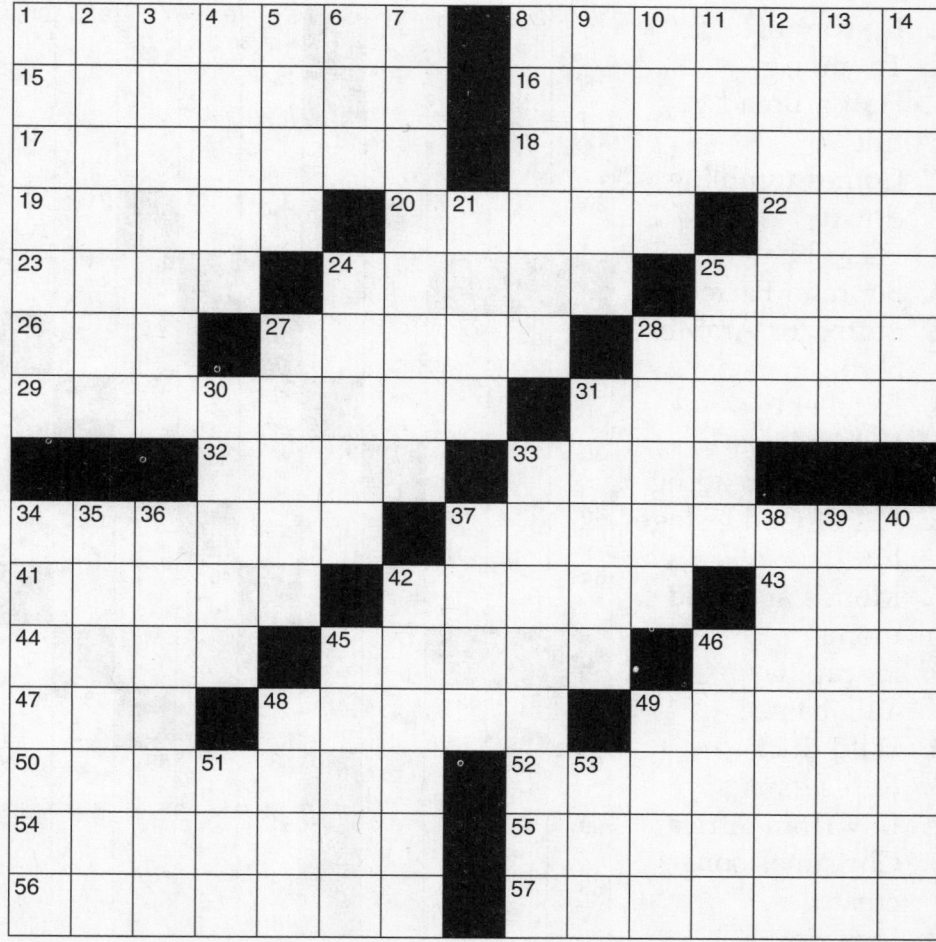

28

ACROSS

1. D.A.'s aide
5. Radarscope signals
10. Area over an eye or eyes
14. Chopped cabbage
15. "And thus shall ye __": Exod.
16. Papal court
17. Categorize
19. Swan genus
20. Jehu
21. Diamond birds
23. Asian holiday
24. Behalf
25. Pleases a glutton
28. In medias __
29. Part of a jack-in-the-green
33. Good motor sound
34. By way of
35. Teach, e.g.
36. Half a Broadway title
37. Comes tumbling down
39. Flax fibers
40. Soprano Farrell
42. Suffix for Arab or Serb
43. Excellent
44. Kind of heat
45. Med.-test reading
46. "__ of God," stage hit
47. Mom's and Dad's moms
49. Its cap. is Tallahassee
50. Wild duck
53. Rap sessions?
57. Lily from Africa
58. Christmas-song creature
60. Incision

61. "Paradise Lost" figure
62. Foil's kin
63. Their teeth are scarce
64. Cleans a meerschaum
65. Millstone support

DOWN

1. Nile menaces
2. Pink item
3. Emerson, e.g.
4. Stereo component
5. He wrote "Western Star"
6. "Waiting for Godot" actor
7. Assassinated Japanese statesman
8. Guides
9. Anagram for trees
10. Chick's pad
11. Wad's relative
12. County in Neb.
13. __ of the Roses
18. Pindaric pieces
22. Medical comb. form
24. Oyster catchers
25. People of intelligence
26. Partner of visual
27. Sing lustily
28. Sunder
30. "Cry, the Beloved Country" author
31. Redeem oneself
32. English writer-critic: 1817–78

34. Director __ Stroheim
35. Female swan
37. "O __, addio," Verdi aria
38. Pool stroke
41. Bald nestlings
43. Take __ (glim)
45. Last
46. Wings on an avis
48. Pianist Rubinstein from Poland
49. Drops a bay
50. Beer ingredient
51. Auk genus
52. Kind of cloth
53. Contain
54. Ape
55. Deadlocked
56. Source; origin
59. Ebro estuary

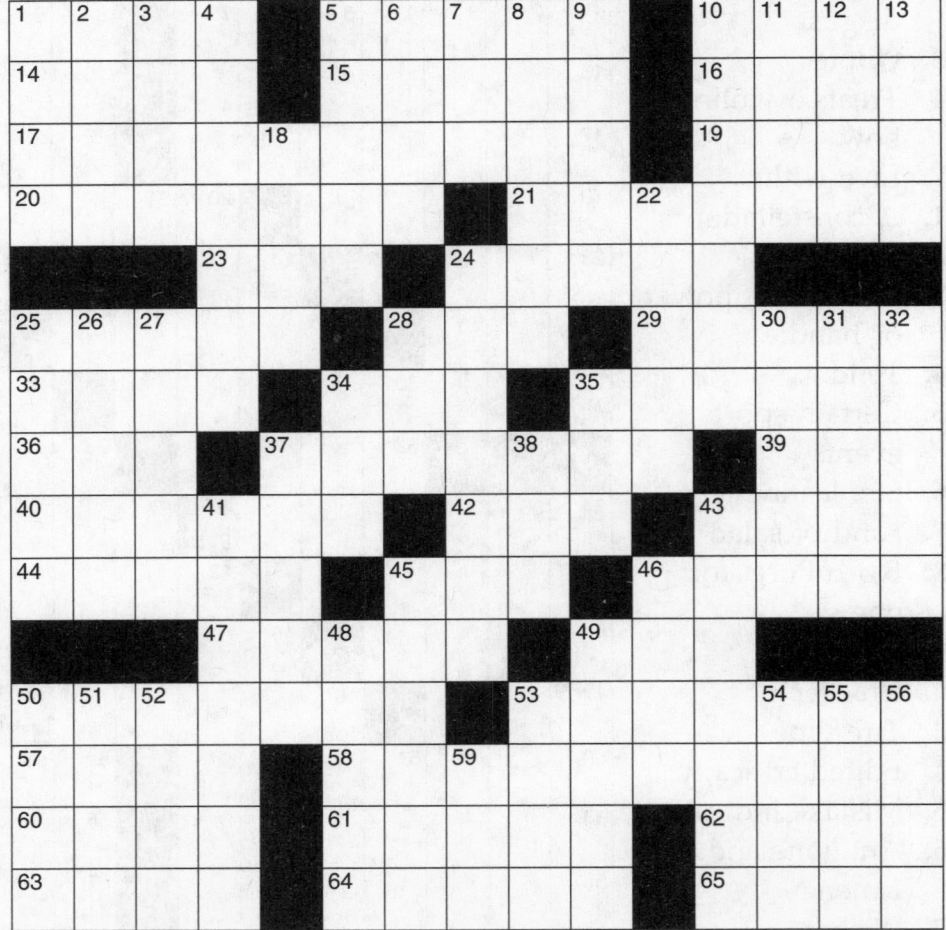

ACROSS

1. Lima locale
5. Asp
10. Coin eater
14. He was Terrible
15. Sawlike organ
16. Item in Caesar's closet
17. — an ear (heed)
18. Ship's upward heaving
19. Middle East gulf
20. Crossword-puzzle fodder
23. Grade
24. Baseball stat.
25. Until now
28. Ave. crossings, sometimes
31. Type of orange
35. Betsey —, Dickens character
36. Organic compound
38. Part of R.S.V.P.
39. More of 20 Across
42. Jailbird
43. Transported horses, e.g.
44. Nothingness
45. Supply
47. Image: Comb. form
48. Mercator work
49. Fla.–Ore. dir.
51. Top sound
53. Still more of 20 Across
61. Tabula —
62. Quaker gray
63. In a line
64. Squirrel gatherings
65. Peddles
66. Kind of clock or bomb
67. Siouan Indian
68. Do a pupil's chore up front
69. Belgian river

DOWN

1. Stack
2. Always
3. Indian princess
4. Like some collegians
5. Have-not's need
6. Waning, as the moon
7. Zwei chaser
8. Former lightweight champ
9. Speeder's trapper
10. "A — Born"
11. N.J. city
12. Curved molding
13. Beach sights
21. Corn unit
22. "Christ Stopped at —"
25. Comet's milieu
26. Synthetic fabric
27. Ogre
29. Wee
30. Butterworts
32. ". . . — upon thine heart": Song of Solomon
33. Rita Hayworth role
34. Hebrew prophet
36. — carte
37. City off.
40. Happening
41. Plea
46. Malaise
48. River island
50. Stagger
52. Kelso or Alsab
53. River to the Ligurian Sea
54. Tense
55. This, in Toledo
56. Bakery worker
57. Singer Turner
58. "Exodus" author
59. Library item
60. Pitcher

30

ACROSS

1. Boiler product
6. "The —," play by Aristophanes
11. Commando
13. Moves stealthily
15. Hairy
16. Eightfold
17. Freer display at D.C.
18. Comments
20. A source of rubber
21. Tailless amphibian
23. Certain palms
24. Luge
25. Cahn output
27. Atl. City marker
28. Hon
29. Seamstress's utensil
32. Former republic of NE Africa
33. They, in Paris
34. Useless but costly object
41. Gleamed
42. Actor Chaney
43. Work translated by Pope
45. Sagacious
46. Chart again
48. In — (wholly)
49. Triple this for a wine
50. Cuddly
52. Heat unit, for short
53. Abstract
55. British motor trucks
57. Figure on Louisiana's seal
58. Gourmet's cousin
59. Amber is one
60. Coal beds

DOWN

1. Saddle appendage
2. Richly embellished ice cream
3. Sounds of hesitation
4. River between Manchuria and Russia
5. Allots
6. Candle fibers
7. Some are co-ops
8. Alphabetic trio
9. Demotic
10. Late British movie star
11. Part of an arrow
12. Stay
13. Muscular
14. Unkempt
19. Highly excited
22. Authentic
24. Seasoning obtained by evaporation
26. Ray
28. Territory in N India
30. Spleen
31. Roof angle
34. Susurrus
35. Antagonistic
36. Ace, as part of a blackjack
37. Hill in the Southwest
38. Make possible
39. Element used in alloy steels
40. Shreds
41. Long oar
44. Drench
46. Kind of numeral
47. Drops heavily
50. Sites: Abbr.
51. O'Neill's — Smith
54. Las' followers
56. Bldg. in Rockefeller Center

ACROSS

1. Pitch indicator
5. Daughter of William the Conqueror
10. London's Albert __
14. Emulate the good doctor
15. Gardener in spring
16. Nichols hero
17. With 57 Across, mason's lament
20. Recreation centers
21. Queen Gertrude's son
22. Grant obtained by Hollywood
23. In person
24. Leyte neighbor
27. Steeplejacks, at times
31. Antarctic cape
32. Gay deceiver
33. Australian honey possum
34. Small ape
35. Billet-doux opener
38. Norris Dam org.
39. Amazon dolphin genus
41. Something bankers lean on
42. Arabian prince
44. Mason's material
46. Jerks
47. Ambassadorial asset
48. Holier-__-thou
50. Quit
53. When the lunch bunch munch

57. See 17 across
59. Sorrel's kin
60. Shopper's concern
61. Leave Logan
62. Sounds of disapproval
63. Snake genus
64. Laurel bestowed on Hollywood

DOWN

1. Modish
2. Woman in a Yeats poem
3. Make one's salt
4. A caboose preceder
5. Role for Walters
6. Soft and fluffy
7. Mas that say "maa"
8. Wimbledon call
9. D.C. building
10. Sam Spade's creator
11. Former labor leader
12. Verse
13. A Balt
18. Came closer
19. Chalet feature
23. Compare
24. Franks' __ law
25. "A Bell for __"
26. S.F. Bay county
27. Street show
28. Horner or Sprat
29. Split

30. Top bananas
32. "Pajama Game" actor
36. Optional course
37. Lessee
40. They outshout words
43. Coaches
45. Harum-scarum
48. Do some sums
49. Fire-engine gear
50. Tapered tuck
51. Biblical oldster
52. Neb. neighbor
53. V. Lopez theme song
54. Monogram pt.
55. Cartouche
56. Place west of Nod
58. N.T. book

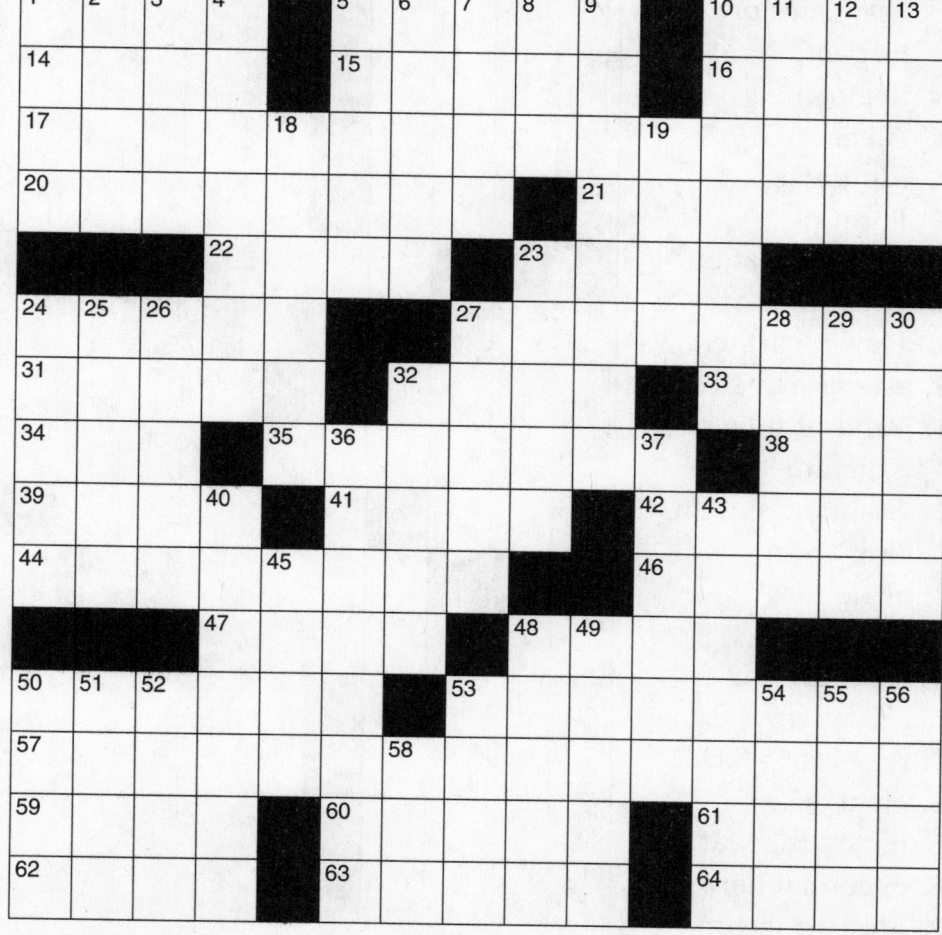

32

ACROSS

1. St. Peter has one at St. Peter's
5. Domesticates
10. Ashen
14. Indigo
15. Endure
16. African river
17. Item in a corset or a collar
18. Oregon or Santa Fe
19. G.I.'s ration in W.W. II
20. Short wave?
21. Actress Anouk —
22. Ornamental pattern, in art
23. An appetizer
26. Distillates of turpentine
29. Regimen
30. A.k.a.
31. Río de la —
33. Form of communication?
36. An entree
39. Haw's partner
40. Aerial maneuvers
41. Kind of tube or sanctum
42. Stimulates, with "up"
43. Staid
44. A dessert
49. Homer's "Odyssey," e.g.
50. "__ war": F.D.R.
51. Spar
55. Enjoy the warmth
56. Stendhal hero
57. Pizarro victim
58. Corner
59. Type of sodium carbonate
60. Glacial ridges
61. Rumpus
62. Mexican gentleman
63. Zola's courtesan

DOWN

1. Metal fastener
2. Stake
3. Ananias, e.g.
4. Greek god
5. A Turkic-speaking people
6. Shelters, in Savoie
7. City in Dade County
8. Widow of Ernie Kovacs
9. Variety of gypsum
10. Tailor's inserted piece
11. Drive off
12. Tex. shrine
13. Middle Eastern republic
24. Stores grain
25. More crumbly or powdery
26. Reckless
27. Ancient leather flask
28. Thailand, formerly
31. Morning star
32. Prune
33. Alcohol burner
34. Printer's mark
35. Marquette was one
37. Specious reasoners
38. Poem by Keats
42. Harvester of a kind
43. Like a stone pillar
44. I.o.u.'s
45. Separated
46. Japanese-American
47. Older brother of Moses
48. Mem. of a pool
52. Handle for Hadrian
53. Scrutinize
54. Scarlett's home

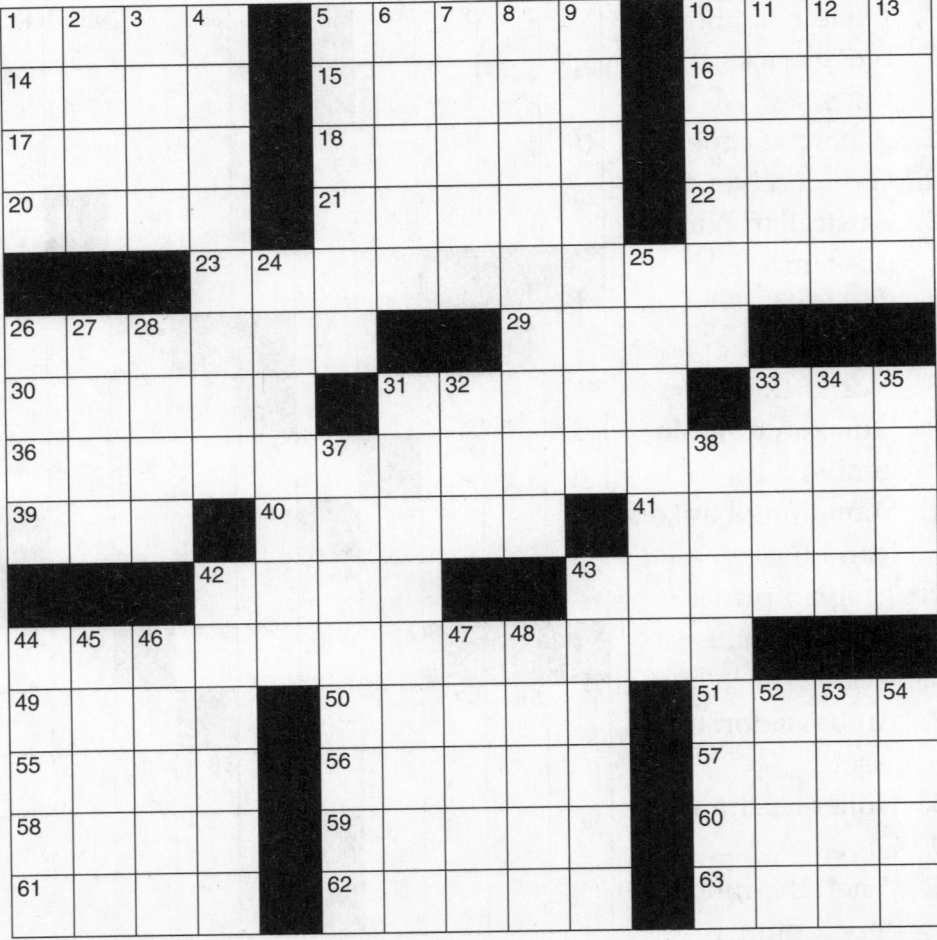

ACROSS

1. _ Major
5. In excess
10. _ mater
14. Get one's goat
15. Danger
16. Roulette bet at Monte Carlo
17. Expensive
18. Loathsome
20. Not important
22. Patterns
23. Soapstone
24. Assign by measure
25. Clean up
28. Decry
32. Metallic element
33. Italian province
35. Old horse
36. Old horses
38. Cheer in Cuernavaca
39. Low point
41. Goddess of dawn
42. Woolen fabric
45. Certain
46. Plausible
48. Writer Ortega y _
50. Other
51. Evergreen
52. Queen Anne's lace, e.g.
55. Containers for lubricants
59. Strong aversion
61. Chamber-music ensemble
62. Comic-strip hero
63. Ordinary
64. Elbe feeder
65. Blackthorn
66. Untidy
67. Depression

DOWN

1. An Indic language
2. Nothing, in Nice
3. Eastern European
4. Making effervescent
5. Shoulder ornament
6. Mediterranean sailing ship
7. Trampled
8. Edge
9. Nourishment
10. Garland
11. Ear part
12. Factory
13. God of war
19. Brainstorm
21. Resinous substance
24. Sapper
25. Pan's appurtenances
26. Lowest deck
27. "To a _" Burns poem
28. Greek island
29. A southern constellation
30. A neighbor of Sudan
31. Plumed heron
34. Picaroon
37. Mariner
40. Made a statement
43. Quack medicine
44. With legerity
47. Former Yankee
49. Computer gate
51. Type sizes
52. Broadway musical
53. Explorer Tasman
54. Flow: Comb. form
55. Burden
56. Exhort
57. Deportment
58. Separate carefully
60. Compass dir.

34

ACROSS

1. Joke
5. L.A. plague
9. Censor
12. Arm bone
13. Kind of boat or buoy
14. Prefix for stock or horn
16. Memorable name in fashion
17. Knowledge, for short
18. Thrust
19. Gape
20. Turn right
21. Peelers
22. Command re an option
25. Semihard, light yellow cheese
27. Mine product
28. Oriental nurses
29. Adages
31. German earth
35. Command re an option
38. Chemical suffixes
39. French ones
40. One who ties shoes
41. Stop on the RR
42. Civil
43. Command re an option
49. Incarnation
50. Bolivian export
51. Japanese aborigine
54. Full of grooves, as a road
55. Small lake
56. Adolescent

57. Certain Swiss paintings
58. Three wise men
59. Author Bagnold
60. Schedule abbr.
61. Dele's opposite
62. W.W. II town

DOWN

1. Punch's partner
2. Lamb
3. Raindrop's cousin
4. Discolors
5. Insult
6. Actor from N.Y.C.: 1939–76
7. Bid
8. Earthy prefix
9. Words on a book jacket
10. Asphyxia
11. Pola of silents
14. Winged
15. Aerie
21. Pocketbook
23. Mexican's enthusiastic affirmative
24. Monks' hoods
25. London gallery
26. "__ Old Cowhand"
29. Radar's kin
30. Exist
31. Rates

32. Donee
33. Regimen
34. To be, in Lyon
36. Private instructor
37. "Thanks __!"
41. Neuters
42. Critic
43. Urban oasis
44. Palate section
45. Spud
46. Speak
47. Ermine in summer
48. Fastener
52. Armstrong or Diamond
53. Ruin
55. Aft. periods

ACROSS

1. Culinary conglomeration
5. Indian state
10. Additions to ltrs.
13. Moslem deity
15. Its capital is Valletta
16. Inlet
17. Dough
18. Violently
19. Pt. or qt.
20. Time period
21. Steno's words of rejection?
23. Repeatedly, to Milton
25. Kind of neckline
26. River to the Ubangi
27. Phrase for a touring stripper?
31. Ancient, in poesy
32. Exist
33. Actor Mischa
34. Hosp. group
35. A sail
37. Acts properly
41. Suffix with musket
42. Disburden
43. Lunched
44. This may be hard to swallow
47. Like a happy medium?
49. Ship with a golden cargo
50. Suburb of Liége
51. __ Anne de Beaupré
52. Substitute dentist's activity?
55. "__, thou art sick!": Blake
59. Summer, to Zola
60. Lovable marsupial
61. German pronoun
62. Painter __ Borch
63. Ethyl acetate
64. Auld Clootie, in Dundee
65. Parts of a cen.
66. Unkempt
67. Erudition

DOWN

1. Some actors
2. Unbalanced
3. __-eyed
4. Shout on the hunt
5. To __ (without exception)
6. Rasputin's tea maker
7. Due to appear
8. Once upon __
9. Lots
10. Petitioned
11. Unaffected
12. Lining fabric
14. Like a kooky cook?
22. Golden Hurricanes' home
24. More faithful
27. Lived
28. Humorist Bill __: 1826–1903
29. Yellow or Black
30. "__ the land . . ."
31. Like an alert ballerina?
34. Naps
36. Unsaturated alcohol
37. Mary's pet's sound
38. Vacation vehicle
39. Catchall abbr.
40. Diocese
42. Stored grain
44. Kind of belt
45. Gide, e.g.
46. Girl watchers
47. Opening for molten metal
48. TV device
50. Win by __
53. Iconoscopes, for short
54. Dogpatch negative
56. Aware of
57. Cooking direction
58. Lake in Ireland

ACROSS

1. Gen. Arnold
4. Nap
8. "Blood Wedding" dramatist
13. Ailing girl in opera
14. State as fact
15. French soup favorite
16. Eager
17. Boxing's square
18. Math word
19. "__ the Wind," film classic of '61
22. Landers or Miller
23. Grant or Peggy
24. Uncooked
26. Companion of yon
29. Uninvited ones
34. Component in perfume or medicine
35. Fox or turkey follower
36. "__ a Song Go . . ."
37. Clarke and West
38. Edwin or J. Wilkes
39. Location
40. Coup d' __
41. Lhasa __ (dog breed)
42. Bodega or boutique
43. Marks off as a poor risk
45. __ Sea (saline lake of Calif.)
46. Suffix with persist
47. Certain weed
48. Partner of fi
51. Bacall-to-Bogart phrase
57. Ionian isle
59. Locality
60. Little __, fictional tugboat
61. County in Ky.
62. Salacious expression
63. Monster
64. Like many curs
65. "¿Cómo __ Vd.?"
66. Home for two peas

DOWN

1. "__ Sierra," Bogart film
2. Belonging to me: Fr.
3. Part of a slangy retort
4. Living room
5. Like campus halls
6. Word before lease
7. Therefore
8. Doone and Luft
9. "Two __ raft" (poached eggs with toast)
10. "Rio" girl
11. Offering to a mendicant
12. Poet's soon
13. Paw's mate
20. "On Your __," Rodgers-Hart 1936 musical
21. Anger
25. One-horse town
26. "Northeaster" painter
27. Heated
28. Tire feature
29. Kind of cut or beam
30. Newspaper pic style
31. Thomas Stearns __
32. Prefix with grade or rocket
33. Dutch painter or British novelist
35. Constantly fail to pass the bar
38. African language
42. Garment of India
44. Harm
45. Tuaregs' region
47. Canary's statement
48. Con man's scheme
49. Musical ending
50. Bani-Sadr's homeland
52. Shopper stopper
53. "__ bien!" (Pierre's approval)
54. Takeout phrase at a diner
55. Killanin's title
56. Parisian season
58. Garden of Eden fruit

ACROSS

1. Pops in Boston and elsewhere
5. Jai __
9. Darkness; gloom
13. Prefix with poise
14. Sparkle
15. On the deep
16. Free spender from the sticks
19. Utter
20. Piquant
21. Sam or Remus
22. Journey that is no junket
23. Metric unit of area
24. Like a thank-you letter
31. Secular
32. Affects, as a virus
33. Friend for Fernand
34. Nursemaid in Calcutta
35. Substitute
37. Cordon bleu
38. Sun. follower
39. Wander
40. First-rate
41. Clumsy
46. Hairy creature
47. A side of New York
48. Thrash
51. What many hail in a hailstorm
53. Botanist Gray
56. Mrs. Cripps of a G. & S. operetta
59. City 200 miles south of Moscow
60. Family in a Wolfe novel
61. Amerinds of the West
62. Kind; sort
63. "__ take arms . . .": Hamlet
64. Peer

DOWN

1. Five-time Presidential candidate
2. Greenish blue
3. Customhouse levy
4. Command to Rover
5. Largest of 50
6. Fuzz
7. Singer Gibb
8. Resident of: Suffix
9. Lodestone
10. Seagoing org.
11. Actual
12. "Citizen __"
14. Cupidity
17. "Cantos" author Pound
18. Spiritual guides
22. Part of M.I.T.
23. How adepts function
24. Creek or inlet
25. Pleasingly mirthful
26. Mother-in-law of Ruth
27. Fort __, N.J.
28. Calif.-Nev. boundary lake
29. Alter; correct
30. Abounding
31. Shish kebab item
35. Part of the epidermis
36. Brit. answer to the Luftwaffe
37. Light delivery vehicle
39. Drive back
42. Tell on a classmate
43. Abutting
44. Manners of walking
45. To live, to Livy
48. Stain
49. Well ventilated
50. Pace
51. Ski lift
52. Pittypat in "G.W.T.W."
53. Transactions
54. Canal built by de Lesseps
55. Church part
57. Psyche component
58. Toupee: Slang

38

ACROSS

1. Thick piece
5. Reading, e.g.
9. Diminish
14. Chanel
15. Bullets, etc., for short
16. Panamanian city
17. Publisher Adolph
18. City on the Truckee
19. Hollywood employee
20. Emlyn Williams play
23. Word with flower or water
24. Entry in a teacher's roll bk.
25. Young member of a pride
29. Dutch disease victim
31. Dir. from Zurich to Lucerne
34. Port in Caesar's day
35. Ratite bird
36. Companion of tear
37. Salinger opus
40. "Just ___ doch-an'-dorris": Lauder
41. Electrical unit
42. Choreographer Ailey
43. Small ape
44. Pompous one
45. Bits of land in water
46. Edict of a sort
48. Holder of an LL.B.
49. "Oats, peas, ___ grow," start of a nursery jingle
57. Yellowstone Park denizens
58. Musical ending
59. Bog
60. Grand
61. Imposing work
62. Rail
63. A Ford
64. Secretary, e.g.
65. Oriental maid

DOWN

1. Dundee native
2. Ness or Lomond
3. Word with head or tooth
4. Brown pear
5. Attic
6. Improve
7. Prefix with potent or present
8. She wrote "A Girl Like I"
9. Bitter
10. Emulates Larry Holmes
11. Der ___ (Adenauer)
12. Rent
13. Spanish queen before Sophia
21. West Indian sorcery
22. Range
25. Kind of train or government
26. "___ ship a-sailing . . ."
27. Aquatic mammal
28. Riviera resort
29. Jannings and Ludwig
30. Imparted
31. Tennis play
32. Berlin's "___ with Music": 1921
33. British naval women
35. Antithesis of Eris or Ares
36. In good health
38. Mary Ann ___ (George Eliot)
39. "___ la vista!"
45. "Give ___ to the Indians," 1939 song
46. Lighter
47. Photographer Adams
48. ___ Ababa
49. Gun sight
50. Pitcher parts
51. Made a hole-in-one
52. Slangy negative
53. Ponselle or Bonheur
54. Weaver's gear
55. Actor Stone
56. Opposite of 52 Down
57. Breton grain

ACROSS

1. Where St. Paul was shipwrecked
6. Tabula __
10. Not of the clergy
14. Kind of artery or vein
15. Ancient kingdom on the Persian Gulf
16. Part of an estate
17. Small, silvery food fish
18. Enchanted
20. Political party meetings
22. Photographer's word
23. Leaping light
24. What F. D. R. said he hated
25. Kind of dome in a Texas team's home
28. Ricochets
33. Pewter, for one
34. "Praise ye the Lord!"
35. Enter
36. Gambling game using 40 cards
38. Word with sum
39. Like a siren
41. "Ars gratia __"
42. Expedient
43. Kind of furnace
44. Hwy.
45. Poetic pugilist
46. Quick as __
50. __ Mountains, near the Black Sea
55. Spot for a 9-year-old
57. "__ ear and out . . ."
58. Exude
59. Incumbent on
60. Val d' __, Italian Alps resort area
61. They caught Dillinger

62. Like Cassius
63. Snub

DOWN

1. File sect.
2. Sir Lawrence __ Tadema, English painter
3. Stead
4. Household powder
5. Risk calculator
6. Old minstrel's instrument
7. Brews
8. Maxim
9. Friendly
10. Intertwine
11. Yearn
12. Angers
13. Homophone for seed
19. Spasm or pang
21. "No seats" sign
24. Strip of shoe leather
25. "All __," early Berlin song
26. Incisions
27. Jealous suitor in "Pagliacci"
28. Place for a home
29. Beyond: Prefix
30. Berlioz's "Les __ d'Eté"
31. "The butler __"
32. Alleges
33. Sun, to skin
36. Merry
37. Formerly
40. Imprecation

41. De Larrocha and Markova
43. Italian navy
45. Copland
46. Atwitter
47. Kipling's "__ Sea to Sea"
48. Idle
49. Gulf of __, Arabian Sea arm
50. __ figure (attract attention)
51. Ever's partner
52. Not so hot
53. "Once more __ the breach": King Henry V
54. Kind of belt
56. Unclose, to Coleridge

40

ACROSS

1. ". . . with the greatest of __"
5. Newscaster Lindstrom
8. Resounded
12. Novel by Durrell
13. Ankara citizens
15. Birthstone for 19 Across
16. G.B.S. play
19. Indian summer mo.
20. Sharp rebukes
21. Beat at Belmont
22. Chorine
23. Analyze sentences
24. "Upon my soul!" is one
26. Antediluvian
27. "For __ a jolly good fellow . . ."
30. Highlander's shoulder covering
31. Guinea or Rock Cornish
33. Emitted, with "forth"
34. Shoemakers' gear
35. Finis
36. Ladder rung
37. Construction workers, of a sort
38. Ripen
39. Kind of card
40. Mystery writer Josephine
41. Berliner's article
43. Snow in Miami
45. Visit often
47. Tinted
48. Complied with
50. Stiff bristle
51. Lillie or Arthur
54. Joseph Conrad story
57. Weed in a grain field
58. Fatigued
59. Word of regret
60. Wee leftovers
61. Where mdse. is sold
62. Oversupply

DOWN

1. She doted on Narcissus
2. Guinness
3. Pew, for one
4. Spike of corn
5. Medal
6. Angers
7. Alias
8. Haley opus
9. ". . . clean hands, and __": Psalm 24
10. Space Age acronym
11. Narrow valley
13. Transports for skiers
14. Scandinavian toast
17. Three-toned chords
18. Aptly named painter of ranch scenes
22. Charleston breakfast dish
23. Welty novel, with "The"
24. Carpenter's tool
25. John Patrick play, with "The"
28. Agent on a mission
29. Bit of marginalia
30. City map
32. U.K. division
33. Solemn
36. Lightning bolt
41. Work for piano and violin
42. Provide with income
44. "The Singing Cowboy"
46. Film actor Lew
48. "__ be in England . . .": Browning
49. Tolerate
50. Neighbor of Wyo.
51. Nautical time signal
52. Rebekah's hirsute son
53. Kind of prof.
55. Not masc. or neut.
56. Racing has-been

ACROSS

1. White House dog in the 30's
5. "The — Wise Man": Van Dyke
10. Gwyn
14. Matured
15. Delete
16. Melville novel
17. Quit in the casino
20. Spring peeper
21. Buenos —
22. Transmit
23. "The Great Commoner"
25. Quit before becoming superannuated
28. Start of an epitaph
29. Baden-Baden, e.g.
32. Spanish river
33. Submarine detector
34. Nephew of Abraham
35. Quit under fire
39. Garland in Oahu
40. Good will
41. Kett of comics
42. Middle of the 16th century
43. Phooey!
44. Renoir's "The Blonde —"
46. Strays
47. Major European waterway
48. Houston athlete
51. Lowest-fare quarters on liners
55. Quit, at ringside
58. Even
59. True's companion
60. Russian range
61. Recess at St. Peter's
62. Peerage group
63. Dido's home town

DOWN

1. Reality
2. Chinese gelatin
3. —-majesté
4. Devoted attachment
5. Paris's lover before he met Helen
6. Ancient Asia Minor area
7. Clock part
8. Brooklyn follower
9. In medias —
10. — game (pitcher's coup)
11. Arab chief
12. Easy gait
13. Deprivation
18. Roman road
19. Shows consideration for, with "to"
23. — arcade
24. "Dies —," ancient hymn
25. Kingdom
26. Waned
27. The Oregon —
28. Hollers' companions
29. One of seven sins
30. French mail service
31. Essence
33. Stews of a sort
36. Scopes trial attorney
37. Actor Sharif
38. Fizzle
44. Practices extortion: Slang
45. Second
46. Undermine gradually
47. Merman
48. "— boy!"
49. Ending with lord or lady
50. — bien
51. Mix
52. Out of kilter
53. Equipment
54. She, in Savoie
56. Mennon or Gideon follower
57. Gun owner's org.

ACROSS

1. Fastener
5. Keep watch secretly
8. Sommer from Berlin
12. "— homo!"
13. Like bacon
15. Poverty
16. Adjective for Ferdinand Marcos
18. "Good —": 1927 musical
19. Actor in "The Sheik"
21. At full speed
24. Initials for Nipper
25. Corpulent
29. Word with clef or drum
30. Charges
31. Companions of radiuses
32. Balaam's rebuker
33. Utah's lily
34. Active causes
35. Tchaikovsky opera, with 50 Down
38. — up (reviewed briefly)
39. Four-hand piano work
40. Diving bird
42. Coop chatter
43. Sea swallow
44. North African gazelle
45. What height is to a hoopster
46. Data: Abbr.
47. Largest Korean port
48. Dormitory partners
51. Tommy-gun lead
54. Elberta pit
58. Prevaricator
59. "... poem lovely as —"
60. Lambs' dams

61. Central lines of planets
62. Short endorsements
63. Triton

DOWN

1. On to
2. German exclamation
3. —-fi
4. Locale of the ischium
5. Major sector of the psyche
6. Hamlet
7. Female gossips
8. Exalted
9. Actor Marvin
10. — Gardens, N.Y.
11. Sullivan and Begley
13. An N.C.O.
14. "Agnus —"
17. Fleming or Hunter
20. Nutty confection
21. Arab garb
22. Social events at which dominoes are worn
23. Undertakes
26. Groups of nine
27. Japanese clay ware, named for its place of origin
28. Kind of curve
30. Parry
33. Takes care of
34. "... nose as sharp as —": Shak.
36. Constantine and Hadrian
37. Outsides of objects
38. Any fashionable resort
41. Relatives
43. Ford's "A — Heal ..."
44. Author of "Emma"
47. Cato's foot
49. —-Locka, Fla.
50. See 35 Across
51. — carte
52. Crossbreed
53. West or Murray
55. Part of i.o.u.
56. Just released
57. Found: Abbr.

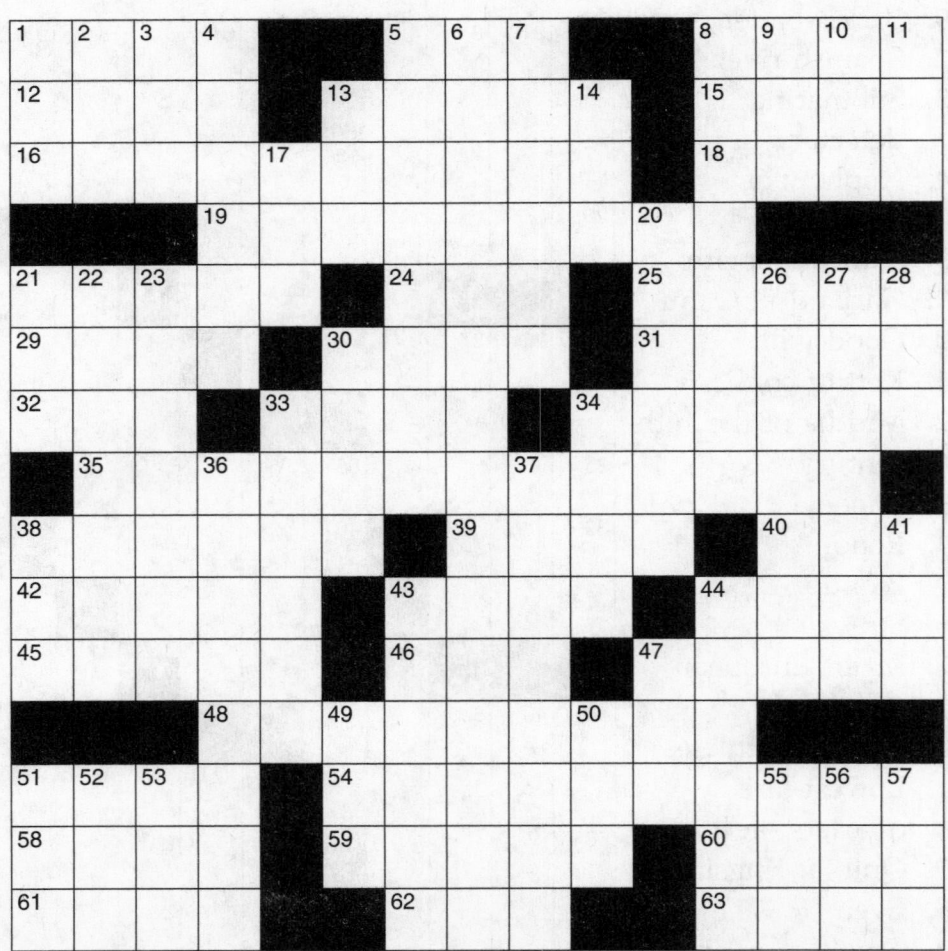

ACROSS

1. Tip, as a hat
5. Like sassy lassies
9. Spill the beans
13. N.Y. island
15. Legendary Irish beauty
16. Chanteuse Horne
17. Crept
18. Descartes or Coty
19. Among
20. This earned many dollars for Anne Nichols
23. Greek war cry
24. Cloth resembling velvet
25. Quickly
28. Let
30. Cow catcher
31. Mil. leaders
32. Jolly boat
36. Letters often rolled in brogue
37. Beginning for cosmic
39. Orphan Annie's Oriental friend
41. Word to a black sheep
42. Affirmatives
44. Dozes
46. Paradise nymph
48. "__ la vista!"
50. Hit a high ball
51. __-fire
53. He has taking ways
55. Music by Shamus O'Connor: 1917
59. Soon
60. Young herring
61. Major Hoople's expletives
63. Fly alone
64. Hibernian export
65. Middle East peninsula
66. Ending for four, six, etc.
67. Club members
68. Negative votes

DOWN

1. __ Moines
2. Pot, in Tijuana
3. Bungle
4. "__ Rainbow," 1947 B'way hit
5. Jeopardy
6. __ Isle
7. Bolognese painter: 1575–1642
8. Encroachment
9. Cajolery
10. Drop, of a sort
11. Cordial flavoring
12. Directed
14. Hoosier comedian
21. __ Paulo, Brazil
22. "__ Anybody Here Seen Kelly?": 1909 song
25. Sean O'Casey product
26. Like a day in June
27. Where to "pile Pelion"
29. Lynn Nolan Ryan's annual stats
31. Ulster, e.g.
33. Border on
34. Follower of hard or soft
35. "Dial" backwards
38. Performing group
40. Flycatchers
43. Airport near Limerick
45. Famous saint, son of a Celto-Roman
47. Start of Finnigin's cable to Flannigan
49. __ rule (generally)
50. Lily, in Lille
51. Rob Roy or buckeye
52. Lycée's relative
54. Abhors
55. Hog food
56. Russian sea
57. Dog in a Barrie play
58. Start of Operation Overlord
62. Fam. member

44

ACROSS

1. Olympic hawk
5. Garden insect
10. Encircle
14. Endure
15. Relative of won't
16. Cry when attacked by a tack
17. Preposition
18. Apple worker
19. Type of car
20. Rubella
23. Bark
24. Mom's spouse
25. Writer St. Johns
28. Handy __
30. Toddler
33. Feast of Lots
34. Plane type, for short
35. Weaned on a pickle?
36. Spicy egg dish
39. Otherwise
40. Colliery center
41. Photo
42. Bishop's jurisdiction
43. Napa Valley product
44. Greek island
45. What Mr. Bonds wields
46. Kind of trench
48. Certain spuds
54. Battle memento
55. Poetic foot or verse
56. Nab
58. Await judgment
59. __ nous
60. Serf of yore
61. Inquires
62. Facing the direction whence a glacier moves
63. Type of catalogue

DOWN

1. World-famous athlete
2. Reverberated
3. Italian town or family
4. Plot
5. Composers' org.
6. Communicate, in a way
7. Injure
8. Arrow poison
9. Hedge on an issue
10. "The Man Who __ Be King"
11. Trick
12. Rickenbacker, Red Baron et al.
13. High deg.
21. Mecca for many retirees
22. Berlin's "__ It Isn't So"
25. Church sections
26. Twofold
27. Eradicate
28. Make amends
29. Alaskan city
30. Utter
31. Opposite of income
32. Ashes, e.g.
34. Item sometimes barked
35. Sounds a half step away from others, in music
37. Places for horseshoers
38. Boundary
43. Had been
45. Gals, to Alfie
46. Agitates
47. Adds liquor
48. Cool desserts
49. File's partner
50. French bridge
51. West Pointer's ". . . __ the fray"
52. Comfort
53. Trig word
54. French Lick, for one
57. Headed

ACROSS

1. Applaud
5. Group of three
10. An absolute failure
14. Speed contest
15. Gamut
16. Always
17. Trite, as a joke
19. N.C.O.'s "As you __!"
20. Kind of horse or ship
21. Cultivators
22. Middle East inn
24. Tipple
25. Steep slope
26. Stories for storeys
29. Cause a cat to scat
32. Delight (in)
33. Makes sheepish sounds
34. Court
35. Singer Burl
36. Trim
37. Scion
38. Suffix for mountain
39. Dishearten
40. Poorest
41. Like stallers' tactics
43. Reliable
44. On one's guard
45. Dread
46. S.A. ungulates
48. Gasp
49. Constrictor
52. Ready to eat
53. Deposes
56. Milieu of the first snake in the grass

57. Songbird
58. Gannets' kin
59. Knight and Bessell
60. Grows weaker
61. Carter's "Why Not the __?"

DOWN

1. Chortle
2. Volcano product
3. Maple-tree genus
4. __ diem
5. Scout units
6. Street show
7. Signs a contract
8. Grow older
9. Consecrate
10. Use caution
11. Defeats decisively
12. Parisian mother
13. Author Harte
18. "Let's give it a __!" (finger-printer's pun)
23. God of war
24. Locales of certain phalanges
25. Barely sufficient
26. Sautéed
27. River embankment
28. Lay upon and beyond
29. Thrown
30. Palm off
31. Number of Ali Baba's foes
33. Main thrust
36. Forms couples
37. Eleventh __
39. Colorist
40. High dudgeon
42. Outsiders
43. Tithes
45. Forcemeat
46. Waste allowance
47. HQ officer
48. Hang fire
49. Cause ennui
50. Possesses
51. One in a D.A.'s office
54. Italian way
55. Johnny __

46

ACROSS

1. Hit the ball hard
5. Nobelist for literature: 1946
10. Economist Smith
14. Cherub
15. Tom Tryon book (with "The")
16. Artist Joan, from Spain
17. One-Time talk-show star
19. Eight: Comb. form
20. On a high plane
21. Destination of the first "piggy"
23. Knievel
24. State flower of N.H.
25. Deceived
28. Natives of Barcelona
31. Change
32. Less psychotic
33. Promise solemnly
34. Jetty
35. Vessels having staves
36. Buddhist god
37. Schisgal play
38. Mint product
39. Shankar instrument
40. Gifts for 40th wedding anniversary
42. Declared
43. Ambiences
44. Lop the crop
45. Bee's objective
47. Discussant

51. Stare at
52. Talk-show star
54. Precognitive person
55. Roman official
56. Volcano
57. Sawbucks
58. Poker play
59. Go easy at the table

DOWN

1. Invited
2. "Blue Angel" star Jannings
3. Sole
4. Tourist
5. Entertained guests
6. Lucy's neighbor
7. Wearing footgear
8. Preacher's talk: Abbr.
9. Hermits
10. Ethically neutral
11. Talk-show star
12. TV funnyman Johnson
13. Open to question
18. Actress June
22. Winglike
24. Rawboned; gaunt
25. Wood for flooring
26. Troy
27. Former talk-show star
28. Warehouse sights
29. Stars that blaze and soon fade
30. Turf
32. __ of time

35. Container for draining and straining
36. Changed the baby's garb
38. Filly's future status
39. Personnel
41. T squares
42. Person receiving a package
44. Irritates
45. Kind of card
46. Molding
47. Date in Trajan's reign
48. Roast, in Dijon
49. Slave of yore
50. Coup d' __
53. Actress Rehan

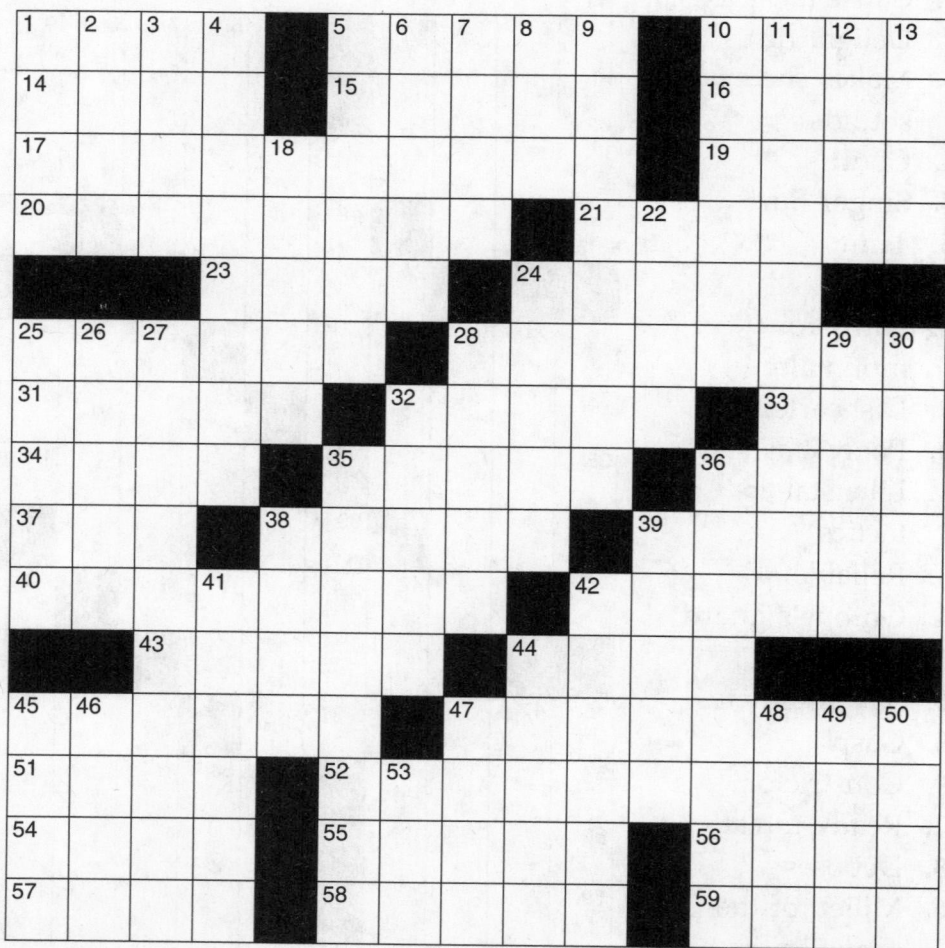

ACROSS

1. Eloper with a spoon
5. Cotton ball
8. Landing craft
12. Suffix with assist and resist
13. "Slip cover"
15. Roman emperor: A.D. 69
16. Where the top brass is scarce
18. Sandarac tree
19. Eastern holiday
20. Keep things going as usual
22. Moves apace
23. Green island
24. "Balm of hurt minds"
26. Evens the score
29. Oodles
30. Companion of rank
32. Indian range
33. Beat the house
34. Traveling bag
37. Reproductive cells
38. Warhol
40. Lode
41. Houston football pro
43. Acted properly
45. Federations of a sort
46. To pray: Sp.
47. Composer Saint-__
49. What the fall guy does
52. Fluffy scarf
55. Captain Pierce on TV
56. General's righthand man
58. Villain's glance
59. Vulgar
60. Cleveland's lake
61. Past performance of a race horse
62. One kind of strike
63. Diner sign

DOWN

1. Pixilated
2. Concerning
3. Glaswegian
4. Rhode Island Red
5. Makes a yarn ball
6. Aid a criminal
7. Tousle
8. Goldbricking
9. Redoubt
10. "... gold in them __ hills"
11. Classify
13. Knocked for __
14. Spirited song
17. Use a flail
21. "Maid of Athens, __ we part ..."
22. Senator Kennedy
24. Tea-party treat
25. Man of property
26. Actor Arkin
27. Chalet features
28. Kind of boarder
29. Clean the deck
30. "Took a powder"
31. Amin
35. Casus belli, at times
36. Place for cocktails
39. "Tall Ship" feature
42. Election winners
44. Anatomical duct
45. Necklace
47. Auto
48. Lincoln and Beame
49. "__ a loaf is ..."
50. Table spread
51. Take on
52. Theda of silents
53. Leave out
54. Planet rulers, in a film
57. Bee follower

48

ACROSS

1. Fascinate
6. Date: Abbr.
10. Leander's lass
14. Lines inside a circle
15. Penn pronoun
16. Sobeit
17. Intensity
18. Palatable
20. Make tracks
22. H.R.E. founder
23. Muse of history
24. Doze
25. "__, O Ship of State"
28. __ Geddes
29. Excluded
30. Kerr play
35. Miller's "__ from the Bridge"
36. Camera motion
37. "If I __ Rich Man"
38. Sign outside a hit show
40. Wordsworth product
41. Corded fabric
42. Smudged
43. Call forth
46. Pinochle combo
47. Degrade
48. Inquisition burnings
53. Anne and George
55. Contemporary of Edison
56. Author Seton
57. Guitar part
58. Chanson subject
59. Ivan or Nicholas
60. Flurry
61. Mature

DOWN

1. Fiddler on the reef
2. Tortoise's competitor
3. Po tributary
4. Mob scene
5. Sullivan, to Keller
6. Gain
7. Snapshot
8. Winnie of fiction
9. Word of disapproval
10. Waste maker
11. Overact
12. Wipe again
13. "The __ Love"
19. Caine or Wayne
21. Walk heavily
24. Sunday talk: Abbr.
25. Goalie's feat
26. Seed covering
27. Angered
28. Prohibit
29. Scrooge's word
30. Spoil
31. Noun suffix
32. "Comus" composer
33. Thatch
34. Sun __-sen
36. Get-up-and-go
39. Victory symbol
40. Alone
42. Gets to work on
43. Abba and family
44. Fictional uncle
45. Academy's statuette
46. Subdued
47. As blind as __
48. Hair style
49. Half: Prefix
50. __ to Cerberus
51. Chimney channel
52. Make one's salt
54. "__ in the stilly night . . ."

ACROSS

1. Pitch indicator
5. Not barefoot
9. Duffers' golf strokes
14. Bullish bellow
15. Bare
16. Kukla's friend
17. Ancient strongbox
18. Russian range
19. Kind of alley
20. Secretly
23. Lincoln Center seat
24. Slight
25. Word with band or box
28. Mercenary of '76
30. Audit maker
33. Whodunit feature
35. Droop
36. Roderick Dhu's group
37. Gratify by favors
41. Spenser or Spender
42. School dance
43. Familiar
44. Dismal
45. Modern eavesdropper's method
48. Compass point
49. Chumps
50. Angers
52. Faultfinding passenger
58. Kayak
59. Eight furlongs
60. Valley
61. Embellish
62. Seaport or gulf
63. In __ (actually existing)
64. Famed colonial family
65. Scottish lake in the news
66. Look for

DOWN

1. King or hermit
2. Wisdom of the ages
3. Every's partner
4. Delicate
5. Smear
6. Protagonists
7. Algerian seaport
8. Erasure
9. Spool for winding thread
10. Edgar __ Poe
11. Parisian cop
12. Slang word after rat
13. But, to Brutus
21. Like some of Koufax's games
22. Mold
25. Trunk fasteners
26. Tennessee city
27. Weary
29. Incline
30. Rudolph's driver
31. S.A. rodents
32. Tarsus
34. Slugger's weapon
36. Network monogram
38. Fish and __
39. Irving's "headless" one
40. First-rate
45. Rouses
46. Decisions for authors
47. Elizabeth and Eve
49. Disdain
51. What partisans take
52. Commanded
53. By and by
54. Military officer
55. Urn
56. Besides
57. Emit fumes
58. Biggin

50

ACROSS

1. Vanquish
5. Low
9. Grate upon
13. Sax or singer
14. Paradise
15. Netherlands city (with "The")
16. Perjurer
17. Oater
19. Kind of cabin
20. Crake
21. Vanity
22. Obstacle race
25. Unyielding
26. Needle-shaped
30. Knowing
32. Magna —
34. Correlative
35. Spiritual food
36. Word repeated before "hurray"
37. Machine part
39. Midwest st.
40. Quotidian
42. Leaves out
43. Meal course
45. Presses for payment
46. Penny-pinching
51. Irish seaport
53. Ointment
54. Audit maker
55. Dust devils
57. Row of seats
58. Justice, Order and Peace goddesses
59. Only
60. Sent for Jeeves

61. Hyalite
62. "Let us —" (raiders' motto?)
63. Ray, of films

DOWN

1. It takes four to walk
2. "The Waste Land" poet
3. They have properties, can't sell
4. Peak
5. Ecce
6. Dote on
7. Ice pinnacle
8. Step above Mid.

9. Sword
10. Like Methuselah
11. Having confidence
12. Shell-game adjunct
15. Do monkey-shines
18. Moon's age on Jan. 1
20. Skater's stunt
23. Bring home the bacon
24. Grasping person
27. Misanthropic
28. Horn sound
29. Makes a gaffe
30. In the center
31. Decline
32. Club i.o.u.'s
33. Be sick

38. All: Prefix
41. Cupid's weapon
44. Helix
45. Humperdinck's name at birth
47. Kind of sanctum
48. Sierra —
49. Turn over
50. Silvery grunt; pinfish
51. Boutique
52. Calabrian coin
55. Abbot's man on first
56. Kindergarten cutup
57. First of a musical trio

ACROSS

1. Willful
11. Shirley MacLaine role
15. One-sided
16. Lamb cut
17. For the most part
18. Attic
19. Isle of exile
20. Coloring matter
22. Black bird
25. Land in a musical
26. Mme., in Mexico
29. False god
32. Pakistanis, Laotians, etc.
36. What "none must hope to find": Pope
39. One of the tides
40. Ward off
41. Table part
42. Teutonic sea god
43. Sandwich filler
44. Tending to ramble
46. Medium's offering
48. Elusive, in a way
49. Witness
50. Hebrew letter
52. "Cry __ River"
54. Lazy
59. Old pronoun
63. "Roads scholar"
64. Reptiles protected by law
67. "__ There"
68. Shipshape
69. Schoolbook
70. Famed W.W. II flattop

DOWN

1. Foppish one
2. Organic compound
3. Precarious perch
4. Where to read about Achilles' wrath
5. Enjoin
6. Air schedule abbr.
7. Tear to pieces
8. Dilettantish
9. Narratives
10. Blissful
11. Brightens
12. Housetop
13. Offend
14. Tiny colonists
21. British thank-you's
23. Help in wrongdoing
24. Certain enlistee
26. Footwear for W. C. Fields
27. Ziegfeld creation
28. Fight sight
30. "Volsunga Saga" king
31. Feudal lord
33. Sponsorship
34. Gullible
35. Carousal
37. Capital of Kentucky
38. Monster
42. "__ sow . . ."
44. Get off at O' Hare
45. Shade tree
47. Grimalkin
51. Paris's prize
53. Perfume base
54. Jigger
55. Resort next to Brighton
56. Mountain goat
57. Strip of wood
58. Locale
60. Snake-dance specialist
61. Mythical apple thrower
62. Early laborer
65. Needlefish
66. Cleo's way out

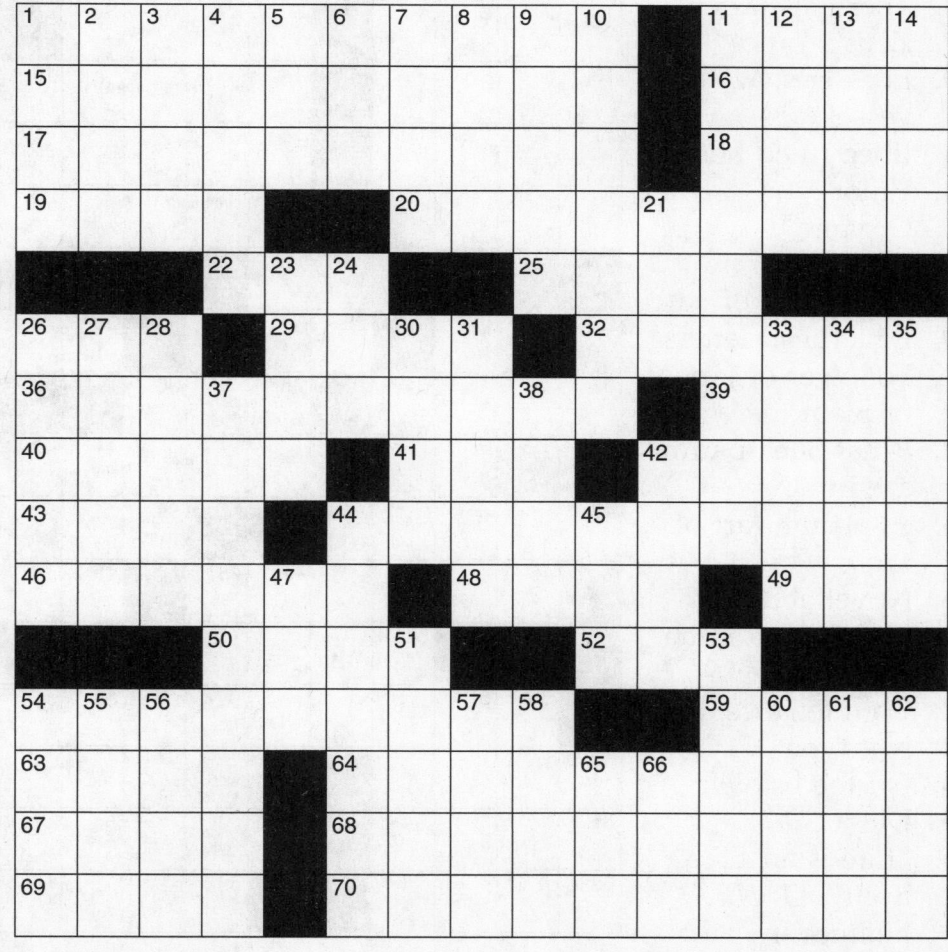

52

ACROSS

1. The __ Reaper
5. Old Glory, e.g.
9. Man the picture
13. Better than never
14. Citrus fruits
16. Competent
17. Like a jalopy
18. Fight site
19. Cheer (for)
20. Line from a nursery rhyme
23. "Exodus" character
24. Extinct relative of NATO
25. Kind of relief
28. Carpenter with six legs
30. Ringed planet
33. Dadaist works
35. Thermal starter
37. Zeus's "juice"
39. Loesser's lazy vessel
43. Rhee ruled here
44. Sailor
45. Organic compound
46. Takes care of
49. Letterhead letters
51. Follower of Japan or Siam
52. What Shea patrons are in
54. __ artium (art of arts)
56. Novel about events on a mine sweeper
62. Countenance
63. Net type
64. On the briny
65. Dies __
66. "Life is an __ itself": O. W. Holmes Jr.

67. 100 Iranian dinars
68. Weaken
69. Camp sight
70. Famous penultimate words

DOWN

1. Satiate
2. Reckless
3. Roman road
4. Jason's helpmate
5. Everglades denizen
6. Cambio currency
7. Approvals at revival meetings
8. Islamic spirits
9. Scroll-like tablet
10. __ Ben Adhem
11. Boor
12. Asian holiday
15. A Yemeni capital
21. Epoch
22. Spot for old toys
25. Take a place in the sun
26. Guthrie namesakes
27. Reproductive body
29. Kind of room or time
31. North Sea feeder
32. Taboos
34. Sugared
36. Great Giant
38. Wheeze's cousin
40. Fundamental
41. Southern Chinese people

42. Embellish
47. Hairdresser's offering
48. This is not Occidental
50. French wine region
53. Insinuative
55. Gape
56. Item on a buggy
57. Mend
58. Grape pigment
59. "Where __ now, the glory . . . ?": Wordsworth
60. Undiluted, as a bar drink
61. River in 43 Across
62. Russian fighter plane

ACROSS

1. Deep sleep
6. Cut down
10. Common rhyme scheme
14. Belief
15. Composer Siegmeister
16. N.Y.C. museum
17. Very seldom
20. Treat in Tijuana
21. Of diodes, triodes, etc.
22. Carpenter and soldier
24. They go before P's and Q's
25. Cow's chew
27. Uinta Mountains' state
30. Designate anew
35. Japanese sash
36. Plummer parts
38. Uneven
39. Complete surprise
43. Indonesian isle
44. "__ from the Vienna Woods"
45. Homophone for heir
46. One of a film trio
49. Kind of shark
50. Pump liquid
51. Mischievous one
53. Start of Caesar's report
55. Make an acronym of, perhaps
61. Facility
64. Carefully picked jury
66. Art of songdom
67. Enlist again, as a G.I.
68. Killer whales
69. Tokyo, once
70. TV's Johnson
71. Grenoble's river

DOWN

1. Burns or Watt
2. Wine measure in Trieste
3. Slight fault
4. Gray's "__ the Spring"
5. Louis XIV, e.g.
6. Free from evil
7. Hamburg's river
8. Roger's follower
9. Asexual
10. G.I.'s fighting need
11. Blessing
12. To me, in Paris
13. Judge's bench
18. Wise old Greek
19. Gaelic
23. Gang's territory
25. Baseball's Ty and family
26. Convoy raider
28. "Loads"
29. Of arteries, veins, etc.
31. Collar
32. It's often pledged
33. English pianist Lympany
34. Rapiers' relatives
37. Town near Omaha Beach
40. Pedro's uncle
41. Devaloka, to a Hindu
42. Serf of yore
47. Actor Will: 1902–78
48. Soprano role in "Don Giovanni"
52. Texture
54. Approximates
55. With competence
56. Gloomy
57. League
58. Offer a new version
59. Be juxtaposed with
60. Small shark
62. Brand
63. In addition
65. Taro-root food

54

ACROSS
1. Entertainer
5. __ fizz (gin drink)
10. "__ That a Shame": 1955 tune
14. Chip in, literally
15. "__ and Sing," Odets play
16. __ B'rith
17. Jazzman Getz
18. Savage
19. Suffix with diet
20. Take __ (be careful)
22. Little sea pike
24. Tanned calfskin
25. Young, inexperienced person: Slang
29. Missile housing
30. Rich cakes
33. Pouch
36. More washed out
39. Crux
40. Ruined a person's chances
44. Part of A.D.
45. Name that means "reborn"
46. Unaccustomed
47. Magnetic units
50. Involved with
52. Holding a purposeful discussion
58. Ewe's plaint
60. Kent/Superman friend
61. Manchester money
62. Miller and Sothern
64. Candelabrum insert
67. Rancor
68. Spots
69. Maternally akin
70. Face shape
71. King Arthur's foster brother et al.
72. Team event
73. Clears, after taxes

DOWN
1. Hinged fasteners
2. Available
3. Perron
4. Lendl's game
5. U.K. air arm
6. Feeling toward a genius
7. Actress Jean from London
8. Giraffe's cousin
9. Excellent
10. Fortas or Burrows
11. Plan of action
12. Detect and expose
13. Timepiece sound
21. Sandpiper
23. Ref's decision
26. All smiles
27. Chroma
28. Consequently
31. Vital verb for Virgil
32. Daube, e.g.
33. E. Fitzgerald forte
34. Best-quality
35. Steadfastness
37. Ending for ethyl
38. Back out
41. Nut containing caffeine
42. Hurled
43. Odd outfit
48. Sum total
49. Zayak is one
51. Beaver state
53. Absurd
54. Katmandu's site
55. Jack
56. Dazzling display
57. Cheerleaders' specialties
58. Pitcher's false move
59. Asian ox
63. Sobriquet for a sibling
65. Hellenic "H"
66. Juan Carlos's title

ACROSS

1. Concentrate
6. Jet speed number
10. __ Wilander, tennis star
14. Greeted the dawn
15. __ Nagy, Hungarian statesman
16. Zaragoza's river
17. Pertaining to a petrified Pa. product
19. Ivan, e.g.
20. Lawyer's advance
21. Stationary
23. Suffix for alcohols
24. Essay
25. Buoy
26. Container: Abbr.
27. Her or his, in Lyon
28. __-Saud
30. Comparative suffix
31. Indian weight
32. Kith and kin
34. Product of a day's work in Pa.?
36. Custom
38. Number of coins in the fountain
39. Poetic contraction
40. Aged: Lat. abbr.
41. Rules to follow
42. Ogre's last word
45. Inert element
47. One, in Glasgow
48. Occupation
49. Curries favor
51. "Hurry up!"
53. Ayes, in Paree
54. Petrified product of Pa.
56. __ time (never)
57. Pierce
58. Subsequent
59. Youth
60. Perfume
61. Travois and monoski

DOWN

1. Serge or buckram
2. Adjust
3. Another example of 1 Down
4. Run-of-the-mill
5. Highway hauler
6. Some Pa. workmen
7. He wrote "Home Town": 1950
8. French vineyard
9. Memorable pianist
10. Bismuth, e.g.
11. Refrains
12. Arnold was one
13. Voodoo
18. Connect
22. Certain muscles
27. Mariner's tool
28. Charged particle
29. Seamstress, sometimes
31. "__ 'em!"
32. Bee chaser
33. Ending for elephant or serpent
34. Optimistic
35. Outside: Comb. form
36. Sailor's garb
37. Detour
41. Nervous Nellie's condition
42. Limited
43. Part of U.M.W.
44. Measures
46. A human Bean
47. Kind of dome or turf
48. A.F.L. branch
50. Pudding starch
52. Cronies
55. It's east of Eden

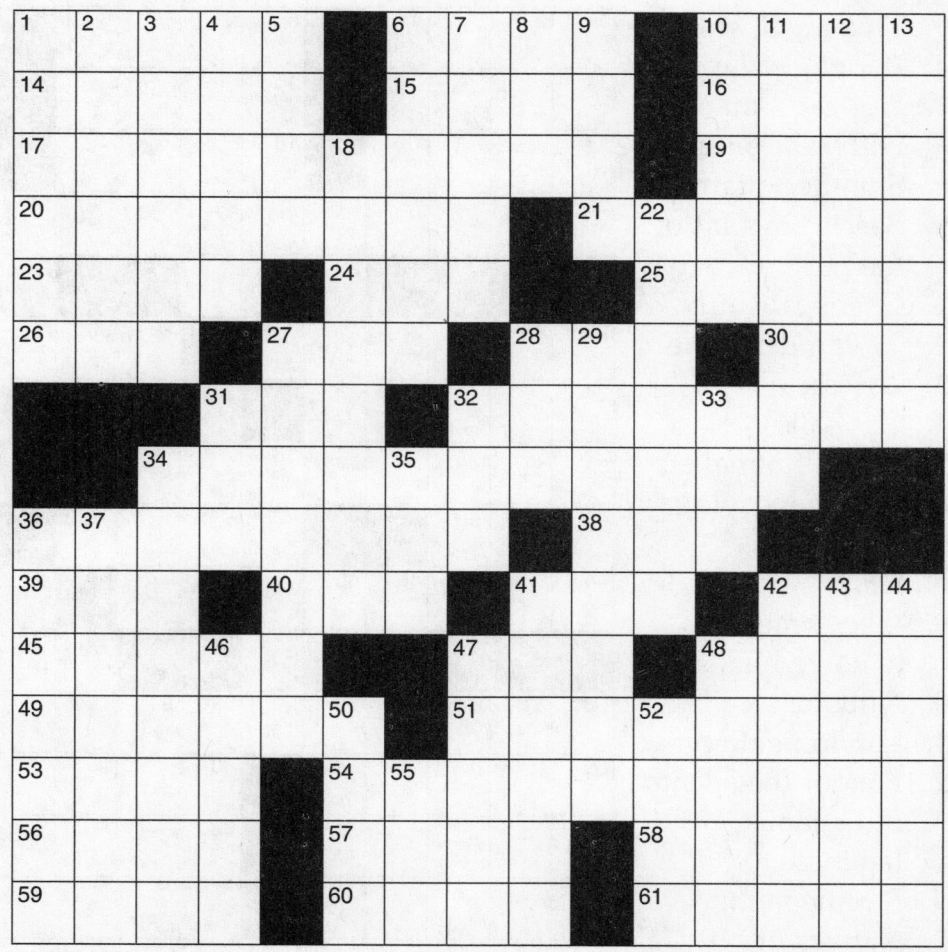

56

ACROSS

1. "Desire Under the —"
5. Bambi and friends
9. Singer Page
14. Richard Wilbur, e.g.
15. Wylie's "Night — Night"
16. Of the bees
17. Notion
18. Datum
19. Sing, Alpine style: Var.
20. L.A.
23. Actor Louis
24. Prevarication
25. Team from College Station, Tex.
29. Tree-lined walks
34. Puppeteer Lewis
35. "... get a man with —": Berlin
36. Summer quaff
37. Beach Boys hit of the 60's
41. Chemical suffix
42. — van der Rohe
43. Assesses
44. Cure-alls
47. Funt's funmaker
48. Hammarskjöld
49. Chart
50. S.F.
59. Like some hallowed halls
60. Nubbins
61. London gallery
62. Pola of the silents
63. Indigenous Japanese
64. Prolific auth.
65. Natives of NE U.S.

66. Brouhaha
67. Eye part

DOWN

1. Typical De Mille film
2. City SSE of Sacramento
3. "— Me in St. Louis"
4. Girdle girder
5. Popular radio tavern
6. Related through Mom
7. Delineate
8. Learning via repetition
9. Heathen, once
10. Highest or farthest point
11. Time's partner
12. Wayne's "— in the Saddle"
13. Name for a señorita
21. "— by land ..."
22. One of the Ladds
25. Rival of BMI
26. Accra's republic
27. Famed Greek physician
28. A grandson of Benjamin
29. Dancing De Mille
30. San — Obispo
31. Puccini's "Vissi —"
32. Freud associate
33. — Aurunca, town NNW of Napoli

35. See 31 Down
38. Alpha's antithesis
39. Kind of paper
40. "— Woman"
45. Stick
46. Worsted yarn
47. Hamburger garnish
49. Loy
50. Honeysuckle, e.g.
51. Say it's so
52. Role for Leslie
53. Heedless
54. Legal surety
55. Lat. catchall phrase
56. Follower of rats or hen
57. Like — of bricks
58. Oriental urges?

ACROSS

1. Beige
5. Scrutinizes
10. Grackle
13. Alda or King
14. Ancient Greek colony
15. Buster Brown's dog
16. Michael Jackson's forte
17. Cross-examine
18. Place for an arras
19. Marie Henri Beyle
21. Fox and Creek
23. Edible grain
24. Biblical halting place: Deut. 10:6
25. Charles Lutwidge Dodgson
29. Ed and Keenan
30. Ames and Errol
31. A lunchtime hr.
34. Work units
35. Farm buildings
36. __ Rios, Jamaican resort
37. Pekoe or hyson, e.g.
38. Hysterical fear
39. NATO member
40. Eric Arthur Blair
43. Cravings
45. Rower
46. Rivulet
47. __ Tom, Alger hero
52. Impel
53. A happening
55. Enameled metalware
56. Musical tones
57. Bakery item
58. Caudal appendage
59. Bend in timber
60. Samuel Clemens
61. Russian lake

DOWN

1. Fall on deaf __
2. Jumbled mass
3. Competition for Atalanta
4. X-quantities to be solved
5. Observes
6. Mrs. Dithers
7. Indigo
8. Nothing
9. Whence some condiments come
10. Fiendish
11. Metal tip on a shoelace
12. Cardiff citizens
15. Spin
20. Speaker's platform
22. Old-make cars
24. Wild horse
25. Harp's cousin
26. In an attractive way
27. Sounds in "The Trolley Song"
28. Eagle's nest
29. Soaked
32. Rizzuto
33. My, in Metz
35. Variety of pear
36. Herbert creation
38. Baffle
39. Quick, sharp blow
41. White-tailed eagles
42. Spoiled
43. Support
44. Ann Arbor's river
47. Japanese Buddhist's church
48. Against
49. Shout
50. Charles Lamb
51. Small, secluded valley
54. Promise solemnly

58

ACROSS

1. Rochester's love
5. Lions' abodes
10. Minor prophet
14. Peak
15. Confess
16. Copperfield's love
17. Plague
18. Return gunfire
19. Host
20. Core; pith
22. Goes by, as time
24. Poor
26. Bury
27. Exercise for a pupil
30. Group of kilns
32. Cleopatra's love
33. Ignored, as advice
38. Desdemona loved one
39. Rural stopover
40. Lay concrete
41. Dynamiter's activity
44. Scarlett's love
46. Suffix with resist
47. British toast
48. Runner for a dresser
51. A cold
53. Salt lake (Lacus Asphaltites)
55. Articulated
59. Business-letter term
60. Robert Schumann's love
62. Italia's capital
63. Nick Charles's love
64. Predictor's pasteboard
65. Kind of rain

66. City south of Moscow
67. Trap having sinkers and floats
68. Zhivago's love

DOWN

1. Mock
2. Simians
3. Robert Stack role
4. Straightening muscles on limbs
5. Grand or petty follower
6. "__ of dreadful note": Macbeth
7. Little hellion
8. Cause heat under the collar
9. A la mode

10. Emulate a chameleon
11. Code inventor
12. Abalone
13. "Simon __"
21. Gaudy sign
23. Prefix with chamber or room
25. Confederate of Jesse James
27. Elia
28. Organic compound
29. Greek portico
31. Lincoln's first love
34. Transitory
35. Valley of a sort
36. Always
37. Former N. African rulers

39. "Airways, __," Dos Passos play
42. Drake's men
43. Taints
44. Quick-drying textile fiber
45. Close
48. Mister, in Madrid
49. Author John le __
50. TV's "Let's Make __"
52. Cheboygan's lake
53. The Flintstones' pet
54. Amor's flappers
56. Cape near Lisbon
57. Arab prince
58. Early 20th-century art
61. Greek nickname

ACROSS

1. Detest
6. Air: Comb. form
10. Musical ending
14. Norman Vincent __
15. Stepped on
16. Spoken
17. First name of a Wharton hero
18. Narrative
19. Julep additive
20. Second looies
22. Baseball's Rose
23. Court issuance
24. One who needs a buyer
26. Price
30. Yoko __
31. Former ring king
32. One who gives permission
34. Hurry off
38. Spotted
39. Advocate at court
41. Senator Kefauver
42. Still untouched
43. Sparks or Buntline
45. "__ Misérables"
46. A son of Seth
47. Aboriginal Australian group
50. "__ boy!"
52. Kind of skirt
53. Passages sunk into the earth
59. Po feeder
60. Oast
61. Heron's kin
62. Goering's greeting
63. Gear at the Grand Banks
64. Gladiator's milieu
65. "Golden __ and girls . . .": Shak.
66. Basic nature
67. __ Warbucks

DOWN

1. Simians
2. One of the "Little Women"
3. Laughter sounds
4. Norwegian king
5. Begin again
6. Reached
7. Arnold, e.g.
8. Gangster's gal
9. City in Texas or Ukraine
10. Make difficult
11. Bay window
12. __ Gabriel Rossetti
13. Tailor
21. Treasure __
25. Red __ (S. African trees)
26. Instance
27. Chooses
28. Tiff
29. Third anniversaries
33. Start
35. Norse god of war
36. Wine: Comb. form
37. Uno, dos, __
39. Make-believe
40. Rosters
42. Venus and Mars
44. Singer Vic
47. Menotti hero
48. "__ cockhorse . . ."
49. Loosened a knot
51. Farther along
54. Currier's companion
55. Taj Mahal site
56. Mr. Flintstone
57. Take care of
58. Collar gadget

ACROSS

1. Connective
4. Follower of Zeno
9. Italian friar's title
12. Charles VII, e.g.
13. __ Alegre, Brazil
14. Labor
15. Restrain
17. Martian, e.g.
18. Kop, to a Boer
19. Huxley's "__ Hay"
21. American folk ballad
23. Inexperienced
25. Desirable tree
26. Expressing sorrow
29. Calumniated
33. Least strict
34. Hied
35. Holmes vehicle
36. Arab princes
37. Phiz
38. Over
39. Huge
40. Before: Prefix
41. Schumann's songs
42. Rolle and Williams
44. Frame of a ship
45. "__ y plata," Montana motto
46. Czech playwright
47. Pitcher in three World Series
51. Put off
55. Where Laos is
56. Upright
58. Record
59. __ du Salut (Safety Islands)
60. Transparent
61. Kith's partner
62. Actor Chaney
63. Province of Umbria
64. Outer: Comb. form

DOWN

1. Medieval Italian chest
2. Parsing word
3. Grime
4. Bath, e.g.
5. Pre-Aztec Indian in Mexico
6. Astral hunter
7. Article
8. Doom
9. Fencing weapon
10. Peeve
11. Partner
14. Subject of an Anouilh play
16. Protagonist of a Wright novel
20. Cross prefix
22. Comedian Olsen
24. Breakfast
26. Parisian pupil
27. Fernando or Lorenzo
28. Live
29. Slump
30. Valerie Harper role
31. Word before drop
32. They have colorful jobs
34. Actress McClanahan
37. "__ Miniver"
38. Noised about
40. Undertaking
41. Race division
43. Suffix with arch or witch
44. MacLaine movie
46. Comfort
47. Kind of end or spin
48. Formerly Christiania
49. Demeanor
50. Escutcheon border
52. Ersatz
53. Majestic
54. Tear
57. Prefix for angle or color

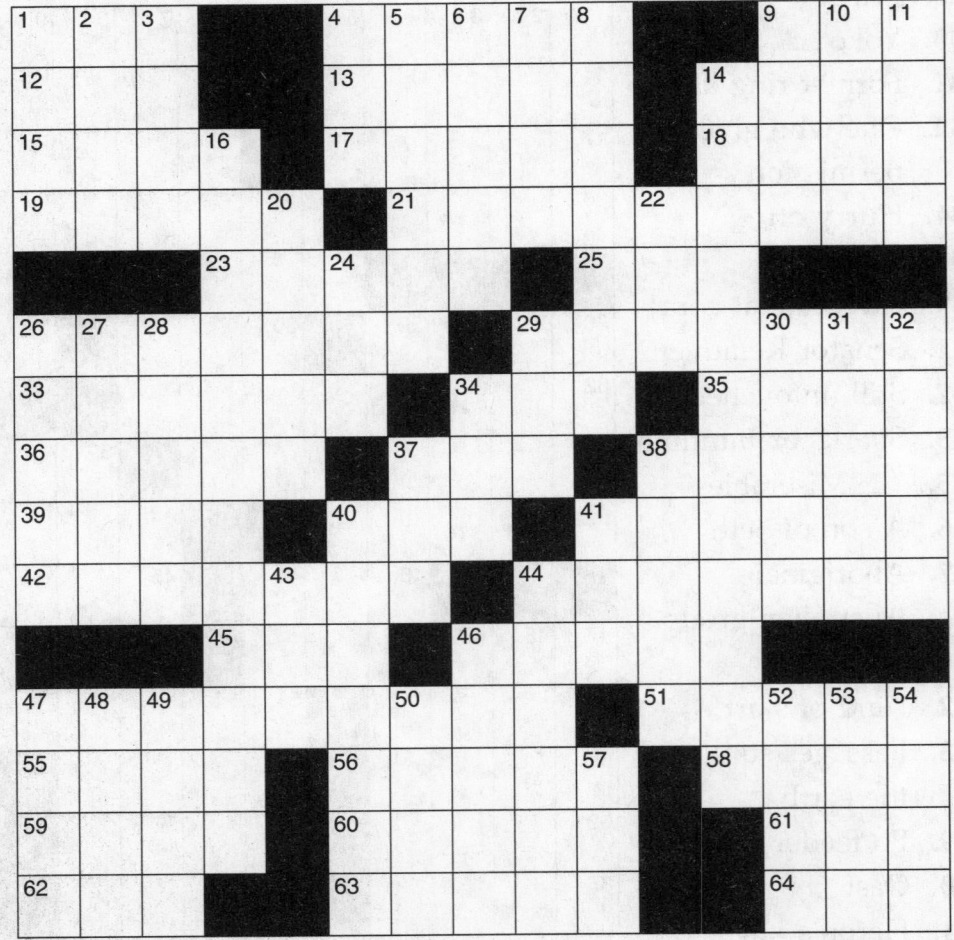

ACROSS

1. Andy's pal
5. Young haddock
10. Fix over
14. Edge
15. Patriot Tom
16. Abba of Israel
17. Di and Margaret
19. Fuller creation
20. Life, for one
21. Not so dull
23. Word form with European or Chinese
24. Bowlers' surfaces
25. Means
28. Burst of energy
29. Ear part
30. Seer of a sort
31. "... the foggy, foggy —"
34. Dictum feared by 53 Across
38. Nov. 1 is their day
39. Set out
40. Puzzler's pet eagle
41. Ho's predecessor
42. Uproar
44. A bridge to Cape Cod
46. Plant for seasoning
47. Felt
48. Tender touches
52. Sweat out a delay
53. Campus group
55. Chemical suffix
56. Assistants
57. Give forth
58. Lion's pride
59. Breakfast item
60. Lairs

DOWN

1. Slithery ones
2. Muck's next of kin
3. Norse god
4. Guard
5. Shells out shekels
6. Maine bay
7. Get up
8. Quarter of four
9. Writer's light
10. Cash in
11. Hard wood
12. Hess and Christie
13. Superhero
18. Dime segment
22. Dinsmore of fiction
24. Away
25. Swiss sight
26. Style, in Sedan
27. Wanes
28. Said "!*!*"
30. Graze
31. Dagger
32. Puzzler's pet toiler
33. Hone
35. French department
36. What holders of a straight do
37. Apselike
41. Shake a leg
42. Most unusual
43. Ice and Stone
44. "A staff is quickly found to — dog": Shak.
45. Tear producer
46. Vaults
47. Ape fish
48. Finale for Friml
49. A few
50. Ireland
51. Fast planes
54. The Tajo is one

62

ACROSS

1. Damage
5. Reduce gradually
10. Scorch
14. Inter —
15. Author Zola
16. Mystery of a sort
17. U. of Michigan team
19. Caen's river
20. Franco Harris, e.g.
21. Used the freeway
23. Lab animal
24. Modern Persian
25. Umpires
30. Franco-Iberian bay
33. Gardener's protective covering
34. Studio stand
36. Drs.' group
37. Biblical giant
38. Old-fashioned
39. Crystalline precipitation
40. Neuralgic symptom
41. Steersman
42. Severe
43. Certain textile workers
45. Ilie and family
47. French seaport
49. Tennyson's "always"
50. Bird dog
52. Ingredient of most bones and teeth
56. Dugout, Gallic style
57. Vanderbilt U. team
59. Teased
60. Now
61. Stadium rooters
62. Little Teresa
63. Aerial maneuvers
64. Celebration

DOWN

1. Turns left
2. "Thanks —!"
3. Get under one's skin
4. Unbranded calf
5. Cylindrical
6. Moslem V.I.P.
7. Bobby or cotter follower
8. Fragrant resin
9. Swallowed again
10. Sings softly
11. U. of Miami team
12. British princess
13. Coarse grass
18. Israeli port
22. Appendage
25. Instrument for Elman
26. Arrest
27. Long Island U. team
28. Genuine
29. Squelched
31. Love, in Sorrento
32. Gapes
35. Bristle
38. Analyzes
39. Begin
41. Gram. past tense
42. Place
44. Pyle and Ford
46. Hindus in a British army
48. Group of Boy Scouts
50. Separate
51. Woodwind
52. "— for All Seasons"
53. Dies —
54. Camping shelter
55. Actual being
58. Start of the 16th century

ACROSS

1. Eared __
5. Brokerage order
9. Tonsorial concern
14. It sailed to Colchis
15. To __ (perfectly)
16. Papal court
17. Honest, in Hamburg
18. Sharpen
19. In a fit manner
20. Prokofiev ballet
23. Utensil on a pencil
24. Carmine
25. A son of Rebekah
27. Bonny belles
31. Attacked
34. Raccoon feature
36. Satcom F4 owner
37. Keen
38. Austrian river
39. "Well, __ for my money . . .": Shak.
41. Choler
42. Pleased
43. She was mad about Adonis
44. Relevant
47. Hindu Kush locale
49. Heavenly Altar
50. "__ Valley P.T.A."
54. Patron of sweethearts
59. Psychologist May
60. Topic for a señorita
61. Ardor
62. Fiancée, to a fiancé
63. Nurture
64. Thank-you __
65. Learned
66. Singer Gibb
67. Chowder

DOWN

1. Buffalo puckster
2. Bobble
3. Old World lizard
4. Courting chair
5. One-third of Africa
6. Town on the Thames
7. What S&L's do
8. Actor Cobb
9. Virgo's neighbor
10. __-dart (blue succory)
11. "Vissi d' __," "Tosca" aria
12. Happy tune
13. Salary
21. Juan's west
22. Russian stream
26. Practical
27. McCartney of Wings
28. Kind of horse or hand
29. Grayish yellow
30. Without
31. Reagan's first Sec. of State
32. Farm unit
33. Author Alice __ Miller
35. Anecdotes
39. Of jays, martins, etc.
40. Cheers up
42. Punkie
45. "Ancient Evenings" author
46. Schwarzenegger
48. Fino is one
51. Earhart was one
52. Mother's kin
53. Extend a lease
54. Loudness unit
55. Seaweed
56. Spanish linear measure
57. Word of assent
58. Fix the dice
59. Fall sound in South Bend

64

ACROSS

1. __ Park, Colo.
6. Strong winds
11. Nos. man
14. Reprimand
15. "__ for naebody": Burns
16. Part of a trip
17. The U.S. Congress
19. Bambi's aunt
20. Hortatory
21. Deflect, as light
23. Done, to a Tuscan
25. Curare relative
26. Anent
28. Precursors of mode
32. "Here's __!"
35. "... how sweet is love itself __": Romeo
38. Bar stock
39. __ throw (short distance)
41. Memorabilia
42. Revels
44. __ prunes
46. Unrefined
47. Anagram for Ashe
48. Top cards
50. Discoverer of six comets
54. Do C.C.C. work
58. "War and Peace" heroine
61. Sweet drink
62. The State Department
64. Needlefish
65. Speech form
66. Type of toast
67. Unit of energy
68. Flavorful
69. "__ a Grecian Urn": Keats

DOWN

1. __ signum (see the proof)
2. Humbug
3. Big trouble's bit
4. Bulldog, for one
5. __ order (align)
6. Waistcoat
7. Berliner's expletive
8. Hideaway
9. Perry's creator
10. Word with praise
11. Stainless
12. Peter's __
13. Prized marble
18. Hen's product: Comb. form
22. Get one's goat
24. Contested
26. Not in harmony
27. Type of performance
29. Euripides drama
30. Compass pts.
31. Not a full prof.
33. Mythical Aztec hero
34. North Sea feeder
36. Knife of yore
37. Art cult
40. Corp. officers
43. Indifferently
45. Landed
48. "__ to Live": O'Hara
49. Coniferous tree
51. Set of names: Comb. form
52. Collar
53. Fermi's subject
55. Gide's "__ Die"
56. Pop
57. Protection
59. Bindlestiff
60. "... __ with seven wives"
63. Received

ACROSS

1. Early love feast
6. A sixth-day creation
10. N.F.L. team
14. Fable's finale
15. __ vu
16. Gray's text: Abbr.
17. Ancient Roman port
18. __ even keel
19. Pioneer heroine Betty
20. Town near Antietam
22. Augury
23. Pit
24. Rio Grande city
26. Trued
30. 2, 4, 6, 8 . . .
32. Word in Texas's nickname
33. Riley's love
35. Strike out
38. Ulna's locus
40. Condensing, in a way
43. Scatters newly cut grass
44. Dail's land
46. Knee, to an M.D.
47. Fix in the mind
49. Reunion and Spectrum
51. Petition
54. Aarhus native
56. Page
57. Kind of range where a miss is strange
63. "__ Do Is Dream of You"
64. Rumanian city
65. Almost inaccessible nest
66. Units of reluctance
67. Split rattan
68. Item found on a spine
69. Net
70. "Sustineo __," U.S.A.F. motto
71. Ruhr city

DOWN

1. Tekoa prophet
2. Mild expletive
3. Ionian gulf
4. Brace
5. Slip by
6. Playa clay
7. Strips
8. Discordant
9. Laundry gear
10. Maugham novel, with "The"
11. "What's in __?"
12. Having a leonine coiffure
13. Pool member
21. Passover feast
25. "__ Love Her," Beatles hit
26. Landon
27. Swag
28. Concerning
29. Voracious underwater creature
31. Swerve
34. U.S.A.
36. Possible prelude to foreclosure
37. Sicilian city
39. On the Laptev
41. Inclined
42. Astronaut Grissom
45. Book by George Sand
48. Llama's kin
50. Detroit sales gimmick
51. Tocsin
52. Martinique mount
53. Cloys
55. Llama's habitat
58. Type of thermometer
59. Kona garlands
60. Part of B.A.
61. Aswan's river
62. Astute

66

ACROSS

1. "__ Side Story"
5. Grain fungus
10. Insecticide, for short
13. Apiece
14. John Ringling or Sheree
15. Three spot
16. Despot
17. Wane
18. Calendar contents
19. Flowed
21. Regard highly
23. W.W. II area
24. Prevent legally
26. Fool
29. Globe
31. Printing mistakes
34. Endemic
36. Third son of Jacob
38. Not any
40. ". . . rode madly off __": Leacock
43. Adjective for Robert Parish
44. Roman road
45. Protein in muscles
46. Somewhat tardy
48. Bad __, German spa
50. Observe
51. Feels antipathy for
53. Devoured
55. Shooting star
58. Napless or sleepless
63. Assert
64. Ferber and Best
66. It's served in Attica
67. Ruffle one's feathers
68. "__ of the Border"

69. Ireland
70. Wright wing
71. Indian in Clive's army
72. Trust, with "on"

DOWN

1. Moistens
2. "__ of Eden"
3. Cicatrix
4. Proverbial crowd
5. Fill with love
6. Mantle
7. Rate
8. Baseball great
9. Affected
10. "Die __ Pintos," Weber-Mahler opera
11. Beloved
12. Seaport in Lebanon
15. Like a drum
20. Coral Island
22. Louis __, former French coin
25. Harsh
26. Finished a flight
27. Sound producing
28. Cochlea canal
30. Carefree
32. Casper's wife, in comics
33. A Merman role
35. Not bonkers
37. Before, to Prior
39. Domestic slave of yore

41. Misery
42. Sample
47. Fish bait in Hawaii
49. Paludous
52. Aurora's big moment
54. Nitrite, e.g.
55. __ nostrum (our sea)
56. Bad
57. Legendary Swiss marksman
59. Western alliance, for short
60. Fatigue
61. Gilels or Jannings
62. Contradict
65. Female rabbit

ACROSS

1. Did the hucklebuck
7. At the nadir
13. Diacritical mark
14. Shows
16. One of Webster's replies to Hayne
17. Old hand
18. He, objectively
19. This makes paints
21. Explorer Johnson
22. Satanic
24. Approaches
25. Uitlander foe: 1899–1902
26. Plexuses
28. Map abbr.
29. Kin of an ophicleide
30. Of perfect happiness
32. Sans twinklers
34. German river
36. Artist-author Silverstein
37. Laden
41. Army engineer corpsman
45. Audibly
46. Kind of sister or story
48. Combine
49. Sugar unit
50. Mexican cornmeal mush
52. Trendy set
53. S.E.C. member
54. Deviation from the rule
56. French business abbr.
57. Brilliant bird
59. Pragmatic person
61. Disintegrate: Brit.
62. Enters the service
63. Annalists' items
64. Fries quickly

DOWN

1. Inferred
2. Nudist
3. Basketball tourn. letters
4. Football foul
5. Remove to a distance, in law
6. Nick Carter's "__ Key"
7. Young hares
8. Oasts
9. Katarina __, figure skater
10. Chemical suffix
11. Marley's partner
12. Prickly plants
13. Stick together
15. Deadfalls
20. On which nelsons occur
23. In a queue
25. Whence a reliever comes
27. Played the paraclete
29. Carplike fish
31. Recent: Comb. form
33. Gift-openers' sounds
35. Touches up a Rembrandt
37. Golf-ball ingredient from the bully tree
38. Howl
39. Nicholas II's surname
40. Condemn
42. Exact
43. Solipsists
44. Adjusts an alarm clock
47. Sounds raucously
50. "__ of robins . . ."
51. "Maria __," 1933 song
54. Opposed, in the backwoods
55. Asian border river
58. Soul, to Simone
60. Kindled

68

ACROSS

1. Generally regarded
8. Musical form
15. Issue
16. Account
17. Balearic island
18. School at Annapolis
19. "__ pro nobis"
20. Draws back
22. French article
23. City on the Danube
24. "__ tu," Verdi aria
25. Lake Balkhash feeder
26. Moral code
29. Large quantity
30. Stone pillar
32. Perform again
34. Rome's St. John __
36. Queenly Spanish name
37. Sleep phenom.
38. Autocrats
42. Ready
46. Diminish
47. Average
49. Union unit
50. TV network
51. River in Devon
52. Germ cells
53. Liq. measures
54. Library procedure
58. Tennis term
59. Members of a pride
61. Analgesic

63. Descendant of Esau
64. Celestial gateman
65. Stripper
66. Toadies

DOWN

1. This hits the spots
2. Kin of a sheikdom
3. Flair
4. Numero __
5. Salts
6. Engrave
7. "Mommie __," C. Crawford book
8. Pertaining to the skull
9. Shucks!
10. Shamrocks' cousins
11. Divest, as of pests
12. Cézanne had one
13. Clam's plate
14. Heavenly
21. Wrath
27. All thumbs
28. Hiawatha's craft
30. Lennon's "__ and Glass"
31. Allegro, e.g.
33. Kind of bird or call
35. Travel abbr.
38. Spotted
39. Hit song in 1953
40. W.W. I poet
41. He wrote "Astrophel"
42. Laundry verb
43. Altar boy
44. Glutton
45. Some beetles
48. What the king of diamonds has
54. Victoria's physician
55. Diminutive suffix
56. This precedes bellum
57. Canter
60. Labor org.
62. Blue Hen St.

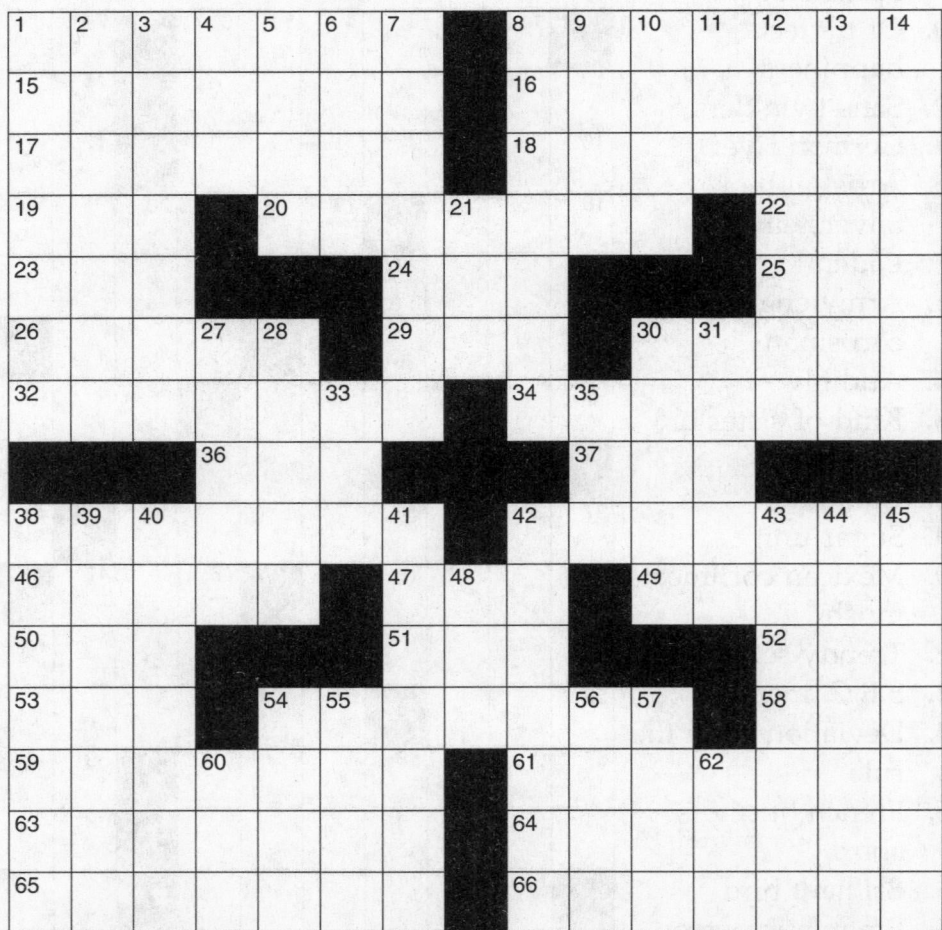

ACROSS

1. Picot feature
5. Chair-back piece
10. "I lift my __ ...": Lazarus
14. Tropical dog
15. Inquiry
16. Winged
17. Is right on the mark
20. Down Under beast
21. Button in a laundry
22. Test
23. Agora
24. March 15 in Milano
25. Biblical passage for a camel
33. Great amount
34. London's "The __ Heel"
35. Norse Healer
36. Kind of saxophone
37. Bedeck
39. Prickly pear
40. Prevail
41. Circuit
42. Factions
43. Show confidence
47. Native: Suffix
48. Banshee's bailiwick
49. Blue planet
52. Pooped
54. Adherent
57. Ignore
60. Campus org.
61. Peerce was one
62. Observe
63. Home of the Jazz
64. Husks of grains of wheat, etc.
65. Discover

DOWN

1. A memorable Bert
2. Hodgepodge
3. Eight: Comb. form
4. Opposite of neg.
5. Orb
6. Quickly
7. Place for a pendant
8. Border on
9. Distant: Comb. form
10. Knight creation
11. Midi city
12. Uxmal aborigine
13. Mouse, to a skunk
18. Receptacles
19. Burdened
23. Exec's reminder
24. Party to
25. Large conical net
26. Garden flower, for short
27. "...could __ fat"
28. Flowers, in Firenze
29. Abbr. at O'Hare
30. Wild card, sometimes
31. Full of fuzz
32. Delete
37. First-rate
38. Rightful
39. Youth
41. Woolf's "__ Lighthouse"
42. Glistening
44. Showy, shallow art
45. Trafalgar Square statue
46. Judges
49. Grayish yellow
50. Much
51. Roll; list
52. Male ant
53. Commune in NW Spain
54. Egyptian goddess of fertility
55. Pace
56. Like flax
58. N.Y.C. gambling initials
59. Vigil

70

ACROSS

1. Down Under birds
5. Jai-alai basket
10. Down Under product
14. A Carnegie
15. "Wait __ Dark"
16. Pelvic bones
17. "The __" (subject of this puzzle)
20. Even if, for short
21. Modify to suit
22. Requires
23. Preminger product
24. High __ kite
25. Koala's "kitchen"
33. Indigo dyes
34. Consumer
35. Numbat's morsel
36. Brief autobiography
37. Drafty places
39. "Money __ object"
40. When Paris sizzles
41. Stopper
42. Ancient Greek theater
43. 1988 bicentennial city
47. Unmatched
48. Amateur radio operators
49. Diving apparatus
52. "And the rockets' red __ . . ."
54. Half a dance
57. Southern lights
60. Alum
61. Prospect
62. Suva is its capital
63. Supporter
64. Allen or Frome

65. Down Under marsupials

DOWN

1. Prepare for publication
2. Long-run TV show
3. Indians' shell money
4. Tasman or Timor
5. Lovable
6. Bivouac
7. Traffic sign
8. Hue
9. Hgt.
10. One-dimensional
11. To the sheltered side

12. Obey
13. Cricket equipment
18. Fastens
19. Tchr.
23. F.D.R. dog
24. "__ Death": Grieg
25. Lower borders of roofs
26. Oneness
27. Quoted
28. Finnish port
29. Seagoing org.
30. Supporting frame
31. Boredom
32. Mouthlike opening
37. He played Hopalong
38. Brazilian macaw

39. One of the Argonauts
41. Fragrant wood
42. Abalone
44. Not a soul
45. Kind of daisy
46. Scottish garment
49. Tale of derring-do
50. Ringlet
51. Russian river
52. Rate; speed
53. Luxuriant
54. Muse of history
55. Son, in Buenos Aires
56. Sale sign
58. St.
59. Neighbor of Eur.

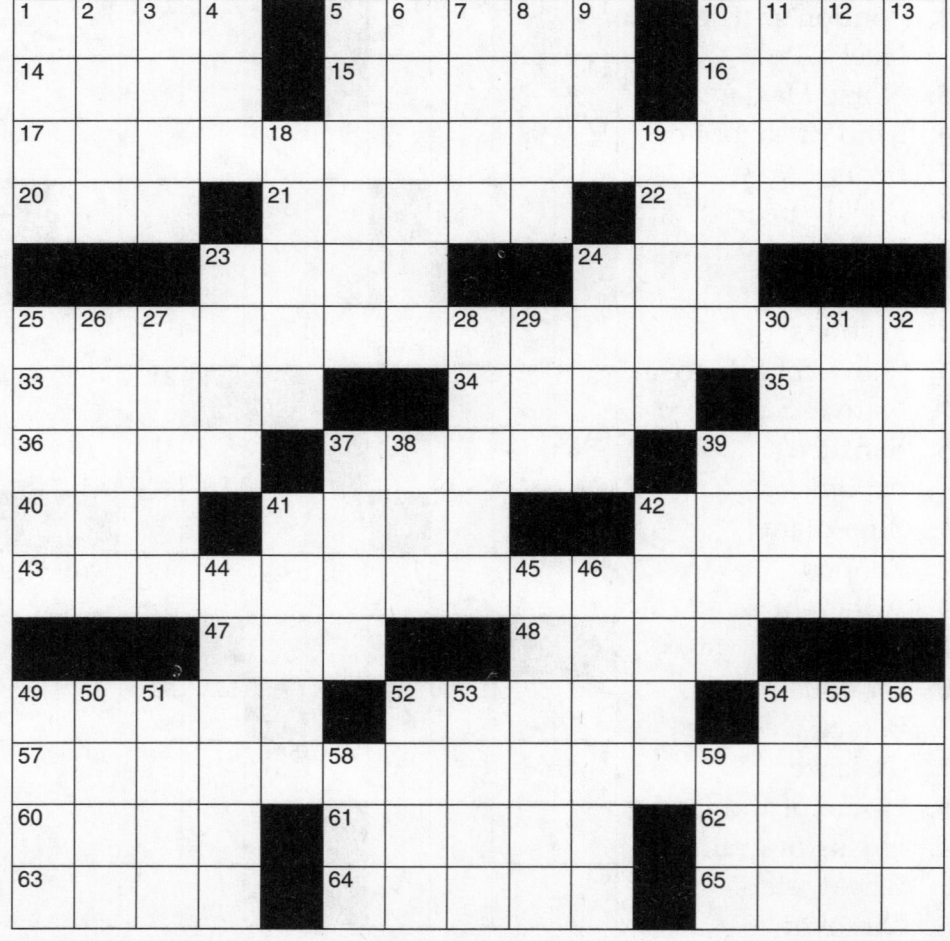

ACROSS

1. Solo
6. As well
10. Enjoy a quid
14. Distributed
15. Perches
16. Pedro's "Ahoy!"
17. "Festina lente"
20. Here, in Paris
21. Watery fluids
22. Zones
23. Eliot work
27. Director Howard
28. Squatter
32. Dali's homeland
35. Bank transaction
38. Site of the Tell legend
39. Saw
43. Berenson's subject
44. Pot item
45. Obliterate
46. Sly
49. Theater sign
50. Cornmeal mush
57. What a bigwig carries
60. Part
61. Nothing
62. Saw
66. Make eyes at
67. Brainstorm
68. Violinist Isaac
69. Brassie, e.g.
70. Cabbage; bread
71. He wrote "Too Late the Phalarope"

DOWN

1. Come clean
2. Cause filtering
3. Jack of old films
4. Mets' div.
5. Afr. country
6. Pecuniary resource
7. British measure
8. Swipe
9. W.W. II govt. agency
10. Combinations of tones
11. Inventor Elias
12. Singer Fitzgerald
13. What E. B. Browning counted
18. Org.
19. "Daily Planet" employee
24. Formal order
25. Tops
26. O'Neill's "___ Christie"
29. Popular sandwich filler
30. Aphrodite's son
31. Liturgy
32. Hit a gnat
33. Young salmon
34. Italian wine city
35. Chaney
36. Teammate of Bill Terry
37. Veneration
40. Negatives
41. A jerk
42. Trampled
47. Conveyed on a flume
48. Petruchio's wife
49. Takes to court
51. Commerce
52. Hayseed
53. Skirt part
54. Atlas feature
55. Explosive, for short
56. First orbiting American
57. Vittles
58. Como, to Carlos or Carlo
59. Frogner Park's locale
63. Soviet plane
64. O. Henry's monogram
65. One ___ time

ACROSS

1. Ancient Syria
5. La __, opera house
10. Hyde or Central
14. Weighty work
15. Group of speakers
16. Woodwind with nasal tones
17. Had creditors
18. Relating to eight
19. Cinder
20. Start of a line by Tennyson
23. Quote
24. Pop
25. Chant
28. Lofty
33. Portuguese saint
34. Kelly or Moore
36. The clear sky
37. Food fish
39. More painful
41. Seine feeder
42. Calamities
44. Some subs
46. "Cara __," 1954 song
47. Misleads
49. Poked quickly
51. "__ Maria"
52. Toothed item
53. End of 20 Across
60. Cab
61. Des Moines native
62. Utilizer
63. Capital of South Yemen
64. Aromatic plant
65. Close
66. "Let freedom __"
67. Disabled
68. __ souci

DOWN

1. Minute particle
2. Up-front group of seats
3. So be it
4. Italian doctor
5. Shoplifters' nemeses
6. Hidden stores
7. Pot builder
8. Girl's name meaning "weary"
9. Refer (to) indirectly
10. Be subsequent to
11. Qualified
12. Leo's lament
13. Ten-gallon cask
21. "Of Thee I __"
22. Hub of a wheel
25. Surrounded by water
26. Ingenuous
27. Gin and __
28. Beiges
29. Onionlike herb
30. Little Tom
31. Spooky
32. Fear greatly
35. First-class
38. Coruscant
40. Answered
43. Hindu god
45. Certain U.S. weapons
48. Pardonable
50. Rifles' kid brothers
52. Thriller episode
53. Gully, usually dry
54. Conestoga team
55. New Rochelle college
56. Sink or __
57. On the Coral
58. Shabby
59. Makes mistakes
60. Gob

ACROSS

1. Retirement accts.
5. Missile acronym
9. Mitigate
13. Hebrew bee
14. Asian capital
15. Checkup feature
16. Treaty org.
17. Preminger and Kruger
18. Garden "snake"
19. Avine collective
22. High, craggy hill
23. Propel a wherry
24. West Pointers
27. Command to a tailor
32. Yoga posture
33. Flag
34. Victorian or Edwardian
35. Feline collective
39. Summertime in N.Y.C.
40. November tally
41. Ignited anew
42. ". . . _ and in his tongue": Shak.
45. Actress Ruth
46. Jimmy's successor
47. Emulate Howard
48. Ursine collective
55. Elevator man
56. _ step, in dancing
57. Cloth measure
59. Marino-to-Duper play
60. Swinburne's "_ the Microscope"
61. Den
62. Cafeteria need
63. Landlocked land
64. Poet Lazarus

DOWN

1. _-Saud
2. Widen a hole
3. Aleutian island
4. _ of the stick
5. Mother: Comb. form
6. Division word
7. This may be over your head
8. Memorable Italian director
9. Incite by argument
10. ". . . Indians, all in _"
11. Lip
12. Give the once-over
14. Peasants, sometimes
20. Of a hope chest
21. Scandal sheet
24. Encrusted
25. Stage whisper
26. Alighieri
27. These raise Londoners
28. Berlin's Sommer
29. Soles' chasers
30. Banks on whom the Cubs banked
31. Weatherman's adjective
33. Presses a suit
36. Momentous
37. Armistice
38. Qualified to make a will
43. Ornate
44. Tellegen of silents
45. Nobelist in Chemistry: 1918
48. "Bright" inspiration for Keats
49. Actress Eilbacher
50. Tennis's Mandlikova
51. Word on a dollar bill
52. Z. Taylor and Tecumseh
53. Range
54. Pickings or Pickens preceder
55. Select
58. Between, in Bari

ACROSS

1. Bagel
5. W.W. II servicewomen
9. Picket
13. "The __ Love"
14. Where to seek what's chic
15. Approve
16. Warm-up for Winfield
19. Beings
20. Impish doings
21. Understands
22. Not __ (zilch)
23. Assagais
26. Slipcover material
30. Thane's group
31. Eastern inn
32. Anguilliform creature
33. Swimming stroke
37. Montpellier Mrs.
38. Poet Dickinson
39. Nautical term
40. Hinged hooks
42. Wall boards
44. Horseshoe part
45. Is busy
46. Quite sore
49. Bayou craft
53. He aims high
55. "Stole __ . . ."
56. Cenobites
57. Tortosa's river
58. N.B.A. team
59. Becomes the plaintiff
60. T.V.A. works

DOWN

1. Bishop's wear
2. __ even keel
3. Daugavpils native
4. Court principal
5. Reportable income
6. Most of Switzerland
7. Supportive
8. Garden legume
9. Vichyssoise base
10. Analogous
11. "Good counsellors __ no clients": Shak.
12. Sizes up visually
14. Swivets' kin
17. Where Pompey rode
18. He's quick on the flaw
22. Marshal
23. Trickster
24. Egret's pride
25. Atelier prop
26. Provides an overhead
27. English hymnologist John Mason __
28. Staircase feature
29. Les femmes
31. Move furtively
34. Eat one's words
35. Blends
36. Paid kidnappers
41. Wedding-cake features
42. Does some handwork
43. Both: Prefix
45. Yokels
46. To __ (as one)
47. Handle harassment
48. Quatre et quatre
49. Boleyn or Hathaway
50. Mr. Eban
51. Semester
52. Hit signs
54. Gambler's marker

ACROSS
1. Bucket
5. Arizona Indian
9. The Crimson Tide, for short
13. 4,840 square yards
14. Toward the mouth
15. Disappears slowly
16. Chopsticks?
18. Beds for Leo and Elsa
19. Actress O'Shea of music-hall fame
20. Ali __
22. Needle feature
23. Encircle
24. Part of a Warsaw bank?
26. Tweed, for one
28. Enclosure for a sandhog
29. Feign
30. "__ the Way," 1957 song
31. Mining car
34. "Shoe the horse, shoe __"
37. Seeming intersection of earth and sky
39. Word with tooth or heart
40. "The orb of the day"
41. Antiochian or Augustan
42. Asiatic bird
44. Strikebreaker
45. Rio kook?
48. Favorite Scrooge utterance
49. Small ape
50. Saudi Arabian province
51. Oz figure
54. Revoke, as a marriage
56. Hamlet?
58. "Mortal __," Huxley book
59. Heal
60. Italian cousin of Mount St. Helens
61. Spot for Sonny Boy
62. Annexes
63. Puma's prey

DOWN
1. NATO, for one
2. Word with tooth or heart
3. Hubbub in Dublin?
4. Opticians' products
5. Hockey great
6. Anglo-Saxon money
7. Overheat
8. Paragons
9. Barnyard sound
10. Ta-ta, in Tours
11. Streep of Hollywood
12. What you have going for you
15. Taste, to a Londoner
17. Intention
21. Illuminated
24. Homophone for 1 Across
25. Not pro
26. Casey's cudgel
27. Late protest singer
28. Trusts
32. Prague comrade?
33. Sabra's dance
35. City ENE of Paris
36. Forward passes in football
37. Sept follower
38. Collar
40. Incited
43. Riddle
44. Polished
45. Ebon or raven
46. Chattered incessantly
47. Athlete with an army
48. Fell for
51. Urchins
52. Bancroft or Boleyn
53. Intimate
55. Rubber tree
57. Word with split or tight

ACROSS

1. Greek letters
5. This precedes Baker
9. Does road work of a sort
14. "Ma, He's Making Eyes ___"
15. Fire's foe
16. Corvette's prey
17. Teen-ager's infatuation
19. "___ say die"
20. Mysterious obj. in the skies
21. Decorated the walls
23. French pronoun
24. Validate
26. Ache
28. Gear features
31. Leading man, now and then
34. Rueful exclamation
36. French cookbook word
38. Shadow: Comb. form
39. Matinee ___
40. Actress Saint's middle name
41. Sound from Tabby's "motor"
42. Third son of Jacob
43. Church part
44. Pinches
45. Massages
47. Crime causing a conflagration
49. Kind of preview
51. Claros or conchas
55. "Ulalume" author
57. Theater districts
60. Welcome ___
61. This may end a dream
63. Court score
65. Central Asian mountain system
66. Any letter in NATO
67. Clothes or family follower
68. Scratches out
69. Relatives of sens.
70. Tear

DOWN

1. Another name for New Guinea
2. Fill
3. ". . . ___ blind desire": Kipling
4. Follower of Aug.
5. Greatly excited
6. Betty of cartoons
7. Flow along or against
8. Kind of board
9. Fountain fare
10. Ribicoff
11. Trophy
12. Asian weight unit
13. Mus. group
18. Battle site in 1914, 1915 and 1917
22. Strange
25. Native of Leghorn
27. Grating upon
29. Kind of door
30. Brother of Hengist
32. What snobs put on
33. Conjunction
34. Arabian gulf
35. Parlor pieces
37. Rank
39. Sort
40. Kenyan native
44. Like blue jays and catbirds
46. Skin layer
48. Dred and Walter
50. Grain sorghum
52. Love, to 25 Down
53. Despoil
54. Bucephalus, for one
55. Former talk-show host
56. Highly seasoned meat dish
58. "The ___ Eagle"
59. Hockey foul
62. Actress Charlotte
64. P.O. concern

ACROSS

1. Inverness is one
5. Kind of strip
10. Struck, old style
14. Across the plate
15. Seed
16. River in a canine's name
17. Gardner's lawyer-detective
19. Caesar's etymological cousin
20. Subject of a book by Adelaide Bry: 1976
21. Anguineous creatures
22. Not so prolix
24. Sometime partners of stars
25. First name of the 18th U.S. President
26. Identity documents
29. Hammett private eye
32. With 40 Across, a patriot
33. Visorless cap
34. Punty
35. Cut of meat
36. Passages for gas, steam, etc.
37. Chevet
38. Form for Frank Lloyd Wright
39. Plods, as through mud
40. See 32 Across
41. Stretch
43. Gripping tool
44. Forage plant
45. Licorice or parsnip
46. Laud
48. One of Adam's boys
49. Hood's quaff
52. ___ Kong

53. Spillane's slugging shamus
56. Setting for a gem
57. Heed Revere's warning
58. Home of the Hawks
59. Items in Trevino's bag
60. Slender candle
61. Blessing

DOWN

1. Clerical mantle
2. Some are rarae
3. Flibberti gibbety
4. Commit a blooper
5. Promising ones
6. Athletic fields
7. Put into disorder
8. Intl. labor group
9. Small French coins
10. Petty ruler
11. Christie's gumshoe
12. Of wrath: Lat.
13. HI before 1959
18. Pine for
23. Formerly, formerly
24. One of the astronauts
25. Male red deer
26. West Indian volcano
27. Coral island
28. Van Dine's suave sleuth
29. Twilled fabric
30. Medicine applicator
31. Beautiful areas
33. Salvation Army founder
36. Dining-table doily
37. Finished a flight
39. NCO's
40. Love, in Lanai
42. Whinnies
43. Commotion
45. A.F.B. in Texas
46. Unit of illumination
47. Libertine
48. Between hop and jump
49. Bullets and bombs, for short
50. Light, gauzy fabric
51. Milesian's land
54. A Gershwin
55. Kind of scene

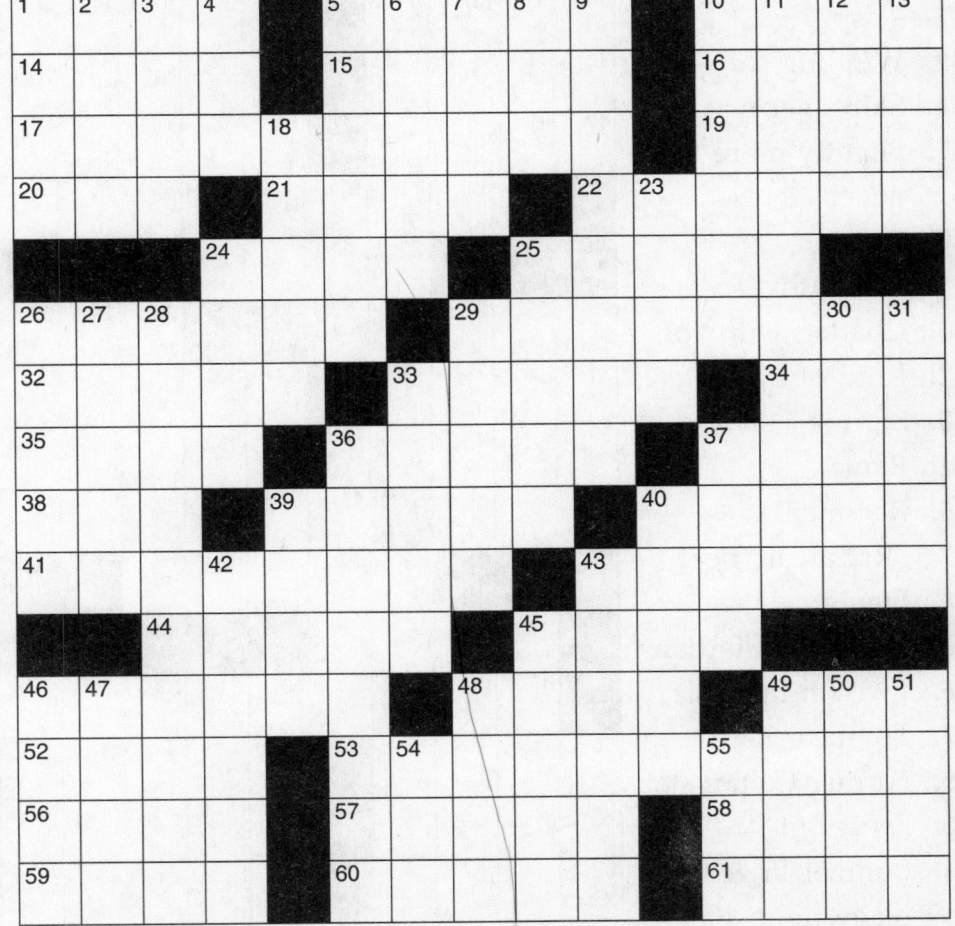

ACROSS

1. Pop
5. Bundles
10. Contest at Belmont
14. Enthusiasm
15. Gothic arch
16. Mine entrance
17. Whitewall, e.g.
18. Consumer advocate
19. Tease
20. A beginning
23. Portion
24. Where Caesar trod
25. Offshoot
28. Like Harvard's "Pudding"
31. Gasp
32. Winding
34. Skip over water
37. Slightly more than never
40. "__ and Sympathy"
41. Chatter, with "on"
42. Kind of eye
43. Storms
44. Rank
45. Regimen
47. "Rubáiyát" poet
49. Finally
55. Manitoban Indian
56. Two on the aisle
57. Toy-bear hero
59. Former Celtics star
60. Fences in
61. Pulitzer Prize playwright: 1953
62. Glut
63. Nettlesome
64. Broadway gas

DOWN

1. Coterie
2. Hodgepodge
3. Mild oath
4. Short narrative
5. Plus
6. Yawning
7. Playground of Venice
8. Kind of number
9. Curative agents
10. Curio
11. __ a dozen
12. Autumn beverage
13. Season in Chartres
21. Eternity
22. Boxer's pinnacle
25. Detect
26. Support of a sort
27. Quechuan Indian
28. Sword handles
29. Botanical exterior
30. Umpire's call
32. Bottleneck
33. Potter's paste
34. Teresa Stratas, e.g.
35. In the thick of
36. Soccer great
38. Seething with indignation
39. Diamondback
43. What some hairlines do
44. Slender fish
45. Andrea __
46. Passive
47. Repeatedly
48. Cryptogamous
50. Nile killers
51. Lowest high tide
52. Surrealist painter
53. Kind of eagle or wolf
54. Trademark
55. TV initials
58. Party member of a sort

ACROSS

1. Chits
5. Do a parent's job
9. Limited amount of time
13. "A part to tear __ in": Shak.
14. Manx's relative
15. Scintillated
16. Baptism, e.g.
17. Item in many still lifes
18. Part of a Dante opus
19. Cleaves
21. Opera star Alda
23. Some scares for Dick Weber
25. Signed a contract
26. Range of influence
28. Suspenseful
30. Word of consolation
31. Red and Black
32. Like one side of Luna
36. "Cabaret" lyricist
37. Grew crops in a fixed order
40. Merry, in Avignon
41. Autocrat
43. Hebrew letters
44. "Grandfather Stories" author
46. Not __ in the world
48. Stock-market declines
49. Sunnite deity
51. Fix rattan furniture
53. Outstanding, as a performance
55. Hammett whodunit, with "The"
58. Lag behind
59. __ Rios, Jamaica
61. 1953 Pulitzer Prize playwright
62. Lower-echelon personnel
63. Spread
64. Author Ephron
65. Rockfish
66. Brimming
67. Punkie

DOWN

1. "G.W.T.W." setting
2. Kind of rain
3. Mother of Solomon
4. More sharply sloped
5. Legendary equestrian
6. Cover one's traces
7. Beast that balks
8. Coral ridge
9. Hit the golf ball with the heel of the club
10. City in Puerto Rico
11. Paid for a hand
12. Modernists
15. What a radar beam does
20. Thinner in density, as gases
22. Hair treatment
24. Shore-dinner tidbit
26. Directive to a typesetter
27. Degs. for would-be Kants
29. Highway sign
31. Ending for hip or poll
33. Father of Electra
34. Storm
35. Oversized chocolate chip
38. Mid-American Indian
39. Lama of renown
42. Auto races
45. Collection agency's tactic
47. Directions to square dancers
48. Dolphin colony
49. Roman villa features
50. Clues
52. A Kennedy
53. Puncture
54. Mouth part
56. Taj Mahal site
57. Undiluted, as whisky
60. Actor Gulager

80

ACROSS

1. Quarrels
7. Pertain
13. Dixie river
15. Soviet republic
16. Changed into gaseous form
17. Horseshoe throws
18. "Cap'n —," Lincoln novel
19. Polliwog
21. — Tyler, English rebel
22. Rivals of the Dodgers
24. Tourist attraction in Pompeii
25. Wait
26. Condition
28. One of three in "cyclic"
29. Musician of '76
30. Sign of coryza
32. Type of scholar
34. Exist
35. Experienced
36. Thatcher et al.
39. Pusher's customer
42. Tommy Dorsey favorite
43. Lew Wallace hero
45. Show disdain
47. Where Sligo is
48. Dark brown
50. Thrive
51. — Jacinto
52. Periods
54. Pious person, in Paris: Abbr.

55. Paul Pry
57. Ocean swell
59. Dürer and Whistler, e.g.
60. Altar-bound
61. Places to stay
62. Winebibbers

DOWN

1. Frugal ones
2. Dry red beverages
3. Virginia river
4. Finnish port
5. Parcel's partner
6. Slander
7. Blows one's top
8. Water bird
9. Triangle side
10. Fish of the herring family
11. Scolding speeches
12. — Island in the Pacific
14. Cite as proof
15. Copenhagen coins
20. Slapstick staple
23. Soap ingredient
25. Auction action
27. Strange
29. Certain pens
31. Zuider —
33. Trough
36. Italian gulf
37. S.A. river
38. Tailor's tool
39. Melodic
40. Bouquet for a belle
41. Meadowlands performer
42. — Marco Polo
44. High points
46. Fall apparel
48. Foresighted fellows
49. Concerning
52. Small barracuda
53. Pudding starch
56. Exclamations
58. Interstice

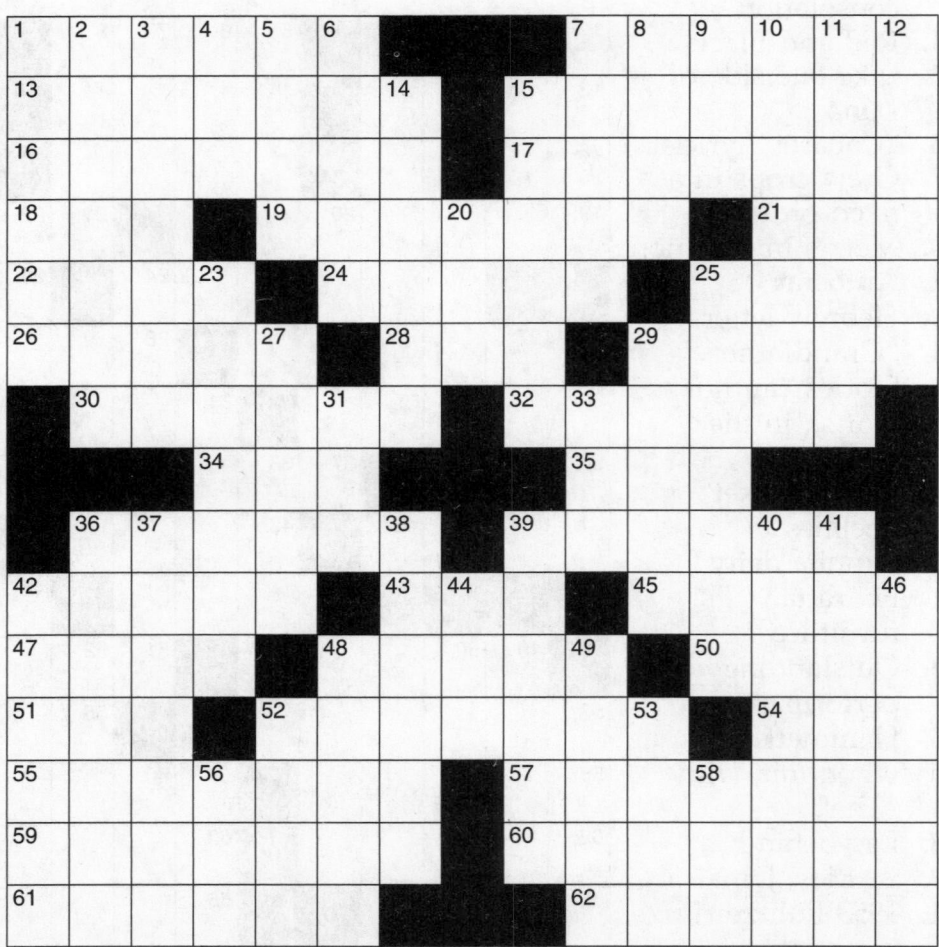

ACROSS
1. Fleecer's aide
6. J.E.H. was one
10. Play tricks
14. TV sound section
15. Comfort
16. Tel __
17. Travel account by 61 Across
19. Hair follower
20. Advice to Kelly
21. Mull over
23. Schisgal hit play: 1964
26. Nanking nurse
27. Kubrick's computer
28. In a tumult
30. Half-track cargo
33. Edition: Abbr.
36. Chinese secretary in piece by 61 Across
39. Sikkim's site
40. Franklin's spouse
41. U.S. doubles co-champ: 1976
43. Manipulates, as prices
44. Site of Brown U., alma mater of 61 Across
46. __ Fell Pike, England's highest peak
47. __-majesté
48. Hibernians
49. Beam
51. "Persistence of Memory" painter
54. Soak flax
55. Levy
58. Vacuous
60. Tart
61. American humorist
66. M.I.T. is one
67. __ gold

68. Sole of a plow
69. Space acronym
70. V.I.P.'s aide
71. B'way dog

DOWN
1. Maxim
2. Vietnamese city
3. Parts of psyches
4. Wagons-__ (French Pullmans)
5. The Roman language, later on
6. Consort of Frey
7. Responded to opportunity's knock
8. Kind of blonde
9. A tide
10. De la Roche locale
11. Undercover agent in story by 61 Across
12. Languish
13. "__ thine"
18. Intention
22. Word of surprise
23. Some shoe-factory employees
24. Of a Russian range
25. Book by 61 Across
29. Certain ladies' rooms
31. "Marvelous __" of the old Mets
32. When Gary Coleman will be 34
34. Fin de __
35. Most clearheaded

37. Feedbox info
38. Boots one
39. On the briny
42. Jitters
45. Sophoclean protagonist
47. Fleur-de-__
50. Vessel of a sort
52. In re
53. Malayan gibbon
55. "The fat __ the fire": Heywood
56. African monkey
57. U.S. satellite
59. Raines or Logan
62. Minor offs.
63. Chess piece
64. Augment
65. Victor at Elchingen

82

ACROSS

1. Raison d' __
5. Ermine
10. Tarot, e.g.
14. __ and branch
15. Uhlan's weapon
16. Source of a bitter drug
17. With 58 Across, a Dryden quotation
20. Small heavenly body
21. Alexander and Darius
22. Protuberance
23. Fruity drink
24. Impassive
27. Acres for grazing
33. "__ all, folks"
34. Bottom of the barrel
35. U.S. cousin of the BBC
36. Weird
37. Direct attention to
39. Mecca for shoppers
40. Compass pt.
41. Arnaz
42. Outmoded
43. Sets right
46. Michaelmas daisy
47. Consumed
48. Examination
50. Laundry workers
54. Dressed
58. See 17 Across
60. Diminutive ending
61. Come afterward
62. Dismiss
63. Observes
64. Crucible product
65. Scads

DOWN

1. Sea eagles
2. Spree
3. Writer Jaffe
4. Infinite time
5. Turned around
6. Torn piece
7. Can. province
8. Discomfort
9. Holden Caulfield, e.g.
10. Mount in NW Israel
11. Jai __
12. Divagate
13. Sandra and Ruby
18. Coalitions
19. Family in an Eliot novel
24. Guide
25. "On __ I Stand," book by Countee Cullen
26. Rowed
28. Michael Caine movie: 1966
29. French homophone for nay
30. Salt's "Halt!"
31. West Scandinavians
32. Librarian's device
37. National Guard of the U.S.
38. Tee predecessor
39. Large dogs
41. Discourage
42. Strass
44. Wives of rajahs
45. Phidian creation
49. Cohan's first wife
50. April 13, e.g.
51. Plexus
52. Boniface, in Bologna
53. Dispatched
55. Wading bird
56. Name of a republic: 1937–49
57. Nancy __, fictional sleuth
59. Dir. from Paris to Vichy

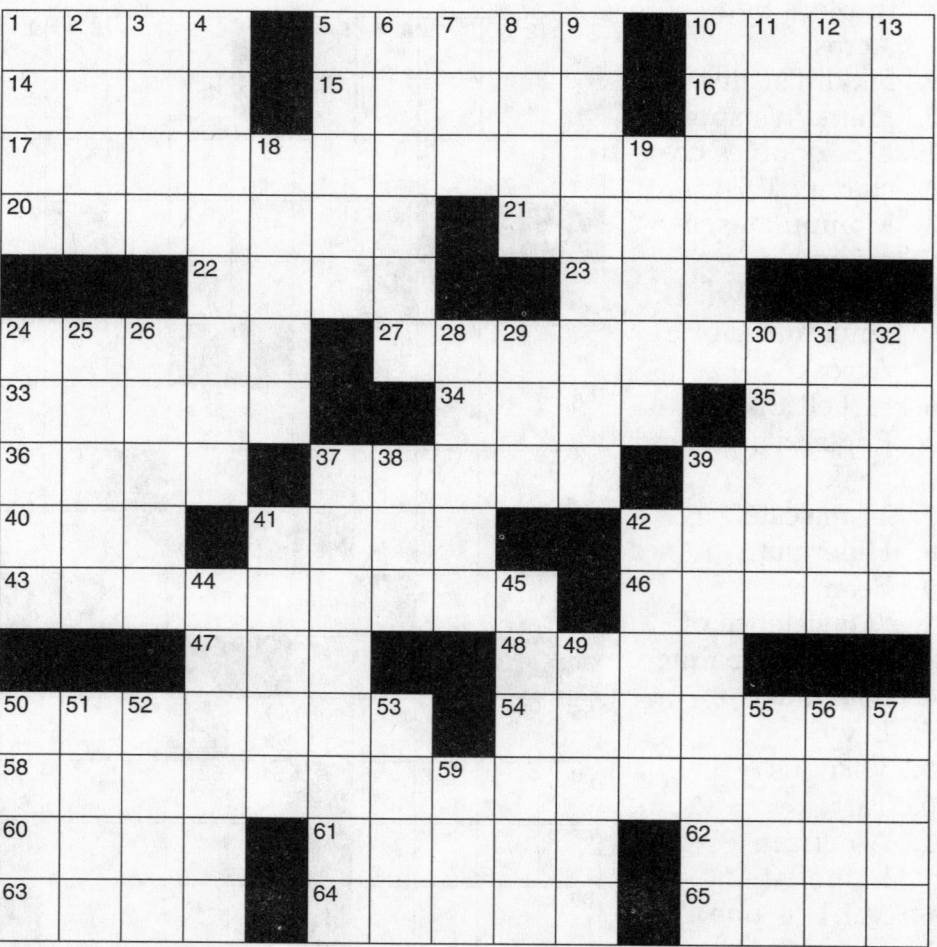

ACROSS

1. Moves restlessly
5. Fish armor
10. Meek one
14. Others, to Octavius
15. Site of the Rodin Museum
16. Persian poet
17. Buck heroine
18. Tapestry
19. Not any
20. Paper money: Slang
22. Showy bird
23. Cowpoke's concern
24. Collar stiffener
26. Inlets
28. A women's club
32. Bulldoze
35. Govt. agents
37. Dawn
38. Spoken
40. Last Trojan king
42. Christmas carol
43. Get to be
45. Roman commoner
47. Monogram of the author of "The Hollow Men"
48. Oklahomans
50. Edible fish
52. Long-run musical
54. Military vacation
58. Stage
61. Like Methuselah
63. Anagram for ache
64. The cheekbone
65. Founder of the Fathers of Oratory

66. Countertenor
67. Famed fiddle name
68. Whilom
69. Put to trial
70. Cabled
71. Fr. holy ones

DOWN

1. British prisons
2. Apportion
3. Woody's frequent co-star
4. Judy Collins, e.g.
5. Box
6. Pet's pal
7. Court order: Fr.
8. Flowering vines
9. Sigmoid letter
10. U. of Texas athlete
11. All-conqueror, Roman style
12. Horse's neck growth
13. Author Harte
21. Courage
22. Tan color
25. Vagabondized
27. Electrical unit
29. Carbon particles
30. Angers
31. Auction
32. Male swans
33. Mountain: Comb. form
34. Home of the Baylor Bears
36. Short snort
39. Surprising winner at Santa Anita
41. Estrange
44. "Lady of the __": Wordsworth
46. Kind of boy or buoy
49. Spicy meat
51. Gear for codders
53. Kind of energy
55. Fend off
56. Biblical sentence
57. Corrects copy
58. Fuel for Flaherty
59. Hearty's partner
60. Stein's "Four Saints in Three __"
62. Grating
64. Symbol of voracity

84

ACROSS

1. Coin drop
5. Actor Peck, to friends
9. Maze entrance
14. Onion, for Ovid
15. Wedding pellets
16. Mead ingredient
17. Careless omission
19. Title holder
20. Fame
21. Auditory
23. Sky sighting
24. Avian activity
26. Bumpkin
28. Cubic meter
30. Deli purchase
33. "__ Rheingold"
36. Collision
38. Wand for Mehta
39. Arden
41. Depot: Abbr.
42. Puppet Mortimer
43. Habituate
44. Bout
46. Author of "Life with Father"
47. Least common
49. Clairvoyants
51. Painter of ballerinas
53. Collars worn in the 16th and 17th centuries
57. G.I. address
59. A son of Seth
61. Lady of Spain
62. March master
64. Potential losers
66. Blake subject
67. Uncluttered
68. Greek W.W. II underground group
69. Cookout residue
70. Party men, for short
71. Repudiate

DOWN

1. Reject
2. Quay
3. Does what Pandora did
4. Gypsy's decks
5. Cheshire cat, e.g.
6. Trailer truck
7. Sonic feedback
8. Tycoon J. Paul
9. This will bar a jar in a car
10. Emergency road service
11. Marked with rings
12. Offshore hazard
13. Novitiate
18. Changes one's course of action
22. One of the Cyclades
25. Fescue, e.g.
27. Verve
29. Kefauver
31. Unit of syllabic length
32. __ 500, auto race
33. Whitetail
34. Tolstoy heroine
35. Lone prospector
37. Misanthrope
40. Hudson Bay Indian
45. Four o'clock china
48. Palomino color
50. Prepared for a paint job
52. It's measured in decibels
54. County in Montana
55. "... __-voice of England" (Tennyson on Milton)
56. Impudent
57. Nick Charles's pet
58. Parisians' peas
60. Old dagger
63. Call, in poker
65. Hungry Horse is one

ACROSS

1. Ghost
6. Waist scarf
10. Moslem leader
14. __ deux, ballet figure
15. Olive for Octavia
16. Lounging slipper
17. Former Mediterranean coin
18. Look ahead
19. Patch of ground
20. Forts
23. Quoits stake
24. Appearance
25. Part of a football team
26. Greek letter
28. Artful
29. Burglar
30. Fencing tactic
33. Backslides
35. Street, in Sevilla
36. Clumsy
39. Deprived
40. Fresh and firm
41. Body in outer space
44. Feminine name meaning "noble"
45. Meager
46. Dom. of former Lion of Judah
49. Football Hall-of-Famer Ford
50. North Sea feeder
51. Indian city
52. Londoner's last letter
54. What ads strive for
57. Metals
59. Mariners' patron saint
60. ". . . long-drawn __ and fretted vault": Gray
61. Dragon, for one

62. Hold back
63. Appraises
64. Part of M.V.P.
65. Killer whales
66. Photo within a photo

DOWN

1. Fits of activity
2. Lozenge
3. Fish-eating bird
4. Ancient theater
5. Composer of "Music in the Air"
6. Styron's "__ Choice"
7. Rider of a sort
8. Sailor's need
9. Learned __, famed jurist

10. "The __ of the Perverse," Poe story
11. Manifold or complex
12. Plant of the lily family
13. Allot
21. Relief carving
22. Typewriter part
27. Consolation for Earl Anthony
31. Ethereal being
32. Interference, in tennis
33. Cotton thread
34. Poplars
36. Wood sorrel
37. Ending for drunk or dull

38. __ choice, in baseball
39. Site of Baldwin-Wallace College
41. Exercise book of a sort
42. Controversial
43. __ choice (lack of an alternative)
46. Casts out via pores
47. Seat of County Kerry
48. Most vigorous
51. Beelike
52. Kind of lens
53. Hence
55. Atmosphere: Prefix
56. __ passu (with equal pace)
58. Gel

86

ACROSS

1. Asian tree
5. Candle threads
10. Retired soccer star
14. A memorable Anita
15. Mete out
16. Wading bird
17. Before long
18. Climbing plant
19. Fox __
20. Gain an advantage over
23. Angler's purchase
24. Prosecute
25. Subordinate ruler
29. "It's __!"
31. Needlefish
34. Different
35. Book of poems by Ciardi
36. Actress Storm
37. Charity organization
40. Corrida creature
41. "Break __!" (actors' good luck saying)
42. Teheran native
43. Simple sugar
44. Shock
45. Defeated
46. Muscle spasm
47. Department or river in France
48. Halftime entertainers
55. Grantland of sports fame
56. School for Pierre
57. Matinée __
59. Concerning
60. Former German money unit
61. Treatment

62. Owner's document
63. Where one-armed bandits are fed
64. "When Irish __ . . ."

DOWN

1. Hirt and Pacino
2. Cote sounds
3. Booty
4. Domestic slave of yore
5. Clout
6. Epic about Achilles, Hector et al.
7. Razor __
8. Hawaiian coffee-growing region
9. Begin
10. Meaningful
11. Spanish river
12. Beast that has his pride
13. Abbr. at Kennedy
21. S.A. bird
22. Shout
25. __ voce
26. Duel personality created by Dumas
27. "Over __"
28. San __, Italy
29. Pale as a poltergeist
30. Life story
31. Anwar's predecessor
32. Coeur d' __, Idaho
33. Varnish ingredient
35. Legal defense org.
36. One-fifth of Papa Dionne's surprise
38. Toothed bars
39. Famed bride of July 1981
44. Thus, to Tacitus
45. Filaments
46. Cornered
47. Lace tag
48. "The world's __ oyster": Shak.
49. Land measure
50. Ending for poet or myth
51. __ contendere
52. Gallic resort
53. 1944 event
54. Angry
55. Free (of)
58. "__ Misérables"

ACROSS

1. Sea flyer
5. Adorn in a finicky way
10. Try for a ringer
14. Jack Sprat's diet
15. Duck, or its down
16. Aimless; pointless
17. Tops
18. French place of learning
19. Total defeat
20. Tale of Venus de Milo?
23. Highest honor
24. Purpose
25. Postures at bat
29. Enrage
33. Instant
34. Jittery
36. Alley __ of comics
37. River in Yorkshire
38. Fry in very little fat
39. Had on
40. Moslemism is one: Abbr.
41. Chrysler Building feature
42. Ballerina Jeanmaire
43. Russian citadel
45. Noisy oil wells
47. Swiss waterway
48. Three, in Rome
49. Tale of autumn leaves?
58. Chester __ Arthur
59. Start of many a limerick
60. Margarine
61. Columbus's return-trip ship: 1492–93
62. Sniggler for wrigglers
63. Tilt, as a ship
64. Spur; stimulus
65. Gives, as to charity (with "out")
66. Kismet

DOWN

1. Exile island of 1814
2. Menace for mariners
3. Space agency
4. Overpower with emotion
5. Runt
6. Paddy product
7. Fan-club hero
8. Pell's partner
9. Make-believe
10. Angry speech
11. Repute
12. Urban eyesore
13. Coteries
21. __ homo
22. Formerly
25. Heron's relative
26. More veracious
27. Usher's beat
28. Cleaner's concern
29. Between: Prefix
30. Not a soul
31. More grievous
32. Musketeers' foils
35. Fr., Ger., Ital. et al.
38. Full of vigor
39. Lycanthrope
41. Cabbage dish
42. Like "a day in June"
44. Bacchante; distraught woman
46. Additional ones
49. Outlaw outfit
50. Hodgepodge
51. Dog in "Peter Pan"
52. Van Gogh's brother
53. "War is __": Sherman
54. Tupelo or tulip
55. Hip bones
56. Raven's haven
57. Be foolishly fond

88

ACROSS

1. Great amount
6. Rescue
10. Arf or woof
14. Decorative
16. Relative of a yucca
17. Never? Well, almost
19. C or F, e.g.
20. Souvenir
21. Mill product
22. __ majesty
23. Wind direction: Abbr.
24. Where a Venus was found
27. Constellation
32. Brainchild
33. Pennsylvania city
35. Haggard novel
36. A playground pair?
39. Bolivian export
40. Prefaces
41. Term in knitting
42. Offerings on a Florida menu
44. Grazes on the lea
45. Curtain support
46. Qualified
48. Elder statesmen
51. "Saki" was his pen name
53. Cave dweller
56. Cheap production?
59. "__ Old Cowhand"
60. Retinue group
61. C.S.A. troops

62. "__ Sorry Now?"
63. Satiny

DOWN

1. Swindle
2. Lake in Ireland
3. Suffix with buoy and exult
4. Miss West
5. Strikes sharply
6. Kind of dance
7. Salt tree
8. Conceited
9. Sprite
10. Bombard
11. "I cannot tell __"
12. City once saved by geese

13. Boat-bottom timber
15. Grandson of Adam
18. Dead Sea monastic
22. What slugabeds do
23. Facing a glacier
24. Gloves for Bench
25. Booth or Newman
26. Met soprano Mitchell
27. Burnt residue
28. Part of a goblet
29. Offspring
30. Piece of pottery
31. Whimpers
33. Made a mistake
34. Agent: Suffix

37. Resist
38. Fencing gear
43. Dolls up
44. Headline-makers in spring
46. Bancroft and Boleyn
47. __ Mawr
48. Budge
49. "O, woe!"
50. Snatch
51. Mode of procedure: Abbr.
52. Golden-rule preposition
53. Part of N.B.
54. Comedian Johnson
55. Chore
57. Rover's offering
58. Crony

ACROSS

1. "Merry Widow" composer
6. Largest of the Marianas
10. Art —
14. Muse of poetry
15. Odd, in Glasgow
16. Hebrew measure
17. Love of objets d'art
18. On the way
20. Stop signs
22. Big Dipper star
23. Engine sound
24. Typhoons
25. Owl sounds
29. Plumed bird
30. "Just — Those Things"
31. Consumer protection agcy.
34. Toboggan
35. Ski resort
36. Letter opener
37. Thesaurus wd.
38. Winter fall
39. "Boys of Summer" figure
40. Rabbit stew
42. Neptune or Poseidon
44. Voiced
45. Author of "The Naked and the Dead"
46. He hides when he rides
50. Land of the wallaby

52. Make amends
53. To — (precisely)
54. Night: Comb. form
55. Mau Mau's home
56. Cause to go
57. Mediocre
58. To be: Sp.

DOWN

1. Counter-clockwise
2. Hoffer
3. Deer
4. Not single
5. Go backpacking
6. Decadent
7. Samovars
8. Painting, e.g.
9. Annual event in Boston
10. "Taxi Driver" star
11. Downs or salts
12. I.O.U.'s
13. Solemn vow
19. Snobbish
21. Not safe
24. Thanksgiving helping
25. Hardy girl
26. Like Medusa
27. Songbird
28. Free from confinement
31. Gripe
32. Home plate, e.g.
33. — Rabbit
35. Race-result list
36. Dispirits
38. More perspicacious
39. Hear the snooze alarm
40. Discontinued
41. To's partner
42. Recipe direction
43. Iron: Ger.
45. He wrote "Serpico"
46. Urges Rover to attack
47. Predisposed
48. Writer Seton
49. 1984, e.g.
51. Card game

90

ACROSS

1. 128 cu. ft. of wood
5. Fabulizers
10. On in years
14. Jai follower
15. Put out
16. Flutter
17. "__ that touch liquor . . ."
18. Zoo denizen
20. Imam's bailiwick
22. Aldrich's "Story of __ Boy"
23. Misdo
24. The Middies
26. Arabic letter
28. Fin __ (decadent)
32. Wading birds
35. Orchestra member
36. Relative of etc.
38. Waldorf, e.g.
40. Electrical unit
41. Gluts
43. Adhesive
44. Conclude
46. Mystical mark
47. Particle of dust
48. Alpine serenade
50. Demonstrated, as strikers
52. Pitcher
54. Lunchtime
55. Double agent
58. Niche object
60. Passable
64. Anticipate
67. Go by plane
68. "Loverly" look
69. Untamed

70. Inveigh
71. Annoyingly slow
72. Defective
73. Christmastide

DOWN

1. Unflappable
2. Salmagundi
3. Knocks
4. Anxiety
5. Permits, British style
6. Like: Suffix
7. Where the Ob flows
8. Cugat's forte
9. Flower features
10. Wheat feature

11. Look
12. At any time
13. Antelope's playmate
19. Juan's goodbye
21. Wield
25. Wedding locale
27. Piecemeal
28. Peace symbol
29. Hard wood
30. Italian coin
31. Go through, as food
33. Apportion
34. Cook in a bit of fat
37. "Pravda" founder: 1912

39. Achievement
42. Next
45. Lapwing
49. Batted first
51. Cole Porter musical, "Hitchy-__"
53. Spur feature
55. Dish out messily
56. Comics character
57. Egg feature
59. Zhivago's love
61. Swain
62. Seed coat
63. Senate Minority Leader: 1987-1995
65. Essential
66. Green

ACROSS

1. Until now
7. Hari, the spy
11. Drive into hard
14. Inept painter
15. Cry of sorrow
16. Opposite of WSW
17. Maroon
18. Those on the late watch
20. Embassy man
22. Incense
23. French pastes
25. Sacker of Rome
26. Sleek fabric
27. Like twice-told tales
28. Home for a parson
30. Kind of line or lock
31. "The Lip"
32. Tame broncos
33. Contend
35. Access to sewers
37. Valet
41. Ovine belle
42. Agreeing motions
43. U.N. arm
44. Learn of
47. Abundance
49. French numbers
50. "__ Is Born"
52. Candlenut tree
53. Deli portion
54. Clerical vestment
55. Croquet gear
57. Green sailor
59. Marked up copy
62. Season in Limoges
63. Anklebones
64. To wit
65. Knight of TV
66. Finds out
67. Anglers' tangles

DOWN

1. N.F.L. goals, for short
2. Crop item
3. Continuance in time
4. Simmered down
5. Shelters for some Cubs
6. Earth goddess
7. Posse's dragnet
8. Outlanders
9. Playground game
10. "Them __ gits"
11. Secluded
12. Lack of vigor
13. "And all the __ women merely players"
19. Manual arts
21. Man on a $10,000 bill
23. Site of one lifeline
24. Length times width
28. Hybrid critters
29. Pussyfoot
32. Show respect
34. Style-setting coterie
36. King's messenger
37. Righteous
38. Man with a portfolio
39. Author Waugh
40. A winning margin
42. "__ an island"
44. Braised porcine dish
45. Tangible assets
46. Made up for
48. Mexican dish
49. __ Thule (remote goal)
51. Breathers
53. French city
56. Monocle
58. West, of films
60. Pipe joint
61. Bad: Prefix

92

ACROSS

1. Coal scuttles
5. Machine tool
10. Garbed
14. Biblical shepherd
15. Assumed name
16. Circle of light
17. __ me tangere
18. Heavy reinforcing seams
19. Say confidently
20. Suburban sign
23. Positive factor
24. Eggy drink
25. Article XXI of the Constitution
28. Deserter
33. Highway sign
34. New Orleans sight
35. Spring time in Paris
36. Numerous
37. Meadowlands events
38. British statesman
39. Choose
40. Like Peary's expedition
41. Rudimentary
42. Road sign
44. Heated argument
45. Inlet
46. Lion's share
47. Park sign
55. Well-informed about
56. Fraction of a pound
57. Meander
58. Sower's flower grower
59. __ Park, Colo.
60. Poker stake
61. Towel monogram
62. Curt
63. Lupine look

DOWN

1. Aaron or Bauer
2. "An ill wind that nobody blows good"
3. Opposite of stet
4. Bridge sign
5. Licit
6. Hebrew letters
7. Joust
8. "What __ God wrought!"
9. Perfumes
10. Put on the cuff
11. Pompeii covering: A.D. 79
12. English country festivals
13. Buzzing insects
21. Pearl Buck heroine
22. Author Vidal
25. On dit
26. Storehouse
27. Fourth-down plays
28. Made-over tire
29. Incessantly
30. Off-target
31. Relating to birth
32. Pugilistic pinnacle
34. French composer
37. Stew ingredients
38. Idyllic
40. Greek letters
41. Quartet member
43. Vogues
44. Upright
46. Scottish court officer
47. Door sign
48. Fencing sword
49. Activist
50. Marsh plant
51. Division word
52. Not a bit
53. "The __ George Apley"
54. Norse giant of myth

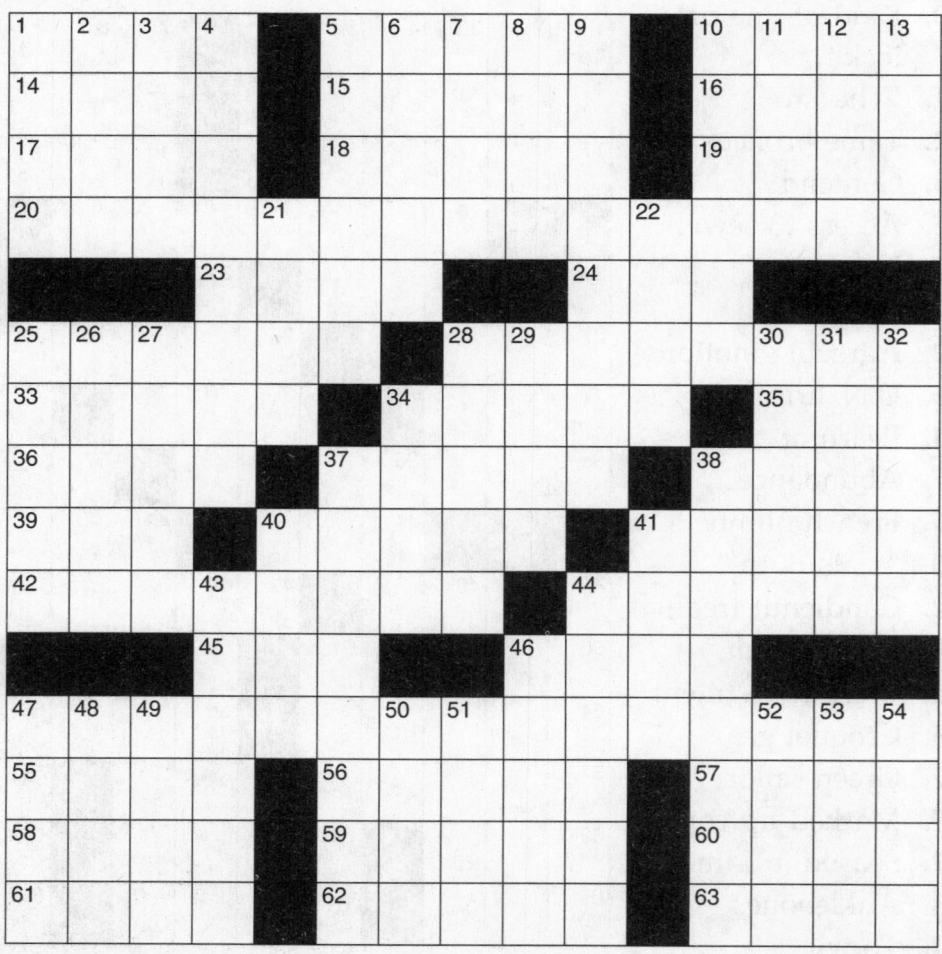

ACROSS

1. "Stop!": Naut.
6. Hastened
10. Shoemakers' tools
14. Concise
15. Site of Guantánamo Bay
16. Boutique
17. Famous Hollywood restaurant
19. Type size
20. Fleet C.O.
21. Showing good sense
22. English native
24. London office break
26. Pair of game birds
27. ___ du Diable
28. Young person
29. These: Fr.
32. Walk slowly
35. Blowhard
37. Umpire's decision
38. Model T starter
40. Altar end of a church
41. More ritzy
43. Balance-sheet entry
44. Muscular twitch
45. Picnic problem
46. Meas. of economic activity
47. Tails of Q's
49. Gas-station sign, of old
53. Showy flower
55. English streetcar
56. Dos Passos trilogy
57. Single
58. Texas state flower
61. One opposed
62. Japanese aborigine
63. Part of TNT
64. Kind of leader
65. Movie critic Rex
66. Actor Buddy

DOWN

1. Not in the field
2. Cape ___ Islands
3. Pleasant odor
4. Compass heading
5. ___ strength (breaking point)
6. Public outburst
7. Sheer; simple
8. Decrease
9. Sunup
10. Appetizing jelly
11. Wind-whipped waves
12. Frenzied
13. Extend across
18. ___ Myra Hess
23. Sought entrance, in a way
25. Cash drawers
26. Swiss capital
28. Parts of ski towlines
30. Gaelic
31. Note for a typesetter
32. C.P.A.
33. West African republic
34. Symbols of villainy in oaters
36. Quebec peninsula
38. Mercury-bearing ore
39. Softens by soaking
42. Rani's garb
43. Windflower
46. Seize eagerly
48. ___ Bell (Emily Brontë)
49. Colleague of Jung
50. Polly and Chloe
51. Rhone feeder
52. Boca ___, Fla.
53. Twofold
54. Part of A.D.
55. Dancer-choreographer Tommy
59. Concern for Crenshaw
60. Pen point

94

ACROSS

1. "La Bohémienne" painter
5. Supple
10. Buddhist language
14. Border
15. Bavarian Alps lake
16. Rainer role
17. Festive
18. Equals
19. Mix
20. June event
23. Buddy
24. Subdue
25. "Winesburg, Ohio" author
29. Containers
32. __ Arabia
33. Tardy
35. Void's partner
37. Devilish child
38. Immortal
41. "Mamma __!"
42. Ooze
44. American Beauty, e.g.
45. Revise
47. Ionesco work
49. Having a spree
51. Hermit
53. Distress signal
54. Polar sight
60. Southwest Indian
61. Support for Grant Wood
62. Get __ the ground floor
64. City in S. France

65. Headstone
66. Preminger
67. Russian refusal
68. Irritable
69. Denials

DOWN

1. Crone
2. Camel-hair robes
3. Doozy
4. Imprinted
5. Jacket features
6. Cake decorator
7. Hemingway novel
8. Wading bird
9. Subjugates

10. Mailer's go-between
11. High: Prefix
12. Secular
13. Concerning
21. "West Side Story" girl
22. __ Lanka
25. Unmodified
26. Put the finger on
27. Super-__
28. Bread spread
30. Light unit
31. David's weapon
34. Adolescent
36. Dip

39. Most magnificent
40. Wooden shoe
43. Fortuneteller
46. Task
48. "Après __ le déluge"
50. Rhett's rival
52. Maternal relative
54. "Bigger __ a breadbox"
55. Sacred
56. Fencing sword
57. Lucre
58. "Do __ others . . ."
59. Remark
63. Gogol story

ACROSS

1. Burden
5. Italian seaport
9. Distort
14. Monthly bill
15. Actor O'Neal
16. Reckon
17. Showed excessive politeness
20. Party to
21. "Play — It Lays": Didion
22. Harper Valley org.
23. Pilot's concern
26. Chick
27. Puppeteer Baird
28. Peete's org.
29. Black bird
30. Salty drops
33. Jostle
37. Ache
39. Diner's "turf"
41. Hindu god of love
42. Norse sea god
44. Kind of heat
46. Disencumber
47. Chou En-__
49. Blind impulse personified
50. Air Force __
51. Theme song of early TV, with "It's"
57. A cont.
58. Pope in 903
59. Roy's missus
60. Latin student's song of joy
65. Moorehead or De Mille
66. Trudge
67. Group attraction in Vegas
68. Toomey or Philbin
69. Creatures with no sweat glands
70. Soprano Mills

DOWN

1. Eye, to a poet
2. Prefix with classicism
3. Loath
4. Note taker
5. Marc and kirsch
6. Novelist Rand
7. Car appurtenance
8. Tchr.
9. Dance souvenir
10. __-Locka, Fla.
11. Fra Lippo__
12. "__ a customer"
13. Tooth-shaped fortification
18. Distrust
19. Home away from home
23. White-water craft
24. Some cockney abodes
25. Gossip
26. Festive
31. Auto acronym
32. "Crazy __," Ephron book
34. Change indicator
35. "Mother __," Kipling poem
36. Walk through snow drifts
38. Overlay with gold
40. Grasshoppers' kin
43. Dark and gloomy, as a cave
45. Affix a "marked-down" label
48. Thought
51. "Horrible" Viking of the comics
52. "Coming __ in Samoa," Mead book
53. Twisted
54. Vim
55. Rudimentary seed
56. Words on an old campaign button
61. "Agnus __"
62. Absalom, to David
63. Prefix with corn
64. Delicacy from the sea

ACROSS

1. Price paid
5. Heavy element
9. ___ au rhum
13. Expletive
14. Cleric's abode
15. Where Persepolis is
16. Syngman of South Korea
17. Lab heaters
18. Slangy negative
19. Strouse refrain: 1960
22. Honeysuckle
23. Above, to Swinburne
24. Coarse; obtuse
26. Alienate
31. As ___ (usually)
32. Pocket case
33. Continent: Abbr.
34. Sondheim refrain: 1973
38. Western Indian
39. Early Coloradans
40. Important occurrence
41. Chemical compound
44. ___ Fisher Hall, N.Y.C.
45. Emblem of sovereignty
46. Maple genus
47. Gershwin refrain: 1930
55. ___ fellow (genial person)
56. Ebbets Field star
57. Pa. port
58. Car part
59. French pronoun
60. Composer of "Put Your Head on My Shoulder"
61. Feral
62. Georges ___ Tour, 17th-century painter
63. Coral formation

DOWN

1. Business abbr.
2. Hawaiian island
3. Printer's direction
4. A 12th-century Archbishop of Canterbury
5. Shaping machine
6. Sicilian city
7. Request for haste: Abbr.
8. Tyrannical
9. Eastern Nigeria
10. "Dove sono," e.g.
11. Judge's seat
12. ___ up (poker term)
14. Partner of ways
20. Japanese-American
21. Law or saw follower
24. Where Cnossus is
25. Talk too much
26. An anesthetic
27. Takes to court
28. Less used
29. Sack material
30. Former, formerly
31. Wet
32. Feminine suffix
35. Counted
36. Embankment
37. Domineer
42. Worked hard
43. Biblical vessel
44. Yearns
46. Confused
47. Theatrical great
48. Cab
49. Brook
50. African river
51. ___-mell
52. "Comus" composer
53. Goddess of victory
54. Unheeding

ACROSS

1. Unadorned
5. Prepare for a test
9. Fragrance
14. Seaweed product
15. "Split City"
16. Axis extremities
17. Plexus
18. Pothers
19. Follow
20. Dengue
23. N.Y.C. opera
24. Kind of kick
25. Pies and cakes, e.g.
30. Tebaldi or Scotto
34. Popeye's Olive
35. Chimes
37. Matched the fire again
38. Framework of parallel bars
40. Muse for Masters
42. Blind piece
43. Nova Scotia's __ Basin
45. Devoured
47. Bacharach's "__ Day Now"
48. Tartan pattern
50. Those in a contest
52. Prejudice
54. Large
55. Electrician's switch
62. Bo or John
63. Tender
64. Darnel
65. Beau __
66. Space
67. Pronom

68. Vexatious
69. Frolic
70. First principle

DOWN

1. Feather branch
2. Teen or golden follower
3. Behind time
4. Reveries
5. Rascal in "The School for Scandal"
6. Make changes
7. Presently
8. Aaron's brother
9. Traffic violator
10. Assembles

11. Additional to
12. Nerve: Comb. form
13. Famed poet's monogram
21. Stronghold
22. Douglas __
25. Tenet
26. Icelandic coin
27. Cast
28. O'Hara's place
29. Roof material
31. Edgar __ Poe
32. Luis of pitching fame
33. A.B.A. members
36. Gun type
39. Aurora's time

41. Insurrection
44. With deftness
46. __-dieu (kneeling bench)
49. __ de Cologne
51. Marbles
53. Fiber for insulation
55. Yield
56. Angers
57. One-third of a 1970 film
58. __ Rabbit
59. Leafy vegetable
60. A Gardner
61. Oboist's purchase
62. Cocktail accompaniment

98

ACROSS

1. Where hippies bed down
5. Construction item
10. Garden growth
14. An early Red
15. Nutty palm
16. Killer whale
17. Western city
19. At hand
20. Most browned
21. Western peak
23. Perform again
24. Fear
26. Yang counterpart
27. Mauna __
28. Facilitates
32. Soft drink
34. Western university
36. Altar above
37. Polly and Pittypat
38. Op. __
39. Fault in the West
42. Type of way
43. "__ to bed": Pepys
44. Sea eagle
45. Lapsang souchong, e.g.
46. Payments of a sort
48. U.S.N. V.I.P.'s
50. __ Beach, Western city
53. Lurches
56. "L' __ c'est moi"
57. Subject of this puzzle
60. Only
61. Broadway musical
62. A.B.A. member
63. Box
64. Dissuade
65. Deprivation

DOWN

1. Skin
2. Bellowing
3. Western attraction
4. Medieval name for a part of Europe
5. Witches
6. Author Harte
7. Moray
8. Rickenbacker, e.g.
9. En __ (all together)
10. Atomistic; unitary
11. Galena and wolframite
12. Shoo's kin
13. Franklin's mother
18. Type of light
22. Hic, __, hoc
24. Family for whom a Western pass is named
25. Useful palm stem
27. Evergreen tree
29. Western capital
30. Canal of songdom
31. Glut
32. Señor's home
33. African port
34. Deplorable
35. Simpleton
40. Wiser
41. When the sun is on the meridian
42. Type of case
45. Poi ingredient
47. Added brandy to coffee
49. Stews' cousins
50. Ending for help or harm
51. On
52. Festivity
53. Adduce
54. At a distance
55. "Simon __"
58. Rosary bead
59. Kindled

ACROSS

1. Breathless
6. Goya's duchess
10. __ dixit
14. Ghanaian export
15. Caron role
16. Area under a poll
17. Oklahoma city
18. Overlord, e.g.
20. Fighting words over Oregon: 1844
22. Places for clodhoppers
23. Kipling's "Drums of the Fore and __"
24. Kowalski's wife
27. Like a Japanese fish dish
32. Part of TV
33. Dependent
35. Harriman nickname
36. Live
38. Polk's party in 1845
39. C.P.A.'s item
41. Cambodian's neighbor
42. Timorous
45. Violin attachment
46. Caribbean land masses
48. Like a small egg
50. Patty Hearst's kidnappers: Abbr.
51. Indigo
52. What 20 Across might have caused
59. Sidney Howard play: 1933
60. Practice for Peter Nero
62. Ring the bell
63. Soprano Gluck
64. Jerk's concoctions
65. Uri hero
66. Clean a briar
67. Three-pipped sides of dice

DOWN

1. Here, in Honduras
2. Trevino's game
3. Playbill heading
4. Eggy dishes
5. A medium used by Degas
6. In the air
7. Famed eighth-century Chinese poet
8. Cordon __ (top chef)
9. Annual Dayton event
10. Wholly
11. Full-house part
12. Notice
13. Counting-out word
19. Supply
21. "Very good" period in songdom
24. Commemorative slab
25. U.S. citizen since 1845
26. Mr. Ness
27. Forearm bones
28. Kind of decree
29. Afghanistan's capital
30. Patti LuPone role
31. Sidetrack
34. Douglas Hyde's land
37. "__ the Saddle," Wayne film
40. Rival of a sort
43. Freight-train unit
44. Big Ben sound
47. "God is and all __": Whittier
49. Most repulsive
51. Where Hue is
52. Reagan's first Sec. of the Interior
53. Tub plant
54. Brooklet
55. Lair
56. Writer Bombeck
57. Hosiery shade
58. 6/6/44
61. Mountain winder

100

ACROSS

1. Child
5. Appeals
10. Former UN member
14. Profuse
15. Unguent
16. __ contendere
17. Eye cheesecake
18. Bower
19. Coffee type
20. R. Graves novel
23. Meas. of speed
24. Bobbled the ball
25. "Is this a dagger which __...": Macbeth
27. Chamber-music group
31. Drugstore cowboy
32. Noble Renaissance family
33. Oyez!
37. S. Maugham novel, with "The"
40. U.S.N.A. freshman
41. Food thickener
42. "__ to the wise..."
43. Cloisters
45. Gripper
46. Indic language
49. Essential or crude substance
50. H. James novel, with "The"
58. Stravinsky
59. Vaunt
60. Jumble
61. River or goose
62. Practical

63. Kind of collar
64. Gaelic
65. Harpy's weapon
66. "The Square Egg" author

DOWN

1. Compact group of people
2. TV's Downs
3. Lake Champlain's Grand __
4. L. Bromfield novel
5. Hymn
6. Enrich
7. Dresden's river
8. Eden's earldom
9. Villein
10. J. R. Lowell book of verse
11. More tender
12. Share
13. Inveigled, with "in"
21. __ buffa
22. Shelter
25. Baal, e.g.
26. Small plum
27. Grasslike plant
28. Belloc work
29. Churns
30. Singer Ritter
31. Urchin
34. A son of Seth
35. Land unit
36. Cardinal

38. Collar
39. Italian province
44. Tribunal
46. Think
47. Radio operator's word
48. Presses
49. Commonly
51. What Iran and Iraq do
52. Jot
53. Shadow
54. Nobel Institute's site
55. Inter __
56. Softly hit tennis ball
57. Hindu ascetic

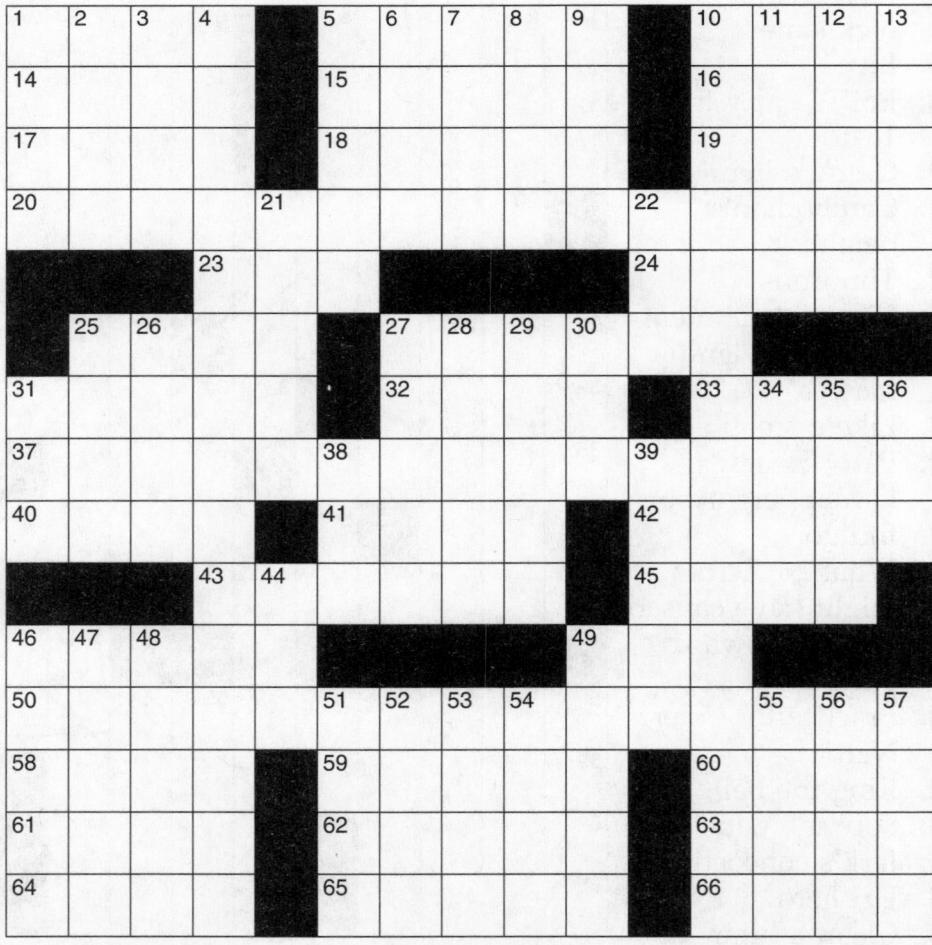

ACROSS

1. Hungarian commercial center
5. Bellhop, at times
10. Relative of a stork
14. Peignoir
15. Peon's ploughed land
16. Fog
17. Clothes carrier
19. Mouse, to a skunk
20. Moe, Curly or Larry
21. Green gems
23. Anklebones
25. Rue __ Paix
26. Waited; sojourned
29. Cutting device
32. Slip
35. Old French money
36. Smell and taste
38. Cote cry
39. Fissure
40. Dull finish
41. Agreement
42. Ump's relative
43. Collect
44. Fairy-tale heavy
45. Palm of Asia
47. Shoe width
48. Malicious burning
49. Airplane stunt
51. Shed
53. Arrange systematically
57. Hockey position
61. Etc.'s relative
62. Pony Express pouches
64. Theater area
65. A Scandinavian
66. Diving bird
67. Recess at Notre Dame
68. Chariot for Claudius
69. Grafted, in heraldry

DOWN

1. Work units
2. Butt of a joke
3. Spain's longest river
4. Most distant
5. Switchboard section
6. Cunning
7. Actor-comic Kaplan
8. Dutch cheese
9. Stormed
10. Reddish African antelope
11. Spud sacks
12. Angered
13. "The __ the limit"
18. Victorian oath
22. Units of reluctance
24. What to do in a think tank
26. Yogi or Dale of baseball
27. More frigid
28. Part of campers' gear
30. "__ Wet," Shute novel
31. High regard
33. Holy: Comb. form
34. Consumed
36. Wee, in Dundee
37. Always, to Milton
41. Easily conveyed
43. Where Wilde spent time in Reading
46. Deep gulch
48. Bitter herb
50. Out of style
52. Eyed amorously
53. Tissue
54. Upon
55. Playing marbles
56. Greek W.W. II resistance gp.
58. French city
59. "__ Rhythm"
60. Slave of old
63. H.S.T.'s successor

102

ACROSS

1. ___ off (intercept)
5. Shoptalk
10. Darn relative
14. First name in scat
15. Light velvet
16. Last of the Caesars
17. Type of bee
19. Part of a travel package
20. Certain bridges
21. Bull Moose, e.g.
22. Cartographic abbr.
23. Parsley piece
25. Ice-cream flavor word
29. Edmonton or Houston team
33. Liver partner
35. "... a bug in ___"
36. Estuary: Sp.
37. Fully prepared
38. Rodgers-Hart song: 1933
40. Hook with a handle
41. Bribe
42. Part of a marathon
43. Inhibit
45. Parts of a comic's repertory
48. Do a tailor's job
49. Zaire, formerly
50. Distinctive theory
52. A cut of meat
54. Diarist's activity
59. "Turandot" character
60. Crashed a soiree
62. Melville work
63. Roman official
64. Prima donna
65. High schooler
66. Introvert
67. Census fig.

DOWN

1. Contained
2. Robert ___
3. He has Alda talent
4. Foolish
5. Sudden burst
6. Like up-to-the-minute news
7. Minute colonists
8. Compass dir.
9. Berlin lang.
10. Involve by necessity
11. One-time movie "tough guy"
12. In ___ (trapped by routine)
13. Flat-bottomed vessel
18. Plant used for flavoring
21. Nice Nelly
23. Dry
24. Rains pitchforks
25. Trunk
26. Lincoln's magnificent obsession
27. Harrison's nickname
28. Clog part
30. "Dolly Sisters" actress
31. Winchester product
32. Newsman Morley
34. Arm support
39. Toast topping
40. ___ Blas, Lesage hero
42. Status symbol
44. Like circus lions
46. Well stocked with
47. How some leave Reno
51. Guide a ride
52. Predicament
53. Batter's mecca
54. Moran of "Happy Days"
55. Disencumbers
56. Monogram ltr.
57. PBS program
58. Tiny pest
60. Barbara ___ Geddes
61. Fuss

ACROSS

1. Filched
6. Health centers
10. Facetious one
14. Cheboygan's lake
15. Vintner's product
16. Scent
17. Place for a bout
18. Nuncupative
19. Leningrad's river
20. Consult formally
22. Rode on a jet
23. Spring occurrence
24. Acquits
26. Hedda of Hollywood
30. Join
32. Kitchen staple
33. __ facto
35. Impends
39. Library patron
41. Theater patron, at times
43. Motionless
44. Molding
46. Rattan
47. Old hat
49. Looked searchingly
51. Conduct affairs
54. No, in Bonn
56. Cupid
57. Group gathered for consultation
63. Instrument
64. Crocus, e.g.
65. Tapestry
66. In addition
67. __ Domini
68. Bungling
69. Forest denizen
70. Eye lasciviously
71. Rent

DOWN

1. Roe source
2. Suffix with fix or mix
3. Russian city
4. TV's Anderson
5. Authorize
6. Like some testimony
7. Freebooters
8. Med. school subject
9. Choice
10. Meeting for consultation
11. Author St. Johns
12. Nomad
13. Hauls
21. Uncanny
25. Harold Teen's leaping flivver
26. Pueblo Indian
27. Lycian poet
28. A Dumas
29. Informal consultation
31. Winning margin, at times
34. Those in favor
36. Jewish month
37. Descartes
38. Sow
40. Lone male at a dance
42. Lukewarm
45. Sincere
48. Soap opera, e.g.
50. Cause by consequences
51. Matched
52. Soap-producing plant
53. Snare
55. Where Saul met a witch
58. French department
59. Composer of "Comus"
60. La __ Tar Pits
61. Moves in small waves
62. Famous Italian family

104

ACROSS

1. Memorable actress Veronica
5. Suffixes for old and gang
10. Being, in Paris
14. Seed covering
15. Characteristic
16. Electromagnetic radiation
17. One who defames
19. Apply asphalt
20. Family member
21. Garland for a wahine
22. Pressed
24. She asks, "Can we talk?"
27. Light refractor
29. Building or bridge
32. Narrow valleys
33. Russian emperors
34. Definite article
35. Good fortune
36. Wilbur and Stevens
37. Prejudice
38. Japanese statesman
39. __ aves
40. "This one" is on him
41. Of single sound source
43. "Sailor on Horseback" author
44. Thrush from Tennessee
46. Arranged in rows
48. A G.I. mailing address
49. Knight of TV fame
52. African gazelle
53. Unsuitably
57. Writes
58. Saltpeter
59. Ascend
60. Ornamental band
61. Greenhouse material
62. Long in the tooth

DOWN

1. Alan or Cheryl
2. Region
3. Tenderhearted
4. Actor Wallach
5. River
6. Teach
7. Bore into
8. Grande predecessor
9. They try hard
10. Send goods abroad
11. Changeover
12. Be delirious
13. Observed
18. Make lustrous
23. Accts. of events
24. Evade in zigzag fashion
25. Fastens anew
26. Angry
27. Planet discovered in 1930
28. Sentences again
30. Chicago airport
31. Cozy place
32. Lamp
33. Pentateuch
36. Frequent activity on Fifth Ave.
37. Fraternal org.
39. Mystic writing
40. Honing implement
42. Breezy
43. Stupors
45. Warren occupants
46. Bugle call
47. Thought
49. Math subject
50. Anagram for "lees"
51. Colored
54. One-thousandth inch
55. Sch. group
56. Epoch

ACROSS

1. Middling
5. Ancient contest
9. Impressionist painter: 1834–1917
14. Waiter's concern
15. Do roadwork
16. Reflection
17. Too bad!
18. Scads
19. Conform; adapt
20. Grazed
21. Innate generosity
23. Title for Jacques
25. Laureate's output
26. Faculties
28. "Tell me __ is fancy bred": Shak.
30. Former Japanese V.I.P.
32. "__ Miss Brooks"
33. Tormé specialty
37. Seed-bearing spike
38. Historic U.S. river
41. Falsehood
42. Little one
44. Compressed mass
45. Pepper of Fla.
47. Flock members
49. Arlington vault
50. Stand in the way of
53. Orchard pest
56. Rattler
61. "A Chorus Line" show-stopper
62. Organic compound
63. Part of a foot
64. Actor Moses from St. Louis
65. Parisian sight
66. May Whitty, e.g.
67. Manipulates
68. Jogs
69. Yet again
70. Nothing more than

DOWN

1. Retinue
2. OPEC vessel
3. Preparations
4. C.I.A. forerunner
5. Church section
6. Festive celebration
7. Word at the bottom of a page
8. Salamander
9. Disagree
10. Some expatriates
11. Toledo tabbies
12. Limber
13. Transmits
21. All hot and bothered
22. Ham it up
24. Horse and carriage
27. Winter creations
28. Forest
29. Emulate a bee
30. Coterie
31. Treat for Trigger
34. Meeting place for Mets
35. Succor
36. Pro-shop item
39. Reckoning
40. Outer garment
43. Proper sphere
46. Elec. unit
48. Dotes on
50. That is: Lat.
51. Harpagon, for instance
52. Place for a barbecue
54. Hidden
55. Thickly packed
57. Artistic cult of the 20's
58. Wheat byproduct
59. Zenith
60. Ruminate
64. Sticky stuff

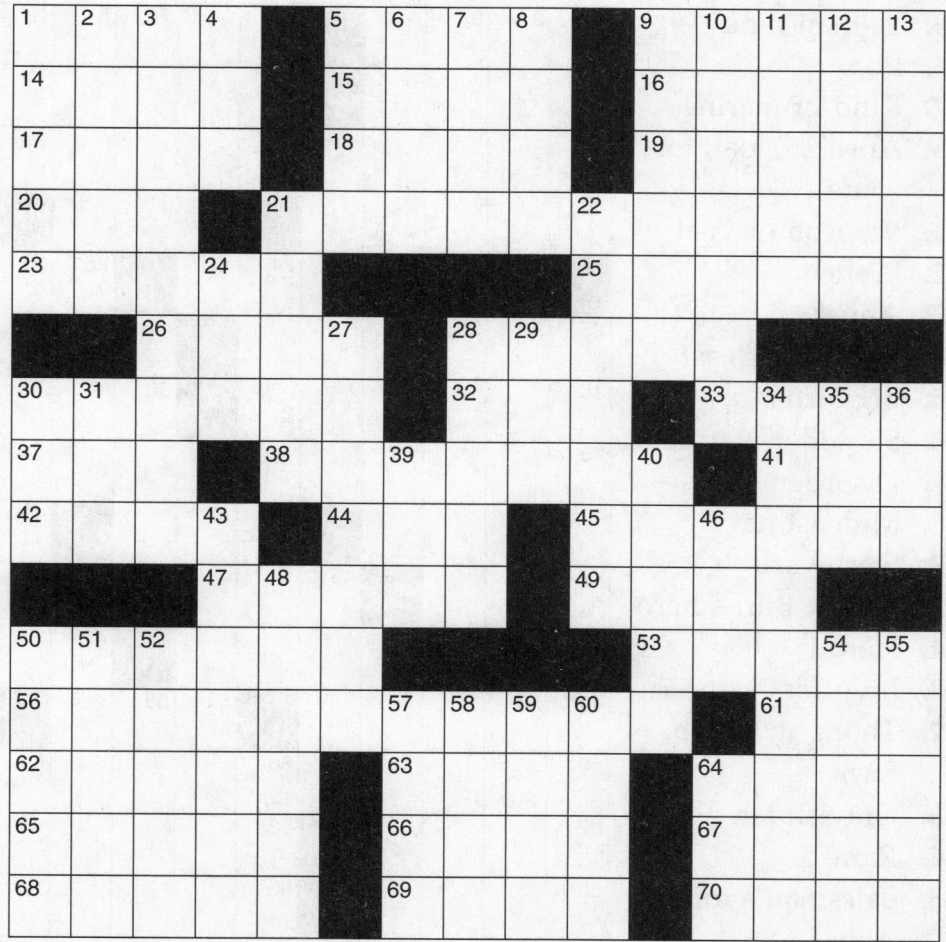

ACROSS

1. Movie mogul
5. Range
10. Own up: Colloq.
14. Endure
15. Splendid attire
16. Function
17. Service that makes people nervous
20. Porridge ingredient
21. Tonga island
22. German city
23. Clock-setting abbr.
25. Material for a trellis
27. Bordeaux wine
31. Actor Ray
32. Prankish fairy
35. __-than-thou
36. Pop
37. Kind of marine
38. April 15 goal, for some
41. Venison or veal
42. Branch
43. Anger
44. Ending for east
45. Big birds
46. Shoulder warmers
47. Disorder
48. Mideast nat.
49. Sternward
52. Robert Burns hero
54. Heron
59. Investors' concern
62. Thought: Comb. form
63. Grayish tan
64. Rara __
65. Salesman's milieu: Abbr.
66. Business plus
67. Defeat

DOWN

1. Remove coupons from bonds
2. Novelist Grey
3. Nick and Nora's pet
4. Hwys.
5. Gabriel or Sebastián
6. Carpentry is one
7. Base of a column
8. "The __ View," 1974 Beatty film
9. Hurricane center
10. New
11. Ages upon ages
12. Veer
13. Noticed
18. Cash in
19. Say nay at the White House
24. Flows
26. Oration
27. Voice of Big Ben
28. Individualist of a sort
29. Alaskan highway
30. Hilarious chap
31. __ apple
32. On a par
33. Thrust
34. Diminishes
37. A hairdo
39. Board members
40. American's main course
45. Saarinen
47. Important
48. Idol
49. Mine entrance
50. Teased
51. Washstand item
53. Certain sale terms
55. Snatch
56. Partner of rant
57. Sponsorship
58. Acid __
60. Basketball org.
61. Old pro

ACROSS

1. Sugar serving
5. Uncloses
10. __ au lait
14. Opposite of written
15. Proportion
16. Earthenware jug
17. House and Senate
20. Annex
21. __ Eleanor Roosevelt
22. Protect with sandbags, etc.
23. God of war
24. "Miss Otis __"
26. Peace conference
29. Elflike creatures
30. Toward the ocean
31. Suffix denoting a collection
32. __ Moines
35. Ultimate D.C. decision makers
40. Elongated fish
41. Roulette bet
42. Where Burma is
43. Uncontrolled gatherings
44. Pattern on a TV screen
46. Eyepiece grid
49. Transmitted
50. Public storehouse
51. Mariner's haven
52. Actor Vigoda
55. U.S. Presidents
59. T.V.A. site
60. Banish
61. Take it easy
62. Scraps for Spot
63. Gets one's dander up
64. Gaelic

DOWN

1. Songwriter Porter
2. Russian river
3. Cry loudly
4. Slippery __
5. Scotland's __ islands
6. Physical discomforts
7. Sicilian menace
8. Afr. republic
9. Weep violently
10. Composers of secret messages
11. In existence
12. Group of warships
13. Far and Middle
18. Swiss river
19. Of unrestrained indulgence
23. Too bad!
24. Paper quantity
25. Sea eagle
26. Top of the head
27. Arthur of tennis
28. Virginia __
29. Harbor sights
32. Do a maid's job
33. Fourth part of HOMES
34. Rigel is one
36. Children's worldwide org.
37. Sight in suburbia
38. Solemn ceremony
39. Malt kiln
43. Becomes mature
44. Ziegfeld offerings
45. French violinist: 18th century
46. Right-hand page
47. Clear sky
48. Infect or spoil
49. Architect's foundation piece
51. Line, as a roof
52. State confidently
53. Mamie's predecessor
54. Tivoli's Villa d' __
56. Suffix with ballad
57. "Repeal" amendment
58. Anger

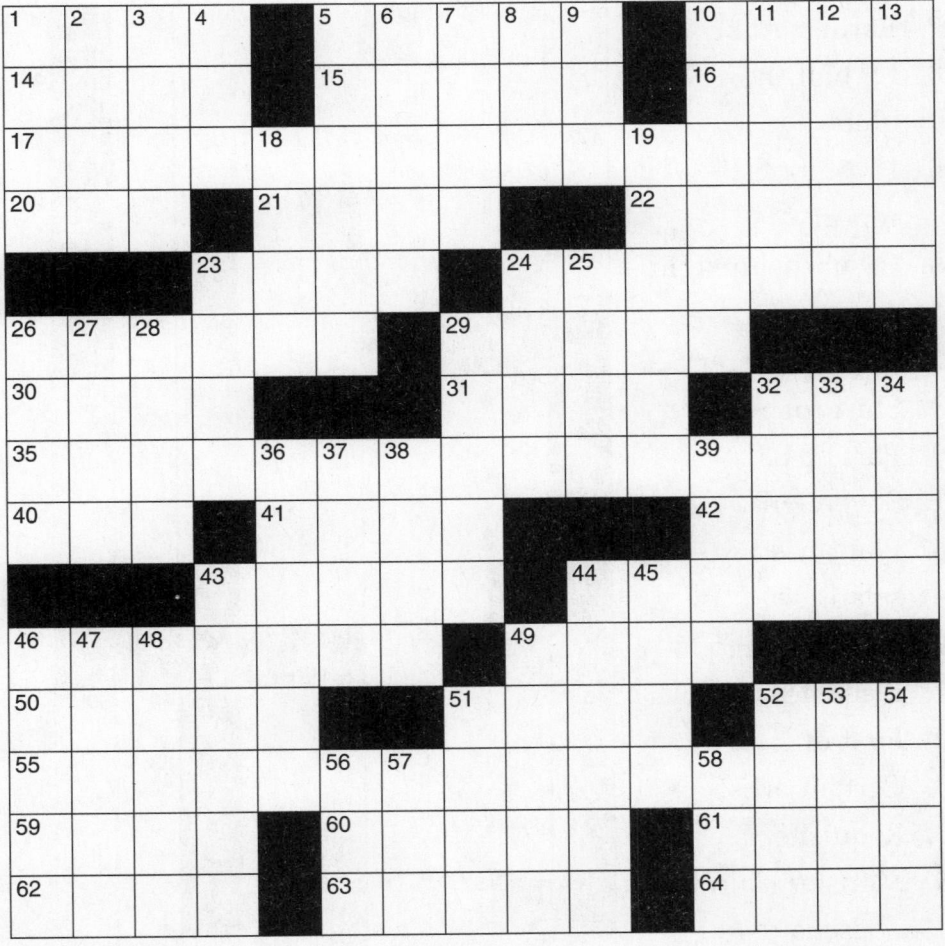

ACROSS

1. Sign that delights angels
4. Humdingers
8. Provokes wrath
12. Face defiantly
14. Strip
17. Base-to-apex measure
18. Daybook's relative
19. Meager
20. Forthwith
21. Fort Bliss locale
22. Mien
24. Blue or yellow flag
25. One of the races
28. Earlier: Abbr.
30. Of half the globe
35. Hyperbolist's report
36. Overwhelmed, in a way
37. Polar explorer
38. Shirt for Scotty
39. Part of E.E.
41. Sovereign
46. Plant used in salads
49. Chinese pagoda
51. Place near Venice
52. First of a series
53. Certain artist
55. Requisite
56. Monster slain by Theseus

57. Space shuttle's org.
58. Operatic role
59. Map abbr.

DOWN

1. Mollusk, also called wentletrap
2. Functions
3. Available
4. Tate treats
5. Earls' wives
6. Inner: Comb. form
7. Burgoo or swivet
8. Empty
9. Go unsteadily

10. Finials, e.g.
11. Cuban crop
13. Subtle
15. Mr. Arnaz
16. Antony's friend
23. Insect sounds
26. Urban dwellings: Abbr.
27. "— Entertainment!"
28. Destines
29. —-Korsakov
30. Popular
31. Opposite of deciduous
32. Office items

33. — Kett
34. Kind of train, for short
39. Black, in poesy
40. Slangy answer
42. Unmixed
43. Start of a Garland vehicle
44. Undaunted
45. Pied-à-—
47. Turns right
48. Earth goddess in opera
49. Zestless
50. Dyestuff
54. Extinct ratite

ACROSS

1. Competent
5. Consumer advocate
10. Peak
14. State of mind
15. Public-relations concern
16. Kind of chop
17. D __ David
18. King of Naples: 1808–15
19. He wrote "Bus Stop"
20. Breakfast order
23. Haggard book
24. Bullring sound
25. Ana and Claus
28. Answers
31. Genetic substance, for short
32. In progress
36. One, to Marie
37. Secular
38. Second breakfast
42. Soho dandy
43. Old __ (London theatre)
44. "The Eve of St. __": Keats
45. Hot time in Paree
46. Dakar is its capital
49. More compact
51. Laugh, in Lyon
52. Romaine lettuce
55. Accompaniment for 20 Across
59. Lather maker
61. Emulate W. J. Bryan
62. Killer whale
63. "__ in Love with Amy"
64. Talked wildly
65. Fervor
66. Cowardly Lion of filmdom
67. Steps over a wall
68. C. Brontë's Jane

DOWN

1. Gather
2. Painter Hieronymus
3. Longest French river
4. Best or Ferber
5. "Jack, be __"
6. Charm
7. Risk
8. Mild oath
9. Examined again
10. Bring into agreement
11. Oblige
12. U.S.S.R. plane
13. Chemical suffix
21. Malory's "Le __ d'Arthur"
22. Yak away
26. Parsley relative
27. Meistersinger Hans
29. Small amount
30. Spherical: Abbr.
32. Emulated Nazimova
33. American organist-composer
34. He wrote "La Vie Parisienne"
35. Switch word
37. Highly volatile fuel: Abbr.
39. Foot muscles
40. Rhone feeder
41. Flemish city
46. TV box
47. She foiled a witch
48. __-camp
50. Outstanding
52. He wrote "Sally in Our Alley"
53. Hollywood award
54. Tasteless
56. Part of Q.E.D.
57. Sitarist Shankar
58. Slow flow
59. Musical syllable
60. Actress Munson

ACROSS

1. Dummies
5. Legal offenses
9. Fleece
14. Viva voce
15. Suffix for axiom
16. Bandleader James
17. Ind. city
18. Strawberry patch?
19. Incensed
20. Manacles manipulator
23. Tennyson product
24. Abstract being
25. Airport label for Caracas
28. Essen exclamation
31. Fodder for Freud
33. Paducah's river
34. Macbeth title
36. New York inst.
37. Wood: Comb. form
38. Politician, publisher and P.M.
42. Heroic poetry
43. Corrode
44. Framework
45. Colorful river
46. December sight
49. Part of i.e.
50. To boot
51. Pop's partner
52. Author Rand et al.
54. Screenwriter for "Accident": 1967
59. European heath
62. Lover's sound
63. Without, in Dresden
64. Corporate checkup
65. Gen. Robert __
66. Foray
67. Malamud product
68. Pool in a range
69. Completes

DOWN

1. One of the recent frosh
2. Kind of code
3. Henry VIII's last wife
4. Drink noisily
5. Kitchen utensil
6. Reception
7. Place
8. Brahms's "__ Festival"
9. Climbs, in a way
10. Spydom's Zelle
11. Failed amendment
12. Cinematics, e.g.
13. Caulfield's spot
21. Vaud vibrato
22. Briefly
25. With 30 down, Byronic pilgrim
26. Cheroots
27. Petrarch specialty
28. Adviser to Odysseus
29. "Motherhood" painter
30. See 25 Down
32. Having wings
33. Stewpot
35. Kind of cone or dive
39. Inigo Jones concern
40. Long-tailed monkey
41. Tribe conquered by the Romans
47. Sponge
48. Well-known mark
51. Chayefsky's butcher
53. Zzzzz
54. Prince Charles is one
55. Actress Kedrova
56. Larger __ life
57. Author Bagnold
58. Beatty movie
59. __-relief
60. Boring routine
61. Half a musical title

ACROSS

1. Mexican food
6. Exotic bird
10. Injure
14. Harden
15. Manganese and malachite
16. Curved molding
17. Meditated, with "over"
18. "Pop __ the weasel"
19. Facts
20. Mixture
22. Deg. holder
23. Weight in India
24. Hammer
26. Kitchen gadget
30. Organize
32. Dog that went to Oz
33. Notices
35. Nocturnal lemur
39. Displayed
41. Matriculator
43. Islamic spiritual center
44. Impression
46. Golden __ of the West Coast
47. Sequence
49. Trample
51. Force
54. Princely Italian house
56. Sanction
57. Mixture
63. Roast: Fr.
64. Gaelic
65. Nigerian seaport
66. Def. alliance

67. So be it
68. Quibble
69. School on the Thames
70. Ointment-yielding plant
71. Not so common

DOWN

1. Apexes
2. Puzzler's favorite ox
3. Ringlet
4. Utah city
5. Collected
6. V.I.P.
7. Historical period
8. Penury
9. Help

10. Mixture
11. Henry __ Wallace
12. Place a new label on
13. Victor at Gettysburg
21. Prickly evergreen shrub
25. A knockout
26. Goblet part
27. World spinner
28. Suffix with Ham or Shem
29. Mixture
31. Sum __ fui . . .
34. One of the Adamses
36. Harvest
37. "__ each life . . ."

38. British gun
40. Reiner or Sagan
42. Morsel
45. Backstage employee
48. Lower in dignity
50. Bank employee
51. Seine tributary
52. Untersee craft
53. Argument
55. Lurch forward on heavy seas
58. "My Friend __"
59. Mount St. Helens production
60. Thickening agent
61. Protuberance
62. Belgian canal connector

112

ACROSS

1. Narrated
5. Sheepfolds
10. Squint
14. León's love
15. City near Kobe
16. Longfellow's bell town
17. Gnomish, in a way
18. Oscar winner: 1958
19. Havoc
20. Battologizes
22. Dorm topic
24. Beyond
25. Frat topic
26. Cudgels
29. British orderly
33. Azimuth
34. Strikebreaker
36. Cinched
37. Snail's motto
41. Bristles
42. Parrot
43. Diminutive suffix
44. Imply
46. Gone, at Logan
49. Tommy of the theater
50. Deliver a haymaker
51. Gust
54. Game fish
58. Be bested
59. ". . . __ face the world with": Browning
61. Gallimaufry
62. Actuaries' concerns
63. Silk voile
64. Rod's partner
65. Siliques
66. Anthony and Clarissa
67. Nixed item

DOWN

1. Actor Jacques __
2. Skip
3. Like an eremite
4. Decay in a forest
5. Italian noblewoman
6. Wicker
7. Hebrew letters
8. Duke Ellington's monogram
9. Huarache
10. Fa la, e.g.
11. Case for trivia
12. Banshee's bailiwick
13. "Lair" of two Baers
21. Harriman nickname
23. Let
25. Butler in 1939
26. Chaliapin and Moscona
27. "Over the Rainbow" composer
28. Apollo 15 astronaut
29. Scenic peninsula
30. Devout
31. St.-Cyr-l' __
32. Fortification
35. Shipper's need
38. Carte carrier
39. Longest human bone
40. Ciceronian collection
45. "__ for tennis?"
47. Kennel adjunct
48. Hereditary
50. Squelched
51. Tab
52. Trademark
53. Canceled, as a stamp
54. Tenor Maison
55. Dairyman's anathema
56. Vienna, to a Viennese
57. "Star Wars" hero
60. __-nod (show drowsiness)

ACROSS

1. Census fig.
5. Verb used with thou
10. Tiff
14. Showed up
15. Our place
16. Singing group
17. "__ Three Lives": Philbrick
18. Brother, in Brest
19. Prefix with drome or dynamics
20. Cheese concoction
22. City in Denmark
24. Too unusual for words
27. Go to bed
28. Gaucho gear
31. __ Vegas
34. Extinct bird
35. "The __ Summer": Kahn
36. Expletive for Major Hoople
38. Designer Oscar de la __
40. Alcohol additive
41. Prevents
43. Sea bird
45. Neither's partner
46. Chilean port
47. P.D.Q.
49. Looking backward
54. Kind of equation
55. African mammals, for short
56. Datum
57. Electron tube
60. Leave out
61. Gem shape
62. Table Bay is one
63. Store event
64. Depend
65. Curved moldings
66. Ogler

DOWN

1. Kind of film
2. Claw
3. Better
4. Famed British air marshal
5. Kin of apostates
6. Shell item
7. Prior, in poetry
8. Type of theatrical light
9. Bara of silents
10. British noble family
11. Like some exhibition games
12. River at Leeds
13. As well
21. Bought before
23. River into the Mediterranean
25. Sally of space trips
26. Laundry workers
29. Stir
30. At a distance
31. Wife of Tyndareus
32. Maturer
33. Like "Candide"
35. Small flags or important knights
37. In a proper manner
39. De __ (superfluous)
42. __ of exchange
44. Imprint
47. Pre-exam activity
48. Futile
50. Medium for "The Answer Man"
51. "Seven Days __," 1964 film
52. Sheer fabric
53. Fragrant compound
54. Wash
56. "Tea __ Two," Youmans song
58. Matador's encouragement
59. Actor Billy __ Williams

114

ACROSS

1. Alpha follower
5. These may revolve
10. Canton is here
14. Let forth
15. Bandleader Shaw
16. Musical finale
17. Number in the news
19. Group of devotees
20. Bishops, e.g.
21. Breaks; rests
23. Ike's post in W.W. II
24. Cuba __, rum drink
25. Frequently
27. Lowest pinochle card
30. Fearsome Greek goddesses
31. What 30 Across do
33. Beer's cousin
34. McEnroe vs. Connors
36. New Year's __
37. __ Mile Island
39. Biblical verb ending
40. Aid
43. Mighty mite
44. Tiny spores
46. Actor Calhoun and boxer Calhoun
48. Player-piano inserts
49. Ampersand
50. Hepplewhite product
52. Maeterlinck's "The __"
57. R.I.P. notice
58. Dec. 31 figure
60. City in Alaska
61. Strong cord
62. Porter of Tin Pan Alley
63. Turned right
64. Drooping part of an iris
65. "If You __ Susie . . ."

DOWN

1. Busy signal
2. Arabian bigwig
3. Buster Brown's dog
4. Part of N.C.A.A.
5. __ Beach, Fla.
6. A fishbowl occupant
7. Elevator man
8. Miss. or Mo.
9. Action in osmosis
10. Happens
11. Common event on Dec. 31
12. Unemployed
13. Feed-bag filling
18. London art gallery
22. Red as __
24. Wrinkles
25. Declaim
26. Cartoon figure on Dec. 31
27. Ben __, Great Britain's highest peak
28. Bread spreads
29. Abound
30. Author Ben __ Williams
32. Jerkins
35. Handel's birthplace
38. Book with a stiff cover
41. Chooses
42. Soprano from St. Louis
45. __ swiss
47. Unique person
50. "Auld Lang Syne" is one
51. C. American tree
52. Radarscope signal
53. Chanteuse Horne
54. Take __ the lam
55. Thespian's quest
56. Sketched
59. Flock member

ACROSS

1. Storybook animal
6. Ollie's pal
10. Tennis great
14. Davy Jones's realm
15. Singer Patti
16. Payoff position at Belmont
17. Start of a quote from "Hamlet"
20. Rent
21. Work at steadily
22. One making a goal
23. Light-Horse Harry
24. They give deductions
26. Quote: Part II
30. Core
31. Like kitsch
32. Actual being
36. Beef order
37. Melodies
38. Quarters for Leo
39. Coffee servers
40. Skirt style
41. Corporeal channel
42. Quote: Part III
44. __ Cup (yachting prize)
48. Road-sign abbr.
49. Spanish wine city
50. "Much __ About Nothing"
51. Henry IV's birthplace
54. End of quote
58. Darling of the demos
59. Be pleased by
60. Unaccompanied
61. Poker pair
62. Antony's friend
63. Yarns

DOWN

1. Orange or Rose
2. Pain's partner
3. Track tournament
4. Outlaw
5. Scrutinize
6. Nimble
7. Sailor
8. Long, long __
9. Predawn workers
10. Neckwear
11. Beach
12. "Iliad" author
13. Pitchers
18. Bread spread
19. "Off with you!"
23. Instruments playing false notes?
24. Phones again
25. Involve necessarily
26. Done, for short
27. Lend an ear
28. Merit
29. Boat basin
32. Emulate Juliet
33. Hindu garment
34. House location
35. Time periods
37. Showing good will
41. Elaine's town
42. Omen
43. "Das Rheingold" role
44. Limits
45. Bea Arthur role
46. Singer John
47. Tracks
50. Sweetsop
51. Louganis's milieu
52. Shakespeare's wife
53. Employs
55. Broadcast
56. Bout ending: Abbr.
57. Dockworkers' org.

116

ACROSS

1. Geometrical figure
5. Commanded
9. Kind of water or cracker
13. Perpetually
14. __ nut
15. Coin of Persia: 1826–1932
16. Key phrase
19. Chicago transportation
20. W.W. II correspondent __ Pyle
21. Passage
22. Oppositionist
23. With: Prefix
24. Aurora borealis
31. Cut
32. "The youth replies, '__' ": Emerson
33. Ages upon ages
34. Exchange premium
35. Turn
37. Caravel of 1492
38. Vessel on a pedestal
39. Inevitable
40. Fat: Comb. form
41. "On the __ toe": Milton
46. Pershing's cmd.
47. Welfare
48. Heap of stones
51. Violinist Isaac
53. Deplorable
56. Hasty, superficial treatment, with "the"
59. Weaving machine
60. Source of mescal
61. Dash
62. Austria's first chartered city
63. Encyclopedia, e.g.
64. Cyrano's outstanding feature

DOWN

1. Yield
2. Ellipse
3. Intelligence
4. Sea eagle
5. Skullcap
6. Longfellow's bell town
7. Take out
8. English cathedral city
9. Winter sport
10. Corps.; assns.
11. Actress Arlene
12. Bet
14. Place to sleep
17. Transmitted
18. Store up
22. Cartoonist Peter
23. Lath
24. Pola of silent films
25. __ to (because of)
26. Split
27. Sgt. or cpl.
28. Spyri's children's story
29. Refreshing
30. Make a sharp, cracking sound
31. Pull with force
35. Gust
36. Wolfert or Eaker
37. Kind of bank or flag: Abbr.
39. Shorthand transcriber
42. Seraglios
43. Noon or midnight
44. Mountaintop nest
45. Vocalized
48. Nursery king
49. By and by
50. Sacred image
51. State flower of Utah
52. Mine car
53. Normandy town
54. Exclamation of woe
55. Unit of force
57. Large tub
58. Brooder of a sort

ACROSS

1. Rum-and-water drink
5. __ law, used by the Franks
10. Rebuff
14. "Hold __ horses!"
15. Historic town in Iraq
16. Bustle
17. Mickey and kin
18. Countenance
19. Actor Skinner
20. Greet, in a way
23. Small drinks
24. Pique
25. Lose
28. Water plant
30. Bleak
33. Utopian
34. Region
35. River in Yorkshire
36. See 56 Across
39. Indian butter
40. Toward the mouth
41. Decided for
42. Goddess of the dawn
43. House at O.S.U.
44. Springs
45. Eur. country
46. Slammer
47. Words after "Fragile"
54. Shaped like a stadium
55. Headdress at Canterbury
56. With 36 Across, like a pinup man
58. __-Lenape, Delaware Indian
59. Criminal offense
60. Madame Bovary
61. Yellowish-brown wool
62. Certain tides
63. Famed couturier

DOWN

1. Training ground for Larry Holmes
2. Louis XV and XVI
3. Cry of pain
4. Superior, e.g.
5. Two-point score in football
6. Baby sitters in Peking
7. Output of St. Helens
8. "__ City" (Pittsburgh)
9. General for whom a sweater was named
10. Author of "Oldtown Folks": 1869
11. Pen name used by Viaud
12. Mine passage
13. Like Buckingham Palace
21. Eucalyptus eater
22. Spanish Mme.
25. Tiny pest
26. Baking potato
27. Dry periods
28. Enlightened Buddhist
29. Conduct
30. Public disorders
31. Napoleon's "Grande" group
32. Devil's trumpets, e.g.
34. Seaport in Spain
35. Drew in by suction
37. Eric the Red was one
38. Architectural order
43. Suffix with care
44. Site of the University of Georgia
45. Talk-show quip
46. Leather band
47. Where cargo goes
48. Assert
49. Darling dog
50. Fencing
51. "__ boy!"
52. Nerve branches
53. Patron saint of sailors
57. Gibbon

118

ACROSS

1. Suggestion
5. "Caveat emptor" notice
9. "It's __ country"
14. Voyaging on the QE2
15. Sewing-machine inventor
16. Settle down for the night
17. Salamander
18. Discordant
19. See 6 Down
20. "I have a __": King
22. Unique individual
24. Jacques' summers
25. Alabama site of a Freedom March
26. Says
28. Sluggish
30. Lennon was one
34. Kind of sister
37. Mortise fitting
39. Like some infections
40. Outline
42. Soprano Galli-Curci
44. Coral island
45. Estimator
47. Peridot, e.g.
48. Mexican food
50. King Arthur's father
52. Pleasure-dome site, in a Coleridge poem
54. "__ again!"
58. Play parts
61. Move
62. Farm-equipment name
63. Weeping one
65. Physicist's abbr.
67. Throat impediment
68. "Roots" author
69. Movie pioneer
70. Icelandic literary works
71. Gotlander
72. Misses the ball
73. Nothing, in Nancy

DOWN

1. Field workers
2. French river
3. Stairway post
4. Straw mat
5. "Eureka!"
6. With 19 Across, famed black abolitionist
7. "__ Hold Your Hand," 1963 song
8. Ukrainian river
9. MOMA offering
10. Offshore flapper
11. Complete defeat
12. Tasso's patron
13. Suffixes with ordinal numbers
21. Conchita's cape
23. Johnny __
27. Title for Jesse Jackson
29. Conger
31. Kin of geom.
32. Behind schedule
33. Ancient region, now part of Iran
34. Minor dispute
35. Jorge of baseball
36. Type of spar
38. Subject of a Styron book
41. Source of a yellowish oil
43. "__ Lady," T. N. Page short story
46. Official who checks accounts
49. Printers' measures
51. Illegal smoke
53. "__ told by an idiot . . .": Macbeth
55. "Rigoletto" composer
56. Wear down
57. Secretary of the Treasury
58. Exclamations from Hans
59. Bird's gullet
60. Mah-jongg piece
64. Sandwich bread
66. Cries of pain

ACROSS

1. Covenant
5. Mail rte.
8. Counterpart
13. "Woe is me!"
14. Greek underground org. of W.W. II
16. Gem State
17. Gold-rush center in 1900
18. Clod
19. Eminent
20. Economists' stat.
21. S.A. plant growing in mountainous regions
23. Mar
25. Pharaohs
26. Hercules' captive
27. Mount
28. Pomme de __
30. Young fellows
31. Pewter ingredient
34. Turkish imperial standard
35. Age or wall leader
37. Glazier's need
38. "My country, __..."
39. Bold Bidder, to Spectacular Bid
40. Bedouin
41. Nobelist Pauling
42. Kind of hole or show
43. Gadget
45. Pontificates on a platform
47. Colonial civil servant
49. Bosh!
51. Day's march
52. Vittles
53. Cartagena child
54. Upper air
55. Galley mark
56. Site of Vance A.F.B.
57. Hampton __
58. B'way sign
59. Old oath

DOWN

1. Throe
2. Isolated
3. Gathering places for certain scouts
4. Monogram of Prufrock's creator
5. Fasten anew, as boots
6. Water chute
7. Moist
8. Intermixes
9. Emulated Héloïse
10. Language spoken around Kazan
11. The mating game
12. Scuttles
15. Athenian's rival
21. Wan
22. Napped leather
24. Race-track bettor's consideration
27. Blackthorns
28. Make trimmings
29. Biblical prophet
31. Meddler's activity
32. __ tizzy
33. Sparks of old flicks
35. Moses' mountain
36. Plods
37. Frost or Burns
39. Furtive movers
40. Stingy
41. Truncated
42. Quickly
43. Moro chief
44. Triple Crown winner: 1935
45. Mink's kin
46. "Crime and Punishment" character
47. Groucho expression
48. Cloches or toques
50. Mary __ Lincoln
53. Born

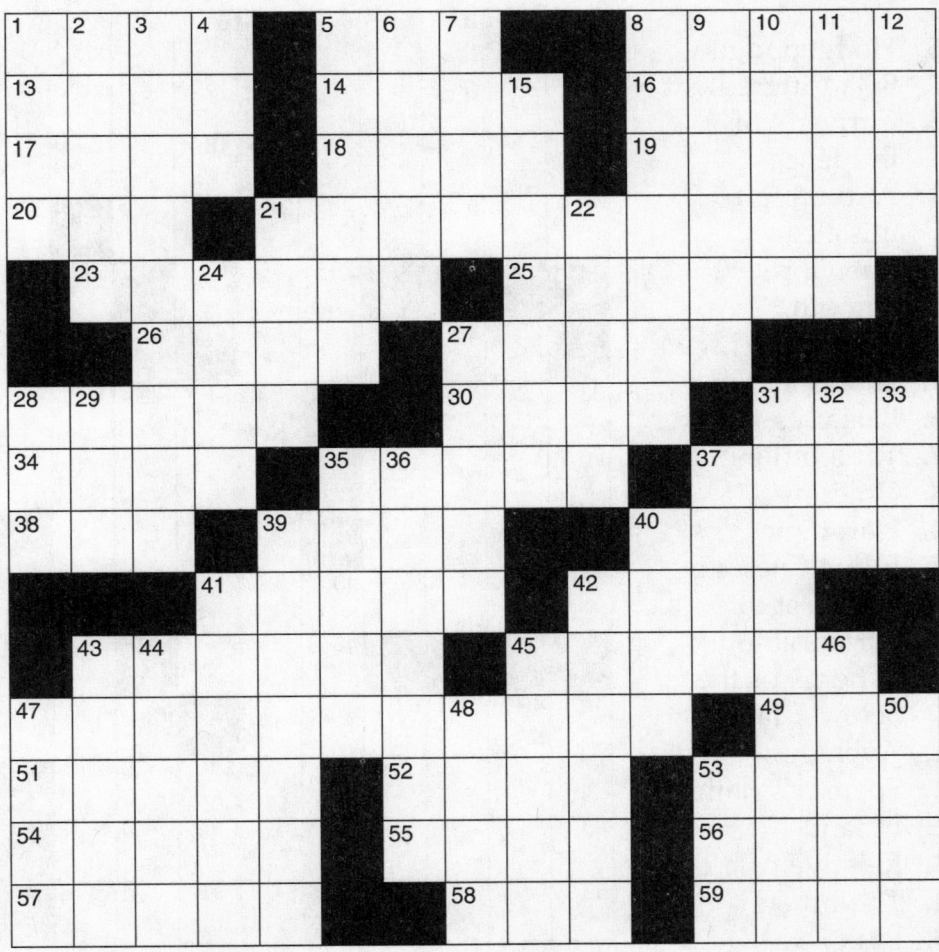

ACROSS

1. Fine violin
6. "And every __ a queen": Kingsley
10. Supplicate
14. Discharge a Tommy
15. Skewed
16. Trick
17. Old-womanish
18. Scotland, to a poet
20. Odds and ends
22. Whirlybird
23. Neither Rep. nor Dem.
24. Afflict
25. Caballeros' partners
28. Asia Minor, once
33. __ Alto
34. Seed covering
35. Tear
36. Hodgepodge
37. Salad ingredient
38. Carnegie of influence
39. Antiaircraft missiles
40. Caen's river
41. Smooth
42. Ireland, to Livy
44. Showy heron
46. Balaam's rebuker
47. Tar's milieu
48. Obvious
52. Harangues
57. Julius Caesar's conquest of 56 B.C.
59. Permissible
60. "The __ of the Screw": James
61. Average
62. Spenser's name for Ireland
63. Relative of a cod
64. The others
65. Plus

DOWN

1. Huxtable and Rehan
2. Carte
3. Cole Porter's "I __ Love"
4. Related
5. Ancient Hispania
6. Spiked the punch
7. Last of a Stein line
8. Musical tone
9. Shopper stoppers
10. Telephone onstage
11. Dwarfish animal or plant
12. Orient, to Napoleon
13. Circle of the seasons
19. Dummkopf
21. Elected ones
24. Fragrant seed
25. Lama leader
26. Out on __
27. Largest of the deer family
28. Sphere of struggle
29. Ham and cheese on rye, e.g.
30. Permission
31. Ria
32. Arabian trading port in Roman times
33. Like Buckingham Palace
34. Molding edge
37. M. Kennedy's "The __ Nymph"
43. Yawp
44. Common Market: Abbr.
45. It was divided "in partes tres"
47. Sordid
48. Orbit
49. __ fortis (nitric acid)
50. Young __ (radical)
51. "__ kleine Nachtmusik": Mozart
52. Word with need or consequences
53. Publicizes
54. Frozen desserts
55. Part of U.M.W.
56. E.r.a. or r.b.i.
58. Classic Japanese drama

ACROSS

1. Brit. fliers
4. Fasten
9. Craving for chalk, e.g.
13. Site of Milton's Pandemonium
14. Forearm bones
15. Summon to court
16. ___ the Great: 912–73
17. Palm that produces nuts
18. Harpsichordist Kipnis
19. Convention activity
21. Partial resemblance
23. Abandon
24. Word with will or wind
25. One "little woman"
26. Philately and golf
31. Grimp
34. Put side by side
35. D. D. E.'s opponent
36. Pickets
37. African cobra
38. View from the George Washington Bridge
41. Pulitzer poet: 1944
43. Painted
44. Stole
45. Prior to: Prefix
46. Budapest, for one
50. Easy and Grub
54. Free of guile
55. Motor
56. Puts out of competition
58. Information
59. Home of the Hawks
60. October lollipop
61. Period in a Jewish year
62. Shed
63. Firearm mechanisms
64. Homework for an ed.

DOWN

1. Prefix with fire or choir
2. Where a sacerdos presides
3. Vagrants
4. Cross
5. A size
6. Drink
7. Silicate
8. Arrau and Duchin
9. Painter commissioned by Victoria
10. Symbol of false friendship
11. Stop up
12. Ethereal
13. Dance
20. Metrical foot
22. Province in Can.
26. Whined
27. Removes rowans
28. Wind sound
29. Being, to Aquinas
30. Clan branch
31. Fear, for one
32. Spare
33. Cuba or Menorca
34. Wear out
36. Loose outer garments
39. Tie Pauline on a track
40. Withered, to George Wither
41. Umiak or shell
42. Peer's realm
44. Breaks open
46. State on the Persian Gulf
47. Lions and Tigers
48. ___ Park (which is not a park)
49. Boris Godunov, e.g.
50. Tuned set of organ pipes
51. Publisher's ponderous product
52. Old Norse poem
53. Trustworthy
57. Place for gobs of gobs

ACROSS

1. Ozark angler's catch
9. Not quite
15. Agua —
16. Fathom
17. Highway stopping-place
18. "Peer Gynt" temptress
19. Exterminator's victim
20. Stamp facsimile
22. Airport closer
23. Debarkation site
25. U.S. Open winner: 1934
26. Smudge
27. Kind of seal
29. Chi follower
30. Hoist
31. Reached
33. Money of sorts
34. Entree
38. A lot
39. Frankie of songdom
40. Tattered Tom's creator
41. Monogram of a famous Phillie
42. Shady place
46. Winter hauler
47. Anatomical meshes
49. Biblical country
50. Work hard: Scot.
51. Cincinnati Kid, for one
53. Track ticket
54. Readied for the printer
56. Maximum
58. Blitzed, in football
59. Vestibule item
60. Quick
61. Contest participants

DOWN

1. Difficulty or scuffle
2. Ancient headband or fillet
3. Heavy overcoat
4. Morse-code word
5. Trepidation
6. "The Lady —," 1935 song
7. Approach or confront
8. Salad choice
9. City on the Seyhan
10. Easter precursor
11. Year in Pope Alexander VI's reign
12. Thwart in battle
13. Cadge; mooch
14. Color close to palmetto
21. Bela's son
24. Gave joy to
26. Tonics
28. Pill dispenser
30. Site of Nixon's famous 1972 trip
32. Nondrinkers: Abbr.
33. The Windy City, for short
34. They gasconade
35. Wrapped, as a rug
36. Barely
37. Set of bells
41. Place for Pompey's calceus
43. Word of warning
44. — dictum
45. Asiatic princesses
47. Rosy-cheeked
48. Aged: Abbr.
51. Mark
52. Confirmation, e.g.
55. Start of many a title
57. Engine: Abbr.

ACROSS

1. Distributed, as seeds
5. Like hoopster Gilmore
9. Hokum
13. Number for Nilsson
14. Pottage trader
15. Brontë's Jane
16. Theatrical duo
19. Most mature
20. Farewell appearance
22. Second half of 16 Across
23. Mineral and vegetable
24. Grassland, to Gray
25. Neighbor of Md.
26. __ Lit. (H.S. subject)
27. Golfers, now and then
29. Turkish dynasty
33. First half of 16 Across
34. York's river
35. Loretta of "M*A*S*H"
36. __ à manger (French dining room)
38. Kind of equation
41. Prom queen
42. Arafat's group: Abbr.
44. Sheriff's asst.
46. Proposed 27th Amendment
47. Greek promenade
49. "Just __" (lyrics by 16 Across)
52. Lowering, of a sort
54. Lethargy
55. "On the Town" hit (lyrics by 16 Across)
57. Gulf of the Arabian Sea
58. Kind of sch.
59. Bone: Prefix
60. Safe companion
61. Bread and whisky
62. Exigency

DOWN

1. Toward the lower back
2. Gold-colored alloys
3. Street of the Barretts
4. Needle, in Nürnberg
5. Chayefsky's "The __ Man"
6. __ last resort
7. Snooky of TV's "Your Hit Parade"
8. Mezzo-soprano Christa of the Met
9. Composer of "On the Town"
10. Lixiviums
11. Small interstice
12. Leghorn lodging
17. Telepathic initials
18. Eight pts.
21. Leaded or unleaded item
26. Piece out
28. Ending for wagon or kitchen
30. Dangle
31. Composer associated with 16 Across
32. Employ
33. Montserrat, Nevis, etc.: Abbr.
35. Highway warning
36. Evening love songs
37. Tree-lined walkway
39. Fatty
40. Contrition
41. River bottom
42. Wiser's correlative
43. In limp or awkward fashion
45. __ up (revived)
48. Uncle Juan
49. List contents
50. "__ hear this!"
51. Don at the tailor shop
53. Author Wister
56. Born, in Bayeux

124

ACROSS

1. What some gliders do
5. Nothing more than
9. Gaze fixedly
14. Butter substitute
15. Infamous alliance
16. Slender candle
17. Wicked
18. Ponder and Pensive
20. Snack named for an earl
22. Mailed
23. Frequent entree
24. Large land mass
25. Disrobe
28. Caught in a misdeed
32. Place often visited
33. Challenges
34. Roman greeting
35. Feudal toiler
36. Bobby Orr was one
37. Locale
38. "Dulce et decorum ___ ..."
39. Thick pieces
40. Large nail
41. Confident
43. Kitchen gadget
44. Numerous
45. Cicatrix
47. Flavorless
49. Describing some TV sets
53. British cream
55. Twofold
56. Worn away
57. Fox terrier of films: 1934–47

58. Peeves
59. Lessened
60. Lone Ranger's trademark
61. An Amerind

DOWN

1. Bladed tools
2. Edison's middle name
3. German negative
4. Bonanza
5. "West Side Story" girl
6. Precise
7. Abundant
8. Compass direction
9. Some are tall
10. British airport runway

11. Church section
12. Marsh growth
13. Vocalized pauses
19. Expedite
21. Cried
24. Sponsorship
25. Cheviot or Romney
26. Italian poet: 16th century
27. Stunted ones
28. Kind of stew
29. Long-nosed animal
30. Call forth
31. Dissuade
33. Moola easily obtained
36. Hunters' hideaways

37. Occasional
39. ___ glass
40. Vamoose
42. Force (oneself) on others
45. Separates
46. Make a squeaking sound
47. Actress Miles of films and TV
48. Eden's earldom
49. Italian province
50. Subject of a Vidal book
51. Superior, e.g.
52. Otherwise
53. "Into a sea of ___": E. Field
54. Amateur radio operator

ACROSS

1. Nursery item
5. Filmdom's Schary
9. Airport abbr.
12. Harness part
13. Island off Venezuela
15. "— Harrington," Meredith novel
16. Candlenut trees
17. Kind of beacon
18. Problem with a blue serge suit
19. N.Y. landmark
22. One-time Mexican president
23. European blackbirds
24. Understand: Colloq.
25. Pool-table covering
28. Marie Antoinette, e.g.
29. Newspaper part
30. Former TV series
32. Polka followers
33. Alop
36. Fix firmly
38. Charge
39. Cpl. once
42. Narrow passes in the Southwest
44. Jack of movie fame
46. Disencumber
47. Order at a service station
48. Louts
50. Philadelphia landmark
54. Site of W.W. I battles
55. Greeting in Maui
56. Secular
58. Tolkien creatures
59. Kitchen gadget
60. Sicilian sight
61. Their: Fr.
62. Two-inch nail
63. Graduated series of boxes

DOWN

1. Rolled tea
2. Wandered
3. Turkish hospices
4. Twig broom
5. Koestler's "— at Noon"
6. Spoken
7. Crooner Vallee
8. Israeli statesman
9. Clear; plain
10. Complications for anglers
11. Certain stakes
14. Place shaded by trees
15. Dropping of a vowel in pronunciation
20. Blockhead
21. — Rivoli, Paris
22. Arabian commander
26. Lacking assurance
27. Resort at the base of the Sierra Nevadas
31. Cloy
33. "Carmen" character
34. Native of Qain
35. Recreation area
36. Prime mover
37. Begs for
39. Stretched out at the poles
40. Creations at Cremona
41. These score six pts.
43. Jewish month: Var.
45. Fairy queen
47. Siouan Indians
49. Reddy or Moody
51. Ancient country in Greece
52. Easy victory
53. "Take — Train," 1941 song
57. Channel — (food fish)

126

ACROSS

1. Hurt badly
5. Lady Macbeth's problem
9. Obscures
14. Worthless: Scot.
15. Aqua ___
16. Rubinstein or Bruckner
17. Spiteful tosses from the mound
19. One heck of a mess
20. Busybody, Yiddish style
21. Pesty little beetle
23. Property claims
25. Israeli desert
26. Israel's Weizman
28. P.L.O.'s Yasir
32. Calming sound
35. Come to pass
38. Hamlet's vacillating infinitive
39. Boxer's ring souvenirs
43. ___ fruit (Jamaican product)
44. Faithful
45. Plastered
46. Las ___, Canary Islands
49. "Sticks and Bones" author
51. Early Puccini opera
54. Duke or Day
57. Relative of a towhead
61. Goes into hysterics
63. Film director Resnais
64. Translucent paper
66. Violinist Ruggiero
67. Year before Raleigh's birth
68. Ending with citron

69. Cheats at hide-and-seek
70. Hawk
71. Abysmal

DOWN

1. Famous Dick
2. Spinning
3. Mossadegh was one
4. Bogart stage and screen role
5. Health resort
6. Vegetable matter
7. Synthetic fabric
8. Function of certain buds
9. Highly skilled worker
10. Offer a new twist
11. Pierce
12. Health faddist's fare
13. Ensconced
18. Greeting meaning "May you live 10,000 years!"
22. Turkish title
24. Feudal toiler
27. Brooklet
29. Colt, e.g.
30. Dugout
31. Classroom event
32. Porgy
33. Icelandic tale
34. Pea pod
36. ___-distant (self-styled)
37. Jug
40. Verse form named after a county
41. Minced oath

42. Existing afresh
47. Male beauty
48. N.C.O.
50. Liquidated, as a hood
52. Molecular components
53. "La" ___" (Max Ophuls film)
55. Braided linen yarn
56. Upright panel piece
57. Kin of a bream
58. Proverbially, this begets another of its ilk
59. Biological variety
60. Bore
62. Device on many a purse
65. Derain offering

ACROSS

1. Disintegrate
8. Cheer
15. Kin of a cookie jar
16. Get
17. Translucent type of glass
18. School figure
19. Tie fabric
20. Factions
22. Early Dr. Kildare
23. Creek
25. One-on-one contests
27. 12-year-old
29. Sounds of laughter
33. Used air-to-ground machine guns
35. Thoroughfare
37. Came
38. One who evades the issue
39. Hot, to a hood
40. Shrove __
41. Arthur Garfield __
42. Metrical foot
44. TV's Verdugo
45. Coq __
48. Plane
53. City northeast of Venice
55. Fight
57. Gear for Ansel Adams
59. Bucolic poem
61. Surplus
62. Ravel-proof edge
63. Tutelary deities
64. Got ready for action

DOWN

1. Acidity
2. Come to a point gradually
3. Giraffe's cousin
4. Tormé
5. Wading bird
6. Gridiron ploy
7. Carried out
8. Be a pain in the neck
9. Outer: Prefix
10. Light greenish blue
11. Vallee
12. Pinafore
13. Lake in Ireland
14. Jersey cagers
21. __ off (irate)
24. ". . . young __ blue surprise": O'Donnell
26. One in a zigzag procession
28. Hoped-for review
29. Kept in line
30. Architectural pier
31. One of the Long fellows
32. Atmosphere: Prefix
33. Mex. girl's title
34. To which Helen was taken
36. Shop tool
37. Eliot's "__ Wednesday"
38. Least clouded over
40. __ the line (behaved)
43. Assets
46. Radio City Music Hall feature
47. Makeup
48. Old minstrel
49. Experience
50. It is so
51. Vague on the screen
52. What "est" becomes tomorrow
54. Name meaning "elfin"
56. Knawel is one
58. Ripen
60. Egg: Prefix

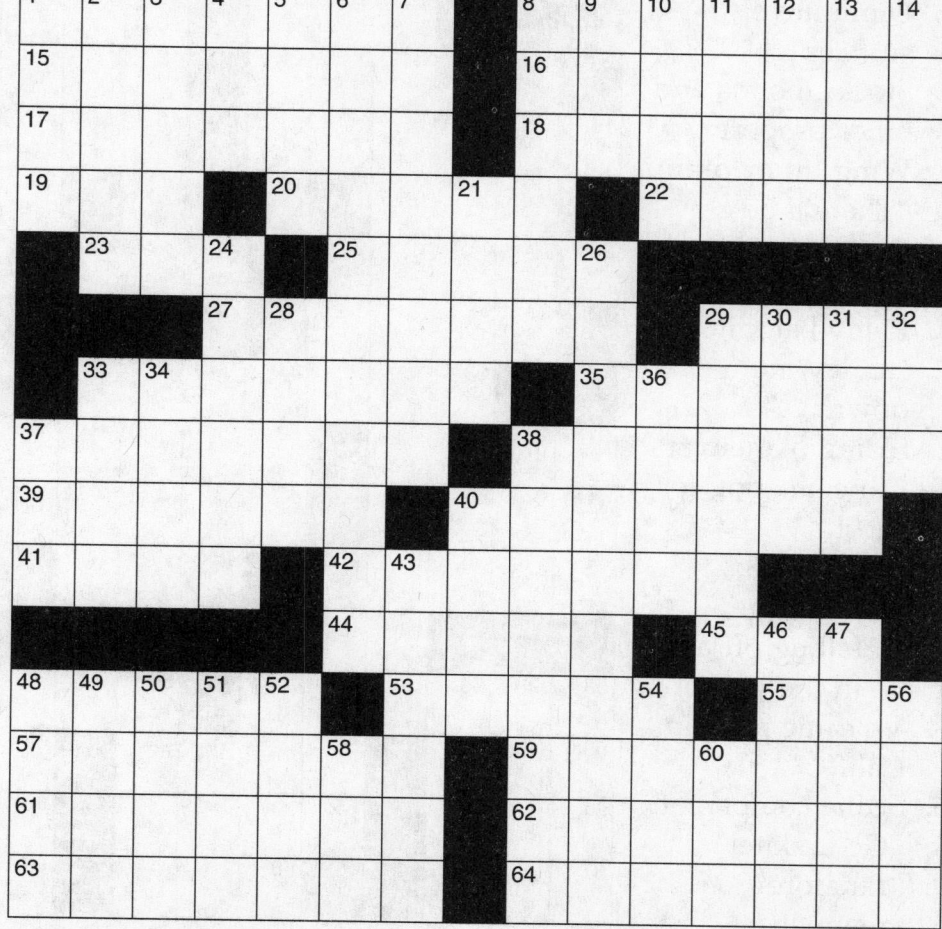

128

ACROSS

1. Prefix with treat or use
4. Cul-de-__
7. Clerical vestment
10. Stage whisper
12. Flag
14. Henna rinse
15. Cure-all
16. King or Alda
17. Pub choice
18. Ye __ Gift Shoppe
19. Bald eagle's cousin
21. Comedians' writers
23. Jenny Lind, for one
25. "__ Fideles"
27. Slave of old
28. Performed
29. Diminutive suffixes
33. Stocks, bonds and other property
36. Wing tip or pump
37. "There'll be __ time . . ."
39. Actress Debra
40. Piggy-bank item
41. "__ lay me down . . ."
42. Skiing maneuver
44. Dancing spot, for short
46. Roman 106
47. N.C. college
49. __ falling off a log
51. __ in the bucket
53. Volcanic peak in Calif.
56. Scone companion
58. "Go __ kite!"
59. "Pinafore" crewman
60. Small case
62. Requisite
64. Dashboard gauge
65. Site of U. of Nevada
66. Lock
67. Miller or Palmer
68. Newsman Rather
69. First of a much-quoted trio

DOWN

1. Good and bad reviews
2. Amin of Uganda
3. Withered
4. Applause, applause, applause
5. Feel pain
6. Rocky formations
7. Style of furniture
8. "Sparky" of the Yankees
9. "I've __ to London . . ."
10. "For __ Know" (old song)
11. Circus attractions
13. Growing out
15. Dawn goddess
20. Brightness
22. Suffers stage fright
24. Slippery customer
26. One way to get a word in
30. "All __ a stage . . ."
31. Unnumbered years
32. Theatrical scene
34. Refugees, for short
35. P.O. item
37. "Troilus __ Cressida"
38. __ polloi
43. Meadow
45. Horse opera
48. He wrote "The Highwayman"
50. Like a gleeful glutton
52. Frog's perch
53. Bring to a standstill
54. Broadway hit
55. Guthrie, the singer
57. Pot money
61. Merkel of movies
63. Historic period

ACROSS

1. Indian princes
6. Skeet feats
10. Creator of Tobacco Rhoda
14. Ooze out slowly
15. Tale: Abbr.
16. Cohan's "__ There"
17. Apportion
18. Inactive
19. Name meaning "black"
20. Alfonso XIII, e.g.
21. Marching instruments
24. Winter headgear
26. Perfect score on a test
27. Floor of a building
29. Builds slopes around a fort
33. Something to fight for
34. Kind of attack
35. Landon
37. Distinctive air
38. Foot lever
39. Cap-__ (from head to foot)
40. Nobel product
41. Kilmer poem
42. __ de menthe
43. Nickname for Chile's cape
45. Plume: Var.
46. Adage
47. Habitual practice
49. French counterpart of 7 Down
53. Pussy-cat's shipmate
56. Clarinet's cousin
57. Judge, in Baghdad
58. Obsession
60. Unerring
61. "Give __ a horse . . ."
62. Expert
63. Prow of a ship
64. Comedienne from Butte
65. Receiver of a check

DOWN

1. With 2 Down, car part
2. See above
3. U.S. holiday
4. What the Stamp Act caused
5. No longer dependent
6. Israeli port
7. See 3 Down
8. Brain tissue
9. Picturesque, as a stage performance
10. American vulture
11. State firmly
12. Seat of the Inca empire
13. Gym dance, at times
22. Kind of stare
23. Walker of football fame
25. Minor or Major
27. Ailurophobe's cry
28. Gibe
30. Magellan's milieus
31. Currency of a sort
32. Sticky mud
34. Clairvoyant
36. A mile has 5,280
38. Police vehicle
39. Jason's ship
41. Siamese
42. Town plat
44. Regard highly
45. Fresh __ daisy
48. Neighbor of Trieste
49. Office bigwig
50. Be adjacent
51. In a pique
52. Tibetan priest
54. Rub clean
55. Behind schedule
59. Political org.

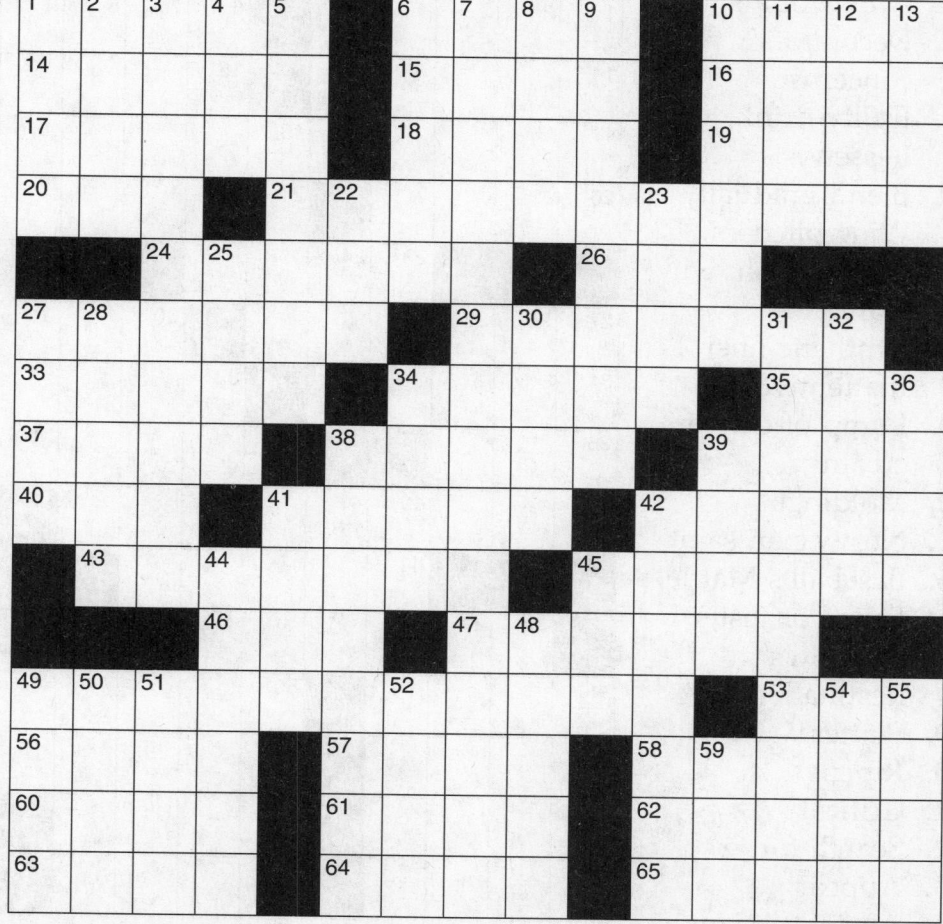

130

ACROSS

1. Hawkeye
6. Agitate
10. Uncovered wagon
14. Skyline sight
15. E flat is one
16. Concert halls
17. Verdi opera
19. Rock follower
20. Otherwise
21. Golfer Lee —
22. Of an epoch
23. Use a letter opener
25. Response to a stimulus
27. Spoiled
30. Punitive
31. Rub out
32. Treated with contempt
36. Annex of a sort
37. Decorators' concerns
38. Fruity drink
39. Lessens
42. Blend gradually
44. Wine pitchers
45. He has cash, will loan
46. Synthetic fiber
48. Inattentive
49. Lump of clay or cream
50. Moldings
52. Norwegian saint
56. Baseball's Mattie, Felipe or Jesus
57. Swallows' destination
59. Platter
60. Ripens
61. Critical
62. Search for
63. Appear
64. Ancient Asians

DOWN

1. "Emerald —"
2. Gemstone
3. Masters of banter
4. Notations on a certain blotter
5. Teachers' org.
6. Wading bird
7. Hognose snake's prey
8. What a good book does
9. Sights seen ahead in a traffic jam
10. Franco of the Met
11. Dote on
12. Psychiatrist's advice
13. Like a redwood
18. Glasgow's "— of Iron"
24. "The Gray Fox"
26. Aviation agcy.
27. Donna or Willis
28. Wreath on a knight's helmet
29. Chalky powder
30. Murmurers in Longfellow's forest
32. Release
33. British stool pigeon
34. Brink
35. Sambar or Bambi
37. Pudding thickeners
40. Kind of 35 Down
41. Pixie
42. Ovine plaint
43. Implement
45. Catfish Row gal
46. Kukla's friend
47. At liberty
48. Belief in an indifferent God
49. Flits
51. Sword for Count of Monte Cristo
53. Praise
54. Status quo —
55. Darius III and Alexander
58. Scottish hat

ACROSS

1. Part of a molecule
5. West Pointer
10. Jack of TV fame
14. Dome on the range
15. Hippodrome
16. City on the Truckee
17. Horns
20. Cagliari's island
21. Kind of bean
22. Scraped by (with "out")
23. Nota __
24. Former Michigan governor
27. Soapy water
28. Moslem potentate
31. To have: Fr.
32. Light tan
33. Growth on a tree trunk
34. Winds
37. Shake __ (hurry)
38. Rose Bowl winner of 1976
39. Bridge expert
40. Crane or Brown
41. __ on it (hurry)
42. Most cunning
43. Buddies
44. Sounds meaning "Don't touch!"
45. Cashmere's kin
48. Cause of nasality
52. Reeds
54. Draft status
55. "R.U.R." or "U.S.A.," e.g.
56. Sicilian sizzler
57. Ogle like an ogre
58. "Farewell the neighing __"
59. Ginza sauces

DOWN

1. Sighs, in Stuttgart
2. "__ yellow ribbon . . ."
3. Actor Sharif
4. Vexatious
5. Co-star in "The Late Show"
6. Jack-in-the-pulpit, e.g.
7. __ vu
8. Chemical ending
9. Put on the bulletin board
10. One of the deadly sins
11. Ages and ages
12. Baxter or Hathaway
13. Ablush
18. Tightwads
19. Cannery items
23. Pouchlike body cavity
24. Assessment amount
25. Egglet
26. Folkways
27. Hustle tickets
28. Kostelanetz
29. Winds of 32–63 m.p.h.
30. "__ You Glad You're You"
32. Endings for prefer and differ
33. Observation posts for Peeping Toms
35. Endures longer
36. Tropical lizard
41. Ganges garb
42. Ate caramels
43. Like a magnet
44. Confuse
45. "Over the hill"
46. Three squared
47. High spirits
48. Buy a poker hand
49. "Tell __ the Marines"
50. Gainsay
51. Madrid wives: Abbr.
53. River isle

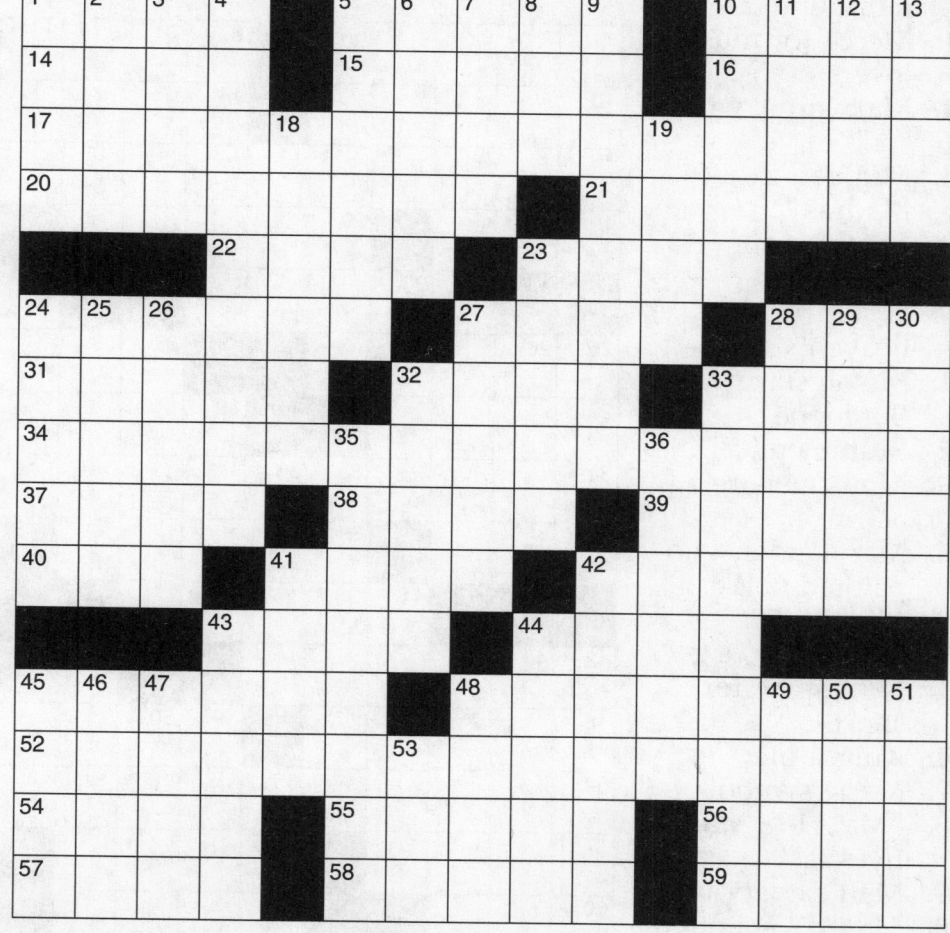

132

ACROSS

1. Masculine, in Mexico
6. Macadamize
10. Metric measures: Abbr.
13. "Mad __ the Boy"
14. "Mene, mene, . . ." e.g.
15. __ accompli
16. Khan men
19. Martinique is one
20. Main __ (boxing attraction)
21. Mockery of a sort
22. More resentful
24. Makes like a ham
25. __ a pistol
27. Malvolio's misdirected emotion
29. Much or many
30. Made more than moribund
31. Mecca for music lovers
34. Marx time, with "A"
38. Mugger, in Madras
39. Moon or sun circles
40. ". . . __ is in heaven"
41. Movie star from Boulogne
42. Mummers
43. Mousquetaire's alarm
46. Marylander who painted G.W.
48. Mephitic
49. Manhattan, e.g.
51. Marsupial, for short
54. Knight life
57. Mass. symbols
58. "Ma, He's Making Eyes __"
59. Man catnapping
60. Milton's synonyms for "alas!"
61. Mulcts
62. Much too plump

DOWN

1. Men who made a star trek
2. Murdered son of Adam
3. Migration wagon
4. Manifest affection
5. "Do unto __ . . ."
6. Model
7. "__ for All Seasons"
8. Means of releasing fumes
9. Means to an __
10. Mariner who found Newfoundland
11. Mr. Pim's creator
12. Madame's "unmentionables"
15. Maniacal fit
17. "__ got sixpence . . ."
18. Maiden's midnight garb
23. M.D.'s Hippocratic __
24. Mr. Kovacs's widow
25. Manner of doing something
26. Mélange; mishmash
27. Mfg. city in Illinois
28. Music to the varsity's ears
30. Manche capital
31. Make spellbound
32. Mohawk's relative
33. Makes lace
35. Mayan roof cover
36. Main river of Switzerland
37. Milkmaid's burden
41. Mr. Cross?
42. Manage somehow
43. Muddled or cruising
44. Meek or humble
45. Midterm trials
46. Muskellunges
47. Make miniatures bigger: Abbr.
49. Moral obligation
50. Men who "get their man": Abbr.
52. Most bills in many wallets
53. Monstrous menace
55. Mailman's pouch
56. Make a heist

ACROSS

1. Arthur or Washington
5. He's sorry now
9. Inside stuff
13. Affirm or confirm
14. Tokyo two-wheeler
16. Tax
17. Ignorant
18. Vermilion Range product
19. Weapon in the ring
20. Despicable
21. Control gate
23. Movie take
25. Emulate the Light Brigade
26. "___ are blue"
29. Jots
30. Electrical unit
31. Umbrella part
33. ". . . ___ and trouble"
34. Rollick or frolic
35. "Cuckoo"
36. Ike's command
37. Squelched
38. Fencing move
39. Food fish
41. Home of the Cowboys
42. Short swims
43. English county
44. He runs "with might and mane"
46. Appraise
47. Polish
49. City on the Wabash
52. Kind of sale
53. Not done purposely
54. Team from Salt Lake City
55. Bull fiddle
56. Variegated
57. Love ___

DOWN

1. ___ Alto
2. Hits too high on the backboard
3. Striking disclosure
4. Give it a whirl
5. Washer cycle
6. Body of troops
7. Fish-eating bird
8. Range in Morocco
9. Freebooter
10. Doctrines
11. "Hail to ___, blithe spirit!"
12. "It ___ to Be You"
14. Breakfast quaff
15. Goblin of German folklore
19. Trifles
22. Russian river
23. Alluring woman
24. White with age
25. Adduce
26. Mist or steam
27. His home is mobile
28. John Hancocks
30. Gruesome threesome
32. Night fliers
34. Creator of Lower Slobbovia
35. Thickens
37. Small harpsichord
38. Get along
40. Decks
41. Was overly fond of
43. Outmoded
44. Horne with a great sound
45. It springs up in spring
46. Coarse
48. Defeat
49. Transport for a trio
50. "With it"
51. Blackbird
52. Horseplay

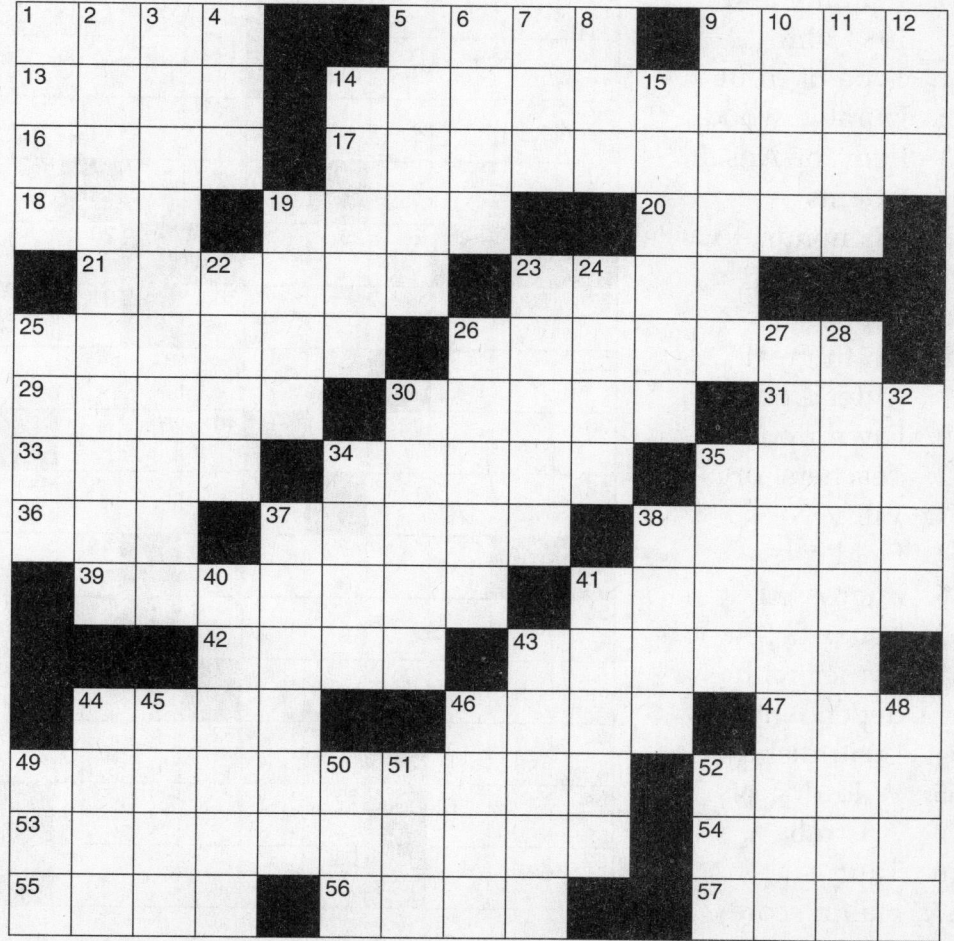

134

ACROSS

1. Brownish gray
6. Humble
11. Drain
14. It hath 30 days
15. Grottoes
16. Wing
17. Humdinger
19. __ king (creamed)
20. Chat
21. New Deal agcy.
22. Kickshaw
24. Grassy field
26. Bailiwicks
27. Cap for a cleric
31. Presses
32. Harem room
33. Rich cakes
35. Etcher's need
38. Kelp and nostoc
40. "Sammy and __," 1983 film
41. Type of trout
42. Durable wood
43. Item for Ansel Adams
45. Diamonds, to a fence
46. Pepo
48. Go to great __ (extend oneself)
50. Fawn upon
52. Teachers' org.
53. Vilify
54. Field role
56. Engrossed
60. "Buzz __!"
61. Earner with dependents
64. Luau dish
65. Wild dog of Australia
66. Taut
67. Half a score

68. Mosquito causing yellow fever
69. Say

DOWN

1. What blunt people lack
2. Guam harbor
3. Russian river
4. Tight spot
5. Wapiti
6. Land measure
7. __ California
8. A Gardner
9. Military subdivisions
10. Umiak user
11. Hardtack
12. Bushed
13. Municipal maps
18. One of Terpsichore's sisters
23. The Argives
25. Feminine suffix
26. Engine for a semi
27. Something not to be rocked
28. Unemployed
29. Tatterdemalion
30. Secret
34. Jerry's partner
36. Scratch causer
37. Fourth-rate marks
39. Wolf in "The Jungle Books"
41. Glass unit
43. Clique
44. Freshen
47. Greek el
49. Deep red
50. Ratify
51. Creator of Moll Flanders
54. What wild winds do
55. Brouhahas
57. Held or Karenina
58. Nuisance
59. Item for some surgeons
62. Tip
63. "__ Only a Paper Moon"

ACROSS

1. Resting
5. Stage
10. Assert
14. Indefinite amount
15. Positioning system for seamen
16. Arnaz
17. Journey
18. Unit follower
19. Clock face
20. Service at D.C.
23. Commercial papers
24. Song
25. Thompson or Hawkins
27. Eur. sea
28. Ending for verb or glob
31. Tamarisk salt tree
32. Distribute playing cards
35. Frozen
37. Pours
39. Hosp. workers
40. Zinc __
41. Rasp
42. On the summit
44. Level
45. Approvals
46. Decay
48. Having weapons
50. Drink
51. Pause
53. 1040A form
60. Calm
61. Right-hand page
62. Dies __
63. Everywhere: Comb. form
64. City in Ill.
65. Monster
66. Require
67. Travels via water
68. Close

DOWN

1. Italian wine region
2. Née
3. Give forth
4. Person supported
5. Sowed
6. Book of Hours
7. Seed coverings
8. River in West Germany
9. Set of nine
10. Totalizer
11. Blood vessel
12. Jacob's twin
13. "Aggravex"
21. Hugh Capet was one
22. Zodiacal sign
25. Bleak
26. Pseudonym of a sort
27. Too
28. __ branch (peace emblem)
29. Sympathized (with)
30. Paradise
31. Jason's ship
33. Part of Q.E.D.
34. Hill dweller
36. Taxpayer's delight
38. An antibody
43. Certain Met supporters
47. "Aida" and "Carmen"
49. Regret
50. Neither liquid nor gaseous
51. Milk: Comb. form
52. Praise highly
53. Image
54. Alaskan city or cape
55. Ice-cream __
56. Brain tissue
57. Importune
58. __ avis
59. "Two of one trade __ love": Dekker

136

ACROSS

1. Drs.' group
4. Offer
7. Mournful melody
11. Virile fellow
13. Fill
14. Landed
15. Largest antelope
16. Dickens villain
17. Golfers' gadgets
18. Form of brainpower
21. Got on
22. Marsupial, Down Under
23. ___ Dame
24. "To be or ___"
28. Where Pusan is
29. Sioux shelter
30. Literary monogram
32. Lupino and Tarbell
33. Praised extravagantly
34. Defeat decisively
35. ___ Aviv
36. Apportions
37. Nit-picking
38. Surprise success
40. Use mineral springs
41. Jefferson Davis's org.
42. Bizarre
43. ". . . they shall beat their swords ___"
49. Source of a bitter drug
50. Ireland, to Gaels
51. Character in "The Rivals"
52. Ponce de ___

53. Dau., bro. et al.
54. Approaches
55. Saxon serf
56. Upward curve in timber
57. Pesticide

DOWN

1. "___ Seasons"
2. Ukases
3. Pyrenees principality
4. Boxer Max
5. Particular
6. Went
7. Skin design
8. Sheltered at sea
9. Pilaster
10. City ways: Abbr.
11. Skirt part
12. Yale man
13. Molt
19. Boat-hull shape, often
20. Kind of bag
23. Protuberances
24. "And ___ the twain shall meet"
25. Uncloses, poetically
26. Farce about V.M.I.: 1936
27. Wash out
28. Travel pack
29. London gallery
31. Piggery

33. Covers walls again
34. Went back over one's path
36. Middle: Prefix
37. Poker player's delight
39. Greek Orthodox Church litany
40. School vehicle
42. Has markers out
43. French islands
44. "High" time for Cooper
45. Mortgage
46. Airfield near Paris
47. Poetic "ever"
48. Draft agcy.
49. Brown October brew

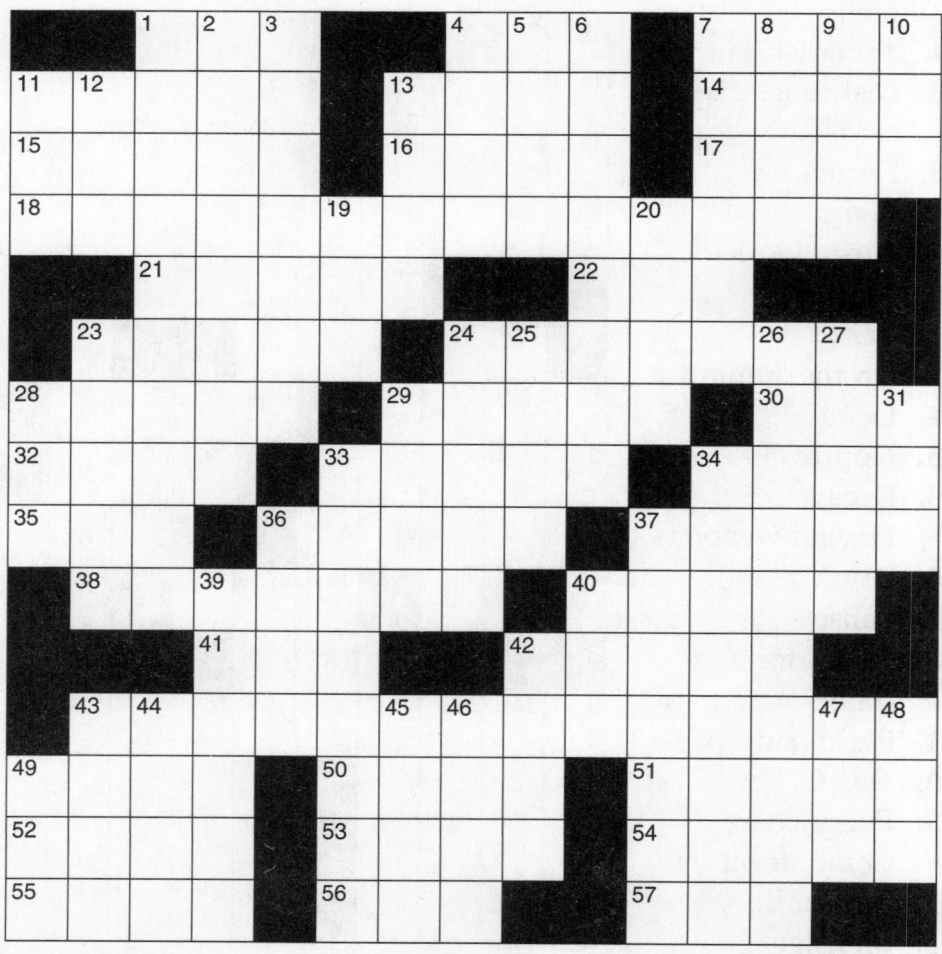

ACROSS

1. Inspired with fear
5. Book of the Bible
9. Taxi driver
14. Nobelist in Physics: 1922
15. Hudson Bay Indian
16. Kukla's pal
17. Tender ears
19. Haley book
20. Girls' ingredients
22. Slatterns
23. Emerged victorious
24. Owns
27. "__ Misérables"
28. Scull implement
29. Opp. of SSW
32. Kazan
34. Love apples
36. Alston Anderson novel: 1965
40. Skunks
41. Word with slip or swipe
42. Pig pad
43. Aunt, in Avila
44. Chem. site
47. Onager
48. Mayday relative
49. Prepare fare for an affair
51. Boys' ingredients
56. Panza's Dapple
57. Drill sergeant's command
59. Queue
60. The __ Lady (Margaret Thatcher)
61. Fibber
62. Welsh, e.g.
63. Lucid
64. Icelandic literary work

DOWN

1. Coll. degrees
2. Rolls 'em in the aisles
3. Caesar's "Alas!"
4. Remains
5. Accumulate
6. Some Slavs
7. Sea birds
8. Remit
9. Sergeant's right-hand man
10. Medicine prepared from the aloe
11. Political group
12. Seize the bait
13. O.K.
18. Kind of story
21. Hindu pundit
24. Mounds
25. Apportion
26. Inane
28. "__, That Kiss," 1931 song
29. Water lifter
30. Requires
31. Serfs in Ethelred's day
33. Mature
34. Cousins of normal schs.
35. N.F.L. scores
37. Eight-limbed animals
38. The Bumsteads' dog
39. Dep.
44. Middle of an atoll
45. Make harmonious
46. Rhythm
48. Pole on a ship
49. Mongoose's enemy
50. Place for a bayonet
51. Unadulterated
52. Russian river
53. Podium
54. __ an egg (bombed)
55. Spiny-finned fish
56. English TV letters
58. Time division

138

ACROSS
1. Tennis calls
5. Former Yugoslav dictator
9. Harmonium
14. Essayist's pen name
15. Sale condition
16. Unsophisticated
17. Part of the Musketeers' motto
19. Brilliant success
20. In an obvious way
21. Lingers (upon)
22. Interpret
23. Mount
24. Acad., for one
27. Three, in Bari
28. Creeper
29. Whitney or Wallach
32. "__ not to question . . ."
34. Unequal
36. Large artery
37. Energy unit
38. Triple
39. Forty
41. Old cars or planes
42. Kind of turn
43. Rulers: Abbr.
44. Cultivator
45. White House inits.: 1945–53
46. Pintail
47. Russian city
49. Lassie, for one
52. Faithless lover
56. Liquid part of fat
57. Alter in form
58. Charlie Chan actor
59. Emanation
60. "When the frost __ the punkin": Riley
61. Bert or Larry
62. Ancient Asian
63. Summer-theater enclosure

DOWN
1. Kind of year
2. Cinders of comics
3. Joust
4. Not so perilous
5. Batu Khan's horde
6. Tristan's love
7. Diminutive
8. Suffix with tuber
9. Thoroughfares having arrows
10. Andretti or Unser
11. One-eighth quart
12. Grandparental
13. Knicks' rivals
18. Monomaniacs' problems
21. Turtle follower
23. Serenade
24. One of fifty
25. Chinese dogs
26. Popular sandwiches
29. Mrs. Bunker
30. Unaspirated consonants
31. What i.e. stands for
33. "__ about time!"
34. Mine output
35. A Gershwin
37. Celtic
40. Curved molding
41. Circles of light
44. Sportscaster Cosell
46. Move furtively
48. Gambling maximum
49. Pen
50. Spiced stew
51. Norman of TV
52. Factual
53. Polyhymnia, e.g.
54. Choirboy's collar
55. A monthly payment, usually
57. Highlander's headgear

ACROSS

1. Augments
5. Meas. at a service station
8. Seagoing pole
12. Legislative body
13. Suffix with sect
15. Sprinter's target
16. Donkey: Ger.
17. Charlie McCarthy's medium
18. Was obligated
19. Composite representations
22. Warner of football fame
23. Corded fabric
24. Inca, e.g.
28. Rain
30. Pride, e.g.
33. Perch
34. Disimpassioned
35. Article in Hamburg
36. Challenge invented in 1913
39. Admiral Nelson's beloved
40. Dark fluids
41. Kind
42. __ Vegas
43. Singles
44. Crows
45. Lemon
46. Lamb's plaint
47. Examine inimically
54. Follow
55. Evicts
56. Use a foil
58. Spoken
59. Mercutio's friend
60. Gaelic
61. Loch of fame
62. Patriotic org.
63. Concerning

DOWN

1. Punchless punch
2. Record
3. Elk's cousins
4. Town west of Caen
5. Take in
6. Job for a young officer
7. Secular
8. Bend
9. Hock
10. Some Gibraltar residents
11. One end of a spectrum
13. A cause of combustion
14. Bridge term
20. Old-fashioned footwear
21. Comparative suffix
24. Ray __, noted boxing trainer
25. One of the Talmadges
26. Condemns
27. U.S. artificial satellite
28. He portrayed Jolson
29. Auto pioneer
30. Dimensions
31. Table Bay is one
32. Necessities
34. Strobile
35. Poet Pound
37. Royal name
38. German sub
43. Suffix with marvel
44. Jerome Hines, e.g.
45. Toyshop display
46. Rhythm
47. Worry
48. Creeks
49. Part of Q.E.D.
50. Sch. at West Point
51. Concept
52. Possessive pronoun
53. Kind of egg
54. Vogue
57. Zodiacal sign

140

ACROSS

1. Faction
5. Certain used cars, for short
10. Tresses
14. Kentucky fort
15. Serviceable
16. Famed cartoonist
17. "Pay ___ mind"
18. Elizabeth's favorite
19. Variety of cat
20. Spot on the skin
22. Athletic miss
24. Spenser opus, with "The"
27. Not Dem. or Rep.
28. Vegas rolls
32. Govt. security
35. Pub pastime
36. Outdo
37. Lloyd's rating
38. Mot ___ (precise phrase)
39. Scanty
40. Nickname for Rosalind
41. Scam
42. Hybrid quadruped
43. Poise and confidence
45. ___ soda
46. Humble
51. Caprice
54. Rub
55. Bates or Mowbray
56. Saint ___, first British martyr
59. Large weed
60. Bronx cheer
61. Roi's mate
62. Nights before
63. Wave-tossed
64. The South
65. A way to remember

DOWN

1. Light rowboat
2. Within: Prefix
3. Recipient
4. One of the glands
5. Fought one-on-one
6. And following: Lat. abbr.
7. Prefix with quote
8. ___ Miss
9. Double trio
10. Spillane sleuth
11. Saudi, e.g.
12. ___ time (P.D.Q.)
13. Name of theatrical fame
21. Class
23. Responsibility
25. Gratuitous, as advice
26. Give ___ (heed)
29. Like ___ of bricks
30. Daft one
31. Sure-footed
32. Western lawman
33. Social dud
34. Dix follower
35. Lackwit
38. Where trash is stashed for cash
39. Architectural support
41. Winnie-the-Pooh, for one
42. Actor Conried
44. Poem part
45. River of song
47. Muscat man
48. Nurmi of track fame
49. Wading bird
50. Foie gras sources
51. Spanish unit of length
52. Dear me!
53. Look intently
57. Wahine wear
58. Jazzman Beiderbecke

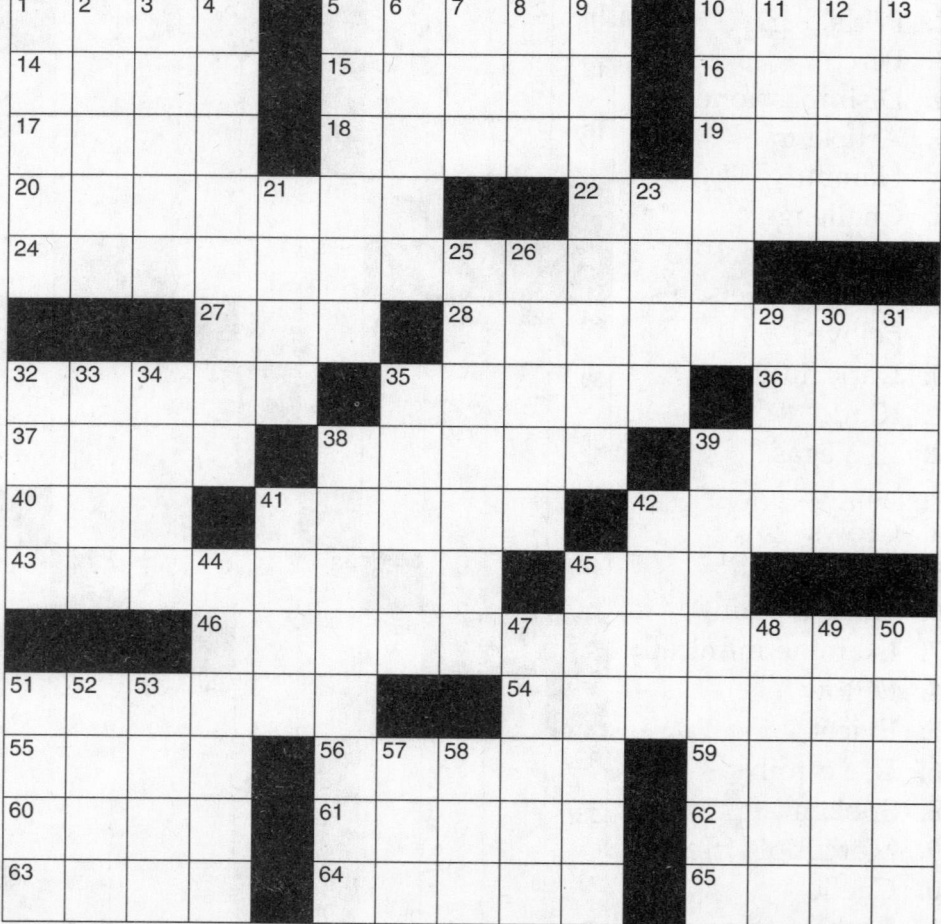

ACROSS

1. Bombay noble
5. __ del Sol, Derby winner: 1982
9. "When You Wish Upon __"
14. Meccan magnate
15. Suffix with class
16. Emulate Zayak
17. Tot's cry
18. Avon produced one
19. Quoted
20. Shopping stops for pops and fops
23. Mirthful, in Lille
24. Pittypat or Polly
25. Enshrined
30. Moccasin
33. Mad as a wet hen
34. Sgts.' bosses
35. Festival
36. Land in Everest's shadow
37. Word after "My country"
38. Blood bank's friend in need
39. Employs
40. Anchor part
41. Kostelanetz
42. Salt, in Savoie
43. Knock for a loop
46. Bethlehem-bound group
47. Arctic explorer
48. Pilocarpine sources
55. Cry "Wolf!"
56. Dresden article
57. Faucet debility
59. Do a grammar assignment
60. "... happily __ after"
61. Gamble chips
62. Gravelly ridge
63. Bratty response
64. Southwestern sight

DOWN

1. Aries symbol
2. Kowloon nurse
3. Iwo __
4. Ibn-Saud, e.g.
5. "The Prophet" author
6. Eastern Canada, once
7. Home in a Mitchell book
8. Seasoned seamen
9. Levitate
10. Evade an issue
11. Jacques of films
12. To __ (right on target)
13. Beatty film of 1961
21. Heron's cousin
22. Some of Manet's concerns
25. Andronicus
26. Greet a new day
27. Where confusion reigns
28. Québec seasons
29. Scale
30. Bearlike beast
31. Then, in Reims
32. Inverted vee
35. Saucerlike bell
37. Interns
38. Challenge giver or accepter
40. Diatom
43. Dairyman, e.g.
44. Pickling fluids
45. Banquet guests
46. He starred on B'way in "How to Succeed..."
48. Taunt
49. End of a popular Stein line
50. Kind of rind
51. Grace Bumbry, e.g.
52. Balled cheese
53. Coastal eagle
54. What a juror does
58. Coal size

ACROSS

1. Slender
5. 160 square rods
9. London's Marble —
13. Put on cargo
14. Debacles
16. — d'Orsay, French Foreign Ministry
17. With 34 and 53 Across, expert's advice re Wall St. pitfalls
20. Dixie
21. Mantles
22. Dan Beard's org.
23. Hop's cousin
24. IBM rival
27. Life-preserver vests
31. "Rory —," Lover novel
32. Evict
33. Laotian's neighbor
34. See 17 Across
37. Kind of sch.
38. Part of N.B.
39. Fulmars' kin
40. National Guard soldiers
42. Dominoes
43. Author of "The Making of an American"
44. Sodom survivor
45. Kind of play
48. Spiced pickling mixture
53. See 17 Across
55. Henri's head
56. Recipient of a gift
57. Ferrum
58. Frontón calls
59. Jeune fille
60. Easy gait

DOWN

1. Skirt feature
2. Trellis piece
3. "Thus with a kiss —": Romeo
4. Meal on a battleship
5. Incite
6. Terra — (literally, baked earth)
7. "Builder" of Yankee Stadium
8. Part of Afr.
9. Vacuum pumps
10. Actress Lenska
11. Make watertight
12. What frightened geese do
15. Hide
18. Peerage entries
19. Huff and puff
23. Former Turkish ruler
24. Soap plant
25. Burns midnight oil
26. Bankers' lures for borrowers
27. Mongrels
28. Cut of beef
29. Fodder plants
30. Sound of escaping steam
31. Lulu
32. Friends of Pawnees
35. Asked
36. "Scram!"
41. Like a Dives
42. Tasty dish
44. Debussy composition
45. Bismarck or Kruger
46. Maréchal —, yellow climbing rose
47. Famed Italian patron of the arts
48. He portrayed Pasteur
49. Diamond from Brooklyn
50. Baltic island
51. Theater curtain
52. He was freer than a theow
54. Place to find peat

ACROSS

1. Fibrous food
5. Speckle
10. Decree
14. Frost
15. Bucolic
16. Prefix with meter
17. Turkish titles
18. Set aside
19. Some stories
20. Light-lunch item
23. Bunch of Brownies
24. Town in NE Italy
25. All smiles
29. Rose essence
33. Tolkien creature
36. Sailing craft
39. London lad's swing, perhaps
40. Sweet snack
43. ". . . blue skies do __"
44. What tax payments may be in
45. Wawaskeesh
46. Espresso ingredient
48. Site of Vulcan's workshop
50. Crushed underfoot
53. Beast of Borden
57. Steakhouse entree
61. Boris contemporary
63. Bird woman of myth
64. Witt's asteroid
65. Stravinsky ballet
66. Banks or Pyle
67. Not any, to Burns
68. Conn. senator
69. Gee-haw controls
70. Cartoonist Silverstein

DOWN

1. Flower part
2. Severity
3. Former senator Alphonse D' __
4. King of Pylos
5. Fastening on a belt
6. "Au Clair de la __"
7. Author Ambler
8. Hide
9. Bern artist's display
10. Register for Pavarotti
11. Nastase
12. Blind impulse, personified
13. Scale notes
21. Imitative
22. J. F. K. letters
26. Medicinal plant
27. Entre __
28. Cavaradossi's love
30. Little feller
31. Integument
32. Give out fumes
33. Auricular
34. Artist Bonheur
35. Staff sign
37. Fille's father
38. Sean Connery, for one
41. Devious; clumsy
42. Proprietor
47. Amendment backed by NOW
49. E.T. and friends
51. Different
52. "The Wreck of the Mary __"
54. Singer Vaughan
55. __ fell swoop
56. Detroit disappointment
57. Blockhead
58. Female wild buffalo
59. "__ Central Park"
60. Draws for Connors
61. Unsound
62. I, to Claudius

144

ACROSS
1. Christie sleuth
7. Doyle's sleuth
13. Wood coating
14. Familiarizes one's position
16. Imminent
17. Wife of Oberon
18. Quieting sound
19. Relative
20. Indonesian island
21. Fort __, Calif.
22. Egg-shaped
24. Secret plot
26. Narrow pass in the Southwest
27. Ancient characters
29. Macadamia, e.g.
30. Choice cut
31. An alcohol
33. Orgiasts, e.g.
35. Simenon's sleuth
37. Headlong
41. Machine rod
46. Verona's river
47. Luxury's soft place
49. Tramp through mire
50. Gists
51. Rolls up, as a flag
53. Approximately
54. Diamonds, to a thief
55. Argon or xenon
56. Pongo, e.g.
58. Downing St. number
59. Spanish mutton
61. Plateful

63. He's dyeing to make a living
64. Cassavas
65. Queen of detectives
66. __ Lupin, Leblanc sleuth

DOWN
1. Concludes, as hoped for
2. Rain __ (in any event)
3. Banking abbr.
4. Mayo and Branco
5. Character in "Hamlet"
6. Cadmus was one

7. Big trouble, informally
8. Bay window
9. Stone: Comb. form
10. __ culpa
11. Dignify; exalt
12. Swizzle stick
13. Cap bills
15. Successors to the Nassers
23. "__ Rosen-kavalier"
25. Raffles, e.g.
26. Be unwell
28. River at Amiens
30. Greek cheeses
32. New Guinea port
34. Doggy doc

36. Unreal; deceptive
37. Widespread, irrational fears
38. Teach
39. Generous
40. Some linemen: Abbr.
42. Arafat's org.
43. Part
44. Basic nature
45. Leather straps
48. Red Cross need
51. One on the move
52. Hoplite's weapon
55. Hereditary unit
57. Sea fliers
60. Zilch
62. Compete

ACROSS

1. He wrote "Ulysses"
6. Jillian or Miller
9. She wrote "Three Weeks"
13. German sub of W.W. II
14. Life story, for short
15. Lieutenant, to G.I. Joe
17. Black eye
18. Broker: abbr.
19. Grown-up
20. Type of house
21. Feel flu symptoms
22. Goddess of agriculture
23. Publish
25. Hardy girl
26. Mather or Maxwell: Abbr.
28. Having a handle
30. "__ Gun for Hire"
33. Evil intent
35. On __ (free)
37. __ ear and out the other
38. Piggery
39. Not married
40. Type of terrier
42. "Eternity and I __": Howells
43. Water: Comb. form
44. TV's "Remington __"
46. H.S.T.'s predecessor
47. Trumpeter Al
49. Rust and alumina
51. Type of orange
53. Narrow reef
54. Food fish
57. Monopolize
58. Author Whitten
59. Long scarf
60. __ gander (look over)
61. Skill
62. Underground drain
63. Jumble
64. Yak away
65. W. German city

DOWN

1. A move in checkers
2. Hautboy
3. Wouk novel
4. Hindu social class
5. A season, in Arles
6. Calculating device
7. Marx Brothers film, with "A"
8. Short letter
9. Candied
10. Magnetite
11. Caesar-Coca TV program: 1950–54
12. Cleopatra's river
16. Dolls named for a film alien
21. First-class
24. Be silent: Mus. dir.
25. Golf gadget
26. Some Mennonites
27. Caprice
29. "__ kingdom come . . ."
31. "Whom shall __ . . . ?": Isa. 6:8
32. Jewish feast
34. Schemes
36. Enticed
38. Concorde
41. Adherent of: Suffix
42. Dismounted
45. Is
48. Meal, in Metz
50. Kefauver
51. Bone: Comb. form
52. Sewing line
53. Dross
55. Toward shelter, at sea
56. A "Coming Home" star
59. Compass pt.

ACROSS

1. Bombay bigwig
5. Mud follower
9. Something to flick
12. Ignore
13. Imogen's Fidele in "Cymbeline"
15. She, in Sonora
16. __ War (famed race horse)
17. "Lost Horizon" director
18. Pherkad is one
19. Optical toy
22. Stanford White extension
23. Distaff busybody
24. O'Hara's Joey
27. Break bread
29. Leaked almost imperceptibly
32. Step __ (hurry)
34. Red or Dead
36. Spanish satirist: 1809–37
38. 24-sided figure
42. Thermoplastic
43. W.W. II zone
44. Poetic times
45. Disclose
48. Cato's "It is"
50. Actor Billy __ Williams
51. Quartet from Mississippi
53. Spy job
55. Like serpentine writing
62. Transported emotionally
63. "...a kiss through __": Hugo
64. Jean or Walter
65. "Ship" follower
66. Stripper, possibly
67. Part of HOMES
68. Thriller prop
69. __-bitsy
70. Start of a Stein line

DOWN

1. Gambol
2. Oriental nurse
3. Judicial number
4. Make amends
5. Recoil
6. "Merry" in a game name
7. Under the "alfluence of incohol"
8. Writer Bret et al.
9. Lowest female voice
10. Word before stick or happy
11. Loser to a tortoise
14. Rhone feeder
15. Shenanigan
20. Hopped-up drink
21. Stone tablet
24. Crocks
25. Lend __ (listen)
26. Kin of a metre
28. Duffer's device
30. Bobbled
31. Loafer
33. Mockery; caricature
35. Borden weapon
37. Faulkner hero
39. "__ of robins..."
40. A daughter of Zeus
41. Inn
46. Religious retreat
47. One of 13 at the Vatican
49. Boy or bit
52. All tuckered out
54. Stud or draw
55. Blow one's own horn
56. Punchbowl site
57. Bedtime-story word
58. Shakes a leg
59. "Quo Vadis?" character
60. Rainbow flower
61. Algonquian language

ACROSS

1. Widow's portion
6. Sees red
11. Shoo!
12. Neckwear
14. "Rear Window" director
17. Dingles
18. Mme. Bovary
19. Unrelenting
20. "Buenos __"
21. Gambol
22. Modern "art"
23. Boston's time, at times
24. Islam's sacred book
25. Goblin
27. Profundity
29. Northern
30. The force is with it
32. Propellers on ships
35. Water
39. Other name
40. __ of vantage
41. Tavern
42. Mil. unit
43. Parsonage
44. Reminder
45. Galatea's beloved
47. "__ a Song Go . . ."
48. Centennial electee
49. Movie of 1947 (see 14 Across)
52. Cancels
53. Bond
54. Lancaster group
55. Elevate

DOWN

1. Lessen money in circulation
2. Scarebabes
3. Tribulations
4. Windup
5. Tell in detail
6. British army orderlies
7. Award never won by 14 Across
8. German pronoun
9. Places
10. Warehouse charge
11. M. Pascal
13. Smelter slag
14. To boot
15. Ardent
16. Truckle
21. Campus figures
24. Experiences
25. __ Islands, south of Tokyo
26. Neighbor of Wash.
28. Supplication
29. Late pianist/comedian
31. Verse stanza
32. Camp David peacemaker
33. Oft-heard expression
34. Area from Cannes to La Spezia
36. Latent
37. Least exciting
38. Like some leaves
40. Convertible carriage
43. Bogs
44. Nutmeg spices
46. Mex., Guat., Arg., etc.
48. Prefix with sphere
50. ". . . and not __ do"
51. Modernist

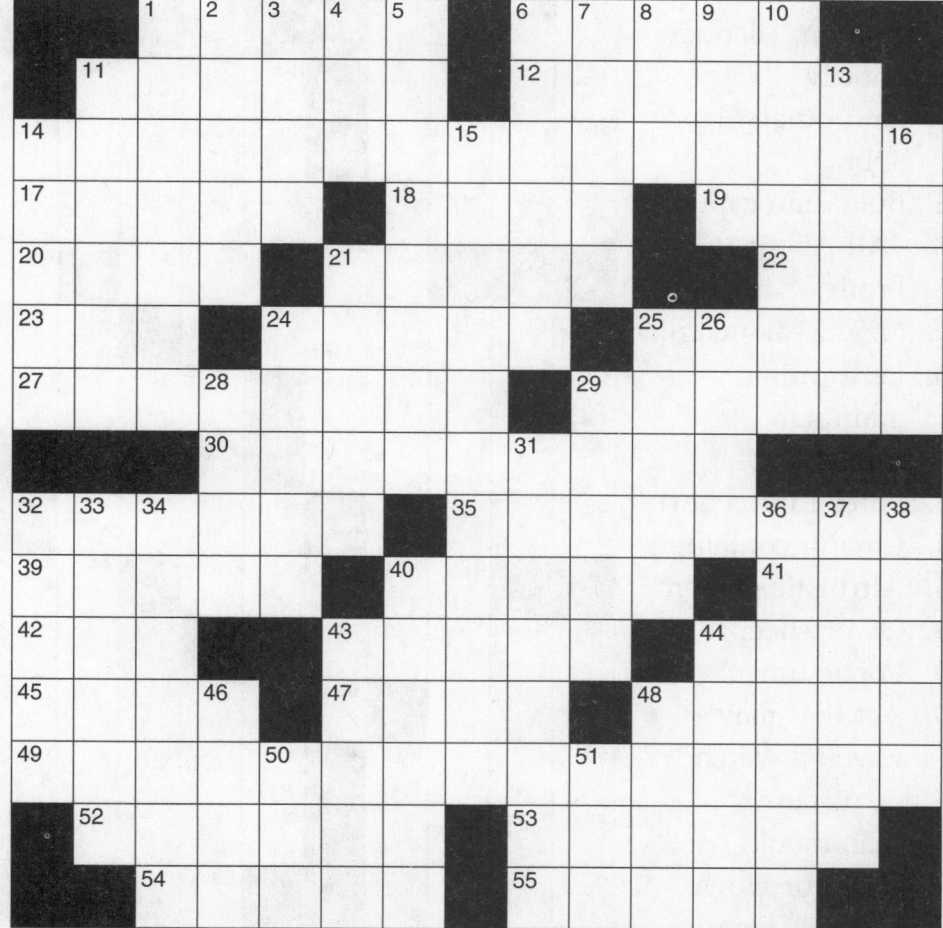

148

ACROSS

1. Watch of a sort
5. Eastern cape
8. Algerian port
12. "How now! __?": Hamlet
13. Satan
15. Quote
16. Like Godiva
17. Ecole student
18. Taj Mahal site
19. Lessee's lessee
22. "Heaven was __ help . . .": Crabbe
23. Malevolent looks
24. Samples
26. Canadian metropolis
29. Salamanders
30. Alaskan islander
31. Shortly
33. And others: Lat. abbr.
36. Bulgarian capital
37. "All About __"
38. Froth
39. New Zealand river
40. Performing mammal
41. Impish
42. Forced into court
44. Chianti containers
46. Altruistic person
48. Ox or sheep
49. Poetic time
50. Act that may wreck a watch
55. __ mecum (handbook)
57. Inventor Howe
58. Hebrew month
59. Level
60. Of certain bones: Comb. form
61. Cause dander to rise
62. Jerk
63. Sparks or Beatty
64. Store event

DOWN

1. Freud's "Totem und __"
2. Ireland's __ Islands
3. Avon great
4. Instrument for a rock star
5. A condiment
6. Pizzeria needs
7. Sutherland, for one
8. Wood sorrel
9. Wolfe book, with "The"
10. Up __ (trapped)
11. Comes close
13. Sidetrack
14. Pre-Easter adjective
20. "Giant" ranch
21. Marble
25. Roofers' gear
26. Specie
27. Baseball's Matty
28. Southpaw
29. "Private Lives" playwright
32. Basis for Ovid's omelet
34. Friend of Jeanne
35. Camera eye
38. Canary's kin
40. Tends
43. Zodiacal sign
45. Warning, for Juan
46. A natural at Reno
47. Ho's partner
48. Comedienne Fanny
51. Vivacity
52. Pelvic bones
53. Invalid
54. Kind of club
56. Terminus

ACROSS

1. Flat hill
5. Fanon
10. Arabian gulf
14. Dinghy equipment
15. Transfer picture
16. Walking tempo
17. CAMEL BACK
20. Finish
21. Amos's friend
22. Stupefy
23. Sniffs
25. __ precedent
27. Wading birds
29. Assume the burden of
33. Jutting rock
34. Lustrous fabrics
36. Age
37. Brutus or Cato
39. Rather of TV
40. Certain fisherman
42. Greeting for 37 Across
43. Imitation pearl
46. Red color
47. Declaim at length
49. Fly
51. Appends
52. Cut, as prices
53. Violinmaker
56. Is unwell
57. Dakota Indian
60. QUARTERBACK
64. Operatic prince
65. Circumference
66. Hot spot
67. Cong. group
68. Plaster of paris
69. Copperfield's first wife

DOWN

1. Speck
2. Merit
3. RESTS UP
4. Onager or dunce
5. Peculiarity
6. Instruments or plants
7. Sore
8. Opposite of long.
9. Pixie
10. Go to a higher court
11. Platform
12. Reverberate
13. Fledgling's home
18. Orient
19. Dense
24. Gymnast Korbut
25. Gleam
26. Eternity
27. Discard
28. Treasure __
29. Barrel part
30. PASSED UP
31. Upright
32. Street show
35. Mine entrances
38. Scandinavian
41. Steeple ornaments
44. Youngster
45. Hunting cry
48. Westerns
50. Far-reaching
52. Screens
53. Sale sign
54. Lien: Abbr.
55. Presently
56. Affectation
58. Pitcher
59. Lab heater
61. Humpty Dumpty
62. Compete
63. Nap or err

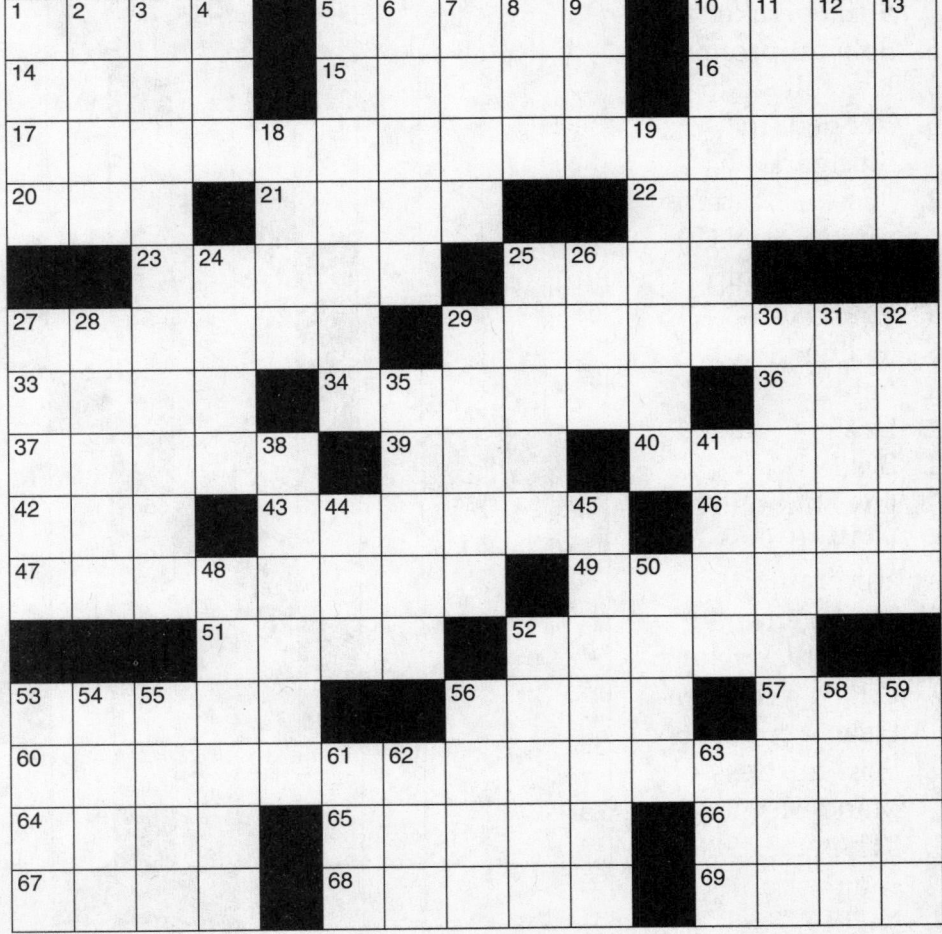

150

ACROSS

1. AMPAS bestowals
7. Suffragette Bloomer
13. Maximilian's empress
15. Queued up
16. Brooklyn Dodgers, to Roger Kahn
18. "__ a man with . . ."
19. Oust
20. NOW aim
21. Repute
22. Conspiracy
23. Inventor of a steam engine
24. Suggestion
25. "When the frost __ the punkin . . ."
26. __ Hawkins Day
27. Strikebreaker
28. Solemn promise
29. Ky. college or city
30. Refined, in Stuttgart
32. "Esse __ Videri" (motto of N.C.)
33. Ceramic chip
35. Equivoque
36. Mulligan
40. Pep __
41. Design
42. Beseech
43. Jewish month
44. W.W. II vice admiral
45. Strategem
46. Tiniest Cratchit
47. C.P.A.'s concern
48. Haze's cousin
49. First mistress of Manderley
53. "The __," 1928 song
54. N.H.L. team
55. Walked triumphantly
56. Take umbrage

DOWN

1. Fall mo.
2. Coptic dialect of Egypt
3. Fine violin
4. Teapot Dome figure
5. Entrench
6. Poland China's place
7. Late photographer Adams
8. Heavy hammer
9. Winged or slippery __
10. Summer cooler
11. Seat belts help to overcome this
12. Make effervescent
14. "To every thing there is __": Eccl.
15. The pipes __
17. Filmic "Incident" of 1943
21. Exclamations
22. Polite
23. F.D.R.'s Georgia retreat
26. Overwhelming quantity
29. Cottontail
31. He played Tarzan in 1970
32. Mercy
33. Conspicuous
34. He manipulates snakes
35. Tartan
37. College-board member
38. Oriental
39. View from Tintern Abbey
40. Certain rockets
41. Ride a bicycle
44. Pelf
47. Caustic
48. Arizona's Lost Dutchman, e.g.
50. Conceit
51. Tug of __
52. Q–U linkage

ACROSS

1. __ buddies
6. Lhasa __ (Tibetan dog)
10. Sea once part of the Caspian
14. Exonerating excuse
15. Club numbered one to nine
16. Little, in Livorno
17. Treasured memento
18. Tasty
20. Catcall
21. Singer Della
23. Expedition
24. Peers
25. Kind of snake
26. Cast
29. Combine
31. Wrangler's gear
32. Bani-Sadr, e.g.
33. Speed inits.
36. Equip
37. Old pro
39. Enviable test score
40. Approval
41. Wilson famed for needlework
42. Masquerade ensemble
44. Animated, in music
45. Cash registers, e.g.
46. Excise
49. Iris used in sachet powder
51. Idolize
52. Short comedies
53. __ Alamos, N.M.
56. Set off dynamite
58. Use a block and tackle

60. Agnes, in Acapulco
61. Body of mores
62. Expunge
63. Key
64. Irish maid
65. Constrict

DOWN

1. Fishhook part
2. Sandwich moistener
3. Storehouse for grain
4. Kimono accessory
5. Modern appliance
6. Succored
7. Airtight pots

8. Dover __
9. Navy's C.I.A.
10. Collection of hives
11. Perch
12. Critical
13. Ne'er-do-well
19. Food warmers
22. Sea accipiter
24. Realty unit
25. Lollobrigida
26. Jeweler's showcase
27. Lease
28. Butts
30. Former capital of Japan
32. "__ my lady . . .": Romeo
33. Pittance
34. Teem

35. High-school affairs
38. Celtic language
43. Begley and Asner
44. Glum
45. Dramaturgy, for one
46. Wheel spokes, e.g.
47. Idyllic locales
48. Stopover site
50. Emulates Cordero
52. Colonnade
53. Pinocchio, at times
54. Peak near the Aegean
55. Buck-and-wing segment
57. Emerson's "Give __ to Love"
59. Smidgen for Spot

152

ACROSS

1. Venue
5. "Cave —"
10. Radar signal
14. Genus of freshwater fish
15. Three-time A.L. batting champ
16. Punjabi potentate
17. Border on
18. Talent for making millions
20. Ornamental handwork
22. All-day rains
23. Belle taken to Troy
24. As to
25. Cotton cloth
27. Called on
31. Eating area
32. Keynes's topic
33. Browning's "— Bratts"
34. Fiddler-crab genus
35. Become greater
40. Tidied (up)
44. Famed twister of words
45. Throws out
46. Dante illustrator
47. What the toxophilite did
48. Characteristic marks
51. Burst inward
54. Criterion
56. Pitcher
57. Two-toed sloth
58. Passover feast
59. Cozy
60. Jupati, e.g.
61. Hebrew months
62. Tupolevs, for short

DOWN

1. Part of a baseball
2. Russian hut
3. Iffy
4. Ultra
5. Remark
6. Property-title receiver
7. Nest, in Nice
8. Not straightforward
9. Of a secret society
10. Trained; oriented
11. Nobelist in Physics: 1914
12. Addition: Abbr.
13. Cries of contempt
19. Ankle: Comb. form
21. Got out of the saddle
25. Ferber et al.
26. Mooring place
28. Scores of autumnal scores
29. Role at a roast
30. Pairs
36. Bit
37. Philanthropist Pratt
38. Gratiano's bride
39. Handled
40. Hue man
41. Elementary texts
42. Sloping walkway
43. Nugatory
48. "Rip —," Presley hit
49. Singer-songwriter Hendryx
50. Like certain controls
52. O.T. book
53. Energy units
55. Scheherazade slept here

ACROSS

1. Stout
4. Tiff
8. Thespian
13. Cutie
15. Sandarac
16. Not a soul
17. Five-and-ten
19. Sag
20. Heaven: Comb. form
21. Braun and Sydow
23. Mineral deposits
24. Tightwad
27. Story
28. Blood-hued
32. Neckpiece
35. Newport, R.I., has one
37. Daft
38. Tightly together
43. Water wheel
44. Compass pt.
45. Permit
46. "Fear God, and — commandments": Eccl. 12:13
49. Forum frock
52. Type of bread
57. Con game
60. African antelope
61. Saki
62. Pivotal
64. Social affair
66. Express a view
67. Some Feds
68. Being
69. Young adults
70. Assists
71. "Take —, She's Mine"

DOWN

1. Total
2. France's longest river
3. Violinist Mischa
4. Posed
5. Sphere
6. Baseball's Hank
7. Ditch
8. Response to a ques.
9. Pigment
10. Travel
11. "Don't tread —"
12. Agts.
14. Dustin Hoffman role
18. Salty sauce, British style
22. Haggard heroine
25. Paid athletes
26. Arabian prince
29. Asian weight
30. Concerning
31. "— la vie!"
32. Rowers' bench
33. Indian of Okla.
34. Farm measure
36. Mil. unit
39. U.S. journalist: 1889–1974
40. Waikiki's isle
41. Not discovered
42. Long period
47. Devilish tot
48. Ancient Laconian city
50. Furniture trimming
51. Kind of angle
53. Varnish base
54. Baked dough with filler
55. Jagged
56. Hermit
57. Blemish
58. Get by
59. "I cannot tell —"
63. — judicata
65. U.S.N.A. graduate

154

ACROSS

1. Apr. 15 collectors
4. Ottoman Empire founder
9. Kind of pipe
14. Detective Archer of fiction
15. Complete
16. Calm
17. Attend
18. Congreve comedy: 1695
20. Citrus coolers
22. Seiling of hockey
23. Midshipman
24. Savor
26. What sachets impart
27. Carpenter's friend
29. Hush!
30. Any bird
31. Kirghizian peaks
33. Ontario TV network
36. Ravel ballet: 1912
39. Heir pursuer
40. Entertainer Gillette
41. Forward
42. Electric-pen inv.
43. Siesta
44. Actress Gless
48. Misbehave
49. What a steed has
50. Trevino won this tournament in '84
51. Event at Hialeah
54. Consider seriously
57. Piper's son
58. Dancer Castle
59. Mrs. Kramden
60. N.T. Book
61. Relaxes

62. "The Screens" playwright
63. Alias, for short

DOWN

1. Ingrid's "Casablanca" role
2. Panpipe item
3. Jaye P. Morgan hit: 1956
4. Night person
5. Netman's apparel
6. "Kiss Me Quick" was one: 1969
7. Pianist Templeton
8. Ship-shaped clock
9. Cole Porter tune: 1929
10. "__ Bayne," Foster song

11. High up
12. Tourist attractions near Carlsbad
13. Sidewalk superintendent
19. Source of vanilla
21. Conductor Caldwell
25. Koran supplement
26. __ Na, musical group
27. Boggs of baseball fame
28. Gardner namesakes
29. It gets chalked
31. Pakistani, e.g.
32. Inadequate
33. Caesarion's mother

34. Ruth's husband
35. Relinquish
37. Altogether
38. Attack time
43. Like the nene
44. Frugal
45. Backpacks
46. "__ We All?," 1929 song
47. Formal customs
48. "There, I've said it __," 1941 song
49. Tumult
50. Mauna Loa goddess
52. Short-order man
53. Lady Hamilton
55. Termagant
56. Hanoi festival

ACROSS

1. Snap up
5. Covent Garden offering
10. Sullen
14. Actress Keeler
15. Mulcts
16. Coin in Cremona
17. Baal, e.g.
18. A square, like Caspar Milquetoast
20. Contrive
22. Solemn
23. Snare
26. Golfer's cheapest purchase
27. Wordsworth's "... Tintern __"
29. Kind of material
31. "Where there __ no Ten Commandments": Kipling
35. Kin of Bronx cheers
36. Havoc
38. By way of
39. Eastern title
40. A square, à la Sinclair Lewis
41. "__ Let Them Clash," Burns poem
42. Sun. text
43. Soporific
44. Suffix with ascend
45. Plane starter
47. Rickenbacker, for one
48. In a quandary
49. Yuk!
51. Rank below baronet
53. A splitting, as of atoms
57. Most recent
60. Foursquare
63. Assert
64. Pulitzer Prize author: 1958
65. Ostracize, in a way
66. Descartes
67. Kitten sounds
68. Avocet
69. Explosives

DOWN

1. Grating
2. Loutish
3. On the square
4. Reporters covet these
5. Tender
6. More, in music
7. Lineman
8. Autumn shades
9. Until now
10. More like stickum
11. Resort near Venice
12. Indic language
13. Baseball's Say Hey Kid
19. "I __ that I dwelt...": Bunn
21. Farm enclosure
24. Lawrence of __
25. Square up
27. Embarrass
28. Cinematic nickname
30. Blanch
32. All square
33. Sibling's daughter
34. Country singer Tucker
36. Chart
37. Nice summer
40. __-woogie
44. Across
46. First prints of movies
48. Mellow
50. __ up (hibernates)
52. Cove
53. Froth
54. "Bus Stop" creator
55. Fume
56. Ensuing
58. Dispatched
59. __ bien
61. Seven, to Severus
62. Wright wing

ACROSS

1. Cuts down
5. Venous fluid of the gods
10. Hounds
14. Square's length times width
15. Orifice
16. "Typee" sequel
17. Coat superficially
18. Noted Abstract Expressionist
20. The Vltava, to a Berliner
22. Place apart
23. Liquid used in dyes
25. Divagate
26. Greek sea god
28. Met mezzo-soprano
32. Furious
34. Firm
36. __ Duarte Perón
37. Large containers
38. Baby's bellyache
39. Wax imprint
40. W.W. II area
41. Pitcher Ryan
42. Château-Thierry's river
43. Agree
45. Esteem
47. Yorkshire river
49. Hung up the receiver: Brit.
52. Topple
56. Mouse, for example
57. Source
59. __ precedent
60. French composer
61. Of musical sound quality
62. Cut
63. Brings to court
64. Candidate list
65. Famous name in motordom

DOWN

1. Source of igneous rock
2. Apollo 16 lunar lander
3. The Iron Duke
4. They supply horsemen
5. Exempt from harm
6. Cote sound
7. Hovels
8. Further
9. Grandiloquent language
10. Uses a divining rod
11. Buddhist sacred mountain
12. Olympic top award
13. Lone
19. Uttered inanities
21. Light
24. Antiseptic solution
27. Type of energy
29. Worthless one
30. Karamazov brother
31. Borecole
32. With, in Nice
33. Acronym for a defense group
35. A cosmetic
38. Debases
39. A North Atlantic sea
41. Parisian nights
42. Horace or Thomas
44. Verdi's "Don __"
46. Group of geese
48. Flynn of films
50. Malodorous
51. College socs.
52. Temple team
53. Offspring of a vache
54. French women's magazine
55. Jazz singer Simone
58. Cole or Turner

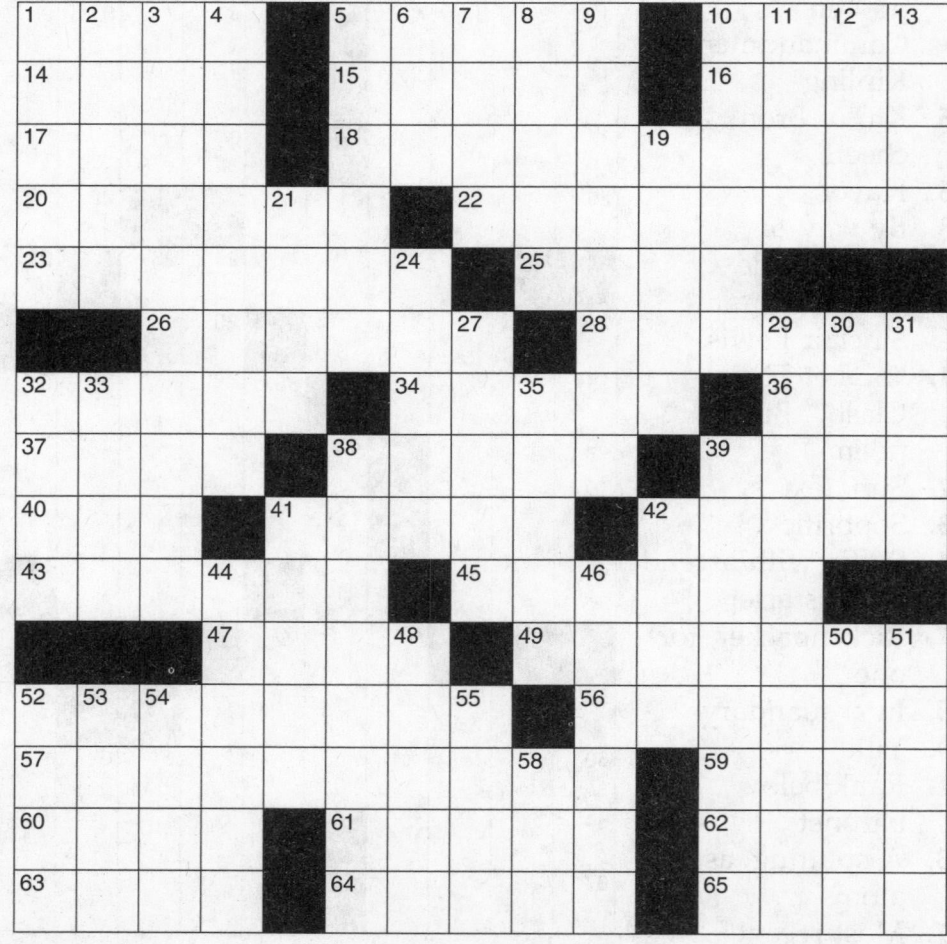

ACROSS

1. Iridescent gem
5. Frat-party garments
10. Orlando rarity
14. Local food store, for short
15. Old-womanish
16. Fundy phenomenon
17. Flap, as a sail
18. Bogged down
19. Mucho
20. Terpsichorean twosome
23. Irks
24. Jerry Pate's turf piercer
25. Getaway
28. Noxious vapors
32. Pillage
33. O'Neill's "__ for the Misbegotten"
35. Carney or Buchwald
36. Hit film of 1933
40. "There! __ Said It Again": Mann-Evans song
41. He spoke for Standish
42. Two-toed sloth
43. Chilean poet's family
45. Abominate
47. Nest
48. Centers
50. Sometime co-star with 20 Across
55. Becloud
56. __-visual equipment
57. Fracas
59. On the Caspian
60. Tree lump
61. Caribbean sight
62. Servants
63. Teasdale and a Roosevelt
64. Lowly laborer

DOWN

1. "__ bodkins!"
2. Riches
3. Winglike
4. Educated class
5. Mexican dish
6. Cat-__-tails
7. Strengthens
8. Give __ up (assist)
9. Political agitation
10. Western vehicles
11. Egyptian delta
12. Aroma
13. Moist
21. Brief swim
22. Sartre's "Nothingness"
25. Puckish
26. Find the answers
27. More bashful
28. Cut, as a lawn
29. W.W. I battle site
30. Diva's numbers
31. Chubby
33. Appends
34. One of the Three Stooges
37. Comaneci or Boulanger
38. Sunday best
39. Surpass
44. Disclose
45. Prattles foolishly
46. Poetic contraction
48. Fragrant wood
49. Prime Minister before Suzuki
50. Otherwise
51. One-on-one encounter
52. The Danube, in Hungary
53. Seine tributary
54. __ contendere
55. Scrooge's expression
58. Decimal base

158

ACROSS

1. Exults
7. Barbara Eden's target in a TV series
10. Hot spot
14. Not more than
15. Forage plant
16. Hoodwink
17. Left port
19. To be, in Paree
20. Puts down turf
21. Palmer's forte
23. Myerson's crown in 1945
24. Kind of upmanship
25. "__ long way to . . ."
29. Sharp
30. Come near, with "on"
32. Some warehousemen
34. Kin of sobrinas
35. Sends out again
36. "Don't give up __"
39. Dye
40. Serves a sentence
41. Belief
43. Affected
44. Quarrel
45. Above, to F. S. Key
46. Device for stimulating emission of radiation
48. Superiority
51. Guam harbor
55. Repeat
56. Guidance
58. Swizzle
59. Be at fault
60. Home-grown
61. Some ophidians
62. Part of E.S.T.
63. Kind of "ship" with a franchise

DOWN

1. It bites in the Atlantic Bight
2. H.R.E. emperor
3. Word with ships
4. Saturates
5. Recipe amt.
6. Kind of rate or rocket
7. Showy flowers
8. __ Doctrine: 1947
9. ". . . wagon to __": Emerson
10. Pindarics
11. Byline information
12. Carson's "Silent __"
13. Indian home
18. Keeps in check
22. Hosts of warships
25. Neighbor of Syr.
26. __ dansant (tea dance)
27. Pinta to Santa Maria
28. Ant cow
29. Held on to
31. Positions in Goren's game
33. Flour made from corn, beans, etc.
34. "__ also serve . . ."
36. Sultry
37. "__ Yankee Doodle . . ."
38. Favorite
40. Extreme conservative
41. __ cropper (fails)
42. Strikes back
43. Maintain
47. Cathedral city of France
49. High crags
50. __ Oreille (Idaho lake)
51. Nick and Nora's terrier
52. Donahue of TV
53. Cleave
54. Mimic
57. Scottish explorer

ACROSS

1. Ruth's native land
5. Stitched
9. Rhyme scheme
13. This place has a lock on New Haven
14. Number in a tub
15. Frond bearer
16. One of Blake's "Songs of Innocence"
19. Color
20. Lubricated
21. Ransack
22. __ qua non
23. Part of a min.
24. Place "above the fruited plain"
31. Largest of seven
32. Prayer
33. Gist
35. Pair
36. Ring a bell
38. Means of self-defense
39. Posed
40. Mint
41. Argus galley
42. "Dilly dilly" followers in a song
47. Charles Schulz's need
48. Suffix with poet
49. Constructed
52. Wooden shoe
54. Buffalo's relative
57. Rarely
60. Sapphic songs
61. Glowing coal
62. First of the James Bond films
63. Palos, once
64. Garden vegetable
65. Twist

DOWN

1. Orpheus-Eurydice tale, e.g.
2. Honolulu's island
3. To the sheltered side
4. Spelldown
5. Author Asch
6. Canal, lake or city
7. One of the Slavs
8. Opposite of pos.
9. Second largest of seven
10. Bouillon base
11. Memorable Belgian musician
12. Maxwell Anderson heroine
14. "To __ own self be true": Shak.
17. Wind
18. Actress Nissen
22. Fokker fighter in W.W. I
23. Large knife of yore
24. Hippies' homes
25. Customary
26. Lariat in Laredo
27. State one's view
28. Danube city
29. Habituate
30. Gentle push
34. Benefit
36. Kin of bop
37. Concealed
38. Norse chieftain
40. Hundred: Comb. form
43. Of least worth
44. Cut of meat
45. Search hurriedly
46. Golden __
49. Betty __ of old comics
50. Solve a mystery
51. Bakery specialist
52. Identical
53. Cleric in Caen
54. Eponym for a great city
55. First-rate
56. Be cognizant of
58. Pen point
59. Elizabeth Blackwell's colleagues: Abbr.

ACROSS

1. Adjective once misapplied to the Earth
5. Like Ferdinand or Isabella
10. One of Niña's gaffs
14. Coin for a descendant of Columbus
15. Obliterate
16. Mata __
17. Italian navigator: 1454–1512
20. One concern of a skipper
21. Maria and Clara
22. Garden tool
23. "__ we forget"
24. Columbus was one
28. Confined
29. __ Amin, Grand Mufti of Jerusalem
32. Caper
33. A Pinta officer
34. Like Lindbergh's flight
35. Where Columbus died: 1506
38. And others: Latin abbr.
39. College or collar
40. Enveloping glows
41. __ Plaines, Ill.
42. Jeanne and Cécile: Abbr.
43. Australian lumbermen
44. Where Vientiane is
45. Actor Linden
46. Columbus's first __ to Spain was made on the Niña
49. Columbus, by birth
54. Parader in October
56. Blue dye
57. Language of millions in India
58. Narrated

59. Bando, Maglie and Mineo
60. Prominent Alaskan family
61. Antarctica is devoid of these

DOWN

1. British tart
2. This gives ade
3. San Salvador's 60 square miles
4. Boat covering, for short
5. Tract
6. What seas do to shores
7. Donated
8. Enzyme
9. Decreased
10. Sidetrack
11. NATO is one
12. Old chest for valuables
13. "The Making of an American" is his autobiography
18. Whence Odysseus sailed
19. What 1492 is part of
23. Admit
24. Rescued
25. Growing out
26. Cartographer's volume
27. Place on the Floss
28. Whence Columbus sailed
29. Viscount Templewood
30. "__ needs a good memory": Quintilian

31. Founder of U.S. Navy tradition
33. Specks
34. Revolved rapidly
36. Explode
37. Martin Alonso Pinzón, e.g.
42. Rani's gown
43. Discussion groups
44. Periods of calm
45. Surround
46. Inlets; creeks
47. Sicilian menace
48. Kind of wind
49. Navigator Vasco da __
50. Life, to Columbus
51. A social sci.
52. Ancient mariner
53. Bow and stern, e.g.
55. Gee-gee

ACROSS

1. Prefix with tasse
5. Aphid, e.g.
9. Former Turkish military title
14. Molecular part
15. Frequent follower of for
16. Tremulous
17. "Ship of the desert"
19. Soothing word
20. Amorous song
21. Pigment containing iron oxide
22. Senator from Kansas
23. Poet who wrote "The Faerie Queene"
24. Lightweight carriage
27. Give a wide berth to
28. Relative of a mesa
29. Players' stock
35. Let forth
36. Savanna
37. Top of a cliff
38. Lengthwise on a lighter
42. Please a gourmand
43. Strong vapor
44. Where matches are brought to thousands
46. Kind of butterfly
50. Rarae __
51. Spread through, causing gradual change
52. Game bird
56. He played alongside Mantle
57. Irregular soldier
58. Public notice
59. Site of a Vichy French naval defeat: 1940
60. Galley gear
61. Naps
62. Accommodations at hostels
63. Pens' business ends

DOWN

1. Pops
2. To be, in Boulogne
3. Secure, as with cables
4. Closest
5. Cyclist
6. Foil a would-be catcher
7. Parched
8. Experiment
9. Like Griselda
10. Pale
11. Sir Patrick of ballad fame
12. Industrial center in Germany
13. Approaching, in poesy
18. '80s TV program
21. Stimulus
23. Bundle, as of papers
24. Musical symbol
25. __ sapiens
26. Moslem commander
27. Hold forth
30. Follower of box or marsh
31. Monomaniac's problem
32. Site of Mount Demavend
33. Ecclesiastical court
34. Kids' mothers
39. Retards
40. Glowing gas
41. Grogshops
45. Back seat
46. Gantry
47. Civil War general
48. Juliet's fiancé
49. Put out bag and baggage
50. Forward or onward
52. Word after Simon
53. Jai __
54. Body established in F.D.R.'s day
55. Russian news agency ITAR-__
57. U.S.N. tar

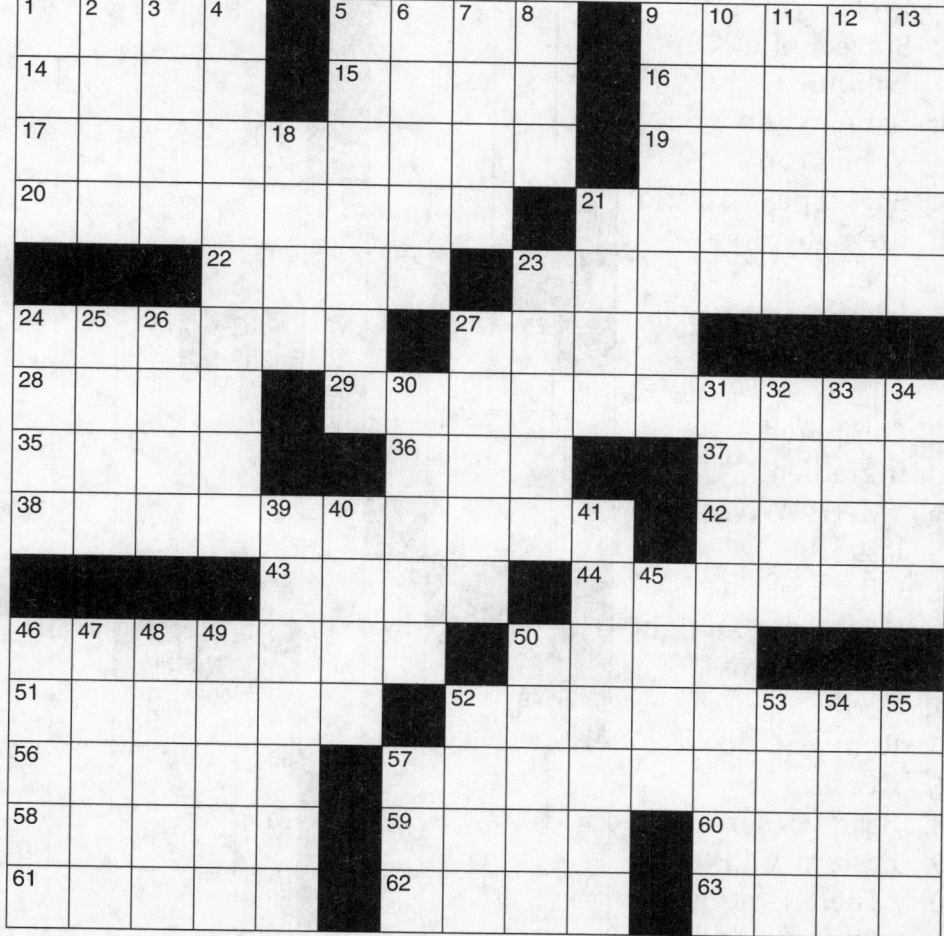

ACROSS

1. Lucre
5. Duchesse, e.g.
10. Whistlers on courts
14. Redolence
15. Finale
16. Charlie Plumb's "__ Cinders"
17. Asian staple
18. Mrs. Chaplin et al.
19. Marianas isle
20. With 48 Across, a Shakespearean line
23. President who became a Chief Justice
24. Glance
25. Tunes
27. Type of parking
30. Prefix with plasm
31. Subject of a Kant critique
33. Batman and Robin, e.g.
36. Shakespearean trio
39. Eternally, to a poet
40. Ukrainian river
41. Shakespearean villain
42. Gunpowder ingredient
43. "Merry Wives . . ." lass
44. Oil cartel
46. Safety and straight
48. See 20 Across
54. Xeric
55. Rousseau novel
56. Deesis
58. Bear's order
59. Eastern V.I.P.
60. "There is no living with __": Addison
61. Fainéant
62. Peep show
63. Darn this thing

DOWN

1. Smugglers' "grass"
2. Dutch cheese
3. Wisdom
4. Area near the pit
5. Sneer
6. In the air
7. Pitch
8. "The Last Time __ Paris"
9. Vane letters
10. Rue
11. Dodge
12. Ampulla
13. Houston
21. Western alliance initials
22. Gapes
25. Relative of smart
26. Road for Cato
27. Darth of "Star Wars"
28. Aide: Abbr.
29. Clark's girl
30. Nice summer
31. Uproar
32. Fish hawk's cousin
33. Martin or Jagger
34. Yen
35. Bear, to Pedro
37. Ukase
38. Metalworker
42. Pester
43. Pismire
44. Sculled
45. Rich copper ore
46. Martinique menace
47. French department
49. Audition
50. Austen heroine
51. Rathskeller quaff
52. Nymph who loved Narcissus
53. Coward
54. "The World __ See It": Einstein
57. George Eliot, __ Evans

ACROSS

1. Pant
5. Charity
9. Plentiful
14. Samoan seaport
15. Appropriated
16. Salt-encrusted depression
17. Wield an ax on an ash
18. French pantomimist
19. Framework
20. How this runs
23. Choir voice
24. "__ Oncle" (vehicle for 18 Across)
25. Finally
28. Neckpiece
30. Enzymes
34. Hammer and tongs
35. Persian rug
37. Part of TNT
38. How this runs
41. Suppositions
42. Former alliance acronym
43. Seer's card
44. Body pouch
46. Limb
47. Straightedges
48. Spotlight
50. Midwest airport
52. How this runs
59. Slayer of Achilles
60. Type of hairdo
61. About 2.2 lbs.
62. Violin maker
63. Mast
64. Spread
65. Circumscribe
66. Cards wool
67. Part of a three-piece suit

DOWN

1. Fishhook
2. Mimic
3. Farm structure
4. Type of pitch
5. Certify
6. Idles
7. How this runs
8. Feature in "Sugar Babies"
9. Houston athlete
10. Yacht basin
11. Stopper
12. Whip
13. Formerly, formerly
21. Reatas
22. Man of Muscat
25. Garret
26. Chewy candy
27. Loam deposit
29. Progress
31. Mart
32. Mistake
33. Winnows
35. Altair or Rigel
36. Maestro Toscanini
39. Instruct
40. Predecessor of Khrushchev
45. Gauguin milieu
47. Shavers
49. Mastic
51. King of Tyre
52. Silvery fish
53. Title
54. Mine wagon
55. Brewer's kiln
56. Finish a bathroom
57. Pub orders
58. Spoils

164

ACROSS

1. Rialto turkey
5. Civil War general
10. Org. in "Trinity"
13. Purim month
14. Purple
15. Liberated Ibsen heroine
17. "Wow!"
19. Author Ludwig
20. __ and Tobago, republic since 1976
21. Viceroy of India: 1943–47
23. A year in Nero's reign
24. Star in Cygnus
25. Wheedle; coax
29. Citadel
32. Gather
33. Formal mall
34. Auto-club insignia
35. French resort
36. Worked at
37. Football kick
38. India __
39. These were all about Eve
40. A Bloomer who took a Ford
41. "Three __," Dos Passos novel
43. Casino patron
44. Hockey's Kindrachuk
45. New Guinea port
46. Foursquare
48. "The Donkey __," Allan Jones hit
53. He's Hawkeye on TV
54. Cole Porter song: 1953
56. Biblical land
57. Famed Greek physician-philosopher

58. Faction
59. Curved plank
60. Put forth, as an effort
61. "__ of Ohio," McKinley epithet

DOWN

1. Coin of Thailand
2. Aroma
3. Bamako is its capital
4. __ Mawr
5. Steve or Miss Jean
6. Unwind
7. Geriatrician's patients
8. Wander aimlessly

9. Stared angrily
10. "In a world __ made": Housman
11. Apple variety
12. Integument
16. "The works"
18. Cash drawers
22. Buy a hand
24. V.I.P.'s in Kansas and Hawaii
25. __ Major
26. __ acids
27. "White Fang" author
28. Simple sugar
29. What time does
30. "Á votre __!"
31. Type of butterfly
33. On the qui vive

36. Distinction
37. Edible seed
39. Deadlocks
40. Censor something said on TV
42. Impractical
43. Progenitor
45. Device for Archimedes
46. "Scots wha __ . . .": Burns
47. He gave his name to the Reo
48. Flatfish
49. Nose: Comb. form
50. Like the Gobi
51. Princess of Tyre
52. Bonn beast
55. Negligent

ACROSS

1. "Simple" letters
4. Art follower
8. "Bag guy" followers
13. PT or U
15. The same, to Seneca
16. Cinched
17. Red letters, once
18. A __ Able
19. Within the law
20. Sight from 51 Across
23. Idol
24. "High" place in a play
25. Attired, in a way
28. Xylophones' kin
33. King of the Visigoths
35. Tokyo, once
36. __ corda: Dir. to a pianist
37. Sight from 51 Across
41. It begins in juin
42. Lab work
43. Safe, as morels
44. Whence signer Caesar Rodney hailed
47. Carter vis-à-vis Reagan
48. Sought a public office
49. Strong __ ox
51. Reagan's California spread
58. Sen. Craig's state
59. She, in Nice
60. Shortly
62. Locket stone
63. __-Hoa, Vietnam
64. Extra large, for one
65. Hebrew measures
66. Normal, in a way
67. Put in stitches

DOWN

1. __ Dhabi, Mideast sheikdom
2. Autumn pear
3. Noted country singer
4. Bride of July 1981
5. Lemon once exported from Michigan
6. Designer Chapman
7. Prefix with bus or potent
8. Many, in Miletus
9. Kind of bandit
10. Put under contract
11. Marine fish
12. When split and cooked, these become spitchcocks
14. Tony of tennis
21. Olga's rival in the 70's
22. Worked hard
25. Studied "the joint"
26. Ant that can fly
27. TV group
28. Reagan adviser
29. Wood-trimming tool
30. Underground group
31. Anoint, old style
32. Sooth follower
34. Rostand's "snooty" hero
38. Saul's uncle or grandfather
39. Lyndon's U.N. delegate
40. Elsa was one
45. Toxophilite
46. Small elms
49. Steve of TV
50. Spectacle
51. Carty of baseball
52. Rib donor
53. Door inscription
54. Politician-labor leader
55. Creator of Mrs. Sarah Battle
56. Lane of The Daily Planet
57. Transude
61. Not used

166

ACROSS

1. Cups, saucers, etc.
7. Action at Aqueduct
13. Stockman
14. Fatty esters
16. At the last instant
18. Crosscut
19. Karpov's forte
20. Méditerranée, e.g.
21. Protection
22. "The __ Hand," Auden work: 1963
23. "Va __!" (Italian's approval)
24. E.M.K., e.g.
25. Leads the pack
26. Break up a prom pair
27. Sells wares
29. Downcast
30. Arbitrator's goal
32. Lifting device
35. It sounds like a glockenspiel
38. Group whose name means "wild cats"
39. Having a bluish-gray hue
40. Banking abbr.
42. Does handwork
43. Seeks truffles
44. Go a round
45. Soldier or slave
46. Bottle size
47. Key letter
48. Plant that may fade without shade
51. Jack must be nimble here
52. Hermetically sealed
53. A use for art gum
54. Play turncoat

DOWN

1. Woodland bird
2. Interweave
3. "My heart __ . . .": Keats
4. Unload
5. Poetic word
6. Kiddie car
7. Fireplace tools
8. At __ (nonplused)
9. Grid "zebras"
10. Map abbr.
11. "__ be born, and. . . ."
12. Sana natives
13. Bullish times
15. Peaceful
17. Fabric sometimes used as a strainer
22. Kind of farm
23. Lancaster et al.
25. Leaves
26. European rabbit
28. Writ that summons new jurors
29. Dissolves
31. Bunker's epithet for his son-in-law
32. Potpourri ingredients
33. Chief ore of a fissionable element
34. U.S. Open winner: 1961
36. Pot-valiant, perhaps
37. Metrical foot
39. Not so hard
41. Servers
43. Ransack
44. Château
46. Dandies
47. Periodically war-torn Turkish city
49. Verily
50. "Une __," Maupassant novel

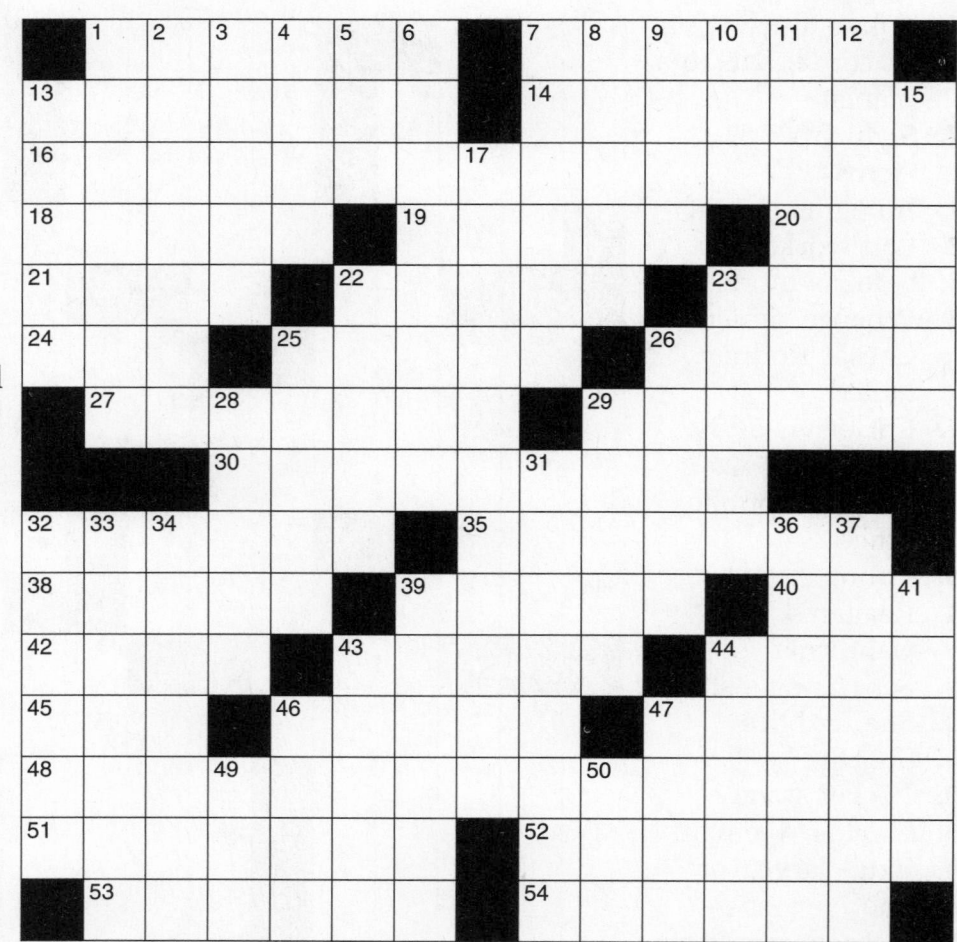

ACROSS

1. Opp. of feminine
5. Wimbledon winner, 1976–80
9. Marine hazard
14. Different: Comb. form
15. __ da capo
16. Buckskin, e.g.
17. Former Spanish kingdom
18. Angelus
19. Akin maternally
20. Date: Abbr.
21. Baryshnikov's partners
23. Proclaim
25. Ethiopian town
26. 100 square meters
27. Had a cold
32. Stiff gait
35. Look sullen
36. Unctuous
37. Sentry's word
38. Ph.D. candidates' bugaboos
39. __-majesté
40. Woody Guthrie's son
41. Parrot's beak part
42. Penguins' enemies
43. Yokels
45. Eur. country
46. Skater Babilonia
47. Harsh
50. Bojangles's forte
55. Follower of Claudius I
57. Lowest deck
58. Status quo __ bellum
59. Increased
60. Go
61. Drudge
62. Conductor Whallon
63. Hamlet and Ophelia
64. Members of a flock
65. Ohio nine

DOWN

1. __ fide (not genuine)
2. Hebrew letter
3. Incline
4. Marian Anderson and Kathleen Ferrier
5. Chatter
6. Mountain nymph
7. Moon feature
8. Marsh bird
9. Chief magistrate of Mecca
10. "__ soit. . . ."
11. Mediterranean port
12. Fictional sleuth's pet
13. Sordor
22. Lets forth
24. Refuge
27. Glides in the air
28. Pete Seeger, e.g.
29. Stead
30. Maxwell or Lanchester
31. Woads
32. Ruler who died in exile
33. Fictional plantation
34. Supporter
35. Imply or connote
38. Expanse
42. Kenyan group
44. Daylong marches
45. Trio of TV fame
47. Loosen
48. Strength
49. "Jove's __ clamours . . .": Othello
50. Related
51. Tract
52. Project
53. Noah's messenger
54. "__ pronounce you. . . ."
56. Has

168

ACROSS

1. Campus org.
5. Biotite, e.g.
9. Kind of school
13. He made tents
14. Sellers
15. Silverdome sound
16. Book by Agatha Christie
19. Opp. of WSW
20. Sluggish
21. Feminine suffixes
22. The Kingston __
23. Beverage for Robin Hood
24. Book by Victoria Holt
31. __ avis
32. Not on the rocks
33. Chitchat
35. Construction-work piece
36. Long-Legs or Warbucks
38. Graph or phone prefix
39. __ boss (casino employee)
40. Mediocre
41. Vexed
42. Book by Norah Lofts
47. Switch positions
48. Soothe
49. Jerk
52. Nome transportation
54. Foofaraw
57. Book by Taylor Caldwell
60. Features on some pitchers
61. Glove material
62. Hindu prince
63. Read the __ act
64. Adjective for a sou
65. Israeli statesman

DOWN

1. Kind of dancer or walker
2. "The __," Peck vehicle
3. Counterweight
4. Dernier __
5. Atmospheric phenomenon
6. Roman road
7. Ante in a "friendly" poker game
8. Dull suffix
9. For the time being
10. Rabble
11. Facility
12. D.D.E. or H.S.T.
14. "__ in the Streets," 1950 film
17. Throwaways at the Trevi
18. Serf
22. Alexandra's husband, for one
23. Farther from the pin
24. __ up (catch)
25. Practice
26. Sister of Thalia
27. "Till the __ Time," 1945 song
28. Knight seen on TV
29. Israeli monetary unit
30. Nominated for office
34. "Whose __?" (Sayers book)
36. Acts on
37. Botanist Gray
38. One of seven in Rome
40. Actress Berger
43. Most tender
44. __ la Société
45. Elbow
46. Actress Lanchester
49. Team follower
50. Siamese
51. Dynamics predecessor
52. Twist
53. Cousin of ogle
54. Melville captain
55. __ vu (paramnesia)
56. Algerian port
58. Loser to R.M.N.
59. Three, to Gina

ACROSS

1. Russian wire service ITAR-__
5. Scrubs
11. Vehicle for A. J. Foyt
14. Lath
15. Part of 34 Across
16. Twelve months, in Mexico
17. Like "Pilgrim's Progress"
19. M.I.T. room
20. Go back to
21. Like the oaken bucket
22. Info
23. Silly
24. Corrida sound
25. One hitting the books
26. Dress a stone
27. Specialist in certain roots
30. Chemical in nail-polish removers
32. Widows
33. MOMA offering
34. Oculist's specialty
35. Torments
39. Chair a meeting
43. State of being undivided
45. Snare
46. Family vehicle
47. Witticism
48. Armistice
50. Counterfeiter's nemesis
51. Dakar or Danzig: Abbr.
52. Gender
53. Riggs's best stroke
54. Reagan, e.g.
56. Like some soldiers: Abbr.
57. Chicken __ (Louisiana dish)
58. Wagner heroine
59. Diocese
60. Fleshly
61. Close a falcon's eyes

DOWN

1. Alexandra was one
2. Like a hydrocarbon
3. Save from ruin
4. Dutch painter
5. Carlyle, e.g.
6. Heart, to Hadrian
7. Word with Baltimore or golden
8. Cloudy
9. Scan
10. Maglie or Mineo
11. Relating to heat
12. Metrical foot
13. "Northwest Passage" author
18. Calendar or chant
22. Motherless calves
24. "__ for the money"
25. Synthetic fiber
28. Become a member
29. Casts evil glances
31. Plaid
35. Shakes a leg
36. Springtime wild flower
37. Unlike a bucking bronco
38. Less complicated
39. Caress
40. Useless
41. Go to the Great Beyond
42. "Hope springs __"
44. Opinion; view
49. Old letters
51. Poet Teasdale
52. Coward of England
54. F.D.R. measure
55. Ga. neighbor

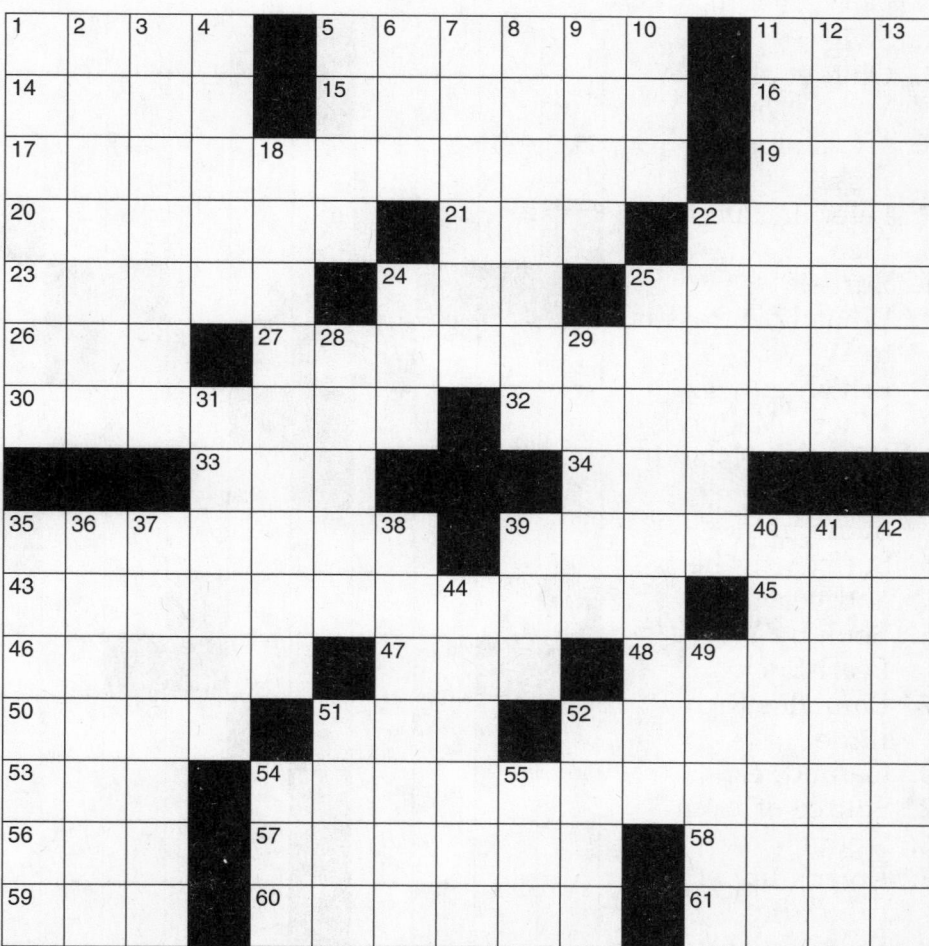

170

ACROSS

1. Attention-getting sound
5. "__ to bury Caesar . . ."
10. Mil. decorations
14. Emulated Arcaro
15. Burrowing animals
16. List abbr.
17. Prolific plant in W. Va.
19. Large hall
20. Sold in small quantities
21. Musical group
22. Noah's eldest son
23. The high cost of leaving
24. Parseghian
27. Family member
29. Wicker's "__ to Die"
31. Swig
33. Ohio et al., to W. Va.
36. ". . . __ forgive those"
37. Peter, in Puerto Rico
38. Burner
39. What 17 Across is to W. Va.
41. British gun
42. Where Aleppo is
43. "Treasure Island" author's monogram
45. Suffix with herb and verb
46. Book by W. Va.'s Pearl Buck
47. Emulates Rich Little
50. Garand, e.g.
52. Source of resin
56. About
57. River's upper tributaries
59. Deity, in Dijon

60. Napoleon's troops
61. Arrived from above
62. Part of a strawberry
63. Packer's Bart
64. "Lang" follower

DOWN

1. Horace's "__ Poetica"
2. 3,600 seconds
3. Selvage
4. Cold cuts
5. Children's marbles
6. One of many W. Va. workers
7. Old Greek flask
8. Pinochle play
9. Suffix with Siam and Japan

10. Gives an account of
11. For W. Va., it's "Montani Semper Liberi"
12. Man or boy
13. Bed part
18. Cheering word
21. Attestation
23. "Peter Rabbit" cartoonist
24. Turkish chiefs
25. Corrodes
26. Meaning of "Semper Liberi"
28. Hebrew ceremonial feast
30. Kin of fulmars
32. Important W. Va. product
34. Man from Dublin

35. Far from foolhardy
37. Sch. affiliates
40. Mozart's "__ Kleine Nachtmusik"
44. Oil well, for instance
48. Greek letter
49. Girls in Toledo: Abbr.
50. Disencumbers
51. "What's __ for me?"
52. Saucy
53. "__ Camera"
54. Smooth and slippery
55. "__ go bragh"
57. Owns
58. Sault __ Marie

ACROSS

1. Lichen
5. Hot Springs and Warm Springs
9. Strain
11. Athens's rival
13. Smokeless powder
14. Visualize
16. "A feast __ famine"
17. Harmonious relationship
19. Grundy or Miniver
20. Heelless sheepskin shoes
22. Aristocracy
23. Petty quarrel
24. Slender, graceful girl
26. Still
27. Coeur d' __, Idaho
28. Canary's cousin
30. Dinner course
32. Camelot character
34. Prescribed quantity
35. Strew
38. Part of a calyx
41. Common food fishes
42. Kind of story
44. Type of dovetail
46. Sets into opposition
47. Coast Guard group
49. Rapturous praise
50. Footed vase
51. Largest of the Ryukyu Islands
53. Afternoon party
54. Lawmen's trawl
56. Misshape
58. Hard cash
59. Bobbins
60. British gun
61. White-tailed fisheater

DOWN

1. Seemingly impossible event
2. "That __ Black Magic"
3. Penitentiary: Slang
4. Caterpillar hairs
5. Place for an epi
6. Agreement
7. Dexterity
8. Difficult question
9. Incursions
10. Repartee
11. Espied
12. Thoroughgoing
13. Beat pounders
15. This: Sp.
18. Variegated
21. Diffuses
23. Unexpected winner
25. Cues
27. Item of value
29. N.Y.C. court tournament
31. Help!
33. Notwithstanding
35. Bakes eggs
36. Short snoozes
37. Kind of equine
39. __ France, 1921 Nobelist
40. Romeos
41. Potato: Colloq.
43. Small nails
45. Undiluted
47. Hank of yarn
48. Pilfer
51. Fairy-tale starter
52. Hebrew musical instrument
55. __-rich-quick scheme
57. Bon __

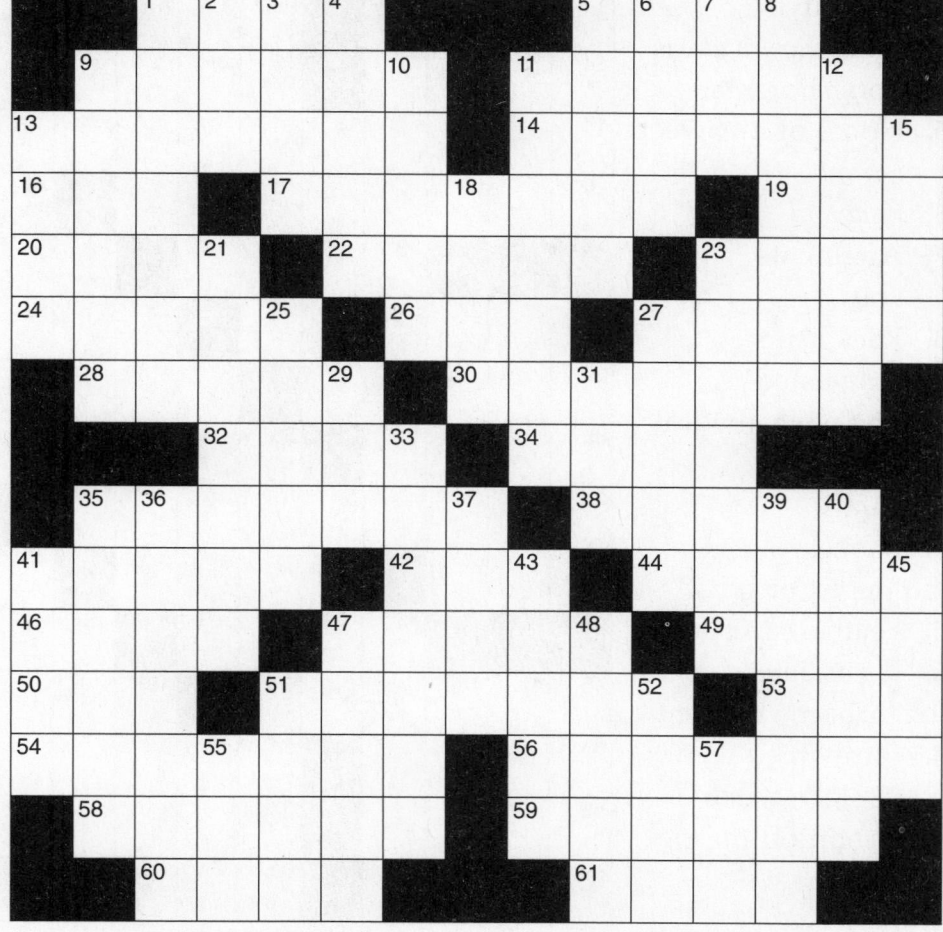

172

ACROSS

1. Rural place
5. Region of France
10. One more time
14. And wife: Lat. abbr.
15. Night sights
16. Lead or heavy
17. Fellow countryman
19. Herbert Hoover, e.g.
20. Take advantage of
21. Did Tuesday's job
23. Genus of shrubs
24. Welcome sight at Stowe
25. Part of a shoe
28. Sign at a crossing
29. Gratuity
32. Morning, in Paris
33. Longshoreman
35. Home of a "Sweet Swan"
36. Fakes
37. Augments, with "out"
38. Racketeers
40. Exhausted
41. English cathedral city
42. Safari
43. Benzenes
44. Elegist or odist
45. Feathered fisheater
46. Repudiate
49. Airborne descent
53. Into which went Gretel's witch
54. Group on the rii of Venezia
56. Observe
57. Brings to bay
58. "Our __," Gershwin musical
59. Geologists record five of these
60. What a playwright counts
61. Happiness

DOWN

1. Tenth part: Prefix
2. Physicist's topic
3. Sugar cube
4. Shipping abroad
5. Put in a stake
6. Peter and Wolfe
7. Army recruiter's verb
8. Mrs. Lennon
9. Actor Peter and family
10. Weapon in "Deliverance"
11. Eight bells
12. In addition
13. Devil's paintbrush, for one
18. Pale
22. Product from sisal
24. Parts of corncobs
25. P.R. man's creation
26. Word in U.S.N.R.
27. Hardhearted
28. Bleak
29. Outward sign
30. Actress Dunne
31. Nuisances
33. Scandal __
34. Contingent upon
36. Fortitude
39. Put away
40. Marine hazard
43. Full of holes
44. Dixie dishes
45. Packs or dips
46. Finished
47. Composer Novello
48. __ precedent
49. Parisian motorist's tire
50. Bobbin
51. Heraldic border
52. Nap
55. Sierra gold

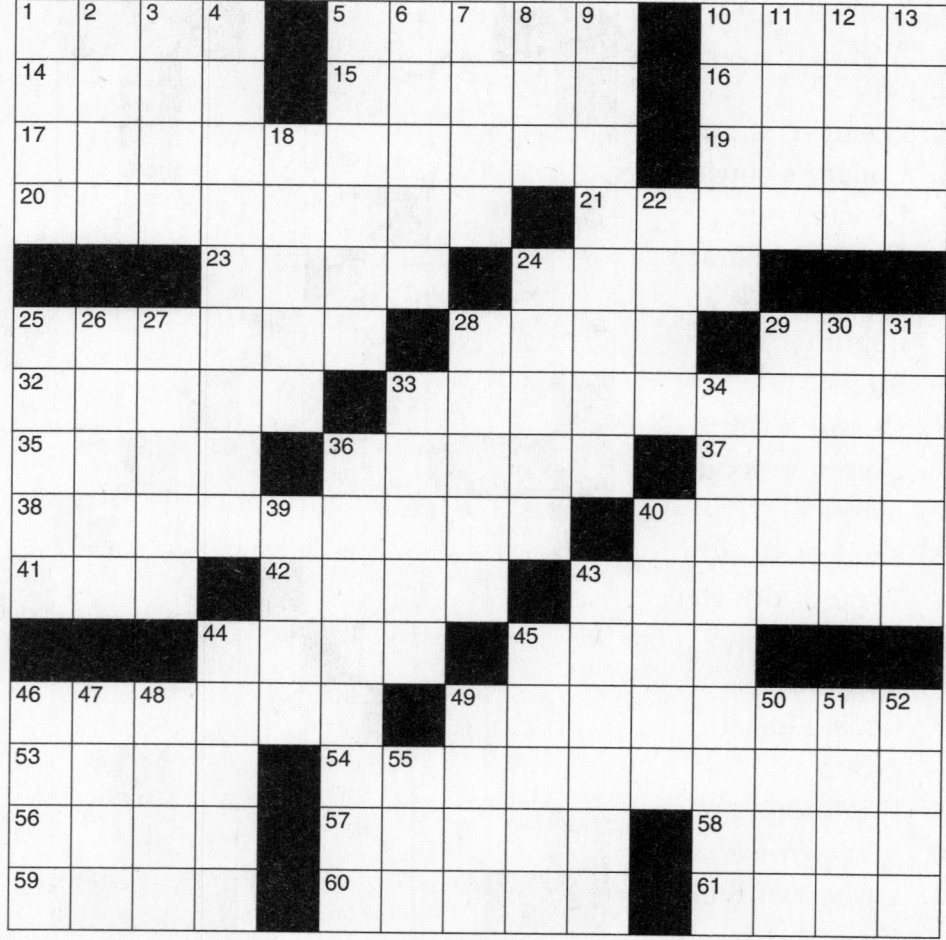

ACROSS

1. Man of Amman
5. One of the Bears
9. "We'll tak _ o' kindness . . ."
13. Star with home-run star
17. Dog star with Canadian star
18. Saul's herdsman
19. Animal
20. "_ in the bag!"
21. Do trucking
23. Midge
24. Doctors' org.
27. Towboat
28. Burton's homeland
30. Smaller
33. Fury
34. Silent star with opera star
39. Do figuring
40. Family member
41. One being decorated
43. Ignited
44. Sibling of dau.
45. Form by carving
46. He has a "prophetable" job
47. "_ Gang" comedies
48. Afghan bigwig
51. Word form with dextrous
55. Two movie stars
59. Red and John
60. Plumlike fruit
61. Hill insects
62. Wait on

DOWN

1. Spring mo.
2. Highway
3. In addition
4. Unrefined
5. Jack's snack
6. As snug _ . . .
7. Cover, as den walls
8. A year _ day
9. Amo, amas, _
10. En tout _ (vanity case)
11. Of bears
12. Some holy paintings
14. Location of a British driver's seat
15. Med. degree
16. Org.
22. Morning song
23. Gather the leftovers
24. Harding or Arbor
25. Flightless bird of yore
26. An ocean: Abbr.
28. Hot dog
29. Be a referee
31. "_ which will live in infamy"
32. Mdse.
35. Broad-minded
36. Law-school grad
37. Novel by Nabokov
38. _ Jima
41. Seals cracks
42. Begin's concern
45. Hijacks
46. Type of automobile
48. Johnson of TV
49. _ Tse-tung
50. Town in Sicily
52. Soda-fountain drink
53. Fall for a trick
54. Dietary need
56. Labor org.
57. Student radical org.
58. Terminate

ACROSS

1. Josip Broz
5. Get out!
10. Applaud
14. Cameo mineral
15. New moon, e.g.
16. Immense
17. Land measure
18. Easy wins
19. Concerning
20. Richard Nixon's Secretary of State
23. Links item
24. Lets up
25. Ladle
29. Graph
31. These make scents
32. Book of the Bible
33. Baron in "Der Rosenkavalier"
37. Slight
38. Flower part
39. Stimulate
40. Hash-house sign
41. Angler's action
42. Creeper
43. Asinine
45. Wine shop
46. Heavy
49. Stein
50. French political song
56. Jacket
57. Valuable wood
58. Shreds of threads
60. Bivouac dwelling
61. Lace again
62. Prefix with Chinese or European

63. Pyrite and siderite
64. Mount
65. Trial run

DOWN

1. MacDowell's "___ Wild Rose"
2. Ruler division
3. Nineveh's partner
4. Team members
5. More nimble
6. Stifle
7. Branches
8. Vipers
9. Navy bugler's "come-and-get-it"
10. Sections of N.Y., S.F., etc.
11. Respiratory organs
12. Concur
13. Equals
21. 1, 66, etc.: Abbr.
22. Suffix for cash
25. Astro or Teapot
26. Light bulb, in comics
27. Said is one
28. Adams and Adams
29. Grove
30. "The ___ is on!"
32. Racine or Rousseau
34. Light talk

35. Fortune's child
36. Historic French town
38. Radar devices
42. Indicator
44. Father of Abner
45. Lifted up
46. Command at sea
47. Step into
48. Compensate
49. ___ ball (19th-century missile)
51. Aid criminally
52. Lug
53. Came to earth
54. Short letter
55. Wraps up
59. Two-year-old

ACROSS

1. Dorothy's pooch
5. You, in Yucatán
10. Away's companion
13. Lei place
14. "On the Beach" author
15. Actress Geraldine
16. Waste allowance
17. Bogart film: 1941
19. Oscar actress: 1982
21. Sudden invasion
22. Narrow margins
23. Habeas corpus, e.g.
24. Straightens
26. Milland film: 1952
30. Hindu queen
31. Recoils
32. Birth-cert. entry
33. It's sometimes the word
34. Home for White's Wilbur
35. Cowboy Ritter
36. "__ pro nobis"
37. "Love Finds Andy __": 1938 film
39. Film segment
41. Disney classic: 1940
43. Tone combinations
44. "Norma Rae" director
45. Sholem Aleichem town
46. Township outside Johannesburg
49. Olivier film: 1948
51. Lancaster film: 1946
54. Pound or Stone
56. Art supplies
57. Eagle roost
58. Movie mogul
59. Eastern cooking pan
60. Ringlet
61. "War and Peace," e.g.

DOWN

1. Young 'un
2. Trireme gear
3. Powell-Loy film: 1934
4. Insult
5. Theater guides
6. Transports
7. Harbor helper
8. Biblical ending
9. Brando-Oberon film: 1954
10. Vegas game
11. Pearl Mosque site
12. Follow a script
15. City on the Tay
18. Monogram pts.
20. "__ kleine Nachtmusik"
23. Complaining
24. Long __ the law
25. Webb-Tierney film: 1944
26. Bara of the silents
27. Howard-Bergman film: 1939
28. Edit
29. Tight spots
31. Nautical pole
37. Port-au-Prince's land
38. "... lily maid of __"
39. Noah's eldest
40. Gather
42. Long journeys
43. Oater high points
45. Martina's rival
46. Put aboard
47. Roy Roger's home state
48. Bandleader Lawrence
50. Coal car
52. Neptune, to a Celt
53. Before, in poesy
55. "Where __ Your Children?": 1944 film

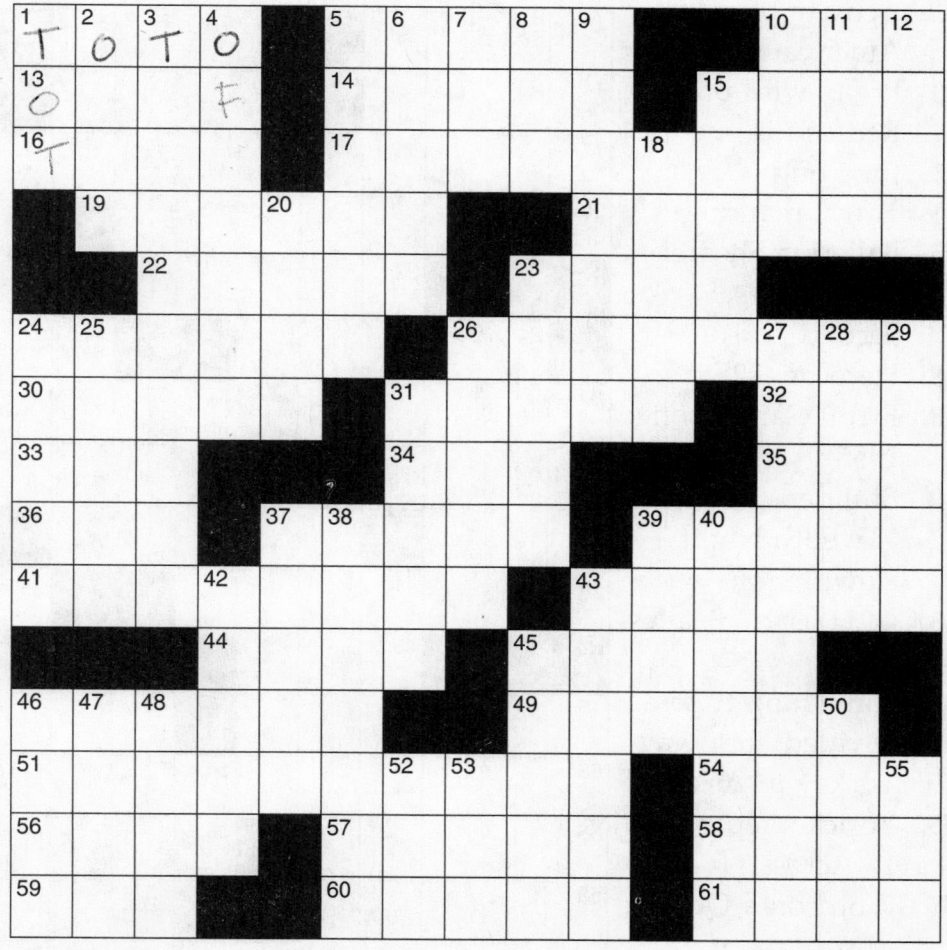

176

ACROSS

1. Poetic sigh
5. C.S.A. soldiers
9. Go over 55 m.p.h.
14. City on the Truckee
15. Señora's stewpot
16. Postpone a decision on a bill
17. Little Hamlet's question
20. Xenophon classic
21. Ratified
22. __ Park, Colo. town
23. Start of a film dog's name
24. Book by Anatole France
26. Activity of many Americans
30. Prefix with port
31. Redford is one
33. June bug
34. Towel marking
35. Ballerina Shearer
36. Apportion
37. Second person
38. Hero of 1927
39. Erroll Garner song: 1955
40. Blunder
42. "Twelfth Night" clown
43. "__ Loser," Beatles song
44. Something to toss
46. Divided, in a way
49. Turkey in Asia
53. Yorick's reply to 17 Across
55. Word on a Québec stop sign
56. Mussolini's daughter
57. Me.-to-Fla. hwy.
58. Punkies, e.g.
59. Woads
60. Prescribes

DOWN

1. Ancient strongbox
2. Not fatty
3. First name of Grandma Moses
4. Subjects of Dr. Carver's experiments
5. Yanks from slumber
6. Dinsmore of fiction
7. Consecrate
8. Witnessed
9. Blocked
10. Progenitor
11. Black
12. Magdeburg's river
13. Legal paper
18. Gobi filling station
19. Yacht basin
24. Where lire gleam under water
25. Lagomorphs
26. Sturdy boat
27. Cato's "that is"
28. Night, in Novara
29. Jane or Zane
30. Oates novel
31. Maxilla or scapula
32. Pot topper
35. Nanki-Poo's father
36. Criminals
38. Jeremiads
39. Supermarket section
41. Unwelcome item on a windshield
42. As __ a pancake
44. Dennis or Duncan
45. Battery terminal
46. Cinch
47. Lucubrate
48. What snobs put on
50. Behind schedule
51. "__ a man with . . ."
52. Sale stipulation
54. Unite

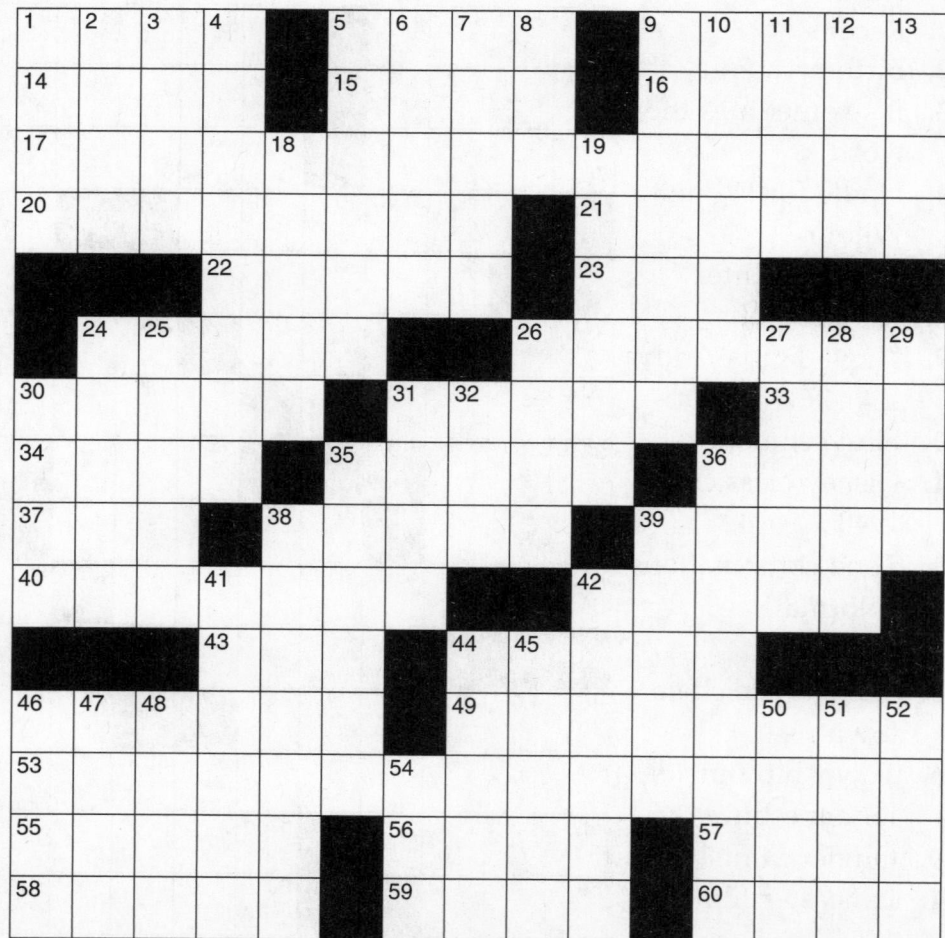

ACROSS

1. Teams
6. Warp's opposite
10. Army off.
13. Schwarzenegger role
14. Milos Forman film
15. "... three men in __"
16. Odysseus's hostess on Aeaea
17. Beige
18. Le __ (Grand Prix stop)
19. Testifies
22. Venerate
23. Type of comedian
25. Raised
26. Vim
29. Finishes the roof
30. One of the Carolines: Abbr.
31. Carthaginian queen's namesakes
33. __ Gay, famed plane
34. Upside-down posture
36. Spanish steps
39. Dough bloater
40. Savile Row mcht.
43. Real
45. __ Lanka
46. Biblical pronoun
47. __ attention (take a cadet's posture)
49. Brief walk
51. Comprehension
54. Enjoined
55. Mild expletive
56. Abbe and Lois
58. Dry
59. Cabell of baseball
60. Discharge
61. Author Rand
62. Martha from Montana
63. Pauses

DOWN

1. New Deal org.
2. Dawdles
3. Come apart
4. Supported
5. Look of contempt
6. Stimulate
7. Apiece
8. Lets go
9. Targets of legislation in 1890
10. __ reason (be logical)
11. "__ in Durango," 1957 film
12. Cooking meas.
15. "__ His Dog": Thomas Mann
20. Brown tint
21. Ability
22. Baseball stat.
24. O.T. book
27. Circular current
28. Assumes an alias
31. Infamous marquis
32. Get top billing
34. Dogged
35. Bhutanese, e.g.
36. N'est-ce __?
37. Pension consultant
38. Substitute
40. Actor Roy from Chicago
41. Most time-consuming
42. Lap robe
44. Food cupboard
46. "M*A*S*H" specialty
48. Lake __, Ethiopia
50. Lounge lizard
52. Actor Donahue
53. Faulkner character
54. Bleat
57. Kin of aves.

ACROSS

1. Charleston, e.g.
6. Indecent
10. The north wind
11. Tear-jerker
13. Comic verse
15. Stubborn
17. Inflexibility
18. Anacreontics' kin
20. Tiny
21. Islet in la mer
22. Parting word in Pamplona
24. Finale for Friml
25. Marsh
26. Injure
27. Diverting
28. Sea cucumber
30. Flaunts
32. Sheltered at sea
33. First letter of the Arabic alphabet
34. Diacritical mark
37. Cuts molars
41. Atlanta university
42. Happen again
44. Aged: Lat. abbr.
45. Yule fuel
46. Writer Ben
47. Con
48. British inc., once
49. Bani-__ of Iran
50. Inaugurate
51. Tar
53. Loser
56. Damascus is its capital
57. Isolate
58. Plaintiff
59. Employing

DOWN

1. Euphemistic oath
2. Underworld talk
3. __-do-well
4. Kind of barn or port
5. Suffix with journal
6. Veins of ore
7. A son of Seth
8. Peruke
9. Spring beauty
10. Sight in many a cellar
12. Tease
13. Blizzard creation
14. Choice cut of meat
16. New and Fair
19. Li'l Abner's land
22. Man-made fiber
23. Shabby
24. Skill
26. Memorable comic Cox
27. Household appliance
29. Couples
31. Alaskan
34. Monastery rooms
35. Overacts
36. Early August
38. Browbeaten
39. Father of Andromache
40. Scam's cousin
43. Raw-silk color
46. "__ the Horrible,"
47. Of the art of flight: Abbr.
49. Lyon product
50. Sudanese native
52. Joanne from W. Va.
54. Sailors' org.
55. "__ Rheingold"

ACROSS

1. Absolute ruler
5. Rainbow flower
9. Orange and jasmine
14. Church part
15. Hawaiian goose
16. English novelist: 1814–84
17. Put off
19. Eldritch
20. Delete
21. Cut a disk out of a metal plate
23. Lets slacken
25. Assignation
26. Nucha or nuque
28. Bowl or cannon
32. Channeled
37. African lake
38. One-pip domino
39. Dolly Varden, e.g.
41. Windy city, for short
42. Impassive
45. Preceded in time
48. Stretching muscle
50. Unit of measurement
51. Mountain nymph
54. Cute marsupials
58. A bursting inward
62. Musical works
63. Italy's chief financial center
64. Fish used in genetic research
66. La __, Argentine port
67. Mother of Apollo
68. Pile Pelion on __

69. Units of loudness
70. Dash
71. Woodwind

DOWN

1. Slender candle
2. Reproductive body
3. Tea-growing area in India
4. Greek wine flavored with pine resin
5. Daughter of Cadmus
6. Split
7. Lifeless
8. Feast at which the Haggadah is recited
9. Betrayal
10. Spaceman's finale
11. Receive for effort
12. __ Sedgwick, tragic heiress
13. Germ
18. Flower part
22. Poe's Arthur Gordon __
24. Point of land
27. Book of the Bible
29. Savoir-faire
30. County in N.C.
31. Maraud
32. Mold
33. Greek peninsula
34. Rialto light
35. Long period
36. Obligation
40. Tropical timber tree
43. Set apart
44. Cigars or crowns
46. Dickens character
47. Electrician's device
49. __ gestae
52. Passage
53. Wooden pin
55. Hire
56. Spring
57. Greens
58. Puckerels
59. Grain sorghum
60. Marshall __
61. __ bene
65. QB Jaworski

180

ACROSS

1. __ hot and cold (vacillate)
5. Nigerian native
9. Secreted
12. __ in the woods
13. Path of a tempest's center
16. Property claim
17. Making an effort, in psychology
18. A twister
20. Dibble, e.g.
21. Torrid
22. Place for a belt
25. Moves slowly
28. Adherent
29. Reverberate
33. Excite
34. Definite article
35. Ottoman peasant
36. Atmosphere
37. Soft, gentle winds
41. Snare
42. Smooth-skinned fruit
44. Squeal or squealer
45. Cut of beef
47. Sum's infinitive
48. Ending for Turk or Finn
49. The north wind
50. Aunt, in Nantes
52. Mining find
53. Huntley
55. Celebrity interviewer
59. Professor of divinity
62. Supreme Greek God
64. Typhoons' cousins
65. Nobleman
66. U.K. honor

67. "M*A*S*H" star
68. Weaver's reed

DOWN

1. 31 gallons: Abbr.
2. Secular
3. Submit
4. Lasses, jocularly
5. School Eden attended
6. Mitchell classic
7. Bikini part
8. Pt. or qt.
9. Arizona pueblo dweller
10. Suffix with tact
11. Metric unit of cap.
13. Glaswegians
14. Small birds
15. He screams for his team
19. Nancy __, L.P.G.A. star
23. Pallid
24. Roman road
25. Thin, crinkled cloth
26. Agitates
27. The southeast wind
30. "Paddle your own __"
31. Wolflike animal
32. Titus __, English conspirator
38. Hibernia
39. Gone by
40. Like a hamster's tail
43. Shooting star
46. Simple tasks
49. Fasteners
51. King of the Huns
53. Smoked fish
54. "__ Comes the Show Boat"
56. On naval operations
57. True
58. Certain
59. Le Duc __ of Hanoi
60. Wood sorrel
61. Sal, in a song
63. Tricky

ACROSS

1. Frighten
6. Half a bray
9. Droop
12. This tool is usually boring
13. Item of dress in Kobe
14. Exclude
16. Pebble mine
18. Aviator __ Balbo
19. French auxiliary verb
20. Make public
21. Respites for warriors
22. Poe's "The __ of the Perverse"
24. Housemaids' implements
26. God of the winds
29. Nickname of a former D.C. team
30. "I __ Have Danced . . ."
31. Bake an egg
33. Map abbr.
36. Garment feature
37. Garfield of the comics, e.g.
38. In a tangle
40. Summertime in N.Y.C.
41. Proclamation
43. Gable
44. Asian sea
45. Elongated lizards
46. Protector of the green
50. Venomous one
51. Small interstice
52. Was a candidate
54. Equestrian's sport
58. Waylay

59. Writer of exposés
61. Employs
62. Specialty of Keats
63. Actress Ekberg
64. Slalom curve
65. __ diem
66. Lift in a shop

DOWN

1. Wise one
2. Short and sour
3. Culture medium
4. Morning call
5. Before, to Bryant
6. Pueblo dweller
7. "__ in the hand . . ."
8. Clever one
9. Orders at the bar
10. Manila hemp
11. Ancient Greek physician
14. Some sites for auto races
15. A Supreme, once
17. Babies' perches
21. A Romanov title
23. Reptiles fond of ponds
25. Get together
26. Sharp and biting
27. Ages and ages
28. Push out
31. Milan's La __
32. Possesses
33. Reddish
34. Inönü, for one
35. Hefty ungulates

39. Not very serious
42. __ Sea, Arctic Ocean arm
44. Worships
45. Went to the bottom
46. Window part
47. Links king before Jack
48. Approaches
49. Very proper one
53. Maple genus
55. Epithet for Tom Joad
56. "I __ Song Go . . ."
57. Uttered
59. Clean a spill
60. Sheikdom __ al-Khaimah

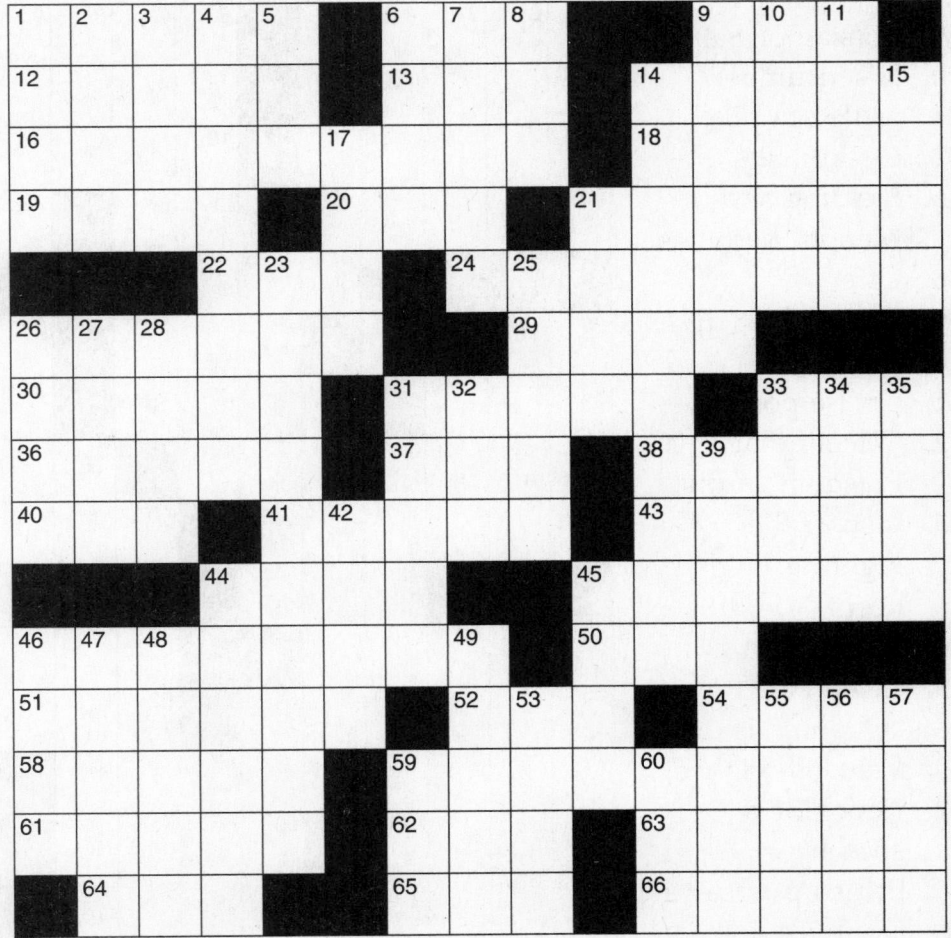

182

ACROSS

1. Chubby
6. Game fish
10. Miami's county
14. Stand for Georgia O'Keeffe
15. Antithesis of written
16. Land of Herod Agrippa II
17. Start of a pessimist's credo
18. Hierarchal system
20. Vexed
22. Credo: Part II
23. "__ est laborare . . ."
24. Impecunious
25. Kind of corner
28. Gump's mate
29. Persian or Siamese
30. Disencumber
31. Little sea pike
32. Cockpits
36. Fielding and Menotti heroines
38. Offer
39. Credo: Part III
40. Saucy
41. Cruise port
42. "Meeting at Potsdam" author
43. Inst. of the Fighting Engineers
44. Credo: Part IV
45. Celebrated
48. "Oberon" is one
50. Valuable violins
52. Conclude a speech
56. British proofreader
58. Dot over dot
59. Toledo's lake
60. Where Beauvais is
61. End of credo
62. Shoe size
63. Devil's-grip, e.g.
64. He wrote "The Big Knife"

DOWN

1. Emulate Tom of Coventry
2. Wash
3. Exploits
4. U.S. poet and religious writer
5. Tradesman, e.g.
6. Sets
7. Caustic
8. Squeal
9. Corrida calls
10. Empties wholly or partly
11. ". . . wings like __": Psalm 55
12. Distributed
13. Corundum
19. Tower on a mosque
21. Go on a tear
25. Asian salt lake
26. Soprano who lost her key
27. A Genesis setting
29. Mail deliverer
31. Indefinitely
33. Tevere feeder
34. Flavoring for a Cannes cordial
35. Ancient ambulatory
37. Linden, tupelo or sour gum
38. Beat repeatedly
40. Make a hitch pitch
44. Loser in 1066
45. Sparkler part
46. Casanova's obsession
47. California county
49. Italian saint
51. Large barge
53. Drug-yielding plant
54. Ballyhoo
55. They might meet in a bowl
57. Get even with

ACROSS

1. On __ with (equal to)
5. Chartres pew
9. Charlemagne's father
14. Cob or colt
15. Kowloon nurse
16. Become a soapboxer
17. Tidy
20. Hermetically close again
21. Cowpoke's poker
22. __ Paulo, Brazil
23. City on the Jumna
25. Enraged
27. Favorite
33. Sleeper, e.g.
34. R.I. rebel: 1842
35. Folkloric giant or dwarf
37. Ornament
39. Tussocks, e.g.
42. Rubens subject
43. Willard and Lazarus
45. __ sheet (bigots' tabloid)
47. Inverted caret
48. Sycophants
52. Anagram for "rose"
53. Eye: Comb. form
54. __ onion (squill)
57. Swerve
59. Less arduous
63. Dessert
66. Gloss
67. Chisholm Trail town
68. Finnish poem
69. Lorenz and Moss
70. Rather and Duryea
71. Resort hotels

DOWN

1. Kabul peer
2. Bolt facet
3. Cry of dismay
4. Annul
5. Discothèque forerunner
6. Simone's soul
7. Snoozes
8. Contribute
9. Least opulent
10. Make a faux pas
11. NASA platforms
12. Virginia willow
13. Famed fiddler
18. Notified via intercom
19. Seine feeder above Rouen
24. Ethnic coif
26. Bruce from Chicago
27. Molière play division
28. Cleveland neighbor
29. Neaten one's appearance
30. Upright: Comb. form
31. "__ Lost That Lovin' Feelin' "
32. Pliny the __
36. Dregs
38. Atlas contents
40. Aura of glory
41. Fellowship sums
44. Unkempt ones
46. Found: Abbr.
49. Jewish eve
50. Gazed
51. Firemen, at times
54. Cummerbund
55. Hebrew bushel
56. Mime
58. Author Jaffe
60. Ham __ (emote)
61. Sicilian sight
62. Sandwich breads
64. Sanction
65. __ out (prevail)

184

ACROSS

1. Worn-out horse
5. "___ of robins . . ."
10. Sound from a clowder
14. Kristi Yamaguchi feat
15. Galileo taught here
16. Spirit of Saint Louis?
17. "Ticklish" color
18. "Westminster Standards" framers
20. Part of R.E.O.
21. Smart's kin
22. Up ___ (cornered)
23. With 50 Across, theologians' rebuttal to cynics
27. Take giant steps
29. Pearl Harbor's locale
30. Plumbing, e.g.
31. Eschew
33. Concrete strip
37. Pilcorn
38. Goes to the land of Nod
41. McKinley's wife
42. Exes' followers
44. Am. Legion members
45. Surround
47. Ballerina's knee bend
49. Part of H.S.M.
50. See 23 Across
55. Divagates
56. Grebe's cousin
57. Little corn grower
60. Outdo in importance
63. Comedian Redd
64. Roller in 1789

65. "Die Fledermaus" maid
66. "The ___ Love," old song
67. Augustan and Caesarean
68. Dead duck
69. Propensity

DOWN

1. Make fun of
2. Leafstalk angle
3. Defame
4. Lodge brother
5. Cochise was one
6. W.S. contemporary
7. Detroit lemon
8. Girl of songdom
9. Milliner's item
10. Writer on population: 1798
11. Don's January
12. Bugaboos
13. ". . . ___ through a glass, darkly": I Cor. 13:12
19. English spa
21. Krait, e.g.
24. Suffix with human
25. Officiates at a tea
26. Antinuclear acronym
27. Pack
28. S. Foster dog
31. Infuse
32. S.R.O. show
34. Stalactite base
35. Tennis term

36. Deadly poison
39. Apollyon's delight
40. Refulgence
43. Mars, Venus, etc.
46. Slip a cog
48. Minus
49. Fiancée's surprise
50. Indited
51. Hang over
52. ___ Culp Hobby, ex-H.E.W. Sec.
53. Of yore
54. Pulitzer Prize novelist: 1981
58. Some bovines
59. Sign in red
61. Gorgon
62. Stir
63. Little pocket

ACROSS

1. Ariz. Indian
5. Dissect a sentence
10. Fastener
14. February 13, e.g.
15. Mrs. Archie Bunker
16. European shark
17. Welsh emblem
18. Boulders south of the border
19. Corrupt
20. Site of Georgian Bay
22. Banquet
23. Protective barrier
24. Transactions
26. Object
29. Coin a part of speech
31. Grand Banks catch
34. Cordwood measures
36. Kudu or dikdik
38. Vehicle for Judd Hirsch
39. Harbor boat
40. "Nana" star: 1934
41. Frankincense
44. Daybreak office
46. Legendary bird
47. Kind of pass
49. Mother of Peer
50. Site of an 1836 siege
52. Kind of surgeon
54. A de Mille
56. John Ford film: 1950
61. Daily phenomenon
62. Adhesive
63. Scoop
64. "L' __ c'est moi"
65. Flirt
66. Gemstone
67. Infamous fiddler
68. Famed Bowdoin alumnus
69. Demolish

DOWN

1. Cachou, e.g.
2. Fancy
3. Far from forceful
4. Made a request
5. Items in Washington's closet
6. Worshipful one
7. Puerto __
8. Part of S.R.O.
9. Exclamations of inquiry
10. Kind of band
11. Locale of Dartmouth and Sydney
12. Sacred bull
13. Stone
21. Swarm
22. Dunaway
25. Newt
26. Early fur baron
27. Aviator Balbo
28. In which Taylor was rough and ready
30. Type of hydrometer
32. Unbars
33. Obtuse
35. "Adam's __," Cukor film
37. W.W. II vessel
39. Teacher's function
42. "Oh me! Oh my!"
43. "Message From __" (Steel novel)
44. Novelist Sharp
45. Winglike
48. Fan
51. Slow, to Solti
53. Struggle
54. Former British colony
55. Word with house or keeper
57. Cuba, for one
58. Calif. valley
59. Foe of Zapata
60. That girl, in Brest
62. Dad

186

ACROSS

1. "... baked in __"
5. Repaired tire
10. Mop the deck
14. Fizzy drink
15. Color called bleu Louise
16. Part of an oriel
17. Equal
18. Value
20. Puncture
21. Ballet performer
22. Not difficult
25. Pleasure, in Paris
26. Work list
29. Family __
31. An arm of HUD
34. Dishonest
36. Epochs
37. Birch's cousin
38. Sonny's sibling
39. Tinters
40. Layer
41. Outline of a figure
43. Peculiar
44. Recess in a church
45. Kind of drama
46. Atmosphere
47. Insect's feeler
48. Star
53. Singer Fitzgerald
57. Frauds
59. Bright light at night
60. Sly gaze
61. Choice
62. Jacket or collar
63. Decoy
64. Frozen rain
65. Charge

DOWN

1. Reptiles in the Nile
2. __ laureate
3. Brainstorm
4. Bore
5. New Deal agcy.
6. Vacant
7. Head, in Milano
8. Ouse feeder
9. Promises
10. Part of a tome
11. Woman soldier in 1942
12. Poker term
13. Porter's relative
19. Concern
23. Hebrew month
24. Pouch
26. Famed Italian baritone
27. Extremely cold
28. Over
29. Sheer cotton fabric
30. Marsh plant
31. Worries
32. Creator of Truthful James
33. Property, e.g.
35. Mother of Horus
36. Something startling
39. Obtund or obtuse
41. Elves
42. Wood sorrel
44. Is not up to par
46. Venerate
47. Actor Duilio del __
48. Ants' creation
49. Ostrichlike bird
50. Imitator
51. __ and void
52. Where Perry triumphed
54. "__ Smile Be Your ..."
55. Pillage
56. Queen or princess
58. Harden

ACROSS

1. Fancy's opposite
5. "Act One" subject
9. Figure of speech
14. A "Silkwood" actress
15. This might be corny
16. Great Lakes acronym
17. Protection
18. Anagram for nail
19. A day's march
20. Place to eat, sleep and learn
23. Also
24. Rowan
25. Jetsam of 1773
28. Domestic hot spot
31. Most logical
36. Asian salt tree
38. Cantabs' rivals
40. Street show
41. Seafarer's expression
44. Show respect
45. Type of mackerel
46. Specialty of 70 Across
47. Shakespeare offering
49. A Gardner
51. Avila aunt
52. Aitch preceder
54. Abbr. on a list
56. Symbol of innocence
64. Aromas
65. Spydom name
66. Swerve sharply
68. Slanted
69. Disastrous
70. A Fitzgerald
71. Singer Simon
72. Marsh growth
73. Jazz player's phrase

DOWN

1. Mark S. Fowler chaired it: Abbr.
2. Melville mariner
3. Nothing, in Noya
4. October 31 alternative
5. Extend a show's run
6. Trans __, range in the Pamirs
7. Controlling power
8. Friendly Islands
9. Turn on __(be very pleasant)
10. He wrote "Our Gang"
11. Hawaiian thrush
12. Melon or squash
13. German donkey
21. A friend of Winnie
22. Draft curves?
25. Items on the agenda
26. Kind of psychology
27. E.T., e.g.
29. "Desire Under the __"
30. Sister's daughter, e.g.
32. Collars
33. Upright
34. Caravansary
35. Seed's outer coat
37. just as
39. Procyon, e.g.
42. Thomas Gray et al.
43. It's now J.F.K. International
48. Perfect, in an Edwards film
50. W.W. II area
53. The clear sky
55. Report on
56. Soft clay
57. Summer quaffs
58. Marina sight
59. Pelagic creature
60. Affluent person
61. Mercyhurst College site
62. Where heros are made
63. One's own person
67. Eur. flyboys

188

ACROSS

1. Churl
5. Carries into a carrier
10. Back of the neck
14. Karenina or Christie
15. Tilted, as the Titanic
16. Musical work
17. N.B.A. team from N.J.
18. "Oro y —," Montana motto
19. Camper's gear
20. Hypocritical sorrow
23. Latin-lesson word
24. Countryside, to Cicero
25. Avocados
33. Twosome
34. Autocrat
35. Peephole or loophole
36. Saharan
38. Capek classic
40. Weak
41. Sign of affection
44. Biddeford's neighbor
47. Silent
48. Largest publications
51. — mode
52. Opposite of pos.
53. Where trials proceed by leaps and bounds
61. Employ
62. What a mob takes a rat for
63. On

64. — mater
65. Type of boat
66. Wolfe of fiction
67. Shine
68. Dark-complexioned, in poesy
69. Prin.'s aide

DOWN

1. Bench for Burger
2. Lollapalooza
3. Aware of
4. Imp
5. Chihuahua and Pomeranian
6. "— Know," Jim Webb song
7. Channel changer
8. Inlet
9. Prestige
10. — bene
11. Mimic
12. Evokers of groans
13. Part of i.e.
21. Leave out
22. Make out
25. Of the ear or air
26. French area, rich in coal
27. Rhine feeder
28. Reliance
29. Slippery one
30. "Remember the —"
31. Co-founder of Rome
32. Check

33. European fish
37. Airport abbr.
39. W.W. II heroes
42. Type of rug
43. Compliments
45. Pops event
46. Margarine
49. Short of breadth
50. Harmless lizard
53. Scot's garb
54. "Aeneid" opening
55. Kind of beer
56. City on Kyushu
57. Aroma
58. Hwys.
59. Rocky peaks
60. What Lady Macbeth curses
61. Owns

ACROSS

1. Style
6. Latin lass: Abbr.
10. Complete failure
14. Where Vulcan forged
15. Supporting column
16. Kazakhstan's Sea
17. Pack of mackerel
18. Meet for McEnroe
19. Treatment
20. Arena
22. Kind of cap or pad
23. Bonilla's bunch
24. Lost intensity
26. Offset, with "out"
30. Floria of opera
32. Words of concern
33. "__ a man . . ."
35. Glowing coal
39. Fur-trimmed cloak
41. Auxin, e.g.
43. Yemeni's neighbor
44. Culinary mélange
46. Church calendar
47. Obvious
49. "Peace and Plenty" painter
51. "__ cut bait"
54. A contemporary of Haydn
56. Prefix with meter
57. Decisive battle
63. Collected
64. Truck type
65. Herd on the move
66. Organic compound
67. Nights before
68. Girdle material
69. Cry from the crib
70. Strike out
71. Movie critic Siskel's TV partner

DOWN

1. Lawful lucre
2. City south of Salt Lake City
3. At the summit
4. Break
5. Biblical dancer
6. Good fellow
7. Sharp response
8. Abound
9. He played Marshal Dillon
10. Game for two
11. Chimp's cousin
12. Runner Sidney of the Olympics
13. What wet madras cloth may do
21. Homes for heros
25. Maple genus
26. Snowflake, to Santos
27. Attention-getter
28. Popular piano piece
29. Prized rodent
31. "Top __ mornin'!"
34. Southwestern flattop
36. Carried
37. Stops
38. Cars of yesteryear
40. Corn holder of a kind
42. __ to (because of)
45. Fishing net
48. Scraped out
50. Provoke
51. Confronted
52. A Massey
53. Endured
55. Gift to Bob Cratchit
58. Dream, to Debussy
59. Monotonous
60. Be foolishly fond
61. Ham's word
62. Call to a queue

190

ACROSS

1. Nice names
5. Tab
9. Poetic initials
12. Baseball's Steady Eddie
13. Scold severely
14. Writer Shere —
16. Shoeless Joe's team
19. Kind of horn
20. Cockcrow
21. Of gulls
22. Lingerie items
24. Moreover
25. Hairpiece, in slanguage
26. Ex-hurlers Lee and Marv
30. Plate umpire's tool
33. Part
34. Part of Q.E.D.
35. Attention
36. Most lean
39. Drs.' group
40. Fish-eating duck
42. Angers
43. Kind of race
45. Dash a liquid upon
47. Bors or Kay
48. Henry or Clare Boothe
49. Opened
53. Well-being
56. Hack or Musial of baseball
57. A Curie
58. World Series champ: 1982
61. Snare
62. Approach
63. Places for roasts
64. Annapolis grad.
65. DNA factor
66. Tennis units

DOWN

1. — game (pitcher's dream)
2. Speak out
3. Singer Davis
4. Where Yankees and Dodgers play
5. "And Quiet — the Don"
6. Croquet area
7. Bat wood
8. World Series champs: 1980
9. Midler hit song
10. Valenzuela's agreement
11. College or collar
12. W.W. II craft
15. English Channel feeder
17. Kind of plank
18. Russian news service
23. Major leaguer, e.g.
24. Van Gogh painted here
26. Corset-factory employee
27. Using speech
28. Doll's word
29. Remain
30. Wife of 53 Down
31. Sloping passage
32. City on the Oka
33. Street show
37. Carlton's craft
38. Oriole catcher: 1955–62
41. Ruthian swats
44. Throw wildly
46. Ballet skirt
47. Mantle or Mays, once
49. Hard look
50. Belief
51. Dwight of the Red Sox: 1972–1990
52. Ennis and Crandall of baseball
53. F.D.R.'s successor
54. To be, in Montreal
55. Arkin or Bates
56. Look over
59. Observe
60. "— Got Sixpence"

ACROSS

1. Defeat
5. Strongboxes
10. Sailing
14. Space
15. Winged
16. Poet Sandburg
17. Brooklet
18. A Doone
19. Garbed
20. Give credence to
22. Mollify
24. Jeanne, e.g.: Abbr.
25. Elopers' aid
26. Mad __
32. Panama or Erie
33. Sierra __
34. Fountain-pen part
37. Bearing
38. Metric ton
39. Pro __
40. A N.Y. time
41. Trim
42. Military caps
43. "And what is so rare __?"
45. Robert or William of films
48. Modernist
49. Summer refreshment
51. Dexterity
55. Mane locale
56. "__ Kick Out of You"
58. Coconut-husk fiber
59. Tribe
60. Japanese-American
61. Gaelic
62. Sentry's word
63. McCarthy's fellow traveler
64. Office item

DOWN

1. Sarcastic remark
2. Pa. port
3. Traffic in
4. Amulet
5. Serving need
6. Lily's relative
7. Partner of wide
8. Lab burner
9. Amphibious vehicle
10. Acquiesce
11. Kind of bar
12. Wipe out
13. Wood for bridges
21. Space-saving abbr.
23. Peel
26. Highest point
27. Declared
28. Dill of the Bible
29. Darken
30. Hair coloring
31. This goes with milk
34. Chevrotain
35. Have __ for (hold a grudge)
36. Supply station
38. Used-car lot items
39. Was jubilant
41. College entrance exam
42. Joint below a femur
43. Passionate
44. Like some tiles
45. Dead certainty
46. Fla. city
47. Asian country
50. Not fer
51. Mob or gang follower
52. Skirt section
53. Sibilant sound
54. Migration
57. Compass dir.

192

ACROSS

1. Cinches
6. Rainwater pipe
11. Almost a knight: Abbr.
14. Soda pop in Boston
15. One of the Keys
16. Trifle
17. De Sica's "Yesterday, Today __"
19. Celestial dessert?
20. Actor Turhan __
21. Domino or Waller
22. "__ Well . . ."
23. Proust's "Remembrance __"
27. Scrutinizes
30. Like some cookies
31. Cupid
32. Indian city
33. "Honest" one
36. Beckett classic
41. Draft letters
42. Young horse
43. Bartók or Lugosi
44. Kind of inflection
46. Halts
49. Dylan's "__ Are A-Changin'"
52. Achilles or Ajax
53. Take __ the lam
54. Goal
57. Outer: Comb. form
58. Dali's "__ of Memory"
62. Fire: Fr.
63. Basilica area
64. A de Mille
65. Football pts.
66. Cotton thread
67. Good earth

DOWN

1. Pierce
2. "And Then There Were __"
3. Warhol or Williams
4. Pendulum's partner
5. Flouts
6. Lazy arboreal clingers
7. Iranian dialect
8. Hockey great
9. Actor Tognazzi
10. Haul
11. Shore-front walkways
12. Stains
13. Pursuit
18. The end, in chess
22. Copy
23. Eject
24. NASA's "not ready"
25. Teri of "Tootsie"
26. Kind of party
27. Seats for the faithful
28. Guidry stats.
29. Carousing noisily
32. C.I.O.'s partner
34. Nut's complement
35. Airport abbrs.
37. Province ceded to Morocco
38. Linguist Chomsky
39. Strong wind
40. "__ thy heart": Emerson
45. Ear: Comb. form
46. Raiment
47. Pi-sigma connectors
48. Kind of library
49. "Property is __!": Proudhon
50. Jinxed
51. Rope fiber
54. Henry VIII's second
55. Some desserts
56. Gob's meal
58. Chum
59. Yalie
60. Wall St. abbr.
61. Kind of trip

ACROSS

1. Rival of Ole Miss
5. After, in Arles
10. Ghanaian seaport
14. Ancient kingdom
15. Literary Becky
16. First governor of "The 49th"
17. French magazine
18. Short-legged dog
19. Presswork with pix
20. Strain
22. Jayhawker
24. Pueblo Indian
25. Joyous celebration
26. Yields as a return
28. Birthstone
33. Grasped
35. Item often having interest
36. Sine __
37. Formerly, once
38. Homophone for a biblical queen
40. Body
41. "Pink Marsh" author
42. Conductor Klemperer
43. Blackjack player's opponent
45. Birthstone
48. Chevet
49. Am. call-up outfit
50. File
52. Crow's kin
55. Tempestuous winds
59. Vent
60. Craft
62. Brainstorm
63. Anagram of noel
64. Corroded
65. Wagnerian cycle
66. __ out (barely managed)
67. "__ thou these great buildings?": Mark 13:2
68. Major ending

DOWN

1. Gripe
2. "I am monarch of __ survey"
3. Promenade
4. Birthstone
5. B.M.I. rival
6. Caused by light
7. Choice
8. Unit of work
9. Plant of the ginseng family
10. Core
11. Selves
12. So long, in Soho
13. Shortly
21. "Second Hand __"
23. Solar disk
25. Cleaving tool
26. Lost to view
27. Goose genus
29. Choral singers
30. Fans' favorites
31. Evangelist McPherson
32. Stingy
33. In the catbird __
34. Explodes
39. Slammer
40. Birthstone
42. Expel
44. Maugham's "__ of Suez"
46. Named a price
47. Gullies
51. Common contraction
52. Take out
53. Berserk
54. Cattle, to Cowper
55. N.B.A.'s Archibald
56. Emulate Edward Bok
57. Cleft
58. Kind of brush
61. Charlotte from Milwaukee

194

ACROSS

1. Royal Norse name
5. Plucky
9. Noggin
13. Betel palm
14. "A __ Able"
15. __ de la Société
16. __ Major
17. Dispatched
18. Crooks' nemeses
19. Hayseed
21. Cypress feature
22. Wkly. arrival
23. "My Sister __"
25. Rabbit fur
28. The first Mrs. Soames Forsyte
30. Crèche figures
31. Ablative, e.g.
33. Horatian creation
37. Slipped away
39. Washington's German baron
41. Poorest
42. Concerning
44. "Of Thee I __"
45. Eight gills
47. Squander
49. Philatelists' books
52. Kiln
54. Liquori specialty
55. Killjoy
61. Iris part
62. Syllogism word
63. Broader
64. Submerge
65. Carol

66. Crème de la crème
67. Kin of Ph.D.'s
68. Russian agency ITAR-__
69. Quebec's Lévesque

DOWN

1. Buccal
2. Marquisette's weave
3. Citric __
4. Queen Esther's predecessor
5. Quebec peninsula
6. Bacteria-free state
7. Mesabi hole
8. Veal Parmesan, perhaps
9. Crosspatch
10. Solitary
11. Caddoan abode
12. Ruhr center
13. C.P.A.'s record
20. Sixteen drams
24. Arrow poison
25. "Le Roi d'Ys" composer
26. Culture medium
27. Squirts
29. Symbol for André Watts
30. Garfield's sound
32. Shebat's follower
34. R.I.P. notice
35. Basso Jozsef __

36. M.I.T. grad.
38. Anagram of must
40. Crying __
43. Comical trio
46. Agreement
48. Retort
49. Titillate
50. Lead-colored
51. Mingle
53. Early stringed instruments
56. Malay outrigger
57. Heap
58. Frigg's mate
59. Network of nerves
60. Sei halved

ACROSS

1. A high school, for short
5. Tartan design
10. W.W. I plane
14. Go on horseback
15. Frankie or Cleo
16. Rich material
17. Freeway spans
19. Jacob's twin
20. Fixes firmly
21. Lunch and dinner
23. Donkey, in Dijon
24. Building crossbeam
25. Stir up
30. Attaches
33. Diminutive
34. A soccer player
36. Strive
37. Rosary beads
38. Word with water or ground
39. Bona __
40. Card spot
41. Villainous expression
42. Knight's helmet
43. Students, in St.-Lô
45. F.B.I. files
47. Prepares potatoes, in a way
49. Le jazz __
50. Type of windlass
52. Chaffs
56. Hawaiian seaport
57. Track official
59. Part of a Jewish year

60. Roman magistrate
61. City near the Comstock Lode
62. Word with halcyon or salad
63. Exclude
64. Tennis segments

DOWN

1. Campus V.I.P.
2. __ Ridge, 1972 Derby winner
3. W.W. II Greek resistance org.
4. Relates
5. Smoothed timber
6. Colleen
7. Some sloths
8. Sluggish
9. Renegade
10. Raveled silk
11. Spends, as an hour or day
12. One of a Latin trio
13. __ ex machina
18. A bid for one's thoughts
22. Brace
25. Day's march
26. Author Shute
27. Bootleg by a quarterback
28. Ceil
29. Terminated
31. Mandate
32. Vetoes on the Volga
35. Stout's Mr. Wolfe
38. Deposed
39. Yankees' griddlecakes
41. Cult's cousin
42. Unisonally
44. Brims on caps
46. __ Heights, Ohio
48. Slyly malicious
50. Libyan neighbor
51. Verdi masterpiece
52. Bartók or Lugosi
53. Fencing weapon
54. Torn
55. Hit-show signs
58. Playing marble

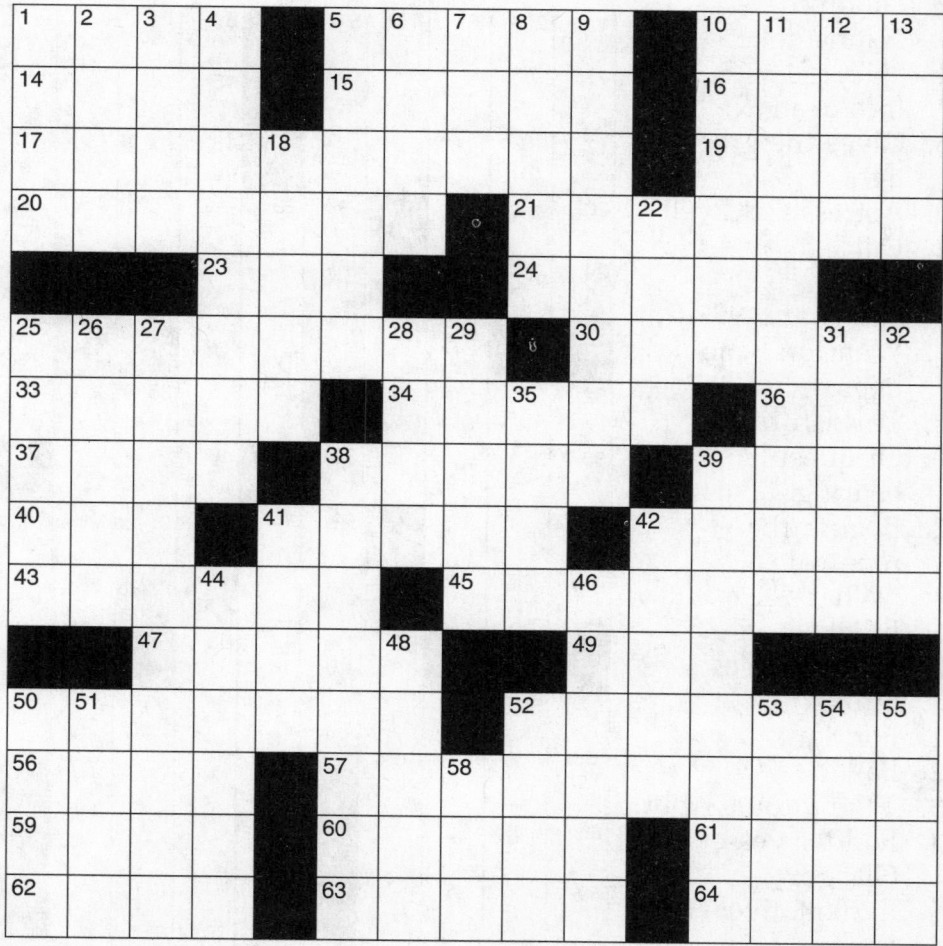

196

ACROSS

1. Wall Street term
6. Worker's recompense
10. Ball of yarn
14. The real "Funny Girl"
15. "__ Old Cowhand"
16. Well-ventilated
17. Eliminated the squeaks
18. Between-meals snack
19. Ditto
20. Comedian Brooks
21. Nifty, to a flapper
24. Rich fabric
26. Kind of nose
27. Dishwasher's partner
28. Having talons
32. Dillon in "Gunsmoke"
34. "No, __!"
37. Info at J.F.K.
38. Gives the green light
40. Actress Caldwell
41. Daft
43. Zilch
44. Smart and 99
47. Wharton School degs.
48. Turkish river
50. Of queenly bearing
52. Begin urban renewal
54. "What's __?": Juliet
57. Union bosses' bunks?
61. For: Lat.
62. Bail
63. Take a tour: Abbr.
64. Fodder vessel, in Glasgow
66. Exploitative person

67. Prefix with phone or gram
68. Coeur d' __, Idaho
69. Tot's counting word
70. German river
71. Steel-mill employee

DOWN

1. Enola Gay's cargo item
2. Judge
3. Day-Hudson comedy: 1959
4. Top pitcher
5. Terminal figure
6. Add chains, snow tires, etc.
7. Bible book
8. Struggles to speak
9. What makeup may do
10. Melon variety
11. Author O'Flaherty
12. Humorist Bombeck
13. Followers of exes
22. Picnic quaffs
23. Mint __
25. Kind of slicker
29. He puts a damper on things
30. Kett of comics
31. When Dracula sleeps
32. A Lisa
33. Similar
35. Quarterback Jaworski
36. Golden __

8. Struggles to speak
9. What makeup may do
10. Melon variety
11. Author O'Flaherty
12. Humorist Bombeck
13. Followers of exes
22. Picnic quaffs
23. Mint __
25. Kind of slicker
29. He puts a damper on things
30. Kett of comics
31. When Dracula sleeps
32. A Lisa
33. Similar
35. Quarterback Jaworski
36. Golden __

39. Emcee Purcell on TV
42. Muscat is its capital
45. Name for a newspaper
46. Transmit
49. Cross-city roadway
51. Hot-air artist
53. Committed a faux pas
55. Gosnold touched it in 1602
56. Mideast V.I.P.
57. Place to see Santa?
58. Alleviate
59. Yemeni seaport
60. Hay bundle
65. __ bonne heure! (right!)

ACROSS

1. ~~Kind of~~ cat
4. Item on a guitar
8. Eaten away
13. Gemstone
15. Città Eterna
16. Boundary
17. Marcello's wish on Jan. 1
20. Designed
21. Slangy refusal
22. Attachment on property
23. Tall tales
24. Grangers' measures
26. Teamster's rig
28. Approached
33. Lily's relative
37. Tears
39. Montélimar's river
40. Spectacle in Philadelphia on Jan. 1
43. Walking __ (ecstatic)
44. Guy on a ship
45. Luxuriate on the beach
46. Town NNE of Paris
48. Desserts
50. Mattress-stuffing material
52. Kefauver
57. Fleming and Hunter
61. Martini base
62. Existent but unrevealed
63. "I do __ . . ." (words for Jan. 1)
66. Dunne from Louisville
67. Certain crosses
68. Farm implement
69. British motorists' needs
70. Point on the Isle of Man
71. Method: Abbr.

DOWN

1. Chewy ~~candy~~
2. "Ernani," e.g.
3. Of the cheekbone
4. Lynn of baseball
5. Sinbad's mount
6. Jan. 1, 1863
7. S.A. beast
8. Olden days
9. 100 dinars
10. All: Comb. form
11. Trigonometric function
12. Kind of collar
14. Describe
18. Luck, in Ireland
19. Some bovids
24. Out of order
25. One of the Yugoslavs
27. Fail, humanly
29. Ishmael's skipper
30. Author Jaffe
31. Purposes
32. Stand in an orchestra
33. Biblical prophet
34. Object shaped like a half moon
35. Arabia's Gulf of __
36. Actor Jannings
38. Tiffin's cousin
41. Actor Rhodes
42. Indigo is one
47. Story of heroism
49. Coral and Red
51. Niña companion
53. Street sign
54. Narrates
55. Government agent
56. Olla-podrida, etc.
57. "__ a bird?"
58. Crooked
59. Poetic contraction
60. Sound
62. __-majesté
64. Thing, in law
65. Capek drama

198

ACROSS

1. Route
5. Buffet dish
10. Cicatrix
14. __ code
15. Encomium
16. Verrett specialty
17. Beautiful birds
20. Meddle
21. Far from fresh
22. Greek theater
23. French dairy product
25. Corrode
28. Word with wing or wood
29. Bird call
30. Formerly
31. Private eye
34. Walked with a certain gait
35. Prynne's stigma
38. Plymouth prisons
39. Headdresses
40. Be flirtatious
41. Dir. from Albuquerque to Denver
42. Invalid's food
45. Dijon dance
46. Proofreading mark
49. Had origin
51. Armadillo
53. Modifies
54. Sherlock Holmes story
58. Fishing need
59. Necktie
60. Feudal bigwig
61. Hand over
62. Urban illumination
63. Gaelic

DOWN

1. Parish head
2. Arched passageway
3. Joined
4. Memorable mime
5. Melampus was one
6. High in pitch
7. Batch
8. Quartz variety
9. Cotton cloth
10. Big brain
11. Belief
12. Make known
13. Ethiopian title
18. Author Deighton
19. Exist
23. Sky traveler
24. Ordinary
26. Maple-tree genus
27. Lewis or Nugent
29. Nickname in "East of Eden"
30. Stable fare
31. White __
32. A wk. has 168 of these
33. Point of view
34. Sch. auxiliary
35. Tale of the Forsytes
36. Put together, as parts of a book
37. Sooner than, to Shakespeare
38. Tar
42. Tulip tree
43. Garden blooms
44. Crushing tool
46. Obnoxious fellow
47. Indo-European
48. Work incentive
49. Oklahoma city
50. Peep show
52. Whimper
53. Biblical book
54. Spark stream
55. __ out (finish)
56. Sgt. or cpl.
57. Absalom, to David

ACROSS

1. __ forth (lectured)
5. To one side
10. Ideologies
14. Lake on the U.S.-Canadian boundary
15. News medium of yore
16. Noted navigator
17. Puccini heroine
18. Epigrammatic
19. Losing racer
20. Babushkas
22. Spirelike
24. Fisheye lens, e.g.
26. Knot
29. Geisha's waistband
30. Roundup item
34. Havens for sightseers
36. What a litterbug does
38. Skyways alien
39. "Eureka!"
41. Ashanti language
42. Pfc.'s, for example
43. Sparrowlike birds
46. Evergreen oak
48. Eydie's man
49. Word now on cigarette packs
51. Mitigated
52. Natives of Erivan
55. Mentor
58. Book signatures
62. Iranian coin
63. Michelangelo piece
65. Eliot's "Adam __"
66. Wickerwork material
67. Places for troughs
68. Pulitzer Prize novelist: 1958
69. Conveyance without wheels
70. "Romantic Comedy" author
71. Quartz variety

DOWN

1. Encloses, with "in"
2. Gold-medalist Heiden
3. What Pizarro called "City of Kings"
4. Mythical maiden of Eire
5. French play divisions
6. Magician's word
7. Breeze
8. Set limits
9. Dutch __
10. "__ the Wind," Lawrence and Lee play
11. Rise
12. Aging filly
13. Doff
21. "Our Town" personae
23. Apposite
25. Dictionary abbr.
26. Blackens
27. Dietary directive to J. Sprat
28. Make amends
31. Patronage
32. Threefold
33. Hafez al-__, Syrian President
35. "__ Wore a Yellow Ribbon," John Ford film
37. Fearful respect
40. Like the Alcan Highway
44. Helped
45. __ Andreas fault
47. Winter melons
50. Created a major disturbance
53. Broods
54. __ in point
55. Swings of a pendulum
56. Switch TV channels
57. Barometer's forerunner
59. Brightest star in Lyra
60. River to the Baltic
61. Kind of pearl
64. Perón or LeGallienne

200

ACROSS

1. Keystone __
5. Sir, in Delhi
10. Monster
14. Fitzgerald
15. Word with glass or house
16. Stomach
17. Horsing around, in "Equus"?
19. Fogginess
20. Longest river in Scotland
21. Asian weight
22. Little Jack __
24. Bettor's note
26. Rickenbacker, e.g.
28. Foundation
29. Swindles
31. Have games with Pogo's team?
35. Korbut
36. Like bone
37. Unite
38. European subways
40. Giants of myth
42. Opposite of hurrah
43. Rope fibers
47. Velvet and army followers
48. Unassisted putout?
50. Report-card time, to some
51. Chapel monk
52. Mountain
53. Snake
54. Aspen activity
57. Electric-company customer
59. Rented

62. On one's __ (alert)
63. Where to look up "Hamlet"?
66. Kin of lui
67. Some looks
68. Wildcat
69. Protection for goalies
70. Out
71. River into the Elbe

DOWN

1. Held on to
2. Pot for puchero
3. Out in left
4. Declare
5. Oriental bean
6. Pleads
7. Vixen
8. Biblical captain
9. Former Senator Birch __
10. Pigments for Opie
11. Catches in the upper deck?
12. Tear down
13. Jug
18. Heat unit, for short
23. Old European coins
25. Glacial ridges
27. CBS logo
29. Bass, sax and guitar
30. New York city
31. Presume
32. Victim of a scam

33. Wyoming county
34. In disorder
39. Italian tongue
41. Little fellows
44. Watering place in Belgium
45. Refers (to)
46. Some sinners
49. Gets up
53. Humorist Bill
54. Footprint
55. Caffeine nut
56. Swallow
58. Gaelic
60. Novel name
61. Rasputin's ruler
64. A.F.T. rival
65. Don Ho adornment

ACROSS

1 Understood
4 Some tracks
9 __ Rizzo ('69 Hoffman role)
14 Santa __ winds
15 Actress Anouk
16 Significant person?
17 Kauai keepsake
18 Small person
20 Legit
22 Caroline Schlossberg, to Ted Kennedy
23 Type style: Abbr.
24 Big Mama
25 Church part
29 Rummy variety
32 The mark on the C in Čapek
33 Calendar period, to Kirk
37 Caustic substance
38 Traditional tune
40 Pub quaff
42 Logical newsman?
43 Long-lasting curls
45 Depicts
49 Health-food store staple
50 Jerry Herman composition
53 Dash
54 Michelangelo masterpiece
56 Journalist Greeley
58 Used booster cables
62 Tina's ex
63 Correspond, grammatically
64 Regarded favorably
65 Pince-__
66 Former Justice Byron
67 Air-show maneuvers
68 Palindrome center

DOWN

1 French
2 __ time (singly)
3 Taipei's land
4 Honolulu locale
5 Fat fiddle
6 Fuse word
7 First name in hotels
8 Big rigs
9 Campus mil. grp.
10 Daughter of Zeus
11 Calendar abbr.
12 Theology sch.
13 Eye
19 __-man (flunky)
21 Hooch container
24 Magna __
26 Rights grp.
27 "Oy __!"
28 __ out (supplement)
30 Hoosegows
31 Footrace terminus
32 Stage actress Hayes
34 MS follower?
35 Love, Italian style
36 Newcastle-upon-__, England
38 Esne
39 Judge's exhortation
40 Prone
41 Name of 13 popes
44 Oscar the Grouch, for one
46 Julia Louis-Dreyfus on "Seinfeld"
47 Pool-ball gatherer
48 Common cause for blessing
50 Strawberry, once
51 "Any Time __" (Beatles tune)
52 Auto-racer Andretti
55 Words of comprehension
56 "David Copperfield" character
57 Ten to one, e.g.
58 Gossip
59 "That's disgusting!"
60 High-tech med. diagnostic
61 Foreman stat

202

by Norma Steinberg

ACROSS

1 "Shane" star
5 Late actor Phoenix
10 "Dark Lady" singer, 1975
14 "__ in a manger . . ."
15 Author Zola
16 "__, from New York . . ."
17 Haircuts?
19 Kathleen Battle offering
20 "__ we having fun yet?"
21 Glowing
22 Kuwaiti structure
24 Opening word
26 Broadway show based on a comic strip
27 Dubuque native
29 Imperturbable
33 Become frayed
36 Former spouses
38 Conceited smile
39 Hawkeye portrayer
40 Recording auditions
42 Garfield's canine pal
43 Pilots let them down
45 Cushy
46 Catches some Z's
47 __ fugit
49 Gullible
51 Sufficient
53 Knucklehead
57 Horoscope heading
60 Police blotter abbr.
61 Prospector's find
62 World rotator?
63 Fake embroidery?
66 Augury
67 "This way in" sign
68 __ carotene
69 Emcee Parks
70 Nursery packets
71 Flowery verses

DOWN

1 Actor Lorenzo
2 Conscious
3 Odense residents
4 Recolor
5 Critiqued
6 ". . . __ a man with seven wives"
7 __ ordinaire
8 "Candle in the Wind" singer __ John
9 Copal and others
10 Vandalized art work?
11 Put on staff
12 Heinous
13 Kind of estate
18 Movie Tarzan __ Lincoln
23 Whoppers
25 Smog?
26 Showy flower
28 Lumber camp implements
30 Verdi heroine
31 Stumble
32 Makes do, with "out"
33 Float
34 Madame's pronoun
35 Eden resident
37 Divan
41 Scoundrels
44 Its usefulness goes to waste
48 Cumin and cardamom
50 Test tube
52 Actor Greene
54 Courted
55 Livid
56 Ann Richards's bailiwick
57 Poor fellow
58 "Be our guest!"
59 Concluded
60 Thunderstruck
64 Part of a year in Provence
65 Cable add-on

ACROSS

1 Hearth debris
6 Atmosphere
10 Columnist Bombeck
14 Room to __
15 Skater Heiden
16 High time?
17 Critical juncture
20 Parade
21 Some oranges
22 Roasting items
25 Sometimes they get the hang of it
26 Woolly one
30 Carnegie Hall event
32 Where Marco Polo traveled
33 Tomb tenant
34 All fired up?
37 Future brass
41 Modeled, maybe
42 Mountain ridge
43 Peruvian of yore
44 Neptune's fork
46 Physicist Niels
47 Work, work, work
49 Its password was "Mickey Mouse"
51 Trotsky rival
52 Straight shooters?
57 Stops rambling
61 Algerian seaport
62 Broadway groom of 1922
63 Sister of Thalia
64 Bridge seat
65 Bank holding
66 Prepare to shave

DOWN

1 Cleo's snakes
2 Flyspeck
3 "Let the Sun Shine In" musical
4 Sea bird
5 Bristles
6 W.W. I grp.
7 Mausoleum item
8 "Road to __"
9 Beginnings of poetry?
10 Involve
11 Beauty aid
12 Folkways
13 Writer Beattie and others
18 Poet translated by FitzGerald
19 Toledo locale
23 Depended
24 Perfumed
26 Senate output
27 On the briny
28 "Gorillas in the __"
29 Hit a fly, perhaps
31 Mean
34 Host Jay
35 Yen
36 Ivan, for one
38 Church front area
39 Expensive rug
40 Fish in a way
44 Aptitude
45 Weight allowance
47 Pack away
48 "Falcon Crest" star
50 "Egad!"
51 Barge
53 McHenry, e.g.
54 Münchhausen, for one
55 Within: Prefix
56 Common sign
58 Sash
59 Cause for overtime
60 Clucker

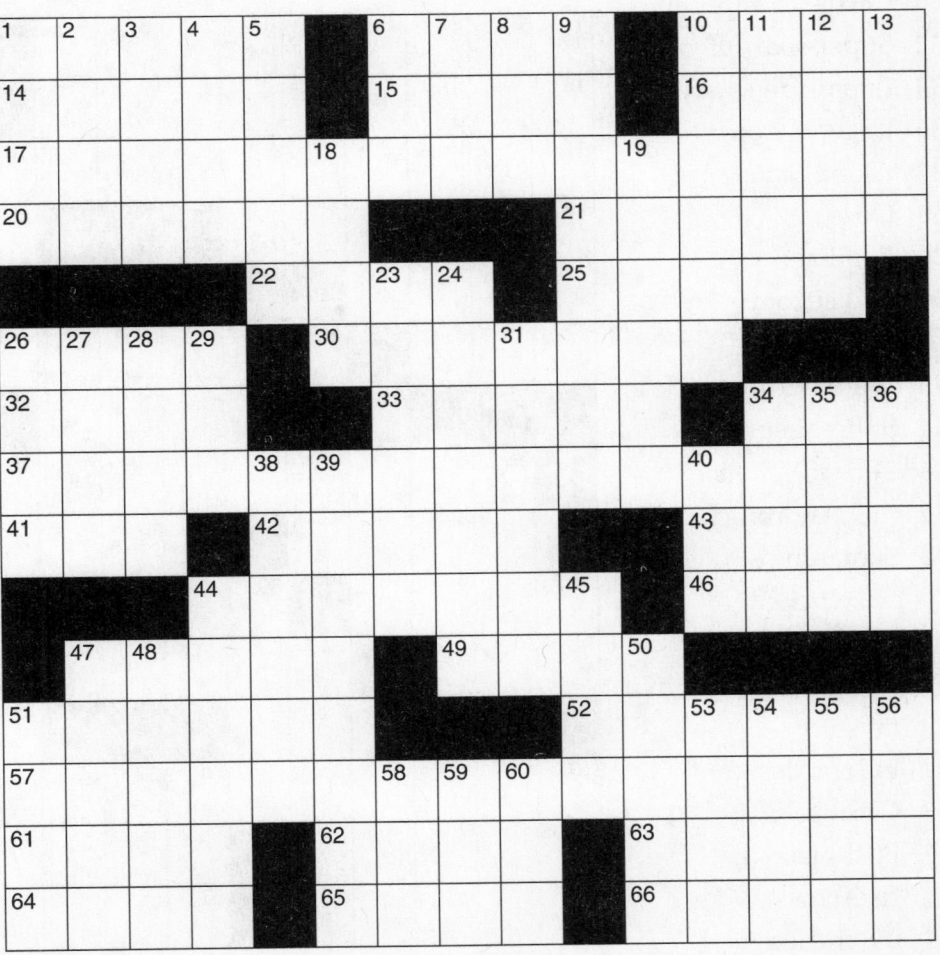

ACROSS

1 Colorful salad ingredient
10 Plant pest
15 Throw some light on
16 El __ (Spanish painter)
17 Acting ambassador
19 Mooring rope
20 The sky, maybe
21 Perry's creator
22 Pop's Carly or Paul
25 It's a drag
27 Country rtes.
28 It has its ups and downs
30 Turner of Hollywood
31 "Duke Bluebeard's Castle" composer
32 Super-soaked
33 Literature as art
36 Urger's words
37 Aloha State
38 Ooze
39 Bombast
40 70's sitcom "__ Sharkey"
43 Watered-down ideas
44 Subsequently
45 Teri of "Tootsie"
46 "__ Andronicus"
48 Samantha's "Bewitched" husband
50 Facetious advice in a mystery
54 Indoor design
55 Carouse
56 Birthplace of 16 Across
57 By and large

DOWN

1 ". . . for __ for poorer"
2 Founder of est
3 Talks Dixie-style
4 Diagram a sentence
5 Competitive advantage
6 Boat's departure site
7 Rocket's departure site
8 It's after zeta
9 Foul caller
10 One more time
11 Schoolmarmish
12 Birthright
13 Bar accessory
14 __ Passos
18 Go with the __
22 Layup alternative
23 Quarantine
24 Be militaristic
26 Manner
28 It can sting
29 Before, in palindromes
30 Actress __ Singer
31 Radar screen image
32 Rouse to action
33 Brief break
34 It's worth looking into
35 Clavell's "__-Pan"
36 Recipe abbr.
39 Mess-hall meal
40 Clint Eastwood's city
41 Kind of scream
42 Obstinate
44 Pelf
45 Miss Garbo
47 Jog
48 Hamlet, for one
49 Nowhere near
50 Fed. medical detectives
51 Sunny-side-up item
52 Lawyer Baird
53 Cambodia's __ Nol

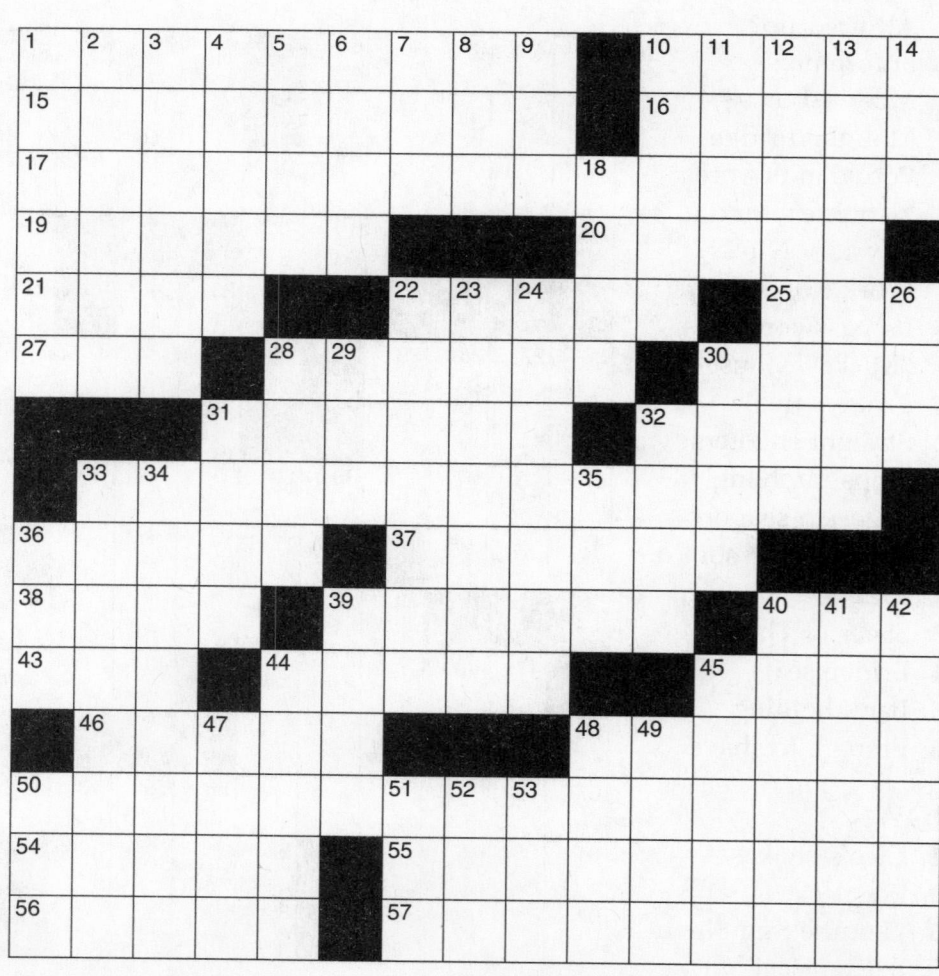

by David A. Rosen

ACROSS

1 Rumble
6 Not fancy?
10 Difficult obligation
14 "__ of do or die"
15 Bing Crosby best seller
16 Guthrie the younger
17 Hearty entree
20 Kibbutzniks' dance
21 Reverse
22 Must
23 Place to crash
25 Kipling novel
26 Tasty side dish
35 Mortgage matter
36 Words before "in the arm" or "in the dark"
37 Detective's cry
38 Them in "Them!"
39 Common key signature
40 Composer __ Carlo Menotti
41 Cpl., for one
42 Feed a fete
43 Stood for
44 Yummy dessert
47 Cherbourg chum
48 Latin I?
49 Lamb Chop's "spokesperson"
52 Oceania republic
55 Windmill segment
59 Eventual bonus?
62 Cream-filled sandwich
63 Debouchment
64 Internet patrons
65 Blubber
66 Yeltsin veto
67 Koch's predecessor

DOWN

1 Calculator work
2 Radar blip
3 Thieves' hideout
4 They're loose
5 "Yikes!"
6 "The Afternoon of a __"
7 In the thick of
8 First name in perfumery
9 Venture
10 Japanese mat
11 Olympic hawk
12 Bed-frame crosspiece
13 "Mikado" executioner
18 Sport whose name means "soft way"
19 Polo, e.g.
24 Circulars
25 Carpenter's woe
26 French bread?
27 High-priced spread?
28 ". . . and eat __"
29 Subj. of a Clinton victory, 11/17/93
30 Key
31 Midway alternative
32 River nymph
33 The Gold Coast, today
34 "À votre __!"
39 Java neighbor
40 Columbus, by birth
42 "Nancy" or "Cathy"
43 Puss
45 Server on skates
46 Dos + cuatro
49 Take third
50 Take on
51 "__ on Film" (1983 book set)
52 Conniving
53 Coach Nastase
54 Rock's Joan
56 Sphere
57 "Cheers" habitué
58 Alternatively
60 Lady lobster
61 Ungainly craft

206 *by Nancy B. Ross*

ACROSS

1 "Charlie's Angels" actress
5 Jimmies
10 One who follows orders?
14 The cheaper spread
15 Campus clubs, for short
16 He jumps through hoops
17 New York cultural site
20 Squirrellike monkey
21 Weird
22 Molly Bloom's last word
23 Smidgens
25 Tempest locale
29 Ambience
30 Vote (for)
33 Woody's son
34 Not on all fours
35 Fido's foot
36 London cultural site
40 Juliette Low org.
41 Dearest ones
42 — of Samothrace
43 Poetic contraction
44 Bad day for Caesar
45 Moulin Rouge attraction
47 1947 Pulitzer composer
48 1987 Michael Jackson album
49 Swiss capital
52 Universal
57 Milan cultural site
60 Spur
61 More frigid
62 It sticks out of a scabbard
63 Emulate Icarus
64 Suspicious
65 Wordsworth works

DOWN

1 Rich soil
2 Tenor Luigi
3 Bucks, e.g.
4 Coed quarters
5 Press type
6 Jimmies
7 Bridge position
8 — degree
9 Compass pt.
10 Phoenix source
11 Yellowstone sighting
12 Singaraja's island
13 Vogue rival
18 Tom Smothers' plaything
19 Manufacturer's come-on
23 Quartet after a breakup?
24 Mischievous
25 "T" to ham operators
26 VCR function
27 Sacrifice site
28 Baked Hawaiian dish
29 City where van Gogh painted
30 Of the eye
31 Skier's garment
32 10-to-12 year-old
34 Gutter locale
37 Dickens waif
38 Lymph —
39 Actress Reinking
45 Informer
46 Puts two and two together
47 — alia
48 Field worker
49 Heat quantities: Abbr.
50 Mr. Saarinen
51 Shankar piece
52 Ballet bend
53 Quick comeback?
54 One of a "Mikado" trio
55 "Winnie — Pu"
56 Musical that opened 10/7/82
58 Kind of painting
59 Sizzling serve

ACROSS

1 Eve's second-born
5 Selves
9 Recipe direction
14 Venetian traveler
15 Baby's cry
16 Nuts-and-honey snack
17 Syllabus
18 Scottish group
19 Bean or Welles
20 Kind of joint between boards
23 Angers
24 British statesman Sir Robert
25 Pursued
28 It can provide a moving experience
29 "__ La Douce"
33 Pregame rah-rah meeting
34 1948 Hitchcock nail-biter
35 Close
36 Island prison of history
37 Days of celebration
38 Roof projection
39 Hammer head
40 CompuServe patron
41 Joseph of the Senate
42 Viewed
43 "All Things Considered" network
44 Be annoyed
45 Utah's state flower
47 Knot in wood
48 The Iron Chancellor
55 Pre-Columbian Mexican
56 Father of Enos
57 Tennis champ Yannick
58 African antelope
59 Suffix with kitchen or usher
60 Old Russian assembly
61 Race to a base, perhaps
62 Bird feeder fill
63 Observed

DOWN

1 Date with an M.D.
2 Heavy Army knife
3 Verve
4 View from Port Jefferson
5 Hosted a roast
6 Big parties
7 Mideast gulf
8 Alternative to a plane?
9 Kind of leave or dinner
10 Group containing Truk, Belau and Yap
11 Too
12 City in Ukraine
13 Hans Christian Andersen, e.g.
21 1934 chemistry Nobelist
22 Heredity units
25 Holiday paper
26 The Tin Man portrayer
27 "Seascape" playwright
28 Person in a booth?
30 Author of "The Cloister and the Hearth"
31 Expert
32 "You __ kidding!"
34 Survey data
37 Baseball practice
41 Road shoulder
44 Hurried
46 Avoid
47 Please, to 48 Across
48 Singles
49 Fanciful, as a story
50 Popular cuisine
51 __ noire
52 Rake
53 Arrived
54 Tatar chief

ACROSS

1 Yahoo
5 Pigeon drop, e.g.
9 Fill one's tank
14 Peace Nobelist Myrdal
15 Rival of Martina
16 Busy airport
17 Freud's home
18 Ticked off
19 Client of 16 Across
20 Princess Margaret's ex
23 Queue after Q
24 Fishing gear
25 Ended a bout early
27 Fishing gear
30 Barbering job
32 Really went for
36 Bakery enticement
38 Tide type
40 Nephew of Caligula
41 1991 Emmy-winning comic
44 Med. sch. subj.
45 Author Dinesen
46 Davis of "Do the Right Thing"
47 Tout's offering
49 Nudnik
51 Highway hazard
52 Uncommon sense
53 Music score abbr.
55 Experimentation station
58 1961 Inauguration speaker
64 Jordanian port
66 Word on a $1 bill
67 Hoedown prop
68 Blender setting
69 Blockhead
70 "If __ You" (1929 hit)
71 Game-show group
72 Tom Smothers amusement
73 Courage

DOWN

1 Cry like a baby
2 Mixed bag
3 Walkie-talkie word
4 Leave time
5 Fight souvenir
6 Eastern region
7 One more time
8 Anti-D.W.I. group
9 Composer of Hitchcock's theme
10 Sounds of satisfaction
11 German coal region
12 "Trinity" author
13 Saucy
21 Attack
22 Giraffe kin
26 Taboos
27 Elephant rider, perhaps
28 Maine college town
29 Best Actor of '39
31 __ Work (rock group)
33 Teammate of Robinson and Hodges
34 "To __ human"
35 B₁₂ quantities
37 Photo finish
39 Betraying clumsiness
42 "Fantasia" ballerina
43 "__ I can help it!"
48 Sharon's land
50 Completely
54 Boris Badenov's boss
55 Reindeer herder
56 Water color
57 Stable home
59 Miss Marple discovery
60 Suffix for stink
61 Waikiki locale
62 Chair part
63 Koppel and Kennedy
65 Old-fashioned do

ACROSS

1 Paint layer
5 Best of old films
9 Plays at Pebble Beach
14 Greengrocer's pods
15 Controversial 70's sitcom
16 Lit
17 Menu appetizer
20 Titter
21 Bambi and kin
22 Hints at the pool table?
23 __ fixe
25 Ta-ta in Turin
27 Hollywood's Barbara or Conrad
30 Menu entree
35 Lew Wallace's "Ben __"
36 Word before mother or lively
37 1975 Clavell best seller
38 Slack-jawed
40 Hoover, e.g.
42 Clean, as a computer disk
43 Beaverlike fur
45 Collars
47 Herbal soother
48 Menu side order
50 Carrel
51 G-men
52 Mr. Carnegie
54 Mystery dog
57 Hacker, e.g.
59 Revises
63 Menu dessert
66 Lady's alternative?
67 Kind of log
68 Hammer part
69 1941 Bogart role
70 Sediment
71 Ocean flyer

DOWN

1 Egyptian church member
2 "The Grapes of Wrath" worker
3 Foot part
4 Provide lodging for
5 Vane dir.
6 Walked unevenly
7 Scruff
8 Each
9 Dentist's anesthetic
10 Risqué
11 Stead
12 Parole
13 Televisions
18 Calculator display: Abbr.
19 Crossword diagrams
24 Newt
26 Pines
27 Hallucinogenic drink
28 Bode
29 Seething
31 Toothpaste once advertised by Grace Kelly
32 Type size for fine print
33 Ponders
34 Underhanded fellow
36 View from the Quai d'Orsay
39 Introduced
41 Barbara with two sisters
44 "Straight up" singer Paula
46 Youth grp. founded in 1910
49 Classic Montaigne work of 1580
50 Dock
53 The M-G-M lion
54 Book after John
55 Lollipop was a "good" one
56 Roman get-up
58 Needle case
60 Sunny vacation spot
61 Ruler until 1917
62 Basted
64 Vein find
65 Ran into

210

by Arthur W. Palmer

ACROSS

1 Not piquant
5 Israelite at the conquest of Canaan
10 Fortune's partner
14 Rustic
15 More than fubsy
16 Part of an été
17 About 17 million square miles
18 Get even, in a way
19 Germany's Oscar
20 Start of an adage
23 Infamous Ugandan
24 "Third Man" director
25 Subservient
28 Mash
30 Computer code
34 Son of Hera
35 Type of window
37 Mason's aid
38 Cornishman
39 Web-footed animal
40 Use a whetstone
41 Four-time Japanese P.M.
42 Mugs
43 Tag words
44 Tithing
46 ABC, for short
47 Making a stand?
48 1905 Secretary of State
50 Shoshone
51 End of the adage
59 Word with fire or no
60 Paris official
61 Pop singer Burdon
62 Some charts
63 Essence
64 Late-night star
65 Fly ash
66 Some homes
67 Crackpot

DOWN

1 Prankster
2 Rummy
3 Anne Nichols stage hero
4 Exciting to the max
5 Welsh dog
6 Incite
7 Wife of Jacob
8 Steep slope
9 Actress Davis
10 Oslo and others
11 Taurus or Aries, e.g.
12 Paw
13 Western Electric founder __ Barton
21 Preternatural
22 Binge
25 Wordless
26 Alpine feature
27 Item in a patch
28 Make powerful
29 Big-band name
31 X'd
32 Type of column
33 Words of explanation
35 "i" piece?
36 Oral stumbles
40 Wood hyacinth
42 Type of gun
45 Like best friends
47 Theta preceder
49 Isle __
50 Patrons
51 Indiana Jones perils
52 Actor Scott
53 Stick in the fridge?
54 Tiny imperfections
55 "Darn it all!"
56 Nabisco product
57 El __
58 Coll. course

211

ACROSS

1 List ender
5 Intrinsically
10 N.Y.C. station
14 Coveted review
15 Love in Limoges
16 "__, Brute?"
17 Part of the eye
18 Rams and Jets, e.g.
19 Newspaperman Adolph
20 "No guarantees"
23 __ Alte (Adenauer)
24 540-1600 on a radio
27 Calpurnia's husband
31 Oner
35 Fluorescent-lamp filler
36 Intoxicating drink of the gods
37 Follower's suffix
38 Unwelcome one
42 Shad delicacy
43 Tight positions?
44 Record
45 Second self
48 Declare
49 Thrall of yore
50 MS. perusers
51 Willy-nilly
59 Concerning
62 Related maternally
63 Assist a prankster
64 __ bene
65 Adder or asp
66 Secure, in a way
67 Not up
68 That is
69 __ Domini

DOWN

1 "The Red"
2 "G.W.T.W." locale
3 Tel __
4 Majesty lead-in
5 Little feet do it
6 Title in Turkey
7 Indulge one's wanderlust
8 Waste reservoir
9 Once, once
10 Bradley University site
11 Another list ender
12 Highest degree
13 Mus' followers
21 Hersey novel town
22 Harem room
25 Control a 747
26 Antiseptic-surgery pioneer Joseph
27 "Lost Horizon" director
28 Tissue gap
29 They may be snowy
30 "Mayday!"
31 Musical form ending a sonata
32 Freeman Gosden radio role
33 Sought office
34 Embark
36 Squealed
39 Society-page word
40 Artist's paste
41 T.L.C. is their forte
46 Nonet, for one
47 Early auto
48 Commercial, in British slang
50 __ Park, Colorado
52 Jeans maker Strauss
53 Writer Bagnold
54 Neck part
55 Miss Cantrell
56 "Voice of Israel" author, 1957
57 Nürnberg no
58 Capital of Manche
59 __ nutshell
60 San Francisco hill
61 I-95, e.g.: Abbr.

212

by Merl H. Reagle

ACROSS

1 Smooth wood
5 Treat like a pariah
9 Pin place
14 Mixed bag
15 "Self" starter
16 "Die Fledermaus" maid
17 Stay tuned, Part 1
20 Writer Danielle
21 She shares the wealth
22 Cut (off)
24 __ gallop
25 Stay tuned, Part 2
34 "O.K., Ahab"
35 Actress Verdugo
36 Borden bovine
37 "Cool"
39 Gounod opera
41 Marion's finish
42 Island crooner
44 Slangy $100 bill
46 Sniggler's wiggler
47 Stay tuned, Part 3
50 Ankh's cross
51 Midwest Indian
52 Disparages
58 Ogden Nash's feet
62 Stay tuned, Part 4
64 Signal to slow
65 Unguarded, in football
66 Radiate
67 Full of vim and vinegar
68 Word to a refusenik
69 Thanksgiving side dishes

DOWN

1 Lays down the lawn
2 Much
3 Not quite Bo Derek
4 "No kidding!"
5 __ Tomé and Principe
6 Hollywood 10 condemner: Abbr.
7 60's spy plane
8 Biblical 950-year-old
9 Gulf of Mexico pirate
10 Cute
11 Aka Edson Arantes do Nascimento
12 Large lodge
13 Minus
18 Boston daily
19 Informal agreement
23 Ill-gotten gains
25 Fish in a John Cleese comedy
26 "__ newt . . ."
27 Listed
28 Boxer's asset
29 Operating
30 Reactions to serialists
31 Fall bloomer
32 Given as a source
33 Falls (over)
38 London daily
40 Ballerina's strong points
43 Speaking skill
45 "Roughing It" writer
48 Hippo's wear in "Fantasia"
49 Dramatist Sean
52 Arts degs.
53 "Cope Book" Aunt
54 Arcing shots
55 Author Hubbard
56 Wordsmith Willard
57 The Graf __
59 N.Y. institution on 53d Street
60 Fedora feature
61 Trans-Atlantic speedsters
63 Prov. on Niagara Falls

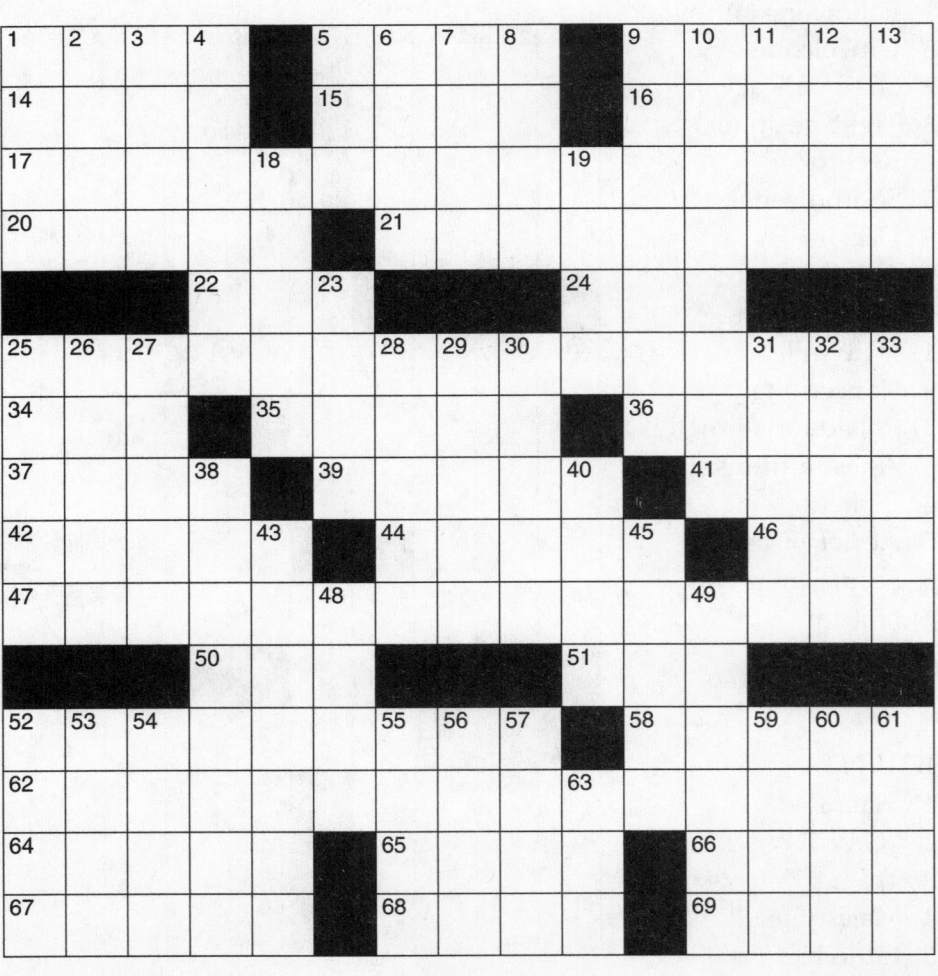

ACROSS

1 "Woe is me!"
5 Inn, informally
10 Dollop
14 Frolic
15 Title holder
16 Burt's ex
17 Jai __
18 Former auto executive
20 Two-pointers
22 Differs
23 Saucer occupants, for short
24 Mozart's "__ fan tutte"
25 Ball girl
28 Vacation spot
30 "Jerusalem Delivered" poet
34 Border lake
35 Car in a procession
37 Spring mo.
38 West Point salutatorian, 1829
41 Language ending
42 Off course
43 City two hours south of Lillehammer
44 Spreads the word
46 Bit of voodoo
47 Grueling tests
48 Sword with a guard
50 Louis Freeh's org.
51 Rubbed
54 Ascendant
58 Two-time U.S. Open golf champion
61 Kind of shark
62 Suffix with buck
63 Pentax rival
64 Sicilian rumbler
65 Poet Robert __ Warren
66 Exhausted
67 Sunup direction

DOWN

1 Bedouin
2 She gets what she wants
3 Amo, __, amat
4 Modern film maker
5 Leaves in a hurry
6 Wows
7 Jet's heading
8 Mercury and Jupiter, e.g.
9 "Well done!"
10 Actress DeHaven
11 Places
12 __ over lightly
13 Kind of crime
19 Mobile unit?
21 Season of l'année
24 Polish producer
25 Cap
26 Having an irregular edge
27 Defame
28 Boil
29 Military chaplain
31 Hot sauce
32 Word with cold or breathing
33 Chocolate snacks
35 Elevations: Abbr.
36 Remark
39 Hardly one with a lilting voice
40 Neoprimitive American artist
45 Unextinguished
47 Kimono sash
49 Paradises
50 Weather line
51 Keep time manually
52 "You are __"
53 Ages and ages
54 Soon
55 Ninth Greek letter
56 Actress Woods and others
57 Pest
59 One who gets special treatment
60 W.W. II hero

214 by Wayne Robert Williams

ACROSS

1 Comic Martha
5 Bamboozle
9 Stoppers
14 Height: Abbr.
15 Face-to-face exam
16 Beau at the balcony
17 Town near Caen
18 Chockablock
20 Headlong
22 Resident's suffix
23 Racetracks
24 Dormitory din
28 Radio transmission sites
30 Offspring, genealogically: Abbr.
31 Celtic Neptune
32 Centers
33 Walk-on
34 Chancellorsville victor
35 Western Indian
36 Enmity
38 Sugar suffix
39 Singer Tillis
40 Word after many or honey
41 Conflict in Greek drama
42 French dance
43 A.L. or N.L. honorees
44 "Phèdre" dramatist
46 Flummoxes
48 Spring fragrance
49 Picture blowup: Abbr.
50 Head count
53 Game of digs and spikes
57 Parts of pelvises
58 Greek poet saved by a dolphin
59 Fit
60 Oodles
61 Mississippi Senator __ Lott
62 Branch headquarters?
63 "Auld Lang __"

DOWN

1 Answer: Abbr.
2 Der __ (Adenauer moniker)
3 Cowardly one
4 Changes with the times
5 Carpentry pins
6 Europe/Asia separator
7 Dark shadow
8 Building wing
9 1984 Goldie Hawn movie
10 Look threatening
11 Actress Thurman
12 Solidify
13 Our sun
19 Xmas tree trimming
21 Spoil
24 Interstate trucks
25 Without rhyme or reason
26 "Schindler's List" star Liam
27 Novelist Graham
28 Hitches, as a ride
29 Surpass at the dinner table
30 Natural alarm clocks
33 Hoofbeats
36 About to occur
37 Pulchritudinous
41 Gum arabic trees
44 Garden brook
45 Completely
47 Juicy fruit
48 Takes it easy
50 Contemporary dramatist David
51 King of the beasts
52 Deceased
53 Large tub
54 Hockey's Bobby
55 Golf-ball position
56 Prohibit

ACROSS

1 Protection in a purse
5 Start, as a trip
11 Actor Max __ Sydow
14 Lawyer Dershowitz
15 Dragon's prey
16 Author Levin
17 Ex-heavyweight champ
19 Galley slave's tool
20 "__ been had!"
21 Bad grades
22 "Is that so?"
24 Colonist
26 Rock's __ Vanilli
27 Brit. ref. work
28 Triangular-sailed ships
30 Pencil name
33 Hotel lobby
34 "Ich __ ein Berliner"
36 "Famous" cookie man
37 Little bits
38 Dumb ox
39 Fourposter
40 Linen shades
41 Leafy shelter
42 Small seals
44 Journalist Nellie
45 Get rid of, in slang
46 Deejay's need
50 Los Angeles player
52 Orbit period
53 Lumberjack's tool
54 Singer __ Rose
55 Noble acts
58 __ time (golfer's starting point)
59 Niagara Falls craft?
60 "Java" player Al
61 "__ day now . . ."
62 The "E" of H.R.E.
63 Chocolate-covered morsels

DOWN

1 Baseball's Roger
2 Extant
3 Middy opponent
4 Epilogue
5 Ran the show
6 Almighty
7 Lobster eaters' accessories
8 Hubbub
9 Second drafts
10 Pew attachment
11 A concertmaster holds it
12 Kind of vaccine
13 Not any
18 Ambitionless one
23 Pub drink
25 Stocking parts
26 Yucatán people
28 Name in computer software
29 7D, e.g.
30 Early Beatles describer
31 "Rag Mop" brothers
32 Legendary bluesman
33 Onward
35 Neither's mate
37 It sometimes comes in bars
38 Cassidy portrayer William
40 Uganda airport
41 Boombox sound
43 Jazz date
44 Long-eared pooch
46 Witch, at times
47 Fine cloth
48 Strive
49 Schick et al.
50 Disk contents
51 The yoke's on them
52 Cosmonaut Gagarin
56 Dada founder
57 __ Na Na

216   *by Christopher Page*

ACROSS

1 Literary Bret
6 From Cardiff
11 Fairy queen
14 Low-cholesterol spreads
15 Winged
16 Señora Perón
17 Rogue
19 Morning dampness
20 Not an expert
21 __ greens
23 Protein source
24 Chicle product
26 Lemon zest source
27 __ monkey
30 1945 meeting site
33 Fruit juice blend
36 __ cit. (footnote abbr.)
38 Canal to the Baltic
39 Hubbub
40 Rowdy one
43 Granada gold
44 Pocket item?
46 Opus __ (work of God)
47 Off-campus nonstudent
49 Circus walker
51 Mexican state bordering Arizona
53 Zhivago's love
55 Diarist Anaïs
56 Cousin of the emu
60 Brownie ingredients
63 Peanuts
65 "__ ever catch you . . ."
66 Stew
68 Avant-garde prefix
69 Sri Lankan native
70 Since: Sp.
71 Possess
72 Prepared to testify
73 $C_4H_8O_2$, e.g.

DOWN

1 Wedding dances
2 Hertz rival
3 Satisfy a debt
4 "Just for openers . . ."
5 Suffix with opal
6 Carroll's carpenter's companion
7 Addition
8 Secular
9 Small porch
10 Regatta site
11 Cab symbol
12 State categorically
13 Floozy
18 Bored
22 Washington news source, maybe
25 Vertical dividing bar in windows
28 Cry of glee
29 __-disant (self-styled)
31 Actress Garr
32 Burn soother
33 Snoozes
34 Abridge, perhaps
35 Do for debs
37 Benin's largest city
41 Bandleader Brown
42 Neither's counterpart
45 Author Paton
48 Coloratura's sounds
50 They're sometimes blind
52 Be finicky
54 Attorney __
57 Thieves' work
58 Wear away
59 "Mary Tyler Moore Show" co-star
60 Souse
61 "__ Good Men"
62 Oriental combat
64 Ye __ Shoppe
67 Russian for "peace"

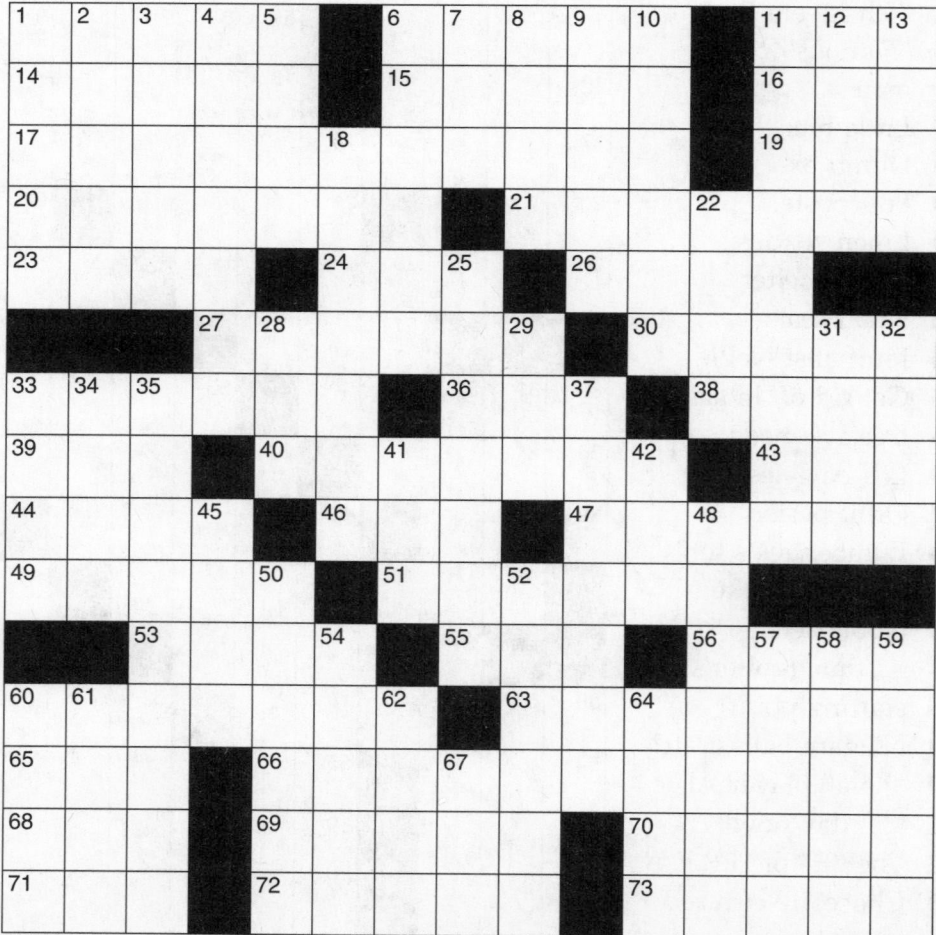

ACROSS

1 Buddy
5 Balance sheet listing
10 Helper: Abbr.
14 New Rochelle college
15 They fly in formation
16 Wife of __ (Chaucer pilgrim)
17 Ordnance
18 Fill with glee
19 Out of the weather
20 Battle in which Lee defeated Pope
23 Sunday talk: Abbr.
24 Activity
25 Fountain treat, for short
26 Battle in which Bragg defeated Rosecrans
31 Singer Coolidge et al.
32 Corner
33 11th-century date
36 Heaven on earth
37 Change
39 Earth sci.
40 Marry
41 Fine poker holdings
42 Hawks
43 Battle in which Grant defeated Bragg
46 John Wilkes Booth, e.g.
50 Tempe sch.
51 Items on a "must" list
52 Battle in which Lee defeated Burnside
57 Retread, e.g.
58 Go along (with)
59 Wrangler's pal
61 Overlook
62 Some are heroic
63 Mideast land
64 Promontory
65 Kilmer opus
66 Niño's nothing

DOWN

1 Spy grp.
2 Baseball, informally
3 Not deserved
4 Not fem.
5 Work to do
6 Infrequently
7 Petticoat junction
8 "Cómo __ usted?"
9 Target MTV viewer
10 Embarrass
11 Nacho topping
12 Rib-eye
13 Ones nearby
21 Dumbarton __ (1944 meeting site)
22 P.D.Q.
23 Item in a hardware bin
27 Fire
28 Nuclear experiment
29 Coffee server
30 Start for fly or about
33 Three-hanky film
34 City once named for Stalin
35 Rick's beloved et al.
37 Herr's "Oh!"
38 "Cry __ River"
39 General Motors make
41 Parcel of land
42 High-hat
44 Words before "I'm yours"
45 Tax
46 "Sweet" river of song
47 Record blot
48 Actress Garr et al.
49 Playwright Clifford
53 Engrossed
54 Mr. Stravinsky
55 Saskatchewan tribe
56 Atop
60 Kind of testing

218 *by Peter Gordon*

ACROSS

1 Bedwear, informally
4 Essen exclamation
7 Move back
13 Sports org.
14 __ tai
15 Ethanol and dimethyl ether, e.g.
17 Germinating
19 One of 38 Across
20 Unchanged
21 Sounds of happiness
23 Hose material
24 One of 38 Across
28 Actress Lupino
29 Distinctive quality
30 Drink cat-style
33 River to the Seine
36 Telecommunications giant
37 Uncommon
38 Theme of this puzzle
42 Missing
43 Dam-building org.
44 Gather
45 Gaze at
46 Afrikaner
47 To and __
48 One of 38 Across
53 Lumberjacks' competition
56 Vote for
57 It is in Spain
58 Concern of 38 Across
61 Beg
63 Fame
64 Nipper's co.
65 Black and tan ingredient
66 Texas city
67 Driver's license info
68 Cobb and Hardin

DOWN

1 Pari __ (at an equal rate): Lat.
2 One of 38 Across
3 Finland, to the Finns
4 "What __, chopped liver?"
5 One of 38 Across
6 Weather data
7 Semi
8 Language suffix
9 Pupil's protector
10 Oscars' cousins
11 Good buy
12 Cubemaker Rubik
16 Antonym's antonym: Abbr.
18 Add color to again
22 Shower's counterpart
25 River in Germany
26 Saturn or Mercury, e.g.
27 Not kosher
30 Pelée output
31 Lover of Aphrodite
32 Bics, e.g.
33 Homeowner's pymt.
34 Sailor's cry
35 Actress Russo
37 More distant
39 Sioux Indian
40 Iris's place
41 Wraparound dress
46 Litters
47 One of 38 Across
48 Type
49 Rathskeller servings
50 "Have __" (interviewer's request)
51 One of 38 Across
52 N.B.A's Thurmond and Archibald
53 Scale notes
54 Eight: Prefix
55 Fill, as bases
59 Yr. parts
60 Singer Sumac
62 Strain

ACROSS

1 Hunter's prey
5 Batter's woe
10 They're big for conceited folks
14 General under Dwight
15 Resort lake
16 Author Émile
17 Cabdrivers do this
20 Start for step or stop
21 Fix, as in gambling
22 Wild talk
23 Uganda's Amin
24 Show biz routine
28 Rummy cry
30 Repetitious goodbye
32 Simile center
33 "What Kind of Fool __"
34 Its symbol is five rings
39 Write
40 Optometrists do this
44 Silent communication
45 Tributes
46 Expert
47 Kind of room
48 Animal stomach
52 Stole
53 Battery's partner
57 Show to a seat, informally
58 What you pay at sales
60 Way of Lao-tzu
61 World traveler of note
62 Lip readers do this
67 Conductor Klemperer
68 Friend of Mercutio
69 Cabin wood
70 Unmixed, at a mixer
71 Hanker
72 Busy bodies

DOWN

1 "Get cracking!"
2 Blake of "Gunsmoke"
3 Succeed
4 Before
5 Having a stiff upper lip
6 Har-de-har-har
7 TV band
8 Stock response
9 Each
10 Metrical Pound
11 Flipping
12 Nostalgic
13 Enclosed with an MS.
18 '93, '94, etc.
19 Aquatic zoo
25 Pudding ingredient
26 "Of Thee __"
27 Big stickers
29 Diamond digit
31 Fine, to a pilot
35 Caustic agent
36 Letter sign-off
37 Slippers for the stubborn?
38 1989 comedy "__ Devil"
40 Page (through)
41 Kiss
42 Victor Herbert work
43 Computer key abbr.
49 Emphasizes, as an embarrassing error
50 Obliquely
51 "Certainly!"
53 Lenten symbol
54 Absolute
55 Imperative to Macduff
56 Overly
59 Dundee dweller
62 Persuaded to marry
63 Not straight
64 Millet's "Man With the __"
65 Doctors' org.
66 Put __ fight

220 *by Robert H. Wolfe*

ACROSS

1 Funeral stand
5 Lick
8 A little night music
12 Like matzoh
16 Della's creator
17 18th-century monarch, too familiarly?
19 Tributary
20 Residents of Meshed
21 Still
22 Miss Merkel
23 Baby food
26 Items that are piled
29 Overwhelms
34 Shah Jahan's building site
36 Salve base
38 Ennoble
39 Lake Ontario outlet, too familiarly?
42 Indian follower
43 TV's Ricky
44 Tangent's cousin
45 Shenanigans
47 Frond holder
49 It makes towels plushy
50 Indy 500 advertiser
52 Actress Thompson
54 Available, as retail goods
59 Bill collector
63 Architectural refinement, too familiarly?
65 Press for
66 Took orders, in a way
67 By and by
68 Bygone platters
69 Those for

DOWN

1 Bare skin
2 Concerning, at law
3 Robt. ___
4 Singer Helen
5 Athletic supporter?
6 Against
7 Indian leader
8 Actress Garr
9 Vicinage
10 Map out
11 Goes down
13 "Do, ___, a female . . ."
14 Kind of reality
15 Academic heads
18 Beaver, for one
23 Turkish bigwig
24 In addition
25 Art sale item
27 Wrap name
28 Chafed places
30 W.W. II foe
31 Know-it-all
32 Full assemblies
33 Pharyngeal invader
35 "The King ___"
37 Aforetime
40 University of Arizona site
41 Surrenderer
46 Last item?
48 Verdun's river
51 Jail-related
53 Overeager
54 Greenish-blue
55 Crank
56 Utah's state flower
57 Adult-to-be
58 Small cut
60 Letters from Wall Street
61 Parmenides's birthplace
62 Stop lights
64 Como's "___ Impossible"

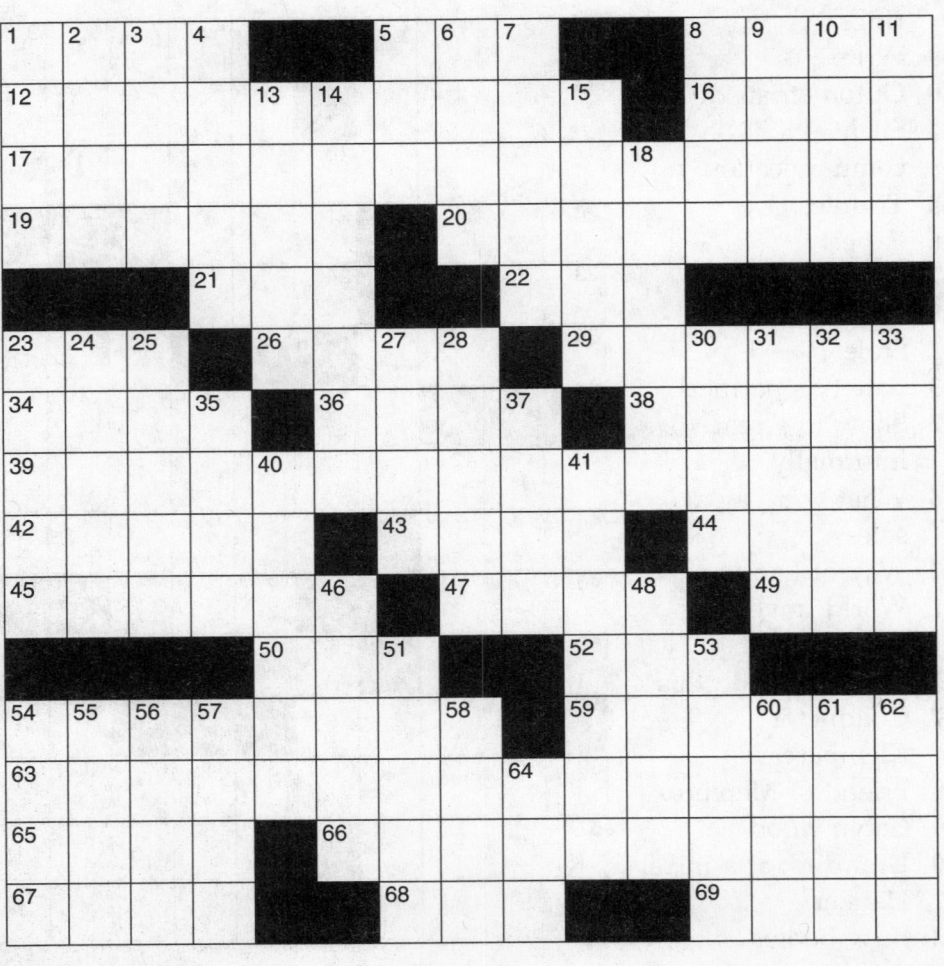

ACROSS

1 Some swabs
6 Ski champ McKinney
12 1964 Hitchcock film
13 Renders drug-free
14 Logical thinker
15 Praises: Var.
16 Lovable
18 Assent
19 River inlet
20 Swiss river
22 Sequel to Buck's "The Good Earth"
23 Group of gangs
26 Bank claims
28 Geo. and Thos., e.g.
29 Adjusts
31 Belles-___
33 "Ars Amatoria" author
35 Word repeated in a Doris Day song
36 Brownies
39 Meal
43 Balkans map abbr.
44 Some boxing jabs
46 Pasta variety
47 Latin I word
49 Drying method
50 "___ the ramparts . . ."
51 Barbara follows it
53 Numbers in parentheses
57 Tough guy of filmdom
59 Break down
60 Oil and water, e.g.
61 Mend a coat
62 Emulated an oenophile
63 Boar or boor

DOWN

1 Libyan strongman
2 Word with blue or believer
3 Atahualpa, e.g.
4 Loading/unloading locale
5 "Flash Gordon," once
6 ___-Mex
7 "___ boy!"
8 Electronic synthesizers
9 Guns N' Roses leader
10 Softens
11 Evaluate
12 Not grandiose
13 Master's and others
14 Skin
17 One that gets hit on the head
21 Stage direction
24 Mr. Sikorsky
25 Smith's need
27 Kind of throat
30 Located
32 Shakespeare's "The ___ of Lucrece"
34 Pays part of
36 Mogadishu's locale
37 Manners
38 The slammer
40 Pain reliever
41 Dismiss lightly, with "at"
42 Blunt
43 Volcanic rock
45 Asparagus servings
48 Publican's offering
52 Indy champ Luyendyk
54 Once more
55 City southwest of Bogotá
56 Actor Ken or actress Lena
58 Append

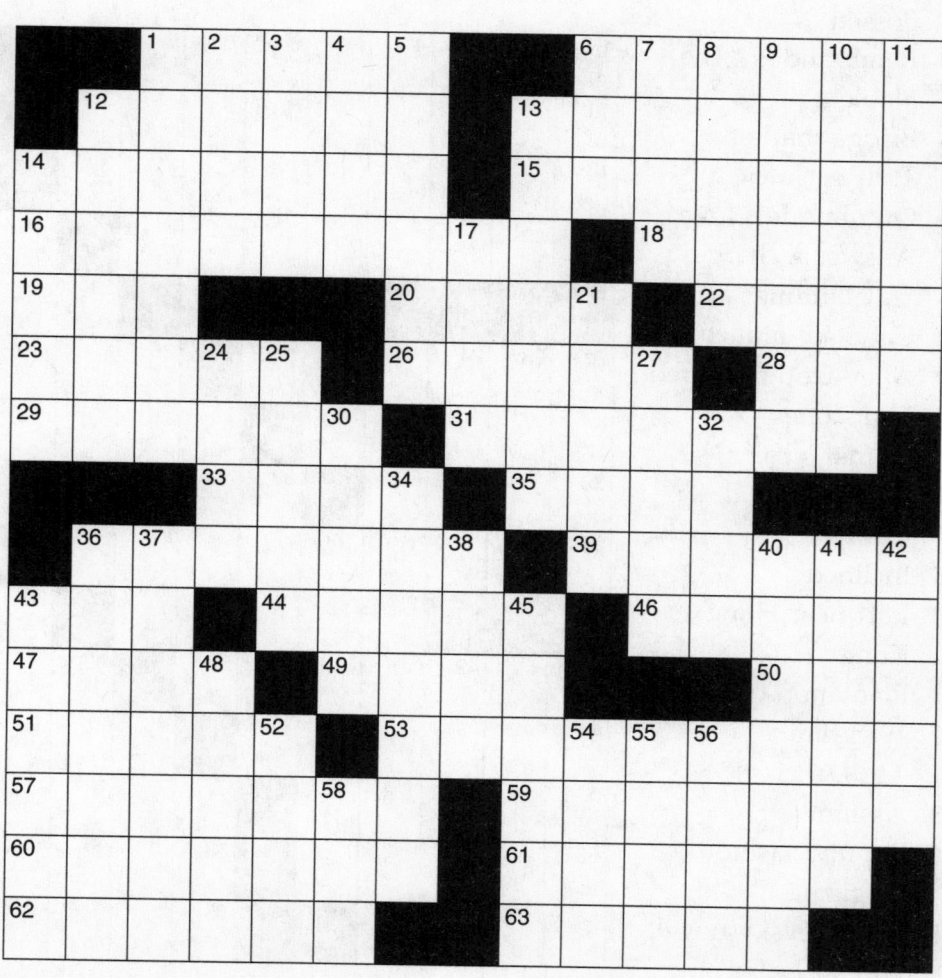

222 *by Daniel R. Stark*

ACROSS

1 It's no loss
10 Grouch
14 Where Croesus's kingdom was
15 Cellular ___
16 Rabelais's amiable giant
17 Monks' hour when psalms are recited
18 One skilled in match play
19 Kind of jumper
20 "Brooklyn Bridge" actress Aquino
21 Hint
22 Calls upon
26 One of the Dionnes
27 Skirt style
28 Bossed
32 Rembrandt's "The Noble ___"
33 Bridge marker
34 Thin necktie
35 Quasimodo's love
37 Answer a charge
38 "I, Claudius" attire
39 Cal State branch site
40 Alley Oop and Fred Flintstone
43 Hefner's color?
44 "O tempora! ___!": Cicero
45 Inclined
50 Port near Hong Kong
51 Plantation crop
52 1985 film "___ Dancing!"
53 Assume
54 Popular fashion magazine
55 Dostoyevsky novel, with "The"

DOWN

1 Hero's tale
2 Peter or Nicholas
3 Melodies
4 Titicaca, por ejemplo
5 Flow (from)
6 Pharmacists' measures
7 Overeager
8 Race track figure
9 Baseball stat
10 Fickle
11 It makes you blush
12 Inca empire locale
13 Assail
15 Connect
19 Marble worker's tool
21 Site of a Margaret Mead study
22 Flower holder
23 Troubles
24 "Anna and the King of ___"
25 Dyed-in-the-wool
26 Cheese coatings
28 "Blowin' in the Wind" singer
29 Digits
30 Dash
31 Extinct bird
33 Leafs
36 Lover boys
37 Take steps
39 Railroad flares
40 Monte Cristo title
41 Menotti's "___ and the Night Visitors"
42 Outspoken
43 Does
45 Producer De Laurentiis
46 Picks, with "for"
47 Hot springs
48 Actress Sommer
49 Act
51 Kind of tent

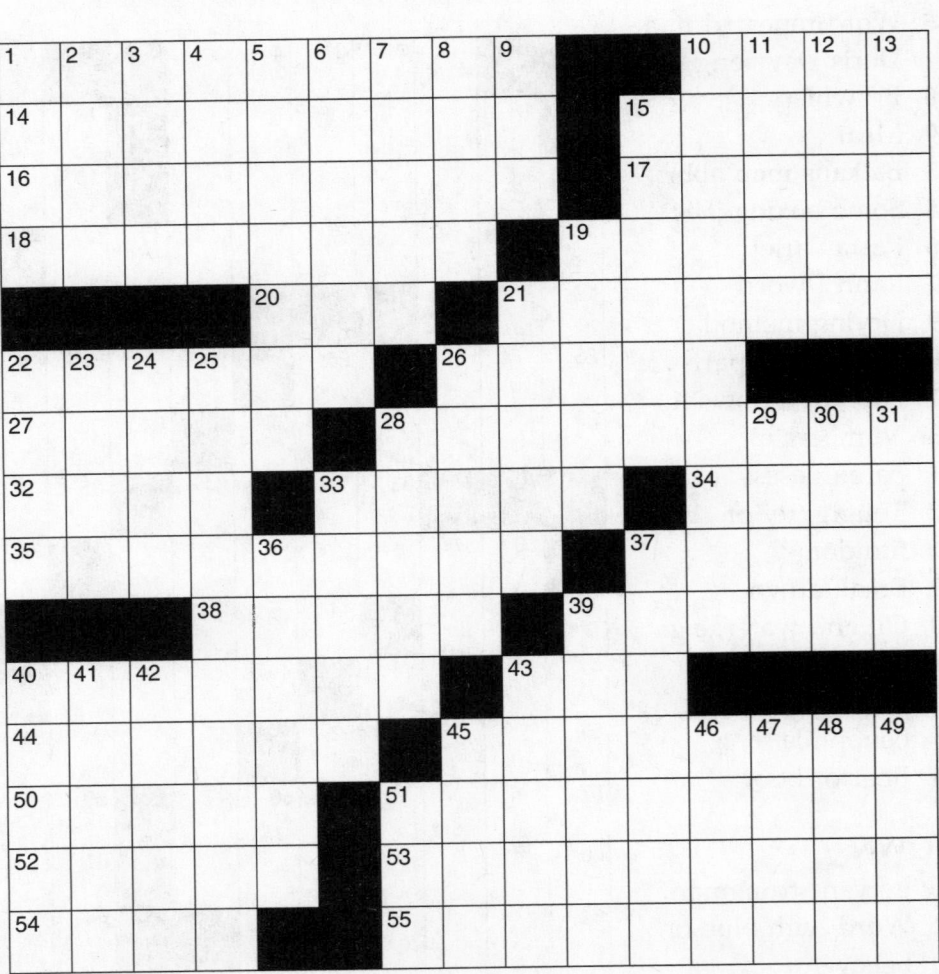

ACROSS

1 Snacks in Santa Rosalía
6 Upright
14 Aligned
16 Elephantine
17 Rainier locale
18 Globe flattener, in a way
19 Interest rate: abbr.
20 Negotiates a puddle
22 __ Khan
23 Superman's mother
25 Lake resort
26 Galway Bay isles
27 Accommodate
29 __ openers
30 Positive, for a shutterbug
31 Mugged a snoozer
33 Husky runners
35 Gouda's cousin
37 Berlin one
38 One kind of clutch
41 Sarge, for one
45 Playwright-lyricist Comden
46 Buff
48 Reuniongoer
49 Harry Golden's "__ in America"
50 Watered silk
52 __ rug
53 Altiplano tuber
54 Where Holstein cows originated
56 Catch some rays
57 Shaven, as a priest's head
59 Fix, as boundaries
61 Rooming-house convenience
62 Foul-ups
63 Quiet firework
64 "Hero and Leander" episode

DOWN

1 Charteris detective Simon __
2 Alligator pear
3 Old telephone exchange
4 Stop __ dime
5 Slangy instants
6 Private eye
7 Kind of town
8 Think alike
9 Resins
10 Actress Zadora
11 Least of the Great Lakes
12 Rallying cries
13 Not an easy boss
15 Blockhead
21 Clod
24 More than enough
26 It's south of the Caucasus
28 Lingerie item
30 Tree with edible seeds
32 Apply makeup
34 Aunts and others
36 Ill-fated bullfighter
38 Place for brooding
39 1996 Olympics site
40 Dutch coin
42 Notarize
43 The eldest Titan
44 Most Scroogelike
45 Fair constructions
47 __-la-la
50 Fable's point
51 Tackles' neighbors
54 "The Incredible __"
55 Hollow
58 Time of yr.
60 __ and away

224 *by George Quincy*

ACROSS

1 __ at Work
4 Diesel-engine submarine
9 Hindu title of address
12 The "A" in U.A.R.
14 Bull: Prefix
15 Pole
16 First name in humor
17 13 Down musical form
19 Kigali's land
21 Soak again
22 Company V.I.P.'s
24 Stately 13 Down dance
26 Americano
28 Carried out
29 Words from Caesar
30 13 Down dance in triple meter
34 Acid
37 Suit to __
38 They often have twists
39 Receipts
40 Neighbor of Leb.
41 13 Down medium for Jean Baptiste Lully
42 Reactor factor
43 Amigo
44 Baby wrigglers
46 13 Down dance, in France
52 English royal house
53 Flood protection
54 Ornamental band
56 13 Down musical form
58 Faithful
62 Female deer
63 __-Bismol
64 Prefix with Disney
65 Snaky shape
66 Deuce toppers
67 Big __

DOWN

1 Miss West
2 Slip
3 60's service site
4 Sundance Kid's girlfriend __ Place
5 Manger locales
6 Literary pen name of old
7 Noisy
8 Woody Herman's "__ Autumn"
9 Give rise to
10 Judged
11 Hot under the collar
13 Highly embellished style
15 Slammin' Sammy
18 Circle
20 Sch. of the Northwest
22 Tart-tongued
23 Stage direction
25 "__ Fideles"
26 First side to vote
27 Old Chevrolet
31 "__ say!"
32 Lon __
33 Western Indian
34 Not now
35 Baby bird?
36 Whom Reps. run against
39 Moderately quick 13 Down dance
41 Made hay?
43 Prayers
45 Drain cleaner ingredient
46 Clearing
47 Former Houston hockey team
48 Climbing plants
49 Marathoner
50 Hang
51 Deplete
55 Writer Anita
57 Inclined
59 Stroke
60 Yorkshire river
61 Long, long ago

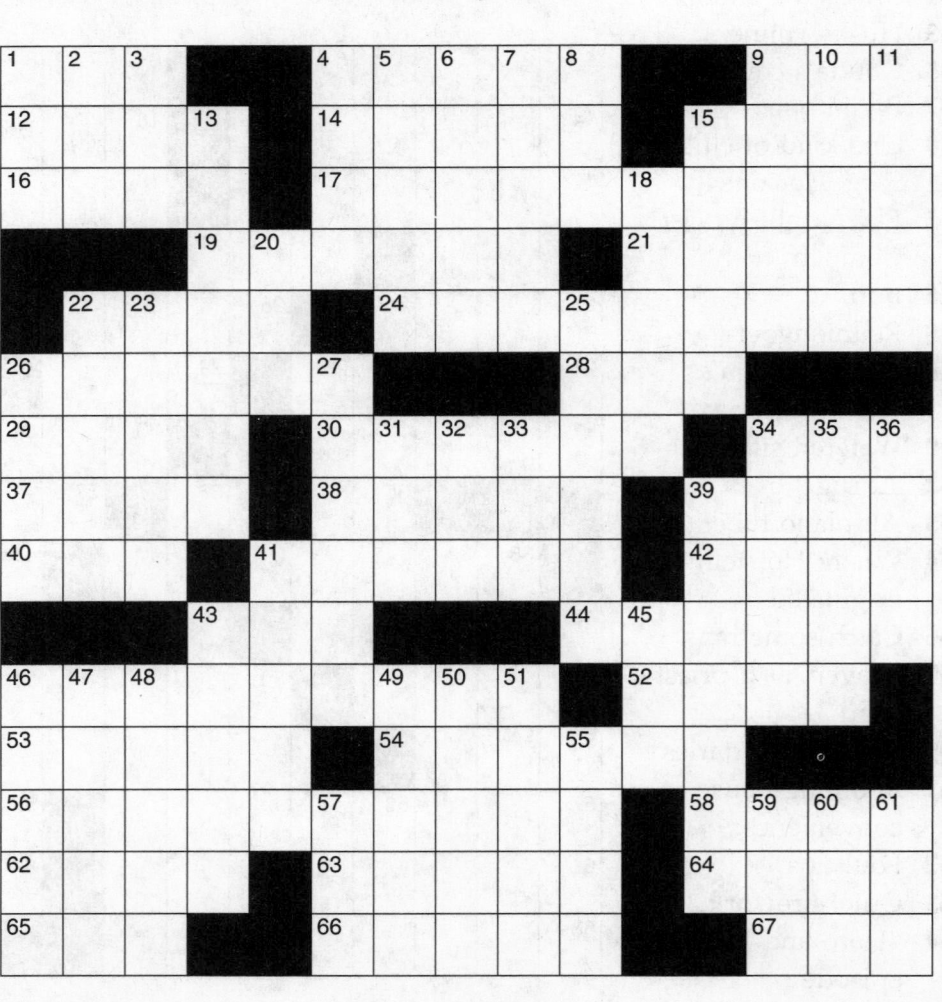

by Manny Nosowsky

ACROSS

1 "Alas"
6 "Chariots of the Gods" author Erich Von __
13 John Denver's "__ Song"
15 Iridescent
16 Jordan River's outlet
18 Extirpates
19 Yodeler's perch
20 Apt to fall apart
22 Astuteness
23 Start of a classic question
25 Twinkle-toed
26 Size up
27 Abram's wife
29 Ship's heading
30 Husky-voiced singer from Vienna
31 Post-kickoff game status
34 Rudolph Valentino, e.g.
36 Kind of suit
38 Israel's Arens
41 "My mamma done __ me"
42 Welles of the Mercury Theater
44 Play money?
45 Fire fighter
47 God of destruction
48 Reagan program: Abbr.
49 1966 musical featuring 30 Across
51 Calif. neighbor
52 Food preservative
54 Get cozy
56 Mark a marker?
57 House Speaker, 1977–86
58 Some car deals
59 Singer James and others

DOWN

1 Former Al-Qubbah Palace residents
2 15 slices, maybe
3 Visored hat style
4 Go to bat for
5 Family tree abbr.
6 Traitorous ones
7 Beatles record label
8 __ a one
9 1969 Nobel Peace Prize winner: Abbr.
10 Of a Plains people
11 Something or someone
12 Lipton competitor
14 Word repeated in a Doris Day song
17 Site of one of Hercules's labors
21 F. Scott Fitzgerald's birthplace
24 Otologist's case
26 Impressionist collection
28 Carpet fiber
30 Resulted in
32 Argentine aunt
33 Mannerism
35 Blowing one's cool
37 "Billy Budd," e.g.
38 Chess or bridge ranking
39 Sir Frederick Ashton ballet
40 Smarts
43 Adam and Eve lacked them
45 Give up
46 Where exes are made
49 Scuttle load
50 Adjust
53 Brother
55 Pick up

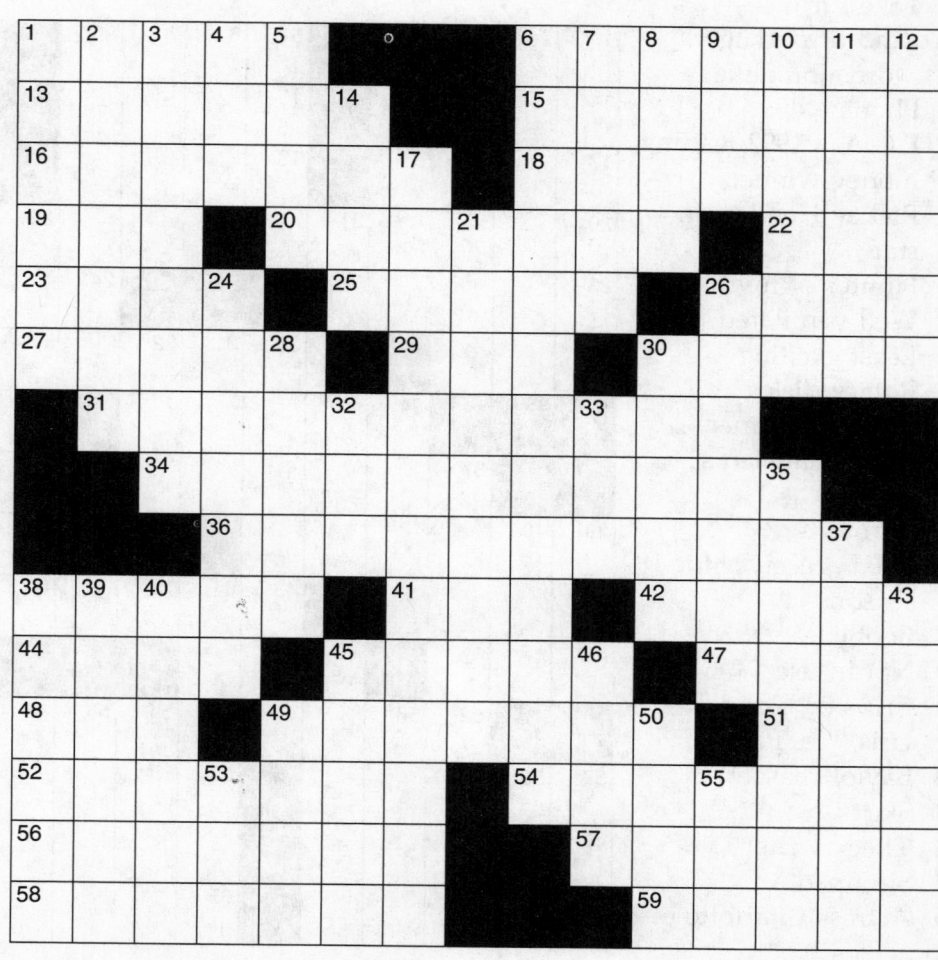

226 *by Janet R. Bender*

ACROSS
1 Wrongs
5 Stockyard group
9 Sail supports
14 Govt. agents
15 War of 1812 battle site
16 Member of a crowd scene
17 Give stars to
18 Basketball's Chamberlain
19 1993 Formula One winner Prost
20 Old "House Party" host
23 Knocks down
24 Reserved
25 1975 Stephanie Mills musical, with "The"
28 Hot time in Paris
29 Take turns
33 Kind of package
34 More albinolike
35 Phobic
37 P.G.A.'s 1992 leading money winner
39 Rickey Henderson stat
41 Hunter of myth
42 Well ventilated
43 Least exciting
45 Rotary disk
48 Sign of summer
49 Mathematician's letters
50 Throw
52 N.F.L. receiver for 18 seasons
57 Booby
59 Not in use
60 Crips or Bloods
61 Uris' "__ Pass"
62 Baylor mascot
63 Skirt
64 Check writer
65 Slumped
66 Actress Charlotte et al.

DOWN
1 Attack by plane
2 Turkish hostelry
3 Stinging plant
4 Fish-line attachment
5 Axed
6 Dancer Bruhn
7 Small brook
8 Loathe
9 Substantial
10 Wheel shaft
11 Noted film trilogy
12 Angle starter
13 __ José
21 Hebrew for "contender with God"
22 Eponymous poet of Greek drama
26 Temper
27 British alphabet ender
30 Elderly one
31 Gumshoe
32 "__ With a View"
33 Columnist Herb
34 Supplicate
36 Thread of life spinner, in myth
37 Savageness
38 Late actress Mary
39 NaCl, to a pharmacist
40 Truss
44 Deviates from the script
45 Party to NAFTA
46 Exact retribution
47 Enters a freeway
49 Persian Gulf land
51 Trevanian's "The __ Sanction"
53 Green target
54 Madison Avenue product
55 Ardor
56 Boor
57 Cutup
58 Noche's opposite

by Sidney L. Robbins

ACROSS

1 Tot's talk, perhaps
5 Encourages
9 First-grade instruction
13 Stinks
15 "Thanks __!"
16 Swing around
17 Like factory workers
19 U, for one
20 Elsie's bull
21 "Mommie __" (Christina Crawford book)
23 "What's __ for me?"
25 Take a potshot
26 Teller of white lies
29 Stage whisper
30 Give the eye
31 Quick bites
33 Advances
36 Baseball's Gehrig
37 Trunk
39 Runner Sebastian
40 Remains
43 Person of action
44 King's address
45 Illegal inducement
47 Mexican dishes
49 Speakeasy offering
50 Saxophonist Getz
51 Candid
53 Waiter's jotting
56 Actress Archer
57 Kind of jury
61 Bucks and does
62 Otherwise
63 Singer __ Neville
64 Lawyer: Abbr.
65 Tackle-box item
66 City inside the Servian Wall

DOWN

1 Tennis shot
2 Run in neutral
3 Body's partner
4 Logician's start
5 Sidekick
6 Sum total
7 Wart giver, in old wives' tales
8 Emphasis
9 On a horse
10 Edit
11 No blessing, this!
12 Shipped
14 Fragrance
18 Marco Polo area
22 Dye color appropriate to this puzzle
24 Vacuum tube
26 Go belly up
27 Borodin's prince
28 Texas' state flower
29 Balance-sheet pluses
32 Golf club V.I.P.
34 Illustrator Gustave
35 Comprehends
38 Patrick Henry, e.g.
41 Bodega
42 Clothing specification
44 Boating hazard
46 Saharan tribesman
48 Newswoman Shriver
49 Intelligence-testing name
51 Actress Thompson
52 Glamour rival
54 River of Spain
55 Leeway
58 "It's no __!"
59 Slippery one
60 Opposite SSW

228 by William P. Baxley

ACROSS

1 Artistic skill
6 Card game also called sevens
12 Holed out in two under par
14 Warned
16 English essayist Richard
17 Burglar
18 Cools, as coffee
19 Pumpkin eater of rhyme
21 Summer drink
22 Employee health plan, for short
23 Horse trainer's equipment
25 Black cuckoos
26 Long, long time
28 Like some schools
29 Sweetens the kitty
30 Smart alecks
32 Traffic circle
33 Charlie Brown's "Darn!"
34 Ex-Mrs. Burt Reynolds
35 Charge with gas
38 Adorned
42 Vineyard fruit
43 Kismet
44 Snick's partner
45 Detest
46 Alternative to eggdrop
48 A Gershwin
49 Drunk __ skunk
50 Analyze a sentence
51 Actor John of TV's "Addams Family"
53 Locale
55 Money-back deal
57 Boot camp denizen
58 Noted family in china manufacture
59 Arabs
60 Cancel the launch

DOWN

1 "L'état __": Louis XIV
2 Army grub
3 Ripening agent
4 Butler's "The Way of All __"
5 __ Aviv
6 Observed Lent
7 Change the hemline
8 __ do-well
9 "La-la" leader
10 Home of the '96 Olympics
11 Poorer
13 Arranges strategically
15 Smart
18 Sullivan's "really big" one
20 Summers, in Haiti
24 Sharp
25 Clowning achievements?
27 Mexican shawl
29 Top-flight
31 Arena receipts
32 Drive in Beverly Hills
34 Epistles
35 Shocked
36 Pencil ends
37 Knocking sound
38 Forbids
39 Bootee maker
40 Most Halloweenlike
41 Doyen
43 Smithies
46 Dwindled
47 High-muck-a-muck
50 Fir
52 Prefix with masochism
54 Item of office attire
56 Fuel efficiency rater: Abbr.

ACROSS

1 Scroogian comments
5 Grandson of Adam
9 Biblical possessive
12 Sheltered, at sea
13 Spot for Spartacus
14 Carnival ride cry
15 "Ho, ho, ho" fellow
18 Seems
19 Hockey's Bobby, et al.
20 Blue Eagle initials
21 Feasted
23 "My salad days when I was __": Shakespeare
30 Favorite dog name
31 Closes in on
32 The East
33 Word in a price
35 Volcano spew
36 Deli cry
37 Cause for liniment
38 Not-so-prized fur
40 River inlet
41 Bucky Dent slew it at Fenway Park in 1978
45 Zorba portrayer
46 Tennis call
47 Sulk angrily
48 Many Dickens stories, originally
52 Civil War currency
56 Merit
57 Nintendo hero
58 One of the Simpsons
59 Sot's problems
60 Jot
61 Prepares the dinner table

DOWN

1 Mexican peninsula
2 Crooked
3 Maids
4 Moon goddess
5 Misreckons
6 Born
7 Indivisible
8 __ Marcos, TX
9 Arid region of India
10 Chick watchers
11 Thus far
13 Take with __ of salt
14 Utility employee
16 It comes in balls
17 Bad news at a talent show
21 "Bull __" (Costner film)
22 Psyche parts
23 Word in a monarch's name
24 Extent
25 National treasuries
26 Tidy up
27 Teen heartthrob Priestley
28 Undeliverable letter, in post-office talk
29 13th-century invader
34 Monastery head
38 D.C. legislator
39 El Greco's "View of __"
42 Nothing: Fr.
43 Pianist Peter
44 Part of rock's C.S.N. & Y.
47 Brotherhood
48 Comic bit
49 "I cannot tell __"
50 Ultimate
51 Madrid Mmes.
52 Dropout's degree: Abbr.
53 Status letters, perhaps
54 "Say __"
55 Dernier __

230 *by David J. Kahn*

ACROSS

1 Colo. acad.
5 Start fishing
9 "Dancing Queen" pop group
13 Mata —
14 Tear to shreds
16 Tactic
17 Singer Antoine from New Orleans
19 Intense anger
20 Carty of baseball
21 — and kin
23 "The Company"
24 Mister twister
28 San Francisco area
29 Antitoxins
30 Laughed, in a way
32 Transfer, as a legal proceeding
36 "Tie a Yellow Ribbon" tree
37 Native land
39 Inform (on)
40 Fantasized
44 Durante's "Mrs."
48 Cosmonaut Gagarin
50 1956 Oscar-winning actress
51 Birthday-suit activity
55 One of L.B.J.'s dogs
56 Munich's river
57 Max or Buddy
59 Till compartment
61 Film hit of 1934
65 Dermatologist's diagnosis
66 Underwater acronym
67 Tevye portrayer on stage
68 Feminist Millett
69 Mikulski and Murkowski: Abbr.
70 Once more

DOWN

1 TV initials
2 Region of heavy W.W. II fighting
3 Heart of the grocery?
4 Champion named 9/1/72
5 — Magnon
6 Goal
7 Acerbic
8 Acropolis attire
9 Bank loan abbr.
10 Longtime Supreme Court name
11 Humphrey, to Bacall
12 TV's "— in the Life"
15 Commotion
18 Act like the Apostle Thomas
22 "— goes!"
25 — Harbour, Fla.
26 Playoff breathers
27 Machine part
28 "— she blows!"
30 Food fish
31 A dwarf
33 Syracuse players
34 Floral container
35 Biblical suffix
38 Moist
41 Novelist Rand
42 City bond, for short
43 Secret lovefests
45 Appearance at a sit-down?
46 Suspect's "out"
47 Top-rated TV show of the 60's
49 Baking potatoes
51 Kind of therapy
52 Moi's country
53 "— my case"
54 "Goodnight" girl
58 Steak order
60 Marie, e.g.: Abbr.
62 Aruba product
63 Nolte's "48 —"
64 Right away

ACROSS

1 Eye site
7 Freshens up baby
14 Canceled
15 P.O.W.'s
16 Partied hearty
17 Fossillike
18 "Liftoff" preceder
19 Early Beatle Sutcliffe
21 Phone button
22 Bottom line
25 Suffix with depend or descend
27 4.0, e.g.
30 "Hey! Jealous Lover" singer
33 Goofs
34 Italian epic poet
36 Showy moths
37 Take in
38 Nursery-rhyme queen's fare
41 Thespian's quest
42 Work unit
43 Shangri-las
44 Timetable divisions
45 Earth and moon, e.g.
47 Letter from Greece
48 Message from the Titanic
49 Satchel binder
53 Willing
57 "__ Lazy River"
59 "__ minute"
60 Twain and others
63 Cloys with adoration
66 Twilight time
67 Voucher
68 Supplies with new hands
69 Iroquoian people

DOWN

1 Computer salesman of renown
2 Maine college town
3 Musical direction
4 Question
5 Plumber's joint
6 Tote board stat
7 Apply lightly
8 __ facto
9 Not under
10 Bundle
11 1977 Streisand hit
12 Abbr. in a military name
13 Compass dir.
15 Nursery-rhyme king's den
20 Gunpowder, e.g.
23 Black numbers
24 '63 film "David and __"
26 Marched
28 Wishes
29 Image in Egyptian art
31 Intersections
32 Tribe of Israel
33 Repeated Jim Varney film role
34 Lifts of a sort
35 Charged at the bench
39 Some Dada works
40 Ovid products
41 Vim
46 Empath's skill
50 __ Janeiro
51 Lark
52 Ziti or fusilli
54 Poet Bradstreet
55 __ Hari
56 German biographer Ludwig
58 Fundamentals
60 Each
61 Oscar-winning Joanne Woodward role
62 Masthead listings, for short
64 Poet's word
65 Boxer's title: Abbr.

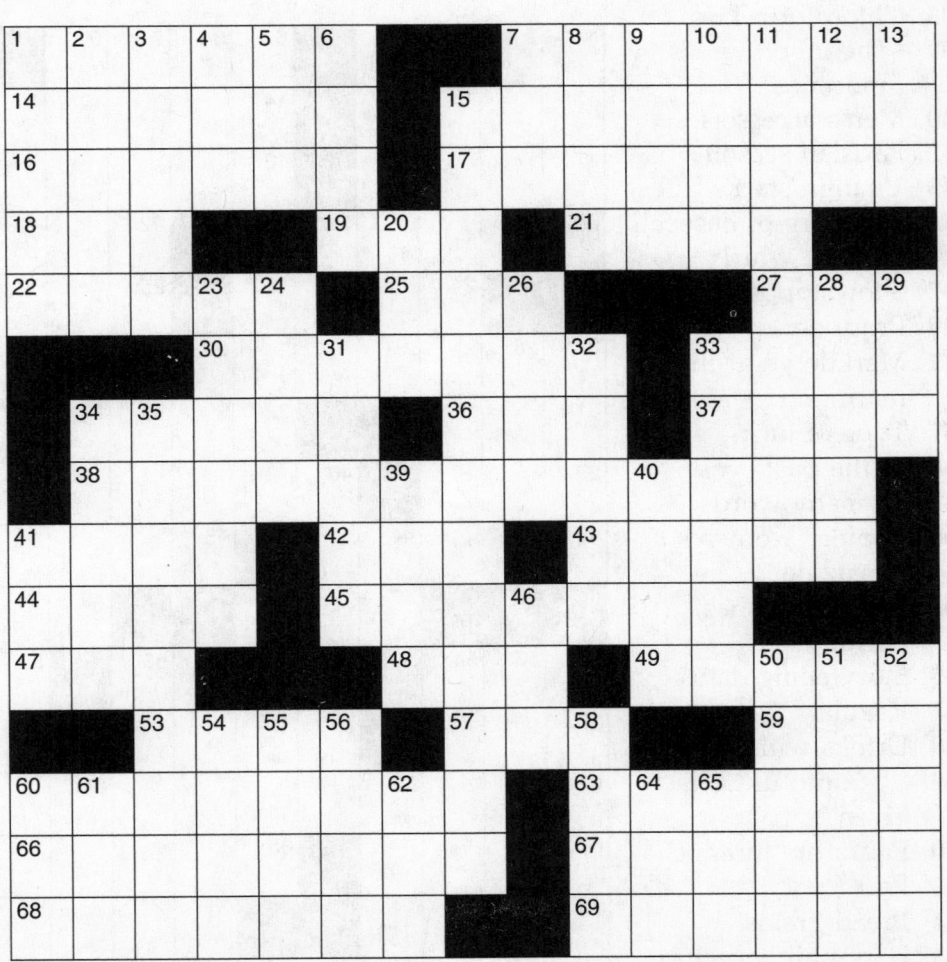

232 *by Jonathan Schmalzbach*

ACROSS

1 Granitelike
5 Paris' __ Monceau
9 Paradigm of happiness
13 Melville book
14 Toledo ta-ta
16 "Guys and Dolls" Tony winner, 1951
17 Lose freshness
18 The Rock Island Line?
20 Argus-eyed
22 Pin down, in a way
23 Born
24 Othello, e.g.
25 Police BBQ?
27 Triathlete
30 Next-to-last Greek letter
31 Non compos mentis
32 Fit together
35 Chloroform kin
39 "The __ of Innocence"
40 Men's accessories
42 Parisian season
43 Vitamin start
45 Sandberg of baseball
46 Give __ whirl
47 Showstoppers
49 Propriety
52 Markdown at the marina?
57 Type of luck
58 In the past
59 __ many words
60 Popular women's magazine
62 Mirror, brushes, perfume?
65 Storytelling dance
67 Regular
68 Drinks with straws
69 ". . . unto us __ is given"
70 Laura of "Jurassic Park"
71 Bread grains
72 Jerry-built structure

DOWN

1 In what manner
2 "What __ mind reader?
3 The Pillsbury Doughboy?
4 Pamper
5 Deli meat
6 Punch's cousin
7 Public uprisings
8 Woo
9 Wheels, so to speak
10 Southwest plain
11 Tours ta-ta
12 "Spanish Guitar Player" artist
15 Meet Morpheus
19 Joshes
21 CD-__ (modern "book")
26 Pioneer Carson
27 Muslim priest
28 Francesco Rinaldi competitor
29 Not e'en once
33 Nathan Hale, e.g.
34 Kind of legs
36 Removal of Junior from a will?
37 Part of Caesar's reproach
38 Enlarge, as a hole
40 Morsel
41 Unnecessary
44 Menlo Park monogram
48 Some TV's
50 Hint
51 Nebraska Indians
52 Economized
53 Tequila plant
54 Asocial person
55 With respect to
56 Truckler
61 __ gin
63 Publican's place
64 Actress __ Dawn Chong
66 As well as

ACROSS

1 Hazard
9 Rumor
14 Took to mean
15 Prevention dose?
16 Lousy tips
17 Be maître d'
18 "A Chorus Line" song
19 Electrical unit
20 Couple's org.
21 High-pitched
24 Moon valleys
27 One of the Chaplins
28 Fineness
29 Crash sound
31 Dire
34 St. Paul's top
35 See 42 Across
36 1964 Berne best seller (and a hint to seven other answers in this puzzle)
39 Falls off
40 D.J. Jazzy Jeff songs
41 Orders of the court
42 With 35 Across, a cleanser
43 Lean
44 So-so grade
45 Hears tell of
47 Least prevalent
50 Comedian's date
51 Wallops
52 Writer Buruma
54 Went chop-chop?
57 After-dinner drink
60 Breezing through
61 Lifeless
62 Italian summit
63 Matter for the Federal Trade Commission

DOWN

1 Butcher's cut of meat
2 Reply to a knock
3 East, in Berlin
4 School org.
5 Country music's Tennessee Plowboy
6 Lacy dress trimming
7 Judge
8 Track-meet measure: Abbr.
9 Amaze
10 From the sticks
11 Nice article
12 Diamonds
13 Asian holiday
14 U.S.N. rank
20 Computer dot
22 One of Adlai's running mates
23 Toodle-oos
24 Beef roasts
25 Princess __ ("Don Carlos" figure)
26 Anwar of Egypt
28 Nuts
30 N.L. M.V.P., 1954 and 1965
31 Becomes gray
32 Intriguing group
33 Like Uriah Heep
34 __ list
35 Tear
37 Tine
38 Jug
43 George Washington, e.g.
44 Harrah's, e.g.
46 Representative
47 Style of type
48 Twine fiber
49 Flavorsome
51 Relative of lotto
53 Born
54 Son of Noah
55 Umberto of Italy
56 Be lucky in the lottery
57 Turn down
58 Bit of advice
59 Latin I verb

ACROSS

1 Game with numbers 1 to 20
6 Crosby to Hope, often
12 Adulterate
13 Deceptive alloys
15 One who's left holding the bag?
16 Pontiac model
17 Definitely not ascetic
19 Gulf War combatant
20 ___ ski
21 Thrombus
23 Mini-peninsula
24 Hautboy, e.g.
25 Capital east of Jerusalem
27 Exact point
28 Roy Orbison's "___ Baby"
30 Silo fan
32 George C. Scott feature
35 Fox
37 English martyr
41 French cooking staple
42 Those opposed
44 Wagner's earth goddess
45 Opportunist
47 Chinese: Prefix
48 Spirit
49 Postulate
51 Flagging conversation?
53 Headstrong
55 Pedigreed
56 Personal personnel
57 ___ in (curbed)
58 American saint and family
59 Sniggler

DOWN

1 A fiancée of Napoleon
2 Kindergarten book
3 Nerve branch
4 Slavic sovereign
5 People of the Five Nations
6 Something you go by
7 Eight-time Norris Trophy winner
8 ___ to say
9 Brown and others
10 Reach in amount
11 More fit
12 Smart
14 Clobber
15 Boy Scouts of America founder
18 January birthstone
22 Tahitian dish
26 Shuttle group
29 Former U.S. poet laureate ___ Van Duyn
31 Bell's ringer?
33 ___ best friend
34 Master hands
35 Lives
36 Ennoble
38 Hatchery
39 Put on a pedestal
40 Like a newborn
41 Sweetie
43 Funereal, in Folkestone
46 Word on a bill
48 Baby
50 Second leader
52 Away from harm's way
54 Wimple wearer

by Jim Page

ACROSS

1 On which Irish linens are made
6 Chase flies
10 Krazy ___
13 Fort Knox deposit
14 Part of U.N.C.F.
16 "Foucault's Pendulum" novelist
17 Festive
18 "The Informer" author
20 Not fair
22 Bits of history
23 Ye ___ Shoppe
24 Mob
27 Stallone namesakes
28 Vex
29 Muddy
33 Mayberry resident
34 European capital
35 Draw ___ on
39 Date
41 Sisal and Bombay, e.g.
42 Bucks for captives
44 Scuffle
46 "Hagar the Horrible" cartoonist
47 Conform
48 Yokel
52 Look for flaws
54 60's hit "Let ___ Me"
55 Brewer of 50's pop
57 Presider in the 103d Congress
59 "Duffy of San Quentin" star
62 Bubbling
63 Remote
64 Circumspect
65 Donnybrook
66 To's opposite
67 Alphabet sequence
68 Put ___ to

DOWN

1 Some dance contests
2 Josie Hogan creator
3 "Sweet Rosie ___"
4 Samuel and Robert
5 Item in a pig's eye?
6 ___-Cat (Aspen vehicle)
7 Playboy nickname
8 Lace tip
9 Most somber
10 Larry who played Tony
11 ___ of the Apostles
12 G.I. Joe, e.g.
15 Character actor Dan
19 Lock up
21 Hardly a Prince Charming
25 Rainbow
26 Artist Georgia
30 Sire's mate
31 Stat for Alan Greenspan
32 All right
33 Mystery writer Lillian
35 Wall Street operator, for short
36 Kind of graph
37 Rock's Brian
38 Turning
40 Playwright Bogosian
43 Mark of the N.H.L.
45 "___ girl!"
48 13 1/2-ton tourist attraction
49 "Murphy's War" star
50 1940 Rockne portrayer
51 Pulled (in)
53 Blacktops
55 Bygone despot
56 Kind of dollars
58 Spiritual leader
59 Not working
60 Wiliness
61 Big Apple sch.

ACROSS

1 Started wrongly?
9 Mouse
15 Number after 1?
16 Ravel's "__ for a Dead Princess"
17 Is in the running
18 Unimak Island inhabitants
19 Home folks
20 Adriatic seaport
22 Endangered whale
23 African tyrant and namesakes
25 Like a wolf's howl
26 Furnish
27 Legal landmarks
29 Digital clock's light emitter
30 La Plata locale: Abbr.
31 Gary Cooper-ish?
33 Like "The Persistence of Memory"
37 6-0, courtesy of Steffi
38 Immortal Pirate
40 French sea
41 It's bound to show the way
42 Site north of Frederick, Md.
47 Emblem on an English shield
48 Fabulous finish?
49 Stories
50 Health org.
51 Film makers' equipment
53 Certain degrees: Abbr.
54 Crumples
56 Aeronautical inclination
58 Army command
59 Casts an absentee ballot
60 Designer Norman Bel __
61 TV address, in short

DOWN

1 Cut the mustard
2 Cheap jewelry material
3 Anyone's game?
4 Angkor __
5 Noted rapper
6 Host of a short-lived talk show
7 Swirls
8 Utah's early name
9 Outpouring
10 Hearty accompaniment?
11 "__ Gotta Be Me"
12 Upset
13 Double __
14 Junk-mail addressee
21 A rug
24 1984 Jeff Bridges role
26 Not loose
28 Manitoba Indians
29 Went under
32 Puts a wrap on
33 No-goodnik
34 Superlative
35 Fed the Colt again
36 Maj.'s superior
39 Frostbite preventers
43 École employee
44 Scroll-shaped ornament
45 Decrees
46 Have an aversion to
48 Acts hangdog
51 Early actress Eleanora
52 God of destruction
55 Downcast
57 Name in voyeurism

ACROSS

1 Spit the kabobs
7 __ Noël (holiday figure)
11 Nosy Parker
12 Accommodating
14 At her small condo, actress Glenn was __
17 "The __ Progress"
18 1903 Nobelist
19 "Go, team!"
20 Time for les vacances
21 Mount
22 Foreign-exchange cost
23 Novelist Buntline
24 French friend's pronoun
25 Failing
27 Hot spots
29 Levels
30 In her corset, actress Beatrice was __
34 Operetta composer
35 Kind of cake
36 Cowcatcher
38 Before time
39 Friday, e.g.: Abbr.
42 "__ may look on a king": Heywood
43 Hold forth
46 Broadway's "High __"
47 Cal. pages
48 Kind of bar
49 V sign
51 The holiday gathering at actress Betty's was __
54 Bolt down
55 Click beetles
56 Retreats
57 Watch mechanism

DOWN

1 Natural
2 Chaffed
3 Axis end
4 Army addresses
5 Guitarist __ Paul
6 Making a stand?
7 Scotland yards?
8 Republic since 1948
9 Unloyal sort
10 Make it keep going, and going, and . . .
11 Lorelei
12 Unvarnished
13 Finished second
15 Canadian prov.
16 Brake equipment
21 Recital works
22 Put on __
24 Miss America prop
26 Clean
27 Deadly reptile
28 Skittish
30 Dugongs
31 Drubbed
32 Did not move decisively
33 Wash
34 Source of fine fleece
37 Gin hounds
39 Bee's target
40 Tyke's four-wheeler
41 Lock
44 Ethnic group
45 "__ du lieber!"
48 Knock for a loop
49 Rel. of college boards
50 Cigar's end
52 Italian __
53 Réunion, e.g.

ACROSS

1 "__ Without a Cause"
6 Musical scale letters
11 Joker
14 Smell
15 Of great scope
16 Electric __
17 Proverb
18 Old-fashioned picture taker
20 Elevator name
22 Victory symbol
23 Norse Zeus
24 Candidate Landon
26 Was sore
28 Having divergent lines
29 Backside
31 DNA shapes
33 Letter getter
35 Seize
36 That lady
39 Make into a spiral
40 Book after Deuteronomy
42 Opposite of SSW
43 __ Mahal
45 12, at dice
46 Leisurely study
48 Eric of "Monty Python"
49 October gems
52 __ Rouge
54 Olive __
55 Sushi go-with
56 National anthem contraction
57 Author Irwin
59 Intercom
62 Smoldering spark
65 Unfashionable
66 "__ a Rainy Night" (1981 hit)
67 On top of
68 Formerly named
69 One of life's certainties, in a saying
70 Deep-__ (discarded)

DOWN

1 Type of computer chip
2 Historical time
3 Ticket booth
4 Discharge
5 Keats poem
6 Recede
7 Beg shamelessly
8 Trapped
9 European freshwater fish
10 Medicine watchdog: Abbr.
11 Uncared-for, as a lawn
12 Eagle's nest
13 Liver or thyroid
19 Extinct birds
21 Rhodes __
24 Jingle writers
25 Greg Evans cartoon
27 Use voodoo on
28 Crate up again
30 __ Jo, of the '88 Olympics
32 Coaxes
34 Mosquito marks
36 Train for the ring
37 __-burly
38 Artist's prop
41 __-fi
44 Diner music maker
45 "Kapow!"
46 Entreaty
47 __ Tuesday
49 Director Welles
50 Irritate
51 Not obtuse
53 Three-toed birds
56 Neighbor of Ark.
58 Both: Prefix
60 Acumen
61 Illiterates' signatures
63 The day before
64 Ruby

ACROSS

1 Fitzgerald's forte
5 Shortening
9 "__ little piggy . . ."
13 Impetuous
14 Sunburn remedy
15 Rule the __
16 Agitate
17 Have on
18 Simone's school
19 Epithet for a TV set
22 Jeanne or Thérèse: Abbr.
23 Believer in God
24 Podunk
30 Eucharistic plate
31 Lascivious looks
32 Set-to
35 On __ with (equal to)
36 High in pitch
37 Mongol monk
38 Bandman Brown
39 Baseball's Doubleday
41 Bank patron
42 Fixation
44 "Queenie" author Michael
46 Get a move on
47 Gambler's tormentor
53 Beau __
54 Flub
55 Eye layer
57 Take back to the car pound
58 Axlike tool
59 60's vocalist Vikki
60 German river
61 "Let's Make a Deal" choice
62 Make a cable stitch

DOWN

1 Last year's jrs.
2 Marcus Porcius
3 M __ Mary
4 Farm machine
5 Maker of cases
6 Not aweather
7 Abbey or Tobacco, e.g.
8 Suffix for 41-Down
9 Alarm bell
10 Catcalls
11 Wee atoll
12 Ending for hip or hoop
15 Extends a subscription
20 School founded in 1440
21 Fragrance
24 October birthstone
25 Place for a necklace clasp
26 Hellenic H's
27 Obliqueness
28 Moray pursuer
29 Aquarium fish
32 Sitarist Shankar
33 Bodement
34 Voting district
37 Politician with a limited future
39 Hurricane of 1992
40 Smile broadly
41 Word before deep or dive
42 Demosthenes, e.g.
43 Impatient one
44 Bumped impolitely
45 Spanish direction
47 Grimm villain
48 "Yipes!"
49 Old fogy
50 Dolt
51 Netman Lendl
52 Garr of "Tootsie"
56 Trump's "The __ of the Deal"

240 *by James L. Beatty*

ACROSS

1 Outbuildings
6 Hobgoblin
10 "— sesame"
14 Mischievous sprite
15 Selves
16 Nuclear reactor
17 Ahead of the times
19 Prefix with marketing
20 Sleep stage
21 Accurate
22 Made an incursion
24 Medicine that's not all it's promised to be
26 Bewails
27 Fictitious
30 Trigonometric function
32 Sashes
33 Oil city of Iran
34 Memorable period
37 Melts
40 It may be penciled in
42 Ott or Gibson
43 Appraised
45 Inland sea east of the Caspian
46 Rephrased
48 Lord Peter Wimsey's creator
50 Caper
52 Uproar
54 Evades
56 — of arms
57 Small amount
60 Woodwind instrument
61 Restaurant special
64 Add-on
65 Swearword
66 Valletta is its capital
67 Not the pictures
68 Nautical chains
69 Stocking material

DOWN

1 Box
2 Busy place
3 Word with eye or final
4 Gunga —
5 Resolve
6 — Arts
7 Monstrously cruel
8 The Almighty
9 River to the North Sea
10 Right to purchase
11 Secondary residence
12 Actress Burstyn
13 Desiderata
18 Electric power network
23 Astound
24 Noted lioness
25 Take new vows
27 Froth
28 French ecclesiastic
29 Love letter
31 Low island
33 Fall bloomer
35 Bellow
36 Piercing tools
38 Instant
39 — one's words
41 Reddish-brown horses
44 Give a little learning
47 Reader's —
48 Miner's nail
49 Cooling-off time
50 Take as one's own
51 Aristocratic
53 Closet pests
55 Espy
57 Kewpie, e.g.
58 Prefix with graph or crat
59 Breakfast fiber source
62 Ballad
63 Blue bird

ACROSS

1 Dogpatch's creator
5 Palindromic term of address
9 Talked, old-style
14 Nose tweaker
15 Willa Cather's "One of __"
16 With sickly pallor
17 Dream
18 Till's bills
19 Rags-to-riches writer
20 Start of an old motto
22 List ender
23 Shooter ammo
24 Part 2 of motto
26 Take-__ (accompaniers)
29 __ of one's own medicine
30 Part 3 of motto
31 Bulldog
32 Twosome
36 Martinique, e.g.
37 Environmentally minded, for short
39 Hook shape
41 "Don't Bring Me Down" rock group
42 Miami's county
44 Blanche in "The Golden Girls"
46 Part 4 of motto
48 Particle
50 Conquering hero
51 Part 5 of motto
54 Aerialist's safeguard
55 Theater people
56 End of motto
61 Sightseeing sight
62 Golfer Isao __
63 Singleton
64 Ball
65 A night in Paris
66 Exterior: Prefix
67 Blackthorn shrubs
68 1949 erupter
69 Creep through the cracks

DOWN

1 Search thoroughly
2 Together, musically
3 On hold
4 Make believe
5 Heath
6 Godmother, often
7 Rings of color
8 Orig. texts
9 Mower's trails
10 Mouth parts
11 White, informally
12 Last name in fashion
13 Nest for 21-Down: Var.
21 See 13-Down
22 "Me" types
25 Thumb-twiddling
26 Fatty __
27 Refrain part
28 1985 Danielle Steel best seller
33 Regretfulness
34 Choir voice
35 Koh-i-__ (famed diamond)
38 Pinch reaction
40 Cut of meat
43 Nitty-gritty
45 Just managed
47 Streets
49 Medea's ill-fated uncle
51 Miss Muffet edible
52 Business as __
53 Zoo heavyweight
57 Related
58 Comic Rudner
59 Spot
60 "Avast!"
62 Actress Sue __ Langdon

ACROSS

1 Mercury or Mars
4 Good old boy
9 Double-crosser
14 1979 film "Norma __"
15 W.W. I battle site
16 Pomme de __ (French potato)
17 Modern bank "employee": Abbr.
18 "__ in Venice"
19 Feeling regret
20 Night photographer's work, with "a"?
23 Common connectors
24 Bother
25 Wears well
27 Kind of budget
32 Dustin, in "Midnight Cowboy"
33 Actress Ward of "Sisters"
34 Exist
35 Like an inept photographer's subject?
39 Christina's dad
40 Snoop Doggy Dogg songs
41 Plays
42 Indy and Daytona
45 Classified
46 Sleep stage: Abbr.
47 Family member
48 Photojournalists' choices?
54 "__ Paradiso" (1966 film)
56 Catalyst
57 Mining area
58 "__ of robins in her hair"
59 San __, Calif.
60 Chemical suffix
61 Mill, to a cent
62 Embellish
63 __ Guinea

DOWN

1 Fat, in France
2 Vow
3 Floor model
4 Owing to
5 Defeats
6 Imps
7 One of the March sisters
8 Netman Arthur
9 Road, in Roma
10 Reflex messenger
11 Composer Satie
12 Prince Valiant's son
13 Fraternity party staple
21 "Jerusalem Delivered" poet
22 __ Lama
25 Author Esquivel
26 Greek
27 Computer sounds
28 Swiss range
29 Trigger
30 Fumbled
31 Grades below the curve
32 Surf sound
33 Open carriage
36 Chaplin persona
37 Shadow-y surname?
38 __-frutti
43 One of the Gallos
44 Affluence
45 Spoiler
47 Vinegar: Prefix
48 British gun
49 Lady of Spain
50 "Holy moly!"
51 Unrestricted
52 Supreme Court complement
53 Brood
54 Topper
55 Single

by Jonathan Schmalzbach

ACROSS

1 Send a Dear John letter
5 Antarctica's __ Coast
10 Stain on Santa
14 Medicinal herb
15 "Golden" song
16 Clinton Transportation Secretary Federico
17 Prefix with bucks or bytes
18 Ad: Part 1
20 Ad: Part 2
22 And others
23 Lennon's lady
24 Clinches
25 Ad: Part 3
28 Ad: Part 4
33 Beats
34 Judge
35 Dogpatch diminutive
36 Cabbies' credentials: Abbr.
37 Jabbed
38 Radio knob
39 And so forth, for short
40 Singular person
41 Gladiator's place
42 Medium in which this puzzle's ad appeared
45 Furnishes for a time
46 Twilights, poetically
47 Richmond was its cap.
48 Queen Victoria's husband
51 Ad: Part 5
55 Sponsor of the ad
57 Snead and Spade
59 15 miles of song
60 Floor pieces
61 Wasatch Range state
62 Prepared to drive
63 Unclogs
64 Glazier's section

DOWN

1 Predicament
2 "__ a song go . . ."
3 CBS's eye, e.g.
4 Genteel snack spots
5 Topper's first name
6 Wings
7 Peculiar: Prefix
8 Clear
9 Downcast
10 Quite an impression
11 Trompe l'__
12 "Dedicated to the __ Love"
13 Noted Chaplin follower
19 Shoshoneans
21 Responsibility
24 Buries
25 Shiftless one
26 __ Bandito of commercials
27 New Mexico's state flower
28 Offenses
29 "The Old __ Bucket"
30 Martian or Venusian
31 Article of food
32 Actress Raines and others
37 Indicates
38 Concocts
41 In addition
43 Adjudged
44 "Buona __" (Italian greeting)
47 Judit Polgar's game
48 Help a crook
49 Bait
50 Spreadable cheese
51 Tempest
52 Browning locale
53 "Do I dare to __ peach?": Eliot
54 Muscat's land
56 Fashionable
58 That girl

244 *by Harvey Estes*

ACROSS

1 Annie, for one
7 Sandwich often on toast
10 "__ 'em!"
13 Took refuge
15 __ rights (police suspect's entitlement)
17 Bomber type
18 Noted Richard III portrayer
19 Congressional funding?
21 Memory unit
22 R. E. Lee's land
23 Three-time World Cup medalist
27 Many a time
29 It borders Tenn.
33 Declaration
36 Taj Mahal, e.g.
39 Most-wanted poster letters
40 Vatican Museum holdings?
43 __ out a living
44 First name in game shows
45 "Brace yourself!"
46 He played Fred on "Sanford and Son"
48 Trading-bloc inits.
50 Particles
51 Make __ story (lie)
54 Famous sewer
57 Vacation slides?
64 Tank gas
65 Forked over
67 Nineveh's nation
68 "Great Expectations" miss
69 Ben in the film "Ben"
70 O.K.
71 Well-__ (rich)

DOWN

1 Cries
2 Campus mil. grp.
3 __-bargain
4 Jalopy
5 Make up on the spot
6 Harebrained
7 Coll. V.I.P.
8 Shade of purple
9 Stumbles
10 Irritated state
11 Bit of brainwork
12 Baseball's Yastrzemski
14 Pic
16 Birdy?
20 Table scraps
23 On __ (theoretically)
24 Call forth
25 Ran at an easy pace
26 Lamb producer
28 Stroller passenger
30 Freighter filler
31 Ohio city
32 Pours
34 Provide weapons
35 Caustic
37 55 letters?
38 Fancy neckwear
41 Start to dominate
42 One at the beginning
47 Hardly svelte
49 Two-door vehicle
52 Admiral in the Arctic
53 Nickname in the Senior P.G.A.
55 Tennis kill
56 Bash, biblically
57 Boom or box
58 Nocturnal bear
59 "Make the __ of it"
60 Votes for
61 "Zip-__-Doo-Dah"
62 Undulate
63 Christmastime
66 Itsy bit

ACROSS

1 Spring runner
4 Pole at sea
9 Dieter's measure
13 Robust drink
14 Delete-key function
15 TV tease
16 Golf ball's position
17 Sedaka and Simon
18 Play the fink
19 "Falstaff"
22 Marked down
23 "The Woman in the Dunes" author
24 It's big in London
25 Hard or soft approach
27 Scout's group
30 Quatrain's pattern
33 Seville snack
35 Sister of Charlotte
37 "The Misfits"
40 Barkin of "Sea of Love"
41 Genealogist's work
42 It may be cured
43 Monaco cube
44 Speech site
46 Actress Carrie
48 Cobbler's tool
49 Imperfect bridge holding
53 Homer #521
59 Blotter entry
60 Waugh and others
61 Eunuch's unit
62 Disk-shaped marine fish
63 Challenger's quest
64 Political abbr.
65 Hound's quarry
66 Semicircular recesses
67 Wordsworth's "We __ Seven"

DOWN

1 Military blast
2 Refuge seeker
3 Duke and earl
4 More than forgetful
5 Favors
6 Tout's post
7 __ Mujeres, Mexico
8 Chester Gould femme
9 Smooth-skinned edible
10 Learning method
11 It makes the mundus go round
12 Actress Washbourne
15 Gordian knot, for one
20 Show amateurish interest (in)
21 Chess's Mikhail
25 Works with Riddick Bowe
26 Facility
27 Belly flop, e.g.
28 Lamb of yore
29 "No way, Sergei!"
30 Elderly
31 Java neighbor
32 Up to snuff
34 Choral voices
36 Tick of time
38 On edge
39 Seaquarium arm
45 Like
47 Swains' requests
48 Like Pegasus
50 Now, in Nogales
51 Autumn beverage
52 Marchers' camp
53 Wear's partner
54 Chase of Tinseltown
55 Pre-rehab Pinocchio
56 __ Hari
57 Underdress
58 "__ Do It" (Porter tune)

ACROSS

1 Kind of fair
7 10th-century English king
12 Walden Pond habitué
13 One found in the stacks
15 Bandit's cry
16 Fine-wooled sheep
18 Beehives, for instance
19 From 8 to 11
21 Venison
22 Alda of "M*A*S*H"
23 "Cheaper by the __"
24 Baseballer Maglie
25 View
26 Antique autos
27 Vain
29 Temporary hair tinter
30 Romance with the past
33 Rubberneck
36 Linked
39 Catamount
40 Thumbs through
41 __ out (relax)
43 Not very competent
45 Furry companions
46 Allocate
47 Leggy one
49 Passengers
50 Birders' society
51 Duds
53 __ piece
54 Volunteers
55 Super buys
56 Expunge

DOWN

1 Mademoiselle's hat
2 Short poems
3 Fire of the mind
4 Actor Parker
5 Letter after sigma
6 Most limber
7 King's fur
8 Consider
9 Rose up, in dialect
10 Newspaper part
11 Inhabitant
12 Dropping sounds
14 Lovers
17 Sixth __
20 Searched thoroughly
22 Old radio favorite "Easy __"
25 __ gin
28 Delight beyond measure
29 Splits
31 Dawdled
32 Teeth holders
33 Bright star in Virgo
34 Mechanic's job
35 Revised
37 Hillary's conquest
38 Political thaw
40 Shells out
42 Hero's exploits
44 Shinbone
46 Actress Van Doren
48 Lifeguard's beat
49 Satisfy
52 One, in Aberdeen

by Trip Payne

ACROSS

1 Wrought-up
6 City near Phoenix
10 Melodramatic cry
14 Cottonwood, in Spanish
15 Burns one up
16 Perambulate
17 One past his prime
20 On the other hand
21 Essentials
22 Summer top
23 Skedaddle
24 Wish
25 Least significant
28 Bluesman Robert
29 Coffee-break brake
32 Independently
33 "You there!"
34 Relief pitcher's feat
35 Hot time
38 Makes like
39 Man with a lift
40 Échecs piece
41 N.Y.C. cultural site
42 Litigant
43 Most fit
44 Sir overseas
45 Biter
46 Plays the zither
49 Picked up on
50 __ Vicente, Brazil
53 It won Hepburn an Oscar
56 One of the O'Neills
57 Iditarod terminus
58 World's largest cobalt exporter
59 Attributes
60 Gumption
61 Register

DOWN

1 Lots
2 Tissue addition
3 Santa drawer
4 Dennis the Menace, e.g.
5 Site of a May 1942 battle
6 Chop finely
7 Work units
8 Dry
9 Camels' destinations?
10 Marquis protagonist
11 Hel's father, in myth
12 Maintain
13 Faxed
18 "Yeah, sure!"
19 Brit's phrase
23 Wards (off)
24 Instructors, for short
25 Mary Stewart's "__, Will You Talk?"
26 Waive one's rites?
27 Physician-turned-wordsmith
28 The Mighty Clouds of Joy, e.g.
29 Farr of "M*A*S*H"
30 Hot spots
31 Nice topper
33 Daisylike bloom
34 Silvery fish
36 Elton John's first hit
37 Make citified
42 Penultimate round
43 From square one
44 Great shakes?
45 "The Maids" playwright
46 Quash
47 What you used to be
48 Flat rate
49 __ Valley, Calif.
50 The joint
51 Prefix with space or stat
52 Mr. Hershiser
54 Postal Creed word
55 Children's author Agle

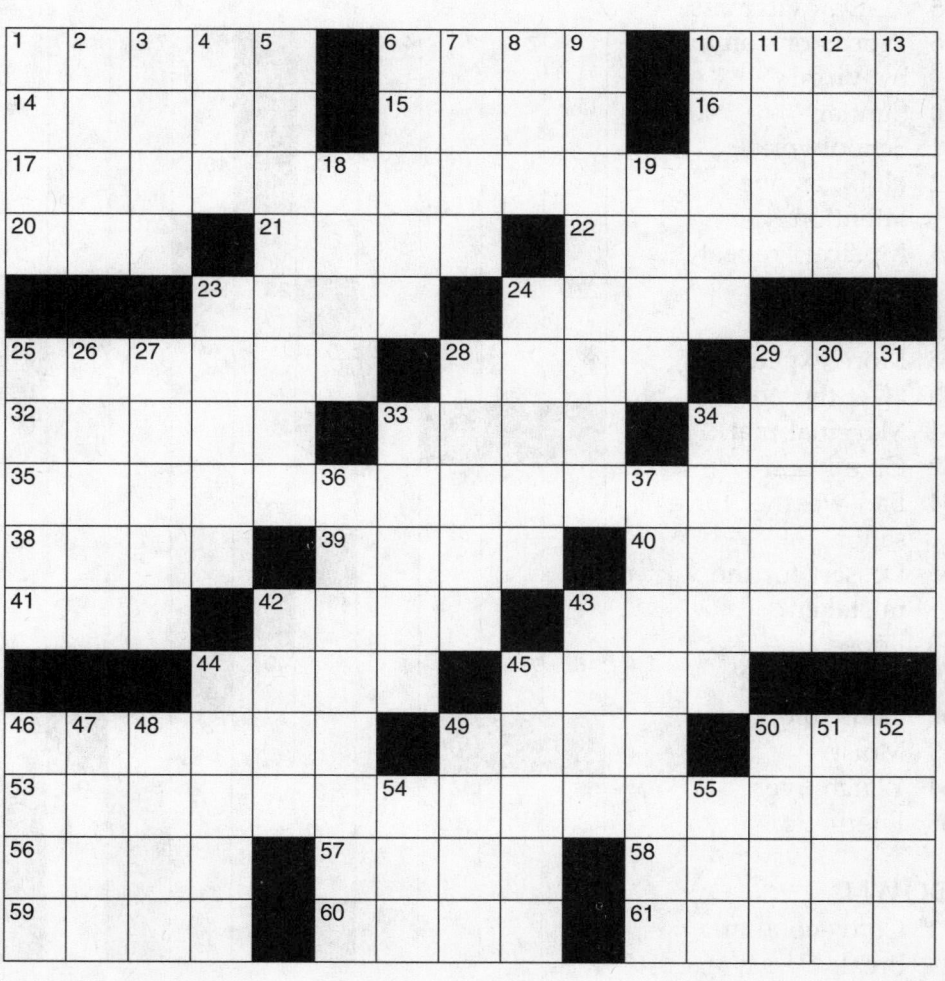

ACROSS

1 Challenge authority
6 Acronym since 1960
10 Off one's trolley
14 Napoleon, twice
15 Shake makers
17 Guys may be attached to them
18 Appendectomy, for one
19 Mimic
21 Covers with a blanket
22 Subject of a Thomas Gray ode
23 Panama, e.g.
25 Physicist's __ jar
29 Hearing aid?
30 Divine __
32 Compelled
33 Superficial pretenses
35 __-Day vitamins
36 Words on romance by Virgil
40 Similar
41 Schoolwork
42 Hold, as one's attention
44 Musical "repeat" sign
45 Calendar mo.
48 More expensive
50 "Get the point?"
51 Marginal mark
52 Give it __
54 Bad weather for a sailor
56 Dessert for the mistaken?
60 Loose
61 Kind of booth
62 Gods' blood
63 Moist
64 Watch over
65 Energetic

DOWN

1 Convene after a break
2 Combo bet at Belmont
3 King's neighbor
4 First name in rock
5 Majesty preceder
6 Bernardo's bear
7 Acts on the basis of 36-Across
8 Churchill successor
9 Sing door-to-door
10 Famous standard maker
11 Mr. Onassis
12 Referee's decision
13 Nine-digit ID: Abbr.
16 Shot the breeze
20 Zoo critters
24 Ten-percenters
26 Honorific of Spain
27 Stuntman Knievel
28 "Hud" Oscar winner
30 Kind of room
31 Walk wearily
33 With worthiness of respect
34 Nets
36 Kitchen staple, once
37 Steinbeck emigrant
38 Brando's "__ Zapata!"
39 Pierce Arrow competitor
43 Nikola the inventor
45 At __ door
46 "thirty-something" character
47 Stick in the salad?
49 Mitchell hero
51 Not a whiz kid
53 Andy Griffith's TV son
55 "Jeopardy!" is one
56 Shrouded
57 Purpose
58 Trim
59 Finale

ACROSS

1 Use a letter opener
5 Dadaist poet Tristan
10 Bus. bigwigs
14 Bear of "very little brain"
15 Grant portrayer
16 Emerald City princess
17 Cogwheel comparison?
20 Skewers
21 Nuke
22 Tool for Bo-Peep
23 Focuses
25 Emmy winner Arthur
26 Totaled car, perhaps?
33 Made a touchdown
34 Got ruined in the wash
35 Manche capital
36 Sci-fi regulars
37 Quieted with Quaalude
40 "Do — say!"
41 Brews
43 Palm (off)
44 Financial success
46 Inflamed toe cause?
49 Big Ben?
50 Mayberry boy
51 Math discovery
54 Nameless one
56 Nolan Ryan was one
60 Mega-marathon?
63 Arabic name starter
64 Christmas Eve flier
65 Eye at the beach
66 Botch
67 Into pieces
68 Source of abundance

DOWN

1 Spring spots
2 Dropped, maybe
3 Isle near Mull
4 Bob Dylan back-up group
5 Make lace
6 Famed cop slapper
7 Anatomical loop
8 Glean
9 Dadaist painter Hans
10 Aiken and Hilton
11 Basso Pinza
12 "Typee" sequel
13 Dropped, maybe
18 Stage remarks
19 Bakery worker
24 Words before "TV" or "each other"
25 Crams
26 Hat-tipping cartoonist
27 Start
28 Curmudgeons
29 Eliot's "Jennyanydots" e.g.
30 Author Calvino
31 The Folger Lady, Mrs. —
32 Jet, at Orly?
33 Levi's mother
38 Bashes
39 Defense mechanism
42 Swimming classes?
45 Hides
47 Dennis the Menace's dog
48 Word with baby or schuss
51 Surrey carriage
52 "Mike and Ike" creator Goldberg
53 Heavy load
54 It's most useful when it's cracked
55 Prefix re honeycombs
57 Buster Brown's bulldog
58 Kaiser, e.g.
59 Like Nash's lama
61 Public works inits.
62 S. & L. accrual

250 *by Cathy Millhauser*

ACROSS

1 "Alice in Wonderland" figure
6 Disney classic
11 Overcrowding antidote, initially
14 In __ (prenatal)
15 Film director Resnais
16 Different ending
17 God
18 Minolta rival
19 Carrie married to Cavett
20 Modern choice #1
23 Former Swedish P.M. Ullsten
26 Ventnor or Vermont, e.g.: Abbr.
27 Sassoon creations
28 Modern choice #2
33 Theda "The Vamp"
34 Example, for example
35 Modern choice #3
42 Triple-layer treat
43 Cocoon-stage insect
45 Modern choice #4
51 Leading
52 She sang "At Seventeen"
53 Give a wave
54 Modern choice #5
59 That, in Spain
60 Suitor
61 Hoople or Houlihan
65 P.R. concern
66 "Unsafe at Any Speed" author
67 Logical starting point
68 First degs.
69 Plumbing tool
70 Gait problems

DOWN

1 Holy city of Iran
2 Tony winner Hagen
3 Comic book squeal
4 "__ Tu" ('74 hit)
5 Illinois State University site
6 Angel
7 Jai __
8 Jazz flutist Herbie
9 Life story: Abbr.
10 Greenhorn
11 Showy flower
12 Welcome culmination
13 Valleys
21 Caesar's salad ingredients?
22 "Arabian Nights" flyer
23 Globe
24 Riffle
25 Earthy prefix
29 Egypt and Syr., once
30 __ the other
31 Milne marsupial
32 It's "hard" for the French
36 "Do-si-do" dos
37 Muff
38 Car monogram of yore
39 Jupiter's mother
40 Courage
41 Bee's charge, in Mayberry
44 Shtick
45 Cycle parts
46 Word in a children's title
47 Contemptuous utterance
48 Coyote State capital
49 Shaver
50 Varmint
51 Bitter
55 Like Robinson Jeffers's stallion
56 End notes?
57 Need a bath
58 Approach the terminal
62 Lord of fiction
63 Alley from Moo
64 Apt. ad info

ACROSS

1 Women's mag
5 One-liners
9 Soccer legend
13 Egg-shaped
14 TV oldie "Green __"
16 Vientiane's land
17 Building code requirement
19 Prod
20 Pilgrim John
21 Most pleasant
23 Madam's mate
25 July 4, 1776, e.g.
26 Opposite of vert.
29 W. Hemisphere org.
32 Mr. Arnaz
34 The lowdown on dancing?
36 Kind of car or sandwich
38 Use a crayon
41 Ratted (on)
42 Armbone
43 By oneself
44 Writer Hunter
45 Hauls
46 Stimulate, as curiosity
47 Measure out
48 Provence city
50 Stalin ruled it
52 "The Bridge of San Luis __"
53 Stephen of "The Crying Game"
54 Late tennis V.I.P.
57 Dawn goddess
59 Lustrous fabric
61 "Faust," for one
65 Shocked sound
67 Summer treat
70 Matures
71 Go 1-1 in a doubleheader
72 Letterman's "Top Ten," e.g.
73 Model's position
74 "Auld Lang __"
75 Not so much

DOWN

1 Divan
2 "Hear no __ . . ."
3 Cooking fat
4 Hightails it
5 Oil alternative
6 U.N.C. and U.Va. grp.
7 In a lofty style
8 Artist's brown
9 +
10 Bulldozer
11 Captain's record
12 Language suffix
15 Church offshoot
18 Arthurian lady
22 Slippery one
24 Sum up
27 Not quite spherical
28 Los Angeles motorist King
29 Of the eyes
30 Magnetism
31 Shades
33 By oneself: Prefix
35 News entry
37 Home port
39 Burden
40 Hall-of-Famer Pee Wee
49 Was in session
51 Motel vacancy
55 Does needlework
56 Mounds
58 "How do you __ relief?"
60 Church nook
62 Writer Wiesel
63 Flagmaker Betsy
64 Picnic pests
65 Cumberland, e.g.
66 In the past
68 One for Wilhelm
69 Numbered rd.

252 *by Joel Davajan*

ACROSS

1 Atop
5 Clubbed
10 Motes
14 New York Cosmos star
15 Chou —
16 Oklahoma tribesman
17 Lord Nelson site
20 Part of an electrical switch
21 Zeroes
22 Hectored
23 Sans verve
24 Medicament
27 Winter woe
28 Ottoman official
31 The Donald's ex
32 Fly like Lindbergh
33 Aits in Arles
34 Prepare for an Indian attack
37 Raison d'—
38 30's actress Grey and others
39 Nighttime noise
40 Beam
41 Sponsorship
42 Feeds a furnace
43 Belgian river
44 Baseball union boss Donald
45 Like llamas
48 Sends quickly
52 Ships' drop-off location?
54 Sea flyer
55 Gnawed away
56 Composition closure
57 Crazy bird?
58 Monopoly payments
59 Formerly

DOWN

1 Goes (for)
2 — Beach, Fla.
3 Airline to Jerusalem
4 Testimonial
5 It's hummed
6 1973 hit by the Rolling Stones
7 Covered
8 The "E" in E.N.T.
9 Prohibit
10 Wampum
11 I-70's western terminus
12 Ilk
13 Golf course 18
18 Of some electrodes
19 Printer's spacer
23 Tree trunks
24 Potato preparer
25 "Requiem for —"
26 Take the plunge
27 Lawyer Roy M. and others
28 "Take — at this!"
29 Type
30 Bridge of — (Euclid proposition)
32 Way up?
33 Blissful state?
35 Produce
36 Wheezing cause
41 Birthright seller
42 TV listing
43 Modern-day Sheba
44 Tops
45 Ex-steelworkers chief
46 Fiery fiddler
47 1962 Bond villain
48 Solar disk
49 Mr. Stravinsky
50 Lawyers' degrees
51 Install in office
53 "— you sure?"

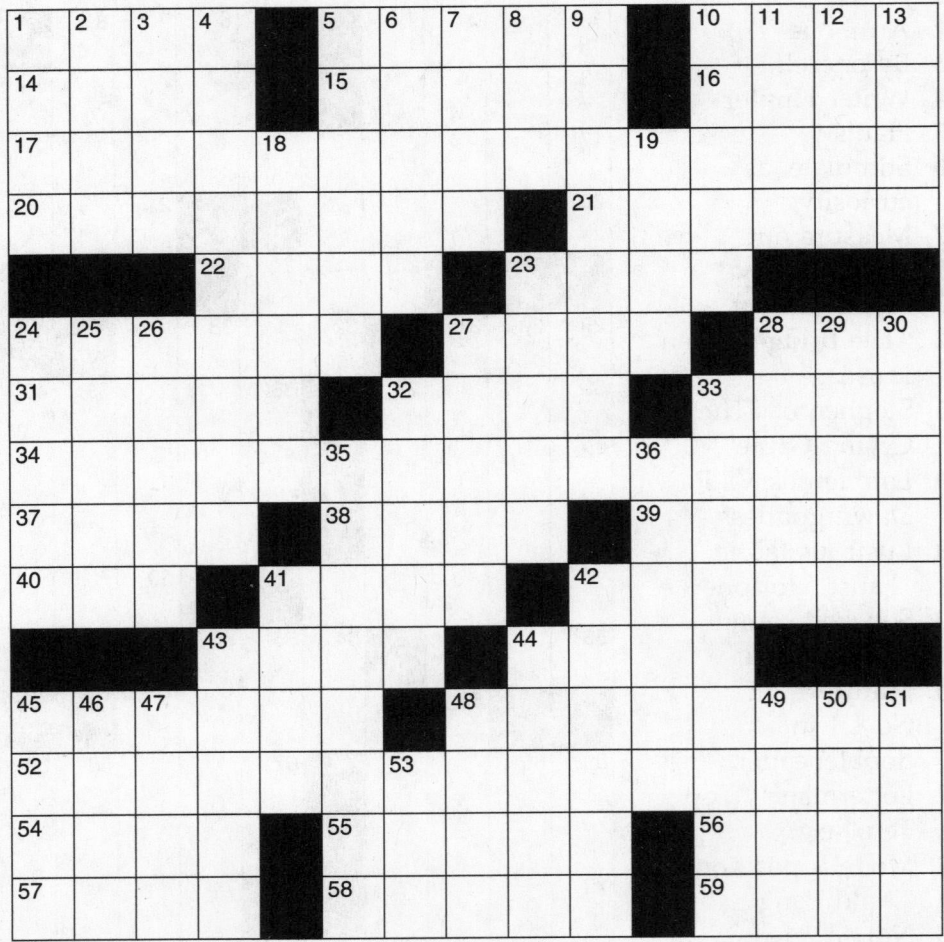

ACROSS

1 Child's getaway
5 Nurse's stick
9 Malpractice target
14 Margarine
15 Part of a cash register
16 Sam or Tom, e.g.
17 Businessperson's oxymoron
20 Crowbar
21 Runner Devers
22 Sums
23 "Get __!"
25 Cut up
27 Vipers
30 Indignant person's oxymoron
35 Actor Erwin
36 Breezy
37 Refer (to)
38 Dinner bird
40 Command to Fido
42 Jewish dinner
43 Mideast language
45 Flood survivor
47 W.W. II grp.
48 Oxymoron for a homely person
50 Cheek
51 Riches' opposite
52 Took a powder
54 Jacob's brother
57 Bare
59 Speechify
63 Coffee drinker's oxymoron
66 Passé
67 Within: Prefix
68 Model married to David Bowie
69 Steeple
70 Slumber
71 Library item

DOWN

1 Monk's hood
2 Lotion ingredient
3 Former talk-show host
4 Fireplace equipment
5 Penn, e.g.: Abbr.
6 Belly dancers
7 Edison's middle name
8 Mathematician Pascal
9 Sine __ non
10 Straighten out
11 Sarcasm
12 Dolt
13 Barbies' mates
18 Enrage
19 Bow of silents
24 Black bird
26 Three-time Super Bowl–winning coach
27 Tin Pan Alley org.
28 One of the Beatles
29 Chrysalises
31 In competition
32 Lindley of "The Ropers"
33 Creativity
34 Indoor balls
36 Writer Loos
39 Busybody
41 Stashes
44 Caesar's swans
46 Certain vote
49 Shylock
50 Magellan, e.g.
53 Lee to Grant
54 Concludes
55 It's seen in bars
56 Against
58 Unit of force
60 BB's
61 Word after "go!"
62 Sea eagle
64 Humorist George
65 "Oh, darn!"

254 *by Joel Davajan*

ACROSS

1 Christiania today
5 Noggin tops
10 Hind's mate
14 Hullabaloo
15 Open-eyed
16 "Damn Yankees" vamp
17 Ike was one
20 Track officials
21 Testify
22 "Rule, Britannia" composer
23 Early Briton
24 Social groups
27 Garlic relative
28 Asian holiday
31 Culture mores
32 Coxswain's crew
33 __ Marquette
34 G.I. newspaper
37 Cures leather
38 "That's interesting"
39 Opt
40 Two-by-two vessel
41 Reared
42 Worth
43 Shed
44 Escape
45 Roman villa locale
48 Apollyon adherent
52 Biblical beacon
54 Seller's caveat
55 Backcomb hair
56 Mechanical memorization
57 Smoker's sound
58 Mead research site
59 Animal team

DOWN

1 Switch settings
2 Eye opening
3 Kind of flow
4 Bell workers
5 Thin metal disks
6 Cognizant
7 Salts
8 Dr.'s graph
9 Most rundown
10 Nodded
11 Pamplona runner
12 Hale of "Gilligan's Island"
13 10 on the Beaufort scale
18 Pressure
19 Spoon
23 Intrinsically
24 Jai alai basket
25 It makes scents
26 Part of the evening
27 Put on cargo
28 Dakota digs
29 Upright
30 Blood and acid, e.g.
32 Beginning
33 Bohemian beers
35 Berlin events of 1948
36 Recap
41 Machetelike knife
42 Wimbledon champ Gibson
43 Code name
44 1980 DeLuise flick
45 Royal Russian
46 "__ girl!"
47 Ski spot
48 Coal stratum
49 Hotcakes acronym
50 Bristle
51 Revenuers, for short
53 "__ sport"

by Albert J. Klaus

ACROSS

1 John Denver's "Christmas in __"
6 "Tuna-Fishing" painter
10 Among
14 "__ Eyes" (1969 song)
15 Actor Richard
16 Bounty rival
17 Refinement
18 Witticisms
19 Vigor
20 1950 Sinatra hit
23 West Bank org.
24 "Just a __"
25 Three strokes, perhaps
28 Actress Sommer
31 Shares
36 Feared test
38 Troubles
40 Weaken
41 1955 Sinatra hit
44 Improve
45 Rig
46 Shut off
47 Beachwear
49 Relax
51 Audit conductor, for short
52 Guy's date
54 Eternity
56 1961 Sinatra hit
64 "Warm"
65 Minnow eater
66 Driving hazard
68 Petruchio's mate
69 Shillelagh land
70 10th-day-of-Christmas gift
71 Swerve
72 Henna and others
73 Follow

DOWN

1 Blue-chip symbol
2 Lively dance
3 Chihuahua change
4 Bar, in law
5 Compass part
6 Half begun?
7 Excited
8 Stucco backing
9 Foot part
10 Swear
11 Ryun's run
12 Basil's successor
13 Niels Bohr, e.g.
21 The Man Without a Country
22 More aloof
25 Propels a gondola
26 Bouquet
27 Bird "perched upon a bust of Pallas"
29 Toddlers
30 Dramatist Rice
32 Goddess of discord
33 Raccoon kin
34 Lawn tool
35 Is apparent
37 Impart
39 Ditto
42 Saw
43 Elevated
48 Stood up
50 Kind of switch
53 Distrustful
55 Run site
56 Prepares the presses
57 Plumber's concern
58 Behind
59 Ale
60 Pennsylvania port
61 Roadhouses
62 They go into locks
63 Relative of Hindustani
67 Volte-face WNW

ACROSS

1 "Spare tire"
5 Ferris wheel, e.g.
9 Shares quarters (with)
14 Furor
15 Airline to Haifa
16 Point with intent to shoot
17 General Bradley
18 Yarn irregularity
19 Roman goddess of flowers
20 Notorious 30's criminal
23 Smoker's intake
24 Subterfuge
25 German physicist Georg
28 Skin problem
31 Chinese veggie
35 F. __ Bailey
36 Shankar's strings
38 Unaccompanied
39 Notorious 30's criminal
43 Killer whale
44 Massenet opera
45 Links position
46 Some flights
49 Janet of Justice
50 Mark's competitor
51 Quite ready
53 Road warning
55 Notorious 30's criminal
62 By radio, e.g.
63 New York Public Library figure
64 Cheater's aid
66 Rubbish
67 War god
68 He wrote "My Way" for Sinatra
69 Misogynist
70 Communications leader?
71 Walter __ Hospital

DOWN

1 To's opposite
2 Reader's aid
3 Seaweed derivative
4 Special Forces cap
5 Put in a straitjacket
6 Not wisely
7 Smear
8 Pipe joint
9 Church drawing
10 Subject of the Teapot Dome scandal
11 Melville novel
12 __ Tyler Moore
13 Native African village
21 Ankle bones
22 Pup's sound
25 Actor Edward James __
26 Love, on bumper stickers
27 Muslim's holy place
29 Watch part
30 "Horrible" comic character
32 Parrot's moniker
33 North, of Irangate
34 Senior leader
37 Ancient letter
40 O'Neill play, with "The"
41 Balderdash
42 Hillock
47 Ransacker
48 Baden-Baden, e.g.
52 Razzle-dazzle
54 Filmdom honor
55 City near Bristol
56 Atmosphere
57 Englishman, in slang
58 Cork's locale
59 "The First __"
60 Normandy river
61 Winged Victory
65 Spoiled

ACROSS

1 They have pins at one end
6 Military bigwigs
11 Put in chips
13 Pan-fried
15 Mary Tyler Moore's old boss
16 Queen Victoria's family
17 Strikes out, perhaps
18 Nautilus habitat
20 Unflattering
21 Cub groups
22 Rock music's Tears for —
24 London essayist
25 Calendar periods: Abbr.
26 Posthumous Forster novel
28 Persuaded
29 San Francisco pants-maker
31 Ancient fly prison
33 Troubles
34 The hunted
35 Offer an apple in Eden
37 Threadbare
40 Spending limit
41 Taunted
43 Quangtri locale
45 Last words
47 Bearded
48 "The — Report" (1976 best seller)
49 Buddy of Irene Ryan?
51 Record number?
52 Hay holders
53 Carbon attachment
55 They're sometimes tickled
57 Put under
58 Bond, once
59 Smarts
60 Lacks

DOWN

1 Painters' equipment
2 Con
3 Egg containers
4 Some eagles
5 Use the peepers
6 Ewe said it!
7 Scores of diamonds
8 Make up
9 Barber's town
10 Less upscale
11 Like abandoned gardens
12 "Hunches in Bunches" author
13 Lamb Chop's voice
14 More than misgivings
19 Shoots an average score
22 Deducted style points from
23 Like Capone's face
26 Ralph of "Happy Days"
27 Touch up
30 Canyon edge
32 Party letters
34 Political tract
35 Purr-fect pets?
36 Show piece
37 Station that went on the air in 1978
38 Like one 1992 Olympics team
39 Ragamuffin's attire
40 Sorority possibles
42 Gave a rap
44 Topsy-turvy
46 L.B.J., e.g.
48 Lena of "Stormy Weather"
50 Picky people pick them
52 Like a star for a 46 Down
54 River to the Irish Sea
56 Bismarck's predecessor

258 *by Kenneth Haxton*

ACROSS
1 Swiss river
4 New Orleans's Vieux __
9 Child shot
12 Pique
14 Mix 'n match collections
15 Fisher's boat
16 Rhapsodic
17 Opening of 4/11/91
19 "My Cup Runneth Over" singer
21 Church teachings
22 Pitch
24 Opening of 3/13/47
26 Dialect
28 Beatles' "__ Mine"
29 Responsibility
30 Pope of 1775
34 Kitchen item
37 Song from "Mondo Cane"
38 Beauty parlor service
39 Nutmeg spice
40 Kind of money
41 Soda fountain indulgence
42 Back up, in a way
43 Actor McKellen
44 Singer Don
46 Opening of 3/26/64
52 Be a breadwinner
53 Flu variety
54 Memorial Coliseum player
56 Opening of 4/23/63
58 Smack
62 Schiller drama subject
63 Composer Bruckner
64 Gab
65 Name suffixes
66 Not in the __
67 "Rosemary" of film

DOWN
1 Timber tree
2 Cuckoo
3 Oil drilling equipment
4 Robin Cook best seller
5 Out on __
6 Stage stand
7 Martini's partner
8 Snake
9 In concealment
10 Advertising ploy
11 Theater critic Kenneth
13 1979 Midler film
15 Electron tube
18 "Turandot" librettist
20 Sixth-century date
22 Eastern capital
23 Often illegal auto maneuver
25 "__ Hell Harry"
26 Magnificence
27 Out of jail
31 ". . . kerchief and __ my cap"
32 Berlin connector
33 Retirees' agcy.
34 Flutter
35 Vast expanse
36 "Roberta" composer
39 Bunkum
41 "Just __"
43 Together
45 Medium grade
46 Crash diets
47 Poe family
48 Nobel physicist Bohr
49 Soames Forsyte wife
50 Certain Jamaican
51 Broadway cars
55 Parking mishap
57 Comics prince
59 "__ Woman" ('72 hit)
60 Astr. or biol.
61 Some popular music

DIAGONAL
1 Opening of 5/4/93

ACROSS

1 Name from 50's TV
9 Baseball's Doubleday
14 Romberg product
15 Filmdom's Lawrence
16 Infant's game
17 Infant's shoe
18 Showed fear
19 Stupidity
20 Sting
24 Mal de __
26 Words of enlightenment
27 Mars sighting
29 Bestow
32 Blow the cover of?
34 Puts back
38 __ Juana
39 Urban noise maker
41 Take this out for a spin
42 University founded in 1253
44 Locust
46 Exhortation
48 Pitcher Ryan
49 "__ of you . . ."
52 Ear-related
54 "The __ From Brazil"
55 Defective stop sign?
58 "I __ You Babe"
60 Yogi's cartoon sidekick
61 Blubbered
66 Like spring flowers
67 Battery type
68 Physicist Freeman
69 Innkeeper

DOWN

1 Person with a collar?
2 One rung on the evolutionary ladder
3 Spike, for one
4 Biblical vessel
5 Coach Bryant
6 Up
7 High
8 Vietnamese money unit
9 Accelerator item
10 Sticks
11 Dostoyevsky's "__ From the Underground"
12 Beethoven dedicatee
13 Singer Della
15 __-Wan Kenobi
19 Star in Cygnus
20 Rabbits' tails
21 "Pagliacci" husband
22 Menachem's peace partner
23 Deface
25 Agony
28 Item of love?
30 Bk. of Revelation
31 Poison
33 Pioneering video game
35 Writer Calvino
36 TV show since 1/14/52
37 Wings have them
40 Wambaugh's "The __ Field"
43 Bogey
45 Male swan
47 1980 Richard Gere portrayal
49 Hooked in a way
50 Definitely not a brain surgeon
51 Chemical compounds
53 Kind of tour
56 Continue
57 South Africa's __ Paul
59 "__ does it!"
61 Phooey's cousin
62 Novelist Rölvaag
63 Medium for Matisse
64 Ending with acetyl or butyl
65 __ Spiegel

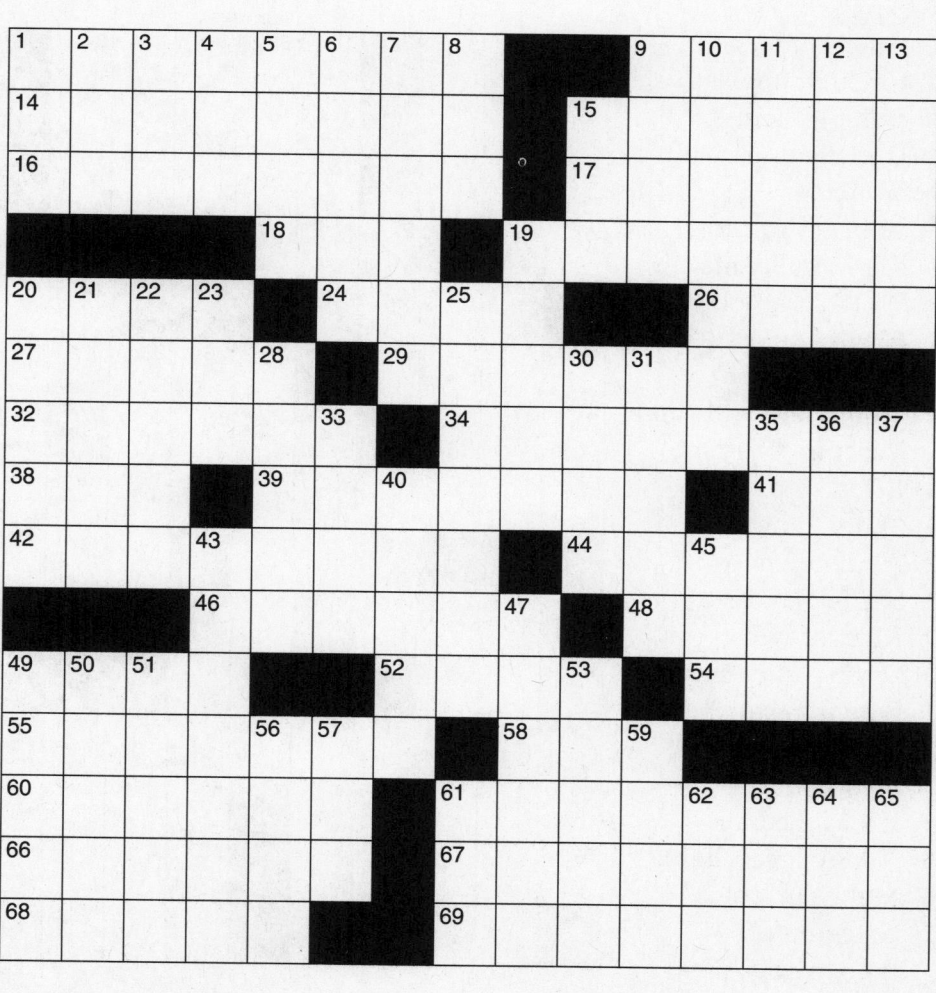

260 *by Harvey Estes*

ACROSS

1 Tiller's place
4 Flop's opposite
9 Merchant R. H. —
13 Money maker
14 Dessert bean
15 Newton knighted in 1705
17 Keg contents
18 "Help!" star
19 1959 Ritchie Valens hit
20 Behave
23 Multicolored
24 — Palmas, Spain
25 On an errand, maybe
26 Mortgage interest
27 Purple Heart, e.g.
30 "Low bridge! Everyone down!" canal
31 Officeholders
32 Circle of angels
33 Belief system
35 Is meticulous, with 53 Across
41 Abbr. in car ads
42 Many millennia
43 Word in an obit
44 Garroway of 50's TV
47 Itty-bitty map
49 "Interview with the Vampire" author
50 E.T.'s ship
51 "Life — beach"
52 Alta. neighbor
53 See 35 Across
59 Kind of wave
60 Scrub a tub, maybe
61 Bolivian export
62 Triangular treat
63 Be a ham
64 It's in the bag
65 NASA green lights
66 Make current
67 Catching of thoughtwaves

DOWN

1 First bone donor
2 Tagalog speaker
3 Most microscopic
4 Seafood dish
5 Water artery
6 An embarrassing problem to face?
7 Is in a slump
8 Celebration
9 The original Goldfinger?
10 "Unto us — is given"
11 Openness
12 American in Habana
16 Brahman, for one
21 Study
22 Pronounced
26 Topper
27 Lack of oomph
28 Edifice extension
29 Spoils, with "on"
30 Trio of mommies?
32 Chance
34 Family nickname
36 Equal a bet
37 Ground-breaker
38 Sweet liqueur
39 Striped apparel, often
40 Heart of Billy Williams
44 Heating pipes
45 "Out of —"
46 Spelling exercise?
48 Gamal of Egypt
49 Fan noise
51 Sailors' keys
52 Litter
54 Went to the bottom
55 Ne plus ultra
56 Diving bird
57 Guitar's ancestor
58 Piece of cake

by *Bill Click*

ACROSS

1 1975 Wimbledon champ
5 __ nova
10 High-ranking NCO
14 Oscar winner for "Moonstruck"
15 Sit up for
16 Ron Howard TV role
17 Irving Berlin song
20 Woolgatherer?
21 Winter forecast
22 Sioux Indians
23 "Gimme a G . . . ," e.g.
25 Org.
26 Word in Amtrak's slogan
28 N.H.L. legend Gordie
30 Wide's partner
33 "La Bohème" role
34 Louisiana inlet
35 One in France
36 Andrews Sisters hit
40 Speaker's pauses
41 Writer Cecil of "The Straight Dope"
42 __ me tangere
43 Q followers
44 Strength, in Variety talk
45 Favor
47 Confused thoughts
49 Secretaries may file these
50 Alpha's opposite
52 Unified
54 Profit by
57 Andrew Lloyd Webber song, with "The"
60 Astound
61 Chisholm, e.g.
62 Tense
63 1/17/94 honoree
64 First-year law school class
65 "Rule, Britannia" composer

DOWN

1 Highest point
2 "Pygmalion" author
3 Beatles recording
4 Goof
5 Tried to save a sinking ship?
6 Steinbrenner to the Yankees
7 Wise
8 Search (through)
9 From __ Z
10 Loses feathers
11 "Mary Poppins" tune, with "A"
12 Take's partner
13 Golfers' gadgets
18 River in Belgium
19 Revolted
24 "Aquarius" musical
25 Gone, but not forgotten?
26 Dinosaur DNA preserver
27 Coffin stands
28 Injures
29 Court cry
31 "Twisted" body part
32 Broadcast anew
34 Boast
37 "The Human Comedy" author
38 "Zip-__-Doo-Dah"
39 Like Nash's "lama"
45 Juries
46 Nothing: Fr.
48 Ripening
49 Like a pitcher's perfect game
50 Siberian city
51 Conductor Riccardo
52 60's hair style
53 Asterisk
55 Avoid
56 Cigar ending
58 Giant Mel
59 "Make __ double"

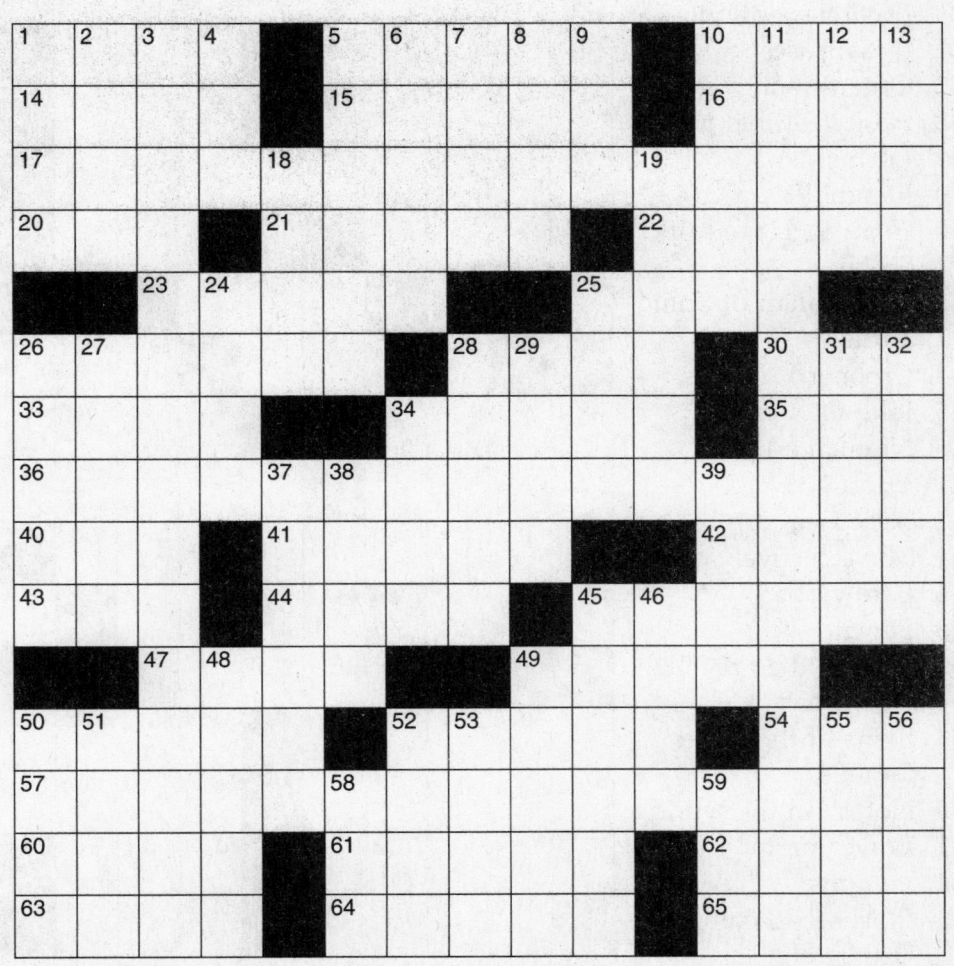

by Thomas W. Schier

ACROSS

1 Say "I do" again
6 March starter
9 Diplomatic skills
14 Dwelling place
15 U.N. member
16 Honolulu hello
17 Scrabble, anagrams, etc.
19 Bottoms of graphs
20 Disney dog
21 Madam's mates
22 Mosque chiefs
23 Ave. crossers
24 "I've been __!"
25 City on the Brazos
27 Ear cleaner
29 __ race (finished first)
30 Lived
33 Oaxaca waters
35 Dictionaries and thesauruses
37 Organic soil
38 Subject of this puzzle
39 Lockup
40 Preambles
42 "You __ Have to Be So Nice"
43 "The Sultan of Sulu" author
44 Crooner Williams
45 Jokester's props
46 Nightclub bits
47 Tricia Nixon __
48 New Deal org.
51 Move furtively
54 Barely open
56 Bewail
57 Start of the French workweek
58 Some of them are famous
60 Not __ in the world
61 Prayer part
62 __ nous
63 Ex-baseball commish Ueberroth
64 Light time
65 Lucy's landlady

DOWN

1 Singer Lou
2 Enemy vessel
3
T	H	I	S
H	E	R	E
I	R	O	N
S	E	N	T
4 Whirlpool
5 B.A. or Ph.D.
6 Like August weather, perhaps
7 Client
8 Computer access codes
9 City vehicle
10 Battle depicted in "The Last Command"
11 Hip joint
12 Not us
13 Freshness
18 Quickly: Abbr.
24 Towel word
26 Connectors
28 Housebroken
29 Circumlocutory
30 Poet laureate, 1843–50
31 Similar
32 Mil. officer
33 __ Romeo
34 Well-mannered
35 Incoherent speech
36 Off Broadway award
38 Is obstinate
41 More erratic
42 Humanitarian Dorothea
45 Where a cruise calls
46 Previn or Kostelanetz
47 Disk jockey Kasem
49 San Diego pro
50 Photographer Adams
51 Masher's comeuppance
52 Politico Clare Boothe __
53 __ the finish
55 Al Hirt hit
56 __ Blanc
59 Itsy-bitsy

ACROSS

1 Hypothetical eccentricities in time
6 Competition
10 Jail unit
14 "__ man with seven wives"
15 Miss Cinders of old comics
16 Singer Guthrie
17 Brightly sunburned
19 Leaning
20 60's space chimp
21 Heroic legends
22 Teen woe
23 Beelzebub
24 Aware of
25 French painter Jean
29 Hesitation sounds
30 __-di-dah
31 Sports sites
33 Mr. Whitney
35 Slippery one
38 Calms medically
40 Car gear
42 Mount St. Helens spew
43 "How dry __"
44 Cylindrical
45 Self
47 Pass receiver
50 "M*A*S*H" character
51 Flake material
52 Boors
54 Cordial
55 They get smashed
56 Clumsy ships
60 One of five
61 Oscar winner for "Sayonara"
63 Lease
64 __ Stanley Gardner
65 Boundary
66 Advantage
67 Philosopher A. J. __
68 Versifiers

DOWN

1 Use Western Union
2 Prayer's closing
3 Effect a makeover
4 School orgs.
5 Airline to Stockholm
6 Cash back
7 Sour brew
8 Under-the-sink item
9 Sups
10 Poolside hut
11 Greenland settler
12 Grassy plain
13 Mislay
18 Botanist Gray
23 Depot
24 Hardy and North
25 Pedro's house
26 Silver holders
27 It misleads
28 Broadway's "Three Men __ Horse"
32 Ocean
34 Permit
36 This, in Barcelona
37 Amorous gaze
39 Place of refinement
41 Baseball stat
46 Reproductive cell
48 Kind of soup
49 Not so clever
51 Exposed
53 Houston sch.
54 Had been
55 Length x width, for a rectangle
56 Prefix with sphere
57 Judicial cover?
58 Mend, as bones
59 Speedy planes
62 Spigot

264 *by Julian Ochrymowych & Amy Goldstein*

ACROSS

1 __ Rica
6 Job for Perry Mason
10 Career summary
14 Top grade
15 "__ We Got Fun?"
16 Son of Seth
17 Jockey's handful
18 Govt. agent
19 Mounties: Abbr.
20 Meaningful silence
23 Prominent features of Alfred E. Neuman
24 Carnaval site
25 Shrimpish
27 University of Maryland player
29 Stumble
32 Antigone's sister
35 Mongolian desert
36 The Monkees' "__ Believer"
37 1987 Edward James Olmos film
40 Actor Chaney
41 Minor profits?
42 Guinea pig or groundhog
43 Emily Dickinson's hometown
45 Air freshener scent
46 Nixon and Schroeder
47 Black-eyed item
48 Shows approval
52 Film in which Hayley Mills played twins
56 Ballet leap
58 One of the Menendez brothers
59 Gaucho gear
60 Elliptical
61 Look
62 Last word of fairy tales
63 Cravings
64 Flexible Flyer, for one

65 Ex-press secretary Dee Dee

DOWN

1 __ diem (seize the day)
2 Puccini product
3 More like a fox
4 Filament material
5 Org.
6 Tabby treat
7 "We __ please"
8 Breeze
9 Mediterranean spouter
10 Against
11 Stimulus
12 Mix of westerns
13 Venomous viper
21 Debts
22 Greek vowel

26 It's south of Saudi Arabia
28 Sign a check
29 Stylish, in the 60's
30 Basque, e.g.
31 Hair splitter
32 Mallorca, por ejemplo
33 Lively dance
34 Whisky-vermouth cocktail
35 Mdse.
38 Place to meet following a tennis match
39 Pick out of a lineup
44 Mertz and Merman
45 Looked too soon
47 Cracker Jack bonus
49 Speechify
50 Library gadget

51 Trains, in a way
53 Cribbage counters
54 Asia's __ Sea
55 Streetcar
56 "The __ Luck Club"
57 Night before

ACROSS

1 "St. John Passion" composer
5 In vogue
9 Carpet variety
13 Nepal's location
14 Leftovers dish
15 Prowess
16 "Lost Horizon" paradise
18 Public sentiment
19 "Message received"
20 Songwriter John
21 Long, deep bow
25 More than a snack
27 First look
30 1901 Churchill novel, with "The"
34 With masts fully extended
35 Imprint on glass
37 Posted
38 Puny pup
39 Dweller in Gulliver's Houyhnhnmland
40 Wash
41 Deuce topper
42 Skater Heiden
43 Idolater
44 Snow remover?
46 Seven Cities of Cibola seeker
48 George Takei TV/movie role
50 Confuses
51 Shore bird
54 Soprano Nixon
57 Dik Browne Viking
58 Town visited by Tommy Albright
63 Subtle twist
64 Like elbowing, e.g.
65 Paris landing site
66 Aromatic herb
67 Prepared brandy
68 Start for "of honor" or "of silence"

DOWN

1 __-relief
2 Ski wood
3 "The Company"
4 Solo of "Star Wars"
5 Plating material
6 Nixon chief of staff
7 Sunny vacation spot
8 Mojo
9 King Kong's home
10 Saber handle
11 To boot
12 __ Burnie, Md.
15 Aborigine's weapon
17 Woodworker's concern
21 City attacked by Cleon
22 Fabric with a raised pattern
23 Near ringer
24 "Jaws" locale
26 Canyon sound
28 Bring up
29 Work __
31 Action star Steven
32 Blitz
33 Typing pool members
36 Designer Chanel
39 Make oneself heard in the din
43 Lecterns
45 "Tumbling Tumbleweeds" singer, 1935
47 Traveled far and wide
49 Eclipse shadow
51 Kind of splints
52 Butler's quarters?
53 Operatic prince
55 "...as a bug in __"
56 Sally of NASA
59 Medic
60 Spanish gold
61 Timeworn
62 TV comic Louis

266 *by Charles Arnold*

ACROSS

1 Guzzles
7 Bebop
11 Certain muscles, informally
14 Dislocate
15 Woodwind
16 Varnish resin
17 Ancient ascetic
18 Letter writing: Abbr.
19 Japanese admiral Yuko
20 Battleship
23 Mesmerized
27 "Or __!" (veiled threat)
28 "Torero Saluting" painter
29 Rioting
31 Despicable
32 Greek market
33 Mitigates
35 Actor Matheson or Allen
38 Dictionary
40 Rogers's partner
42 Wily
43 Topple
45 Fudd of cartoondom
46 Director's cry
47 Bee activity
49 __ Downs (English racetrack)
52 Contented sound
53 __ fixe
54 Bluff, with a gun
57 Nuclear defense grp.
58 Russia's __ Mountains
59 Slanted
64 Petition
65 Scoop (out)
66 To wit
67 "__! We Have No Bananas"
68 Whirlpool
69 Like Parmesan

DOWN

1 Neighbor of Ont.
2 Raises
3 "__ Gratia Artis" (M-G-M motto)
4 Enemy
5 Dear, as memories
6 Two-track
7 Oedipus's mother
8 Lodging
9 Swedish painter of "At the Granary Door"
10 "Fiddler on the Roof" star
11 Straighten
12 Wash up
13 "Waverley" novelist
21 Burstyn and Barkin
22 Labor org.
23 Iranian dollars
24 Theater backer
25 Stand-in
26 Actress Garr
30 Transistor predecessor
31 "__ Misérables"
34 Cronus, to Romans
35 Meek
36 "*The* woman" for Sherlock
37 Traffic sign
39 Choose
41 Prefix with meter
44 Just as much
46 Bill's partner
48 Vexing
49 Emerson piece
50 Aspect
51 Noted White House resident
52 Multicolored pattern
55 Slender nail
56 Sirius, e.g.
60 Drs.' org.
61 Tennis call
62 __ de France
63 Dancer Charisse

ACROSS

1 Forlorn
4 Poker actions
10 Is appropriate
14 Actress MacGraw
15 State boldly
16 British title
17 Cover
18 Animated myope
20 Type of lily
22 Neighbor of Switz.
23 Oriental tea
24 Plant with cup-shaped flowers
26 Skirt opening
27 Communists
28 Clamorous advertising
32 Part of a book
34 Down the __
35 Word of rejection
36 Escape vehicles
37 Misprint
38 Mr. Kadiddlehopper
39 In the past
40 False temptress
41 Targets of 40 Across
42 Ta-ta
44 Fictional plantation
45 Gypsies
46 Cold dessert
49 One of the Borgias
52 Rimsky-Korsakov's "Le Coq __"
53 Rival of Brown
54 Aussie hopper
57 Actor Cariou
58 First name in mysteries
59 Flair
60 Any person
61 Son of Seth
62 Small piano
63 The "o" in Cheerios

DOWN

1 Latin beat
2 1979 sci-fi hit
3 Musical instrument from Down Under
4 Collide head-on
5 Vietnamese and Nepalese, e.g.
6 Point of contention
7 Match parts
8 Afore
9 Tot toter
10 Allegiance
11 Venetian troublemaker
12 1982 Disney film
13 Work long and hard
19 Works long and hard
21 Portents
25 Pindar piece
26 Wooden shoe
28 Beast of burden
29 Uproar
30 S-shaped curve
31 Resistance units
32 Tiff
33 Okefenokee resident
34 Small combos
37 Strunk and White's "The __ of Style"
38 Transport
40 Botanist's concern
41 West of Hollywood
43 Big quackers
44 Seat of power
46 Philosopher Kierkegaard
47 Russian writer Bonner
48 Religious principle
49 Ontario tribe
50 Merit
51 Town near Caen
52 Dream pictures artist
55 Hiatus
56 Legendary Giant

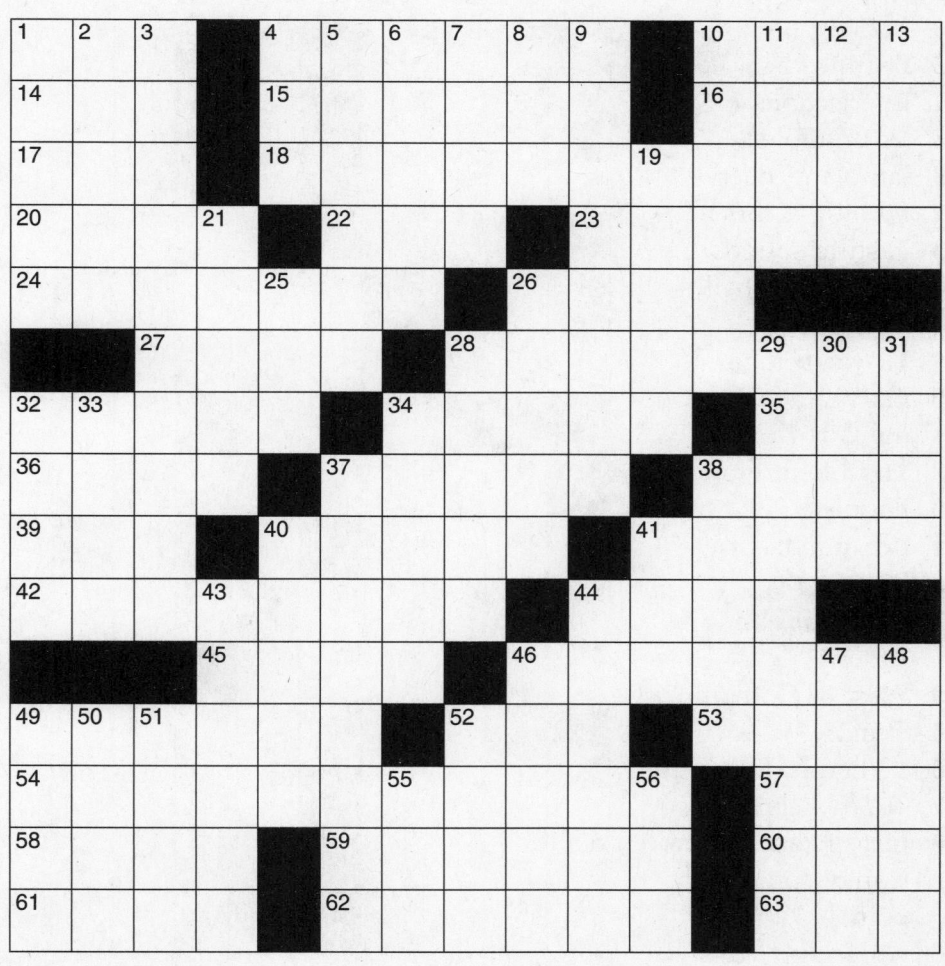

ACROSS

1 It goes from stem to stern
5 Ten Commandments word
10 Companion of Ollie
14 Dancer Pavlova
15 Champing at the bit
16 A billion years
17 Con game
18 Vacant
19 Soap unit
20 Stoves that don't work?
23 "Diamonds __ a girl's . . ."
24 "Gidget" star
25 Perform perfectly
28 Hägar the Horrible's honey
30 It was banned in 1973
33 Beatniks beat it
34 Interjections
36 __ in apple
38 Iamb and dactyl
39 Filming actors?
43 Pasture sounds
44 Carl of baseball, informally
45 Tic-toe bridge
46 Lady __, founder of the Girl Guides
48 Trouble in France
50 Frame
54 Itch initiator
56 Partake of
58 Calendar abbr.
59 Arson?
63 West of Gotham City
65 "I'm __ duck"
66 __ hemp (fiber plant)
67 "I Spy" star
68 List of candidates
69 It may come with points
70 Grown-up grigs
71 Biblical king with 10 wives
72 Muffs

DOWN

1 North African fortress
2 Concert cry
3 Filling surrounder
4 "Mrs. Battle's Opinions on Whist" writer
5 Île de la Cité site
6 The __ Man (tarot card)
7 Actor John
8 First name in supper club entertainment
9 Drift
10 Not at a distance
11 Logician
12 Flight approval
13 22° 30'
21 Baking potato
22 Lump
26 "Rock of __"
27 Young 'un
29 Thrilled response
31 Tony of "Who's the Boss?"
32 License
35 Pen
37 Trans-Atlantic flier
39 Emerson, the __ of Concord
40 Game originally called "fives"
41 Descartes conclusion
42 Fashion
43 Sot's spot
47 Big __, Calif.
49 Not staccato
51 A sew-and-sew?
52 Hubbub
53 Is foppish
55 Grind
57 Kind of attraction
60 Run in place
61 About
62 No __ (register button)
63 Plane downer
64 Like threatening bills

ACROSS

1 Speleology topic
5 Plane egresses
10 Pedestal topper
14 C.I.A. profiler Philip
15 Paradigm
16 Savvy about
17 Canine laryngitis?
19 Mutant heroes of modern comics
20 Not gross
21 Gain
22 Fanciful
24 Doubtful story
25 Fancies up
26 Record lists
29 Uses a cheat-sheet
30 "The Many __ of Dobie Gillis"
31 Watkins __, N.Y.
32 Gridiron period
36 Candid
37 First-aid contrivance
38 Stage curtain
39 Encircle
40 Way with words
41 Sneak preview
42 Posh
44 Like some hair
45 Words preceding film credits
47 Kingsley et al.
48 Warned with a horn
49 South of France
50 Shocking word
53 The least concern
54 Experimental canine?
57 Adjective for an antique store
58 TV exec Spelling
59 Hors d'oeuvre spread
60 Former empire
61 Acknowledge
62 Like certain trays

DOWN

1 "Three Coins in the Fountain" lyricist
2 Chills
3 Third piece of three
4 "A mouse!"
5 Richard Sheridan play, with "The"
6 Be gaga over
7 Chow __
8 Lobbying acronym
9 Winter sport
10 Canine underwear?
11 Frighten to the core
12 Cut flowers
13 "West Side Story" beau
18 Lady Gregory cohort
23 Deprive (of)
24 Stylish canine?
25 "__ You Glad You're You?" (1946 hit)
26 Stop (up)
27 Snake dancers
28 Maintain
29 Succeed, informally
31 Endocrine, e.g.
33 Loads
34 Juice flavor
35 Rations
37 Not get hit?
41 Dither
43 Miniature
44 Failing business's woe
45 Trunk items
46 Gangsters
47 Plains critter
48 Commandment word
49 Vidal's Breckinridge
50 "Gil __"
51 Courtroom ritual
52 Comply with
55 Contemptuous cry
56 Bath, for one

ACROSS

1 Tick off
5 Jerry Herman musical
9 Scarf
14 Tennis's Ivanisevic, often
15 "Fatal Attraction" villain
16 Bust finds
17 Diner's card
18 1953 Leslie Caron role
19 Long time
20 #1 song for Robert Palmer
23 At that point
24 Bookbinding leather
25 At regular intervals
28 Innocent one
29 Entirety
32 Communion table
33 TV's "Batman," e.g.
34 Oil of __
35 Learning method that "works for me"
38 "Indecent Proposal" director Adrian
39 Jokesters
40 One quadrillionth: Prefix
41 Vane dir.
42 Ill will
43 #, & or %
44 Either star of "Tea and Sympathy"
45 To you, to Yves
46 Empty-calorie lover
52 Craze
53 Novel featuring Doctor Long Ghost
54 Bear in the sky
55 Keats or Wordsworth
56 Mash preceder
57 Sardine containers
58 Wash
59 Light submachine gun
60 Noted Renaissance name

DOWN

1 Doll's cry
2 Like some tea
3 Ward (off)
4 Yuletide snack
5 Ice cream treat
6 Xenophobe's fear
7 Pinochle combo
8 Turnoffs
9 It fell in 1979
10 Attach, as a feed bag
11 King Harald's father
12 Folk tales
13 Slalom shape
21 Beloved
22 Energy
25 Humorist Mort et al.
26 Artful dodges
27 Pay the penalty
28 "Tootsie" Oscar winner
29 Out on __
30 Milk: Prefix
31 Popular disinfectant
33 Checking places
34 "Hold on . . ."
36 Happy, for one
37 1934 song "The Very Thought __"
42 Goddess of Hades
43 One of the Virgin Islands
44 Filled turnover
45 Give __ of one's own medicine
46 Nonsense song of 1918
47 Hand or foot
48 Exclude
49 Mr. Kristofferson
50 Does not exist
51 Life of Riley
52 Crowd around

ACROSS

1 Enjoys at leisure
5 Lucifer
10 Likely
13 "Flower Song," e.g.
14 Harden
15 A Guthrie
16 Start of a quip
19 Part of a flick?
20 French holy women: Abbr.
21 First
22 Egg: oval::___: pyriform
23 Supports
25 1973 Elton John hit
28 Burnt, in cooking
29 Environmentalism: Abbr.
30 Large: Prefix
31 "The Conqueror Worm" writer
34 Middle of the quip
38 Foreign exchange listing
39 Come to ___
40 O.K. Corral figure
41 Unstable
42 Elegant
44 Know-it-alls
47 Highlander
48 Treasured violin
49 Repugnance
50 "Whiffenpoof" syllable
53 End of the quip
57 Rotunda resting place
58 Prospero's sprite
59 Kind of ox
60 TV "clutter"
61 Curt
62 Arguments for

DOWN

1 "Völsunga ___"
2 Infuriates
3 Material for a topi
4 Had a session
5 Kind of anguish
6 Choler
7 Wash sites
8 Dernier ___
9 That girl
10 Spinning
11 Argue
12 Lincoln's in-laws
15 "For want of ___ the horse was lost"
17 Understanding words
18 Black ___ (sensational 1947 murder case)
22 Tiresome one
23 Coaxes
24 Boxlike sleigh
25 Slightly wet
26 Be heartsick
27 Time for mad dogs and Englishmen
28 Nuts
30 Grades
31 Vegetables
32 Not just mine
33 Glimpse
35 Kind of food
36 Capital
37 Kind of cutlet
41 Lecher
42 Kine
43 Lascivious look
44 Brazilian dance
45 "The way of a man with ___": Proverbs
46 Windmill arms
47 Rubbernecks
49 He's got it coming
50 Smudge
51 To boot
52 Bids
54 Topper
55 Long start
56 Little dickens

272 *by Fred Piscop*

ACROSS

1 Land for development
6 Small nail
10 __ Observer (1992 mission)
14 Move like a chopper
15 Greek liqueur
16 Wanted G.I.
17 __ Gay
18 Comics canine
19 __ fide (in bad faith)
20 Heirloom tool?
23 Carte start
24 Run an art show
25 Red giant, e.g.
28 TV's "__ Academic"
31 N.L. cap monogram
32 Schlemiel
33 Knock for a loop
35 Casino request
39 President Lincoln's tools?
42 Hightail it
43 Hummer's instrument
44 Month in which D.D.E. was born
45 Astronaut Grissom
47 Cornell's Big __
48 Disturb, with "up"
49 Peloponnesian War participant
52 Antipollution grp.
54 Secret military tool?
59 100 kurus
60 __ du Lac, Wis.
61 Puts out
63 In a frenzied fashion
64 Former Hawaii Senator Hiram
65 Annual visitor
66 Kind of loaf
67 __-eyed
68 Actress Georgia

DOWN

1 Word ignored in indexing
2 Gossipy Barrett
3 Admit
4 Home of the 1962 Mets
5 Park way
6 Flub, as a grounder
7 Wife of Boaz
8 Conqueree of 1521
9 Goofball
10 Class to which all of us belong
11 Look for
12 Esther of "Good Times"
13 Dispatch
21 Attaches
22 Joint: Prefix
25 Drenches
26 1 on the Mohs' scale
27 Way off
29 Transported
30 Until now
33 Our longest bones
34 Level
36 Commandment starter
37 Certain raingear
38 C.P.R. specialists
40 1945 blast site
41 Augured
46 Doesn't tip
48 Lunatic
49 Goo
50 Word of mouth
51 Play for __
53 Bel __ cheese
54 Decked out
55 __ time (right away)
56 1988 Dick Francis thriller, with "The"
57 Throw barbs at
58 Kitchen addition?
62 Pitcher Maglie

ACROSS

1 Cleo player
4 Nods
7 Healing waters
10 Bottom-of-letter abbr.
13 Greek nickname
14 "Barney Miller" regular Jack
15 1964 Murray Schisgal play
16 Vietnam's My —
17 Place for coming to grips?
18 Prom flowers
20 Toast word
21 Oven for a singer?
23 Peking finale
24 Mr. Buchwald
25 Sign maker
27 "Damn Yankees" team
30 "— well . . ."
32 Pope's "An — on Man"
33 Immensely
34 Man's name meaning "red"
35 "Le Coq —"
36 Amenable
37 Big name in top 40
40 Backbiter?
43 Govt. help for mom-and-pop stores
45 "Alice" role
46 Radar reception
47 Come about
49 "Runaround Sue" singer
50 Get in return
51 Skipper's command
53 Jazz's — Winding
55 Oxlike critter
56 Sea for a singer?
61 First name in tyranny
62 More sluggish
63 By way of
64 Literary monogram
65 Long spell
66 Exactly right
67 Charley Weaver's Mt. —
68 Author Harper
69 —-Cat (arctic vehicle)
70 Kidnapping grp., 1974
71 Bandleader Brown

DOWN

1 Religious leader
2 It's south of Georgia
3 Tubular pasta
4 Award for "Wings"
5 Actress friend of Prince Andrew
6 Take up like a sponge
7 Quenches
8 Washington waterway
9 Staved off
10 Grain for a playwright?
11 Revulsion
12 Like apple juice
19 Forte for an actress?
22 Flavor sensor
26 Arcane
27 Annoyer
28 Menu phrase
29 Voyage for an actor?
31 Mauna —
38 "Xanadu" rock grp.
39 Rare aquatic
41 Half a dance
42 Keystone figure
44 Plowed lands
47 #1 hit for the Chi-Lites, 1972
48 Wicked one
49 Family name of F.D.R.'s mother
52 Squash
54 It comes straight from the heart
57 Puppies' barks
58 Baudelaire's "The Flowers of —"
59 Orderly
60 Senate votes

274 *by Harvey Estes*

ACROSS

1 Jam maker
8 Mounds of arms
14 Facsimile
15 Tour follower
16 Occupy
17 Treadmill
18 They may try you
19 RR depot
21 Borders
22 Look up and down
23 "No bid"
25 Curve between musical notes
26 "Agnus __"
27 Crustacean catcher
29 Before
30 Scopes Trial defender
32 Fit into the schedule
34 Coal container
35 Razor-billed bird
36 Reindeer relative
40 Like this answer
43 Constellation next to Scorpius
44 Membership fee for 39 Down?
46 Shipping letters
48 "__ Was a Rollin' Stone" (1972 hit)
50 Picker-uppers
51 Stories
52 Uses a knife
54 Sullivan Award grp.
55 Sommelier's offerings
56 "Four Quartets" poet
58 Temporary
60 Sprays, perhaps
61 Ruin, as plans
62 Naguib's successor
63 Originally

DOWN

1 Shooter supporter
2 Took back
3 Highest orbital points
4 Get wider
5 Whopper juniors
6 Henri's here
7 Dupe
8 Bathing suit top
9 Bit
10 Takes to the street edge
11 Uniform attachment
12 Visualize
13 Is incensed
15 Comprehends
20 Drink opener
23 Resolve, as differences
24 Consoles
27 Kid corrals
28 City on the Loire
31 Baseball stat
33 Ring result
36 Where nautical rope is wound
37 Uzbek lake
38 Duelers' equipment
39 W.W. II craft
40 Masters tournament location
41 Freeloader
42 Cracker toppers
45 Certain code carrier
47 Ruthless ruler
49 Book containing legends
51 Florentine painter
53 Spot
55 "Star Trek" Klingon
57 Finish'd
59 Youngster

ACROSS

1 Apple competitor
4 Gambler Holliday
7 Fifth-century pope
12 Green
14 The "S" in T. S. Eliot
16 Men of La Mancha
17 Farmer's tipcart
18 Cartridge type
19 Aviatrix, for short
20 Point of no return?
21 Hidden theme of this puzzle
24 Last word of "Finnegans Wake"
25 Make an appeal
26 White House monogram
27 Outfit
29 Make an appeal
30 Miners' sch.
32 Out of sorts
33 Friend of 21 Across
35 Affected by pollen
38 "Clan of the Cave Bear" heroine
39 Chosen number?
42 Anwar's successor
43 Pickpocket
44 Slangy hello
45 New York eng. sch.
46 Like 33 Across's apple
50 Suffix meaning "small one"
51 Pack animal?
52 Laid-back
53 Quick to blush
56 London barrister
58 Game officials
59 Making out
60 Hot time in Chile
61 Umpteen's ordinal?
62 Green lights

DOWN

1 Hosp. hookups
2 Doctors often carry them
3 Franciscus TV drama of the 60's
4 "Dream Lover" singer
5 With no letup
6 Price abbr.
7 Material
8 Pro follower
9 Dog, for short
10 Proof goof
11 Minimal ante
13 A bit obtuse
14 Maze word
15 Droopy-eyed
19 Corset result, perhaps
21 Where fat cats get thin
22 "I'm glad that's over!"
23 Sealy rival
28 N.H.-Vt. neighbor
30 Open
31 Whirligig
32 Actor Gerard
33 Boxer's title, briefly
34 Short shot?
35 Daphne and hazel
36 It's like home?
37 Bomber Boomer
39 Beethoven's only opera
40 Sight saver?
41 Peaked
43 Cockpit display
44 Mrs. Rockefeller
47 Former capital of Bolivia
48 Underground event
49 ___ gland
54 It ended in 1806: Abbr.
55 Two or go follower
56 X
57 Football linemen: Abbr.

276 *by Sidney L. Robbins*

ACROSS

1 Wealthy person
5 Takes advantage of
9 "The Forsyte __"
13 Likeness
15 Kind of stick
16 Sheriff Tupper of "Murder, She Wrote"
17 Social hangout
19 Sea swallow
20 Home turnover
21 Knock out of kilter
23 Illuminated
24 Terminator
25 Bear up there
29 Steep slope
33 Crier of Greek myth
35 Wakens
39 Bettor's challenge
43 Show fright
44 Weird
45 Followed orders
48 N.Y. Police __
49 Exodus priest
53 Mauna __
55 Responded unintelligibly
58 "Last stop! __!"
62 Abner's pal and namesakes
63 Diamond coup
66 Relative of the clarinet
67 Auction actions
68 Indian boat
69 Part of Halloween makeup
70 Church nook
71 Endure

DOWN

1 Informal greetings
2 Eastern V.I.P.
3 Wind instrument?
4 They'll be hunted in April
5 Big sports news
6 Loudly weep
7 "Holy moly!"
8 Kind of loser
9 Beelzebub
10 Change
11 Watkins Glen, e.g.
12 "Lou Grant" star
14 Lod airport airline
18 Nobelist Wiesel
22 Esteem
25 German link
26 Kind of squad
27 Lemonlike
28 Singer Lane
30 Cuomo's predecessor
31 Son of Prince Valiant
32 Australian hopper
34 Long Island town
36 Tool storage area
37 Limerick site
38 Barber's cut
40 Wane
41 Bullring shout
42 Receive
46 Pass
47 Cabbage patch item
49 Visibly happy
50 Caribbean getaway
51 "__ has it . . ."
52 Start
54 Actor Guinness
56 Old lab burner
57 Trapdoor
59 Milky gem
60 Arm bone
61 Pueblo town
64 Employee card and others
65 Still and all

by *Alex K. Justin*

ACROSS

1 Dumbfounded
5 Acquire, as expenses
10 Singer Campbell
14 Colombian city
15 Hughes' plane, Spruce __
16 1890's Vice President __ P. Morton
17 1959 Rodgers and Hammerstein hit
20 "You can __ horse to . . ."
21 Bridal path
22 Predicament
24 Obote's successor
26 1956 Comden-Green-Styne collaboration
33 On __ (counting calories)
34 Man with a title
35 Russian space vehicle
36 Pride and envy, e.g.
37 Old hat
38 "Aurora" painter
39 Kind of cap or cream
40 Radio host of note
41 First U.S.-born Saint
42 1930 Gershwin musical
46 Sigmatism
47 Achy
48 Whiz kid
51 Blotto
54 1983 Herman-Fierstein musical
60 "Metamorphoses" poet
61 Wish granters
62 TV's Oscar
63 Hitches
64 Mill material
65 Murder

DOWN

1 Part of a play
2 Star of TV's "Wiseguy"
3 "Waiting for the Robert __"
4 Puts out of commission
5 Desert critter
6 Persona __ grata
7 How some packages are sent: Abbr.
8 R. & R. org.
9 Ring leader?
10 Sticking together
11 Decreasingly
12 Demonic
13 Garibaldi's birthplace
18 Keats or Shelley
19 Popular street name
23 Invent
24 Snaps handcuffs on
25 Gentle, as breezes
26 Grounds
27 Kingly decree
28 Passenger ship
29 Gobble
30 "__ man with seven . . ."
31 Curtain material
32 Nine-to-five routine
37 Conks out
38 Mutinied
41 __-comic (play type)
43 Long narratives
44 Alan, Larry or Stephen
45 Tap-dance
48 Crushing news
49 Four-star review
50 __ rain
52 Admiral Zumwalt
53 Actress Moore
55 Chicken's counterpart
56 Atmosphere: Prefix
57 Prefix with lateral
58 Omicrons predecessors
59 Thesaurus listing: Abbr.

ACROSS

1 One who reunes
5 Bic or Parker products
9 Lox's partner
14 Computer offering
15 Face shape
16 Shade of white
17 No ifs, __ or buts
18 Soho so-long
19 Lounges lazily
20 Start of a quip
23 Consumed
24 Israeli airport
25 __ chango (magician's command)
29 "That was close!"
31 Horror film frightener
34 Oscar de la __
35 Mimi Sheraton subject
36 Obstinate one
37 Middle of the quip
40 Hor.'s opposite
41 __ of March
42 French avenue
43 It's north of Calif.
44 Chance __ (meet accidentally)
45 Not present
46 Columbus univ.
47 One, in Orléans
48 End of the quip
55 His beloved was Beatrice
56 Old newspaper section
57 Hide
59 Rags-to-riches writer
60 Roughneck
61 Bombeck, the columnist
62 Hops brews
63 Sea eagle
64 Cooper's was high

DOWN

1 Internists' org.
2 Give temporarily
3 Remove, as a knot
4 Daydream
5 Spud
6 Dodge
7 European defense grp.
8 Dross
9 Swell, as a cloud
10 Have nothing to do with
11 Course game
12 A Gardner
13 Fleur-de-__
21 Old Nick
22 Coasters
25 Utah city
26 Allude (to)
27 __ nous
28 Editor's mark
29 Part of NOW
30 Breaks up clods
31 Company B awakener
32 ". . . in tears amid the __ corn": Keats
33 Ism
35 Rover's playmate
36 Tormé and Gibson
38 Raise the end of
39 Cacophonous tower
44 Does a groomsman's job
45 Whosoever
46 Bewhiskered animal
47 Author Sinclair
48 Fabric texture
49 "Come Back, Little Sheba" playwright
50 Prod
51 Rating a D
52 Aboveboard
53 Florida's __ Beach
54 Pollster Roper
55 A tiny bit
58 Ecru

by Fred Piscop

279

ACROSS
1 "West Side Story" girl
6 200 milligrams
11 Low island
14 1968 song "All __ the Watchtower"
15 River to the Missouri
16 Fuss
17 Seaver's nickname
19 Robert Morse Tony-winning role
20 House cleaner, in England
21 "Absolutely"
22 Legal profession
24 Queen Victoria's house
26 Freight charge
27 Half-wit
28 Better than a bargain
29 Polynesian carvings
33 "Hail, Caesar!"
34 Netman Nastase
37 Sheepish
38 Cup's edge
39 Battery part
40 Anti-prohibitionists
41 Disfigure
42 Get extra life from
43 Portaged
45 Patriotic uncle
47 Rocket's cargo
49 Crib-sheet contents
54 Earthy colors
55 Veneration
56 Hand-cream ingredient
57 "Harper Valley __"
58 Decorative shrub
61 Sock in the jaw
62 Address grandly
63 Coeur d'__, Idaho
64 Flood relief?
65 Pave over
66 Coiffed like Leo

DOWN
1 "Concentration" objective
2 Hello or goodbye
3 Type type
4 Opening
5 Stone, for one
6 Kitchen gadgets
7 Garage-sale words
8 Spitfire fliers, for short
9 Work up
10 Electronics whiz
11 Western spoof of 1965
12 "What __" ("I'm bored")
13 "__ Sixteen" (Ringo Starr hit)
18 Package-store wares
23 Skater Zayak
25 Place for posies
26 Call back
29 Wrecker
30 "__ had it!"
31 News locale of 12/17/03
32 Shoe part
33 Auto option, informally
35 Wallet contents, for short
36 Shoebox letters
38 Alan or Cheryl
39 Kind of buildup
41 Gauge
44 Inertia
45 Finn's pal
46 Once again
47 "Where's __?" (1970 flick)
48 Part owner?
50 Half of a Western city name
51 Pulitzer-winning novelist Glasgow
52 TV exec Arledge
53 Basted
55 Cinema canine
59 __ out (missed)
60 Descartes's conclusion

280 *by Stephanie Spadaccini*

ACROSS

1 Casper or Balthazar, e.g.
6 Rope material
10 Chorale part
14 Florida city
15 Jai __
16 La Scala presentation
17 NO UNTIDY CLOTHES
20 Walking on air
21 Macadam ingredient
22 __ Cruces, N.M.
23 Prepared
24 Harem
26 Subordinate Claus
29 Apocalypse
31 Gene material
32 Seldom seen
34 "QB VII" author
36 Lump of jelly, e.g.
39 GOVERN, CLEVER LAD
43 "You said it!"
44 Writer Shere
45 Approve
46 W.W. II grp.
48 Agrippina's son
50 German pronoun
51 Answer to "What's keeping you?"
55 Mount near ancient Troy
57 Item in a lock
58 "I" affliction
59 1990 Bette Midler film
62 BLATHER SENT ON YE
66 Neighborhood
67 Le Mans, e.g.
68 Conductor Georg
69 Back-to-school time: Abbr.
70 Bouquet
71 Friend of Henry and June

DOWN

1 Word on the Oise
2 Long (for)
3 Food critic Greene
4 Arm bones
5 Fried lightly
6 Actor Charles of "Hill Street Blues"
7 Overhead trains
8 Not shiny
9 A captain of the Enterprise
10 Dance, in France
11 On __ (doing well)
12 1979 treaty peninsula
13 Authority
18 Alternate road
19 Los Angeles suburb
24 Obviously pleased
25 Big name in viniculture
26 Physics unit
27 Zhivago's love
28 "It Came __ Outer Space"
30 Mezz. alternative
33 "It's true," in Torino
35 French resort town
37 Forest florae
38 __ B'rith
40 Fingernail polish
41 Realism
42 Salon selection
47 Rossini character
49 Potemkin mutiny site
51 Jots
52 Skiing's Phil or Steve
53 Tiptoe
54 Air Force arm: Abbr.
56 Illinois city
59 Cassandra
60 Falana or Montez
61 Opposing
63 Dracula, sometimes
64 Sgt., e.g.
65 Frozen Wasser

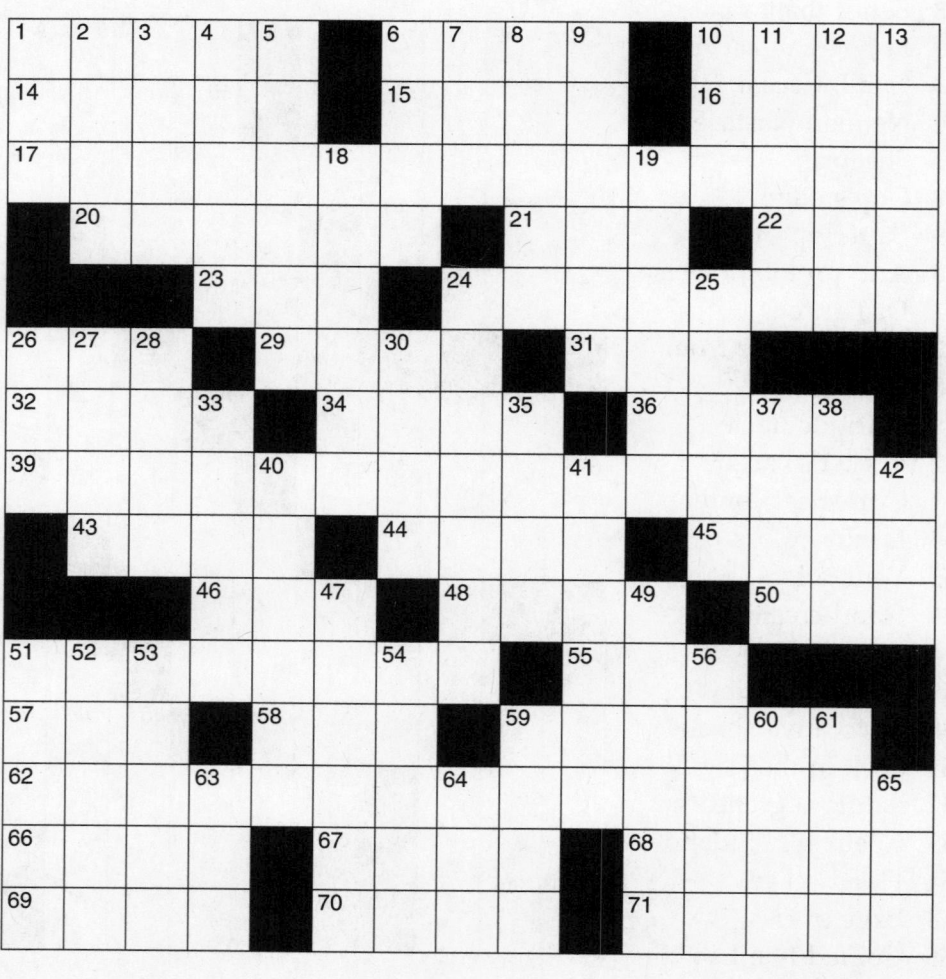

ACROSS

1 Funny pages favorite
11 Composer Satie
15 Exciting adventure
16 "I came," to Caesar
17 Recruiter's objective
18 Professional suffixes
19 Three after B
20 Cousin of "Eureka!"
21 Shows how
23 Stout
24 Hawaii's state bird
26 Screen's partner
27 Post
29 Show anger, in a way
32 According to
33 They make a bloom blossom
35 Satisfied subscribers
37 Profligate
40 Tubular pasta
43 Victoria's Secret selections
47 Blown-up photo: Abbr.
48 Discovery of 1781
51 Stevedore's, e.g.
52 Philatelist's item
54 Little pest
56 One over due
57 Shade maker
60 Twosome
61 Season in St. Lo
62 Turner and Pappas
63 Way back
66 Furniture wood
67 Crudity
68 Guinness Book suffixes
69 Creator of 1 Across

DOWN

1 Start of a Gardner title
2 C.B.ers' names
3 Brennan and Ford
4 Calendar abbr.
5 Match play?
6 Chung's former partner
7 Singer Nina
8 Real ending in London
9 1978 Yankee hero
10 Renowned costume designer
11 Bounce
12 Amend
13 Whole amount
14 "Pow!" places
22 Quakers
25 Loop for a lobe
28 Oscar __ Renta
30 Like Gen. Schwarzkopf
31 Prefix with cycle or sex
34 Gym exercises
36 TV host, 1955–82
38 N.Y.C. div.
39 Bambi's aunt
40 Break
41 Pipe openings
42 Show anger, in a way
44 Hospital personnel
45 Feature of many court buildings
46 Increase the angle of elevation
49 Without cause
50 Long, bony fish
53 Mardi Gras sights
55 Friendly Islands
58 First ed.
59 Actress Olin
64 Dutch painter Gerard __ Borch
65 Thrash

282 *by Norma Steinberg*

ACROSS

1. "Major Barbara" playwright
5. Sierra Club founder John
9. Phrygian king
14. Per capita
15. __ facto
16. "Have __ day!"
17. Proctor's cry at the end of a test
18. Pierce
19. Coast
20. Imprisoned feline's call?
23. Cornucopia
24. "Star-Spangled Banner" contraction
25. Avaricious
28. Nostalgic song for cows?
33. Greenstreet's frequent co-star
34. Monk's hood
35. Flag
36. Neighbor of Afr.
37. Bluish-gray cat
40. Famous diarist
41. Beginning (then)
43. Harness part
44. Desert plant
46. Rex Stout's canine sleuth?
48. Disclaimer
49. Kind of shot
50. Temperament
51. Kind of relationship for crows?
57. Isaac's mother
58. Pierre's breakfast choice
59. Cheer (for)
61. Blazing
62. In addition
63. Author Vidal
64. Sales prospects
65. More than misled
66. Tom Joad, e.g.

DOWN

1. Get __ (ready)
2. Reagan Secretary of State
3. Wile E. Coyote's supply company
4. If
5. 1990 Kathy Bates film
6. Author Sinclair
7. "...ere __ Elba"
8. Kind of cop
9. Old word for a harasser
10. Get by will
11. Parisian house of design
12. Plat portion
13. Comment before "I told you so"
21. Computer add-on
22. Cons
25. Learn through research
26. Awaken
27. Goof
28. Pattern
29. TV lawyer __ Marshall
30. Leonardo's hometown
31. Author Jong
32. Of the kidneys
34. Singer Laine
38. Whiff
39. "__ newt..."
42. Word before march
45. Experience
47. Fancies
48. Tipped, in a way
50. Verdun's river
51. Eatery
52. Kathleen Battle offering
53. Holiday season
54. Takeout shop
55. Kitchener
56. Actress Spelling
57. Former baseball all-star Bando
60. Driver's aid

ACROSS

1 Sibelius's "__ Triste"
6 Where pins are made
10 Masochist's start
14 "Tempest" spirit
15 Late king of Norway
16 Popular rapper
17 Impractical idealist
19 Venus's home
20 Legal add-on
21 "__ goes" ("Slaughter-house-Five" refrain)
22 Casserole tidbit
24 Port, e.g.
26 Son of __
27 Gardner of "Mogambo"
28 Hollywood comer
31 Butler portrayer
34 First king of Israel
35 Leprechaun's land
37 French state
38 Father: Prefix
39 Oscar-winning song of 1958
40 "The Wind in the Willows" character
41 Deadlocked
42 Peacocks do it
43 Hook and crew
45 Kind of ball or card
46 He talked horse sense
47 Super-remedy
51 Hamlet's weapon
54 Jolts
55 Copacabana locale
56 Send forth
57 Performer of prodigious feats
60 Set of type
61 Sea into which the Amu Darya flows
62 Persian
63 Deuce topper
64 Caravel of 1492
65 Strong tastes

DOWN

1 "Star Wars" villain
2 Went up
3 Like some pads
4 Et __ (footnote abbr.)
5 Slippery
6 Spirit
7 Scads
8 Make antimacassars
9 Bad influence
10 Cruel employer
11 Folic, e.g.
12 "Heigho! the derry oh" setting
13 Tribe in the Winnebago nation
18 Early center of Celtic learning
23 Sharing adjective
25 Daydreamer
26 Take __ for the worse
28 Makes replete
29 Navy battle site of 1813
30 Comics bulldog
31 Masterpiece
32 Superior to
33 Site of a "Road" film
34 Redeemed
36 "Delta of Venus" author
38 Immature adult male
42 Livelihood
44 Art today
45 Bridle
47 Arum lily
48 Nordic
49 Chinese weight
50 Actress Anderson, et al.
51 Deprived, poetically
52 Subject in Virgil's "Eclogues"
53 Furniture wood
54 Don __
58 "Exodus" role
59 Blue Eagle agcy. of the 30's

284 *by Stanley Newman*

ACROSS

1 Fight locale
6 Rhyme scheme
10 Fitzgerald specialty
14 Lonesome George
15 Third Vice President
16 Nope
17 Of one of the senses
18 Neck of the woods
19 Linger
20 Hot stuff
22 No contest, e.g.
23 NASA affirmative
24 Suitor
26 Man with a horn
30 Can't stand
32 Hideouts
33 Untrustworthy sort
34 Former nuclear agcy.
37 Being broadcast
38 The Rumba King
39 Colleague of Scotty
   and Spock
40 Road material
41 Showed the world
42 Keepers of the flame
43 Obsolete typewriter
   necessity
45 Memorable shepherd
46 Public fuss
47 "— you!"
48 Congressional caucus
49 Hot stuff
56 Coin in the Trevi
57 Nobelist Wiesel
58 Herbert Hoover, by
   birth
59 Reckons
60 Hirschfeld's
   daughter
61 — garde
62 Letter closing
63 Lincoln in-law
64 Actress Evelyn

DOWN

1 Arab nobles
2 Lopsided win
3 Iberian river
4 "Hud" star
5 Attentive
6 By surprise
7 Ambience
8 — Rabbit
9 Pentagon pooh-bah
10 Inferior
11 Hot stuff
12 Isherwood
   collaborator
13 "Take — Train"
21 — to mention
25 Taipan frypan
26 Like crazy
27 Superboy's girlfriend
28 Hot stuff

29 Sportscaster Cross
30 Hot stuff
31 Bit of wampum
33 Beyond question
35 Sommer of the
   screen
36 Zodiacal border
38 Window type
39 Sample soup
41 Outlaw
42 Apple Computer co-
   founder
44 Slant differently
45 Spelldown
46 Bad news on Wall
   Street
47 Place
48 Give away
50 Miscellany
51 Barnum's soprano

52 Robert Indiana
   painting
53 On vacation
54 It's blowin' in the
   wind
55 Some carpenters

ACROSS

1 Bit of lowlife?
6 Unyielding
10 Spacewalk, e.g.: Abbr.
13 "Reflections on Violence" author
14 Occupied with
15 Lose it
16 Brit's potato chip
17 Headliner
18 Hunt hint
19 Example
21 Riddler of old
23 Burnish
24 Careening
25 Use face cream
27 "Perpetual Peace" writer
28 First name in daytime talk
29 Brit. ref. work
30 Mr. Bones, in a minstrel show
33 Hard-rock band named for an inventor
35 Train schedule abbr.
37 French pupil
38 Nahuatl speakers
40 Cable TV inits.
42 Oklahoma city
43 Writer Hubbard
44 Guides
46 Refute
47 By __ and bounds
48 Bearlike
49 Set apart
53 Flip talk
54 Spice
56 Missile depots
57 Comic Kamen
58 Art Deco master
59 Bar, legally
60 "__ luck?"

61 Env. enclosure
62 Expressionless

DOWN

1 Spore sacs
2 Daybreak
3 Discordia's counterpart
4 Readers' perusal
5 Woolly fabric
6 They're thrown at meets
7 Became a competitor
8 __ glance
9 Abandon
10 Hitch
11 Boast of
12 High point
15 Spielberg film
20 Don't do it

22 Smooth
25 At the home of
26 Sans esprit
28 Concerned citizens' org.
31 Alamo competitor
32 Hammett detective Beaumont
34 Flip __ (decide randomly)
36 Kind of ballot
39 Signs of a cold
41 Wood sorrels
45 Literary works
46 Einstein
48 U.S. Grant's school: Abbr.
50 Countertenor

51 Saturday TV fare, slangily
52 Glimpse
55 Paleozic, e.g.

286 by Harvey Estes

ACROSS
1 Taj Mahal, e.g.
5 Leader from Talah Minufiya
10 Braces
14 Spy in a 1962 exchange
15 Wide open
16 "Listen up," old style
17 Chuck-a-luck equipment
18 Defunct award
19 Villa Maria College site
20 Start of a quip
23 Copied
24 Davis's home: Abbr.
25 Carmichael's "__ Buttermilk Sky"
26 Chaps
28 Scrap for Rover
31 Overlord
33 Subject of equitation
35 "Deep Space Nine" character
36 QB's want them
37 Quip, part 2
43 Union initials
44 Modern site of ancient Tyre
45 Minute __
46 Lower
49 Mount
51 Onetime soldier
52 Twaddle
53 Tram load
55 Advance stealthily
57 Quip, part 3
62 Mavens
63 Attorney chaser
64 Garden dweller
66 May, for one
67 David Copperfield's mother
68 Sheltered spot
69 Inspected
70 First name in comedy
71 Coaster

DOWN
1 Jot
2 Final copy: Abbr.
3 Repairer
4 Censor, in a way
5 Vegetarian football game?
6 Family data
7 Dungeonlike
8 By the item
9 Rides herd on
10 Pronoun in a wedding vow
11 MOMA work
12 Field-guide listing
13 Make fun of mercilessly
21 "Is it soup __?"
22 Carnival day
26 Marcus Loew founded it
27 Debussy's "Le Jet d'__"
29 Writing on an urn
30 Irrelevant facts, slangily
32 Locale in a Beatles song
34 Go soft
36 Disposable
38 On the other hand
39 Fish-line material
40 Flying cross, e.g.
41 More than aloofness
42 Partygoer
46 Ballet movement with the toe
47 Manhattan type
48 "Becket" co-star, 1964
49 Word in a detergent ad
50 Chic
54 Unwelcome tenant?
56 Decodes
58 Gone, with "up"
59 Fraternity
60 Bring home
61 Moolah
65 Kind of school

by Jonathan Schmalzbach

ACROSS

1 "... more than one way to skin __"
5 Supply a party
10 Beast of burden
13 Fads
15 Speak publicly
16 Caltech rival
17 Cereal "fruit"
19 "__ of these days, Alice ..."
20 Outdoor
21 Spiritual punishment
23 Meadow
24 Jockey Cordero
25 Civil War flash point
32 Nom de crook
33 Upset
34 Small dog, for short
37 Split
38 Grew ashen
40 Coffee, informally
41 Hat-room fixture
42 Salon offering
43 More painful
44 U.S. commodore in Japan, 1853–54
47 Letter-shaped metal bar
50 Señor Guevara
51 Lovebirds' destination, maybe
54 Paul of "Casablanca"
59 __ Altos, Calif.
60 County of Northern Ireland
62 Had a little lamb?
63 First name in cosmetics
64 Novelist Françoise
65 Roll of bills
66 Looks (to be)
67 Unattached

DOWN

1 With the bow, in music
2 Bellyache
3 Malarial symptom
4 Part of T.V.A.: Abbr.
5 Hooded snakes
6 Exist
7 Diamond cover
8 To be, to Satie
9 "__ the Fox" (classic fable)
10 In the midst of
11 From the time of
12 Girder material
14 __ of justice
18 Yesterday: Fr.
22 "__ luck?"
25 David's instrument
26 Downwind, nautically
27 Wedding sine qua non
28 Add to, unnecessarily
29 Smut
30 Prior to, in poems
31 Crimson
34 Henry VIII's VIth
35 "Reply completed," to a ham operator
36 Queen of Scots
38 Word before bull or stop
39 Grasshopper's rebuker
40 Baseball's DiMaggio
42 Mexican snacks
43 Isn't miserly
44 Cosmo, e.g.
45 Reverberations
46 At what time?
47 Wedding acquisition
48 Flora and fauna
49 Let up
52 Type of wine
53 Kitty starter
55 Kind of estate
56 Therefore
57 Major rug exporter
58 Unit of force
61 Rep. foe

ACROSS

1 Bend
5 Exchange
9 Polite form of address
13 Actor Calhoun
14 Make __ for (argue in support of)
15 Ray of Hollywood
16 This puzzle's mystery subject
19 "The Joy Luck Club" author
20 Fuzzy
21 Rule
22 Yield
23 Dubbed one
24 1951 movie with 16 Across
31 Stumble
32 River to the Caspian
33 Veterans Day mo.
35 Daly of "Gypsy"
36 Competition for Geraldo
38 Trig function
39 Wynken, Blynken and __
40 They're sometimes wild
41 Earth mover
42 1957 movie with 16 Across
47 Thumbnail sketch
48 16 Across's "Cat on __ Tin Roof"
49 Étagère piece
52 County north of San Francisco
54 Neighbor of Ind.
57 1946 movie with 16 Across
60 "__ known then what . . ."
61 Cancel
62 "A" code word
63 Greek portico
64 Use épées
65 Half a fortnight

DOWN

1 Stew
2 "Damn Yankees" seductress
3 Green land
4 __ Affair
5 Play's start
6 He coined the term "horsepower"
7 Pallid
8 Caress
9 MGM's Louis B. and others
10 "__ know is what . . ."
11 Sick as __
12 Dawn
14 Put up with
17 Novelist Waugh
18 Disney mermaid
22 Horn, for one
23 Iranian chief, once
24 Letter abbr.
25 Richard of "Bustin' Loose"
26 Newswoman Ellerbee
27 Tend to
28 Refrain syllable
29 Confederacy's opponent
30 Three trios
34 Exceedingly
36 Eight: Prefix
37 Through
38 Latched
40 Law professor Hill
43 Airline to Spain
44 Outpouring of gossip
45 Bit of fall weather
46 Miss O'Neill
49 Publisher Adolph
50 Sloop
51 Defense means
52 Diner's guide
53 First-class
54 Man or Ely, e.g.
55 16 Across's "__ With Father"
56 Plumber's concern
58 Travel (about)
59 16 Across's "The Last Time I __ Paris"

ACROSS

1 Unhappy
5 Man with the world on his shoulders
10 Israeli carrier
14 "Mona __"
15 Scarlett's love
16 Comic Rudner
17 What we celebrate on July 4
20 Honor, with "to"
21 Form 1040 amount
22 Buntline and Rorem
23 Sean Connery, e.g.
24 Duke's home
27 Fifth Avenue name
28 Catch in the act
31 Gaucho's rope
32 Golfer Ballesteros
33 Old Russian assembly
34 What we celebrate on July 4
37 Bronze and Iron
38 Some intersections
39 Think
40 Stag party attendees
41 Scorch
42 Ranch
43 Tools locale
44 __ de foie gras
45 Book after Nehemiah
48 Fortification
52 What we watch on July 4
54 A lulu
55 Miss Brooks portrayer
56 Muck
57 Witnessed
58 Stocking material
59 Some whiskies

DOWN

1 Happy
2 Green shade
3 Employed
4 Seasons, as meat
5 Teen hangout
6 Dean Martin's "__ Amore"
7 __-majesté
8 Arm of the Treasury Dept.
9 Ill
10 Construct
11 Island near Venice
12 Mighty mite
13 Costly cloth
18 Hangover soother?
19 Son of Seth
23 Baseball and hockey stats
24 Father of Hector and Paris
25 Danny of the N.B.A.
26 Weighed down
27 Passover feast
28 Blue entertainment
29 Hotpoint rival
30 Sang to the moon
32 Golf legend Sam
33 Doctor's instrument
35 Intangible
36 Egypt's __ Church
41 "Good night, __" (old TV phrase)
42 Briny
43 Like Samson, once
44 Kind of truck
45 Heroic poetry
46 "Auld Lang __"
47 It's better known for its bark than its bite
48 Third degrees, usually
49 Seaman's shout
50 Nod off
51 Rams' dams
53 Dernier __

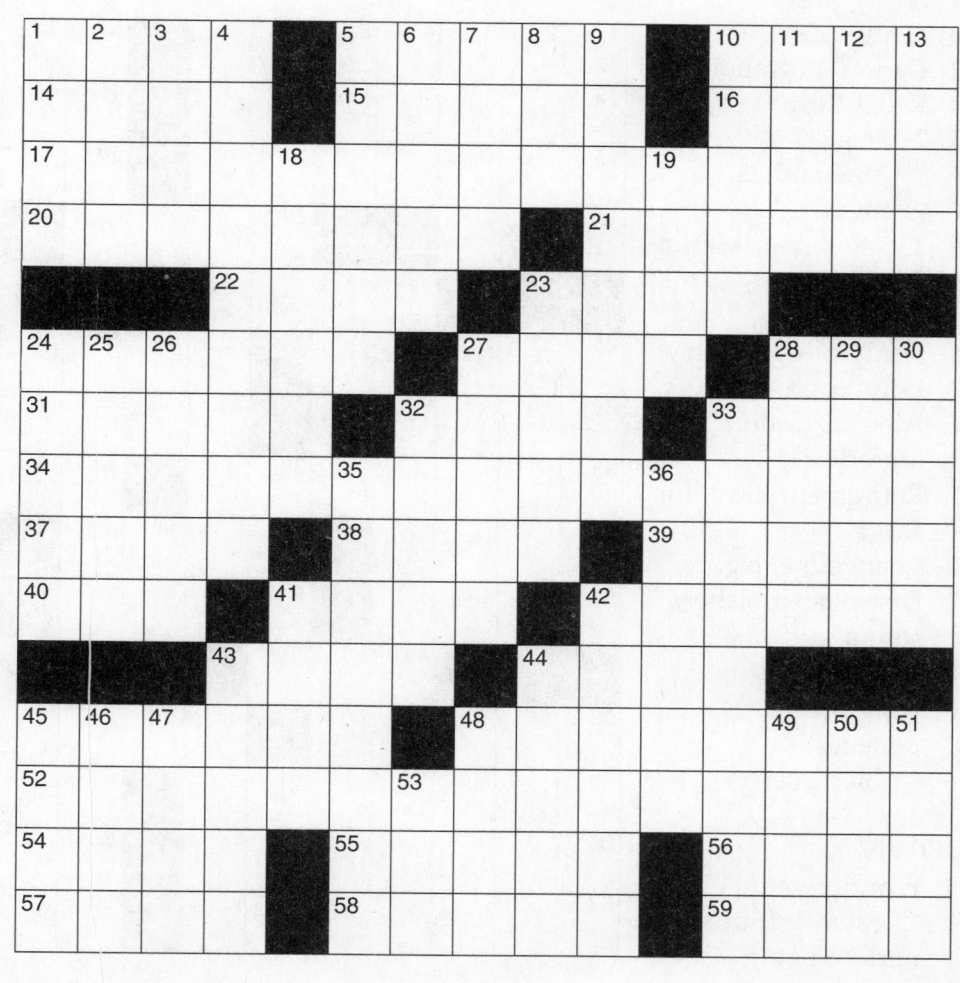

290 *by Harvey Estes*

ACROSS

1 On the __ (very angry)
8 For the well-to-do
15 November winner
16 Savannah's place
17 "Evil Ways" band
18 Bar members
19 Dynamite's kin
20 Christian Science founder
22 Popes "An __ on Man"
23 __ way (incidentally)
25 Murals and the like
26 Free-for-all
29 Play callers
31 Ill-fated sibling rival
35 Put on a pedestal
36 Ark builder
37 Singer Falana
38 String player
40 "Hop to it!"
42 Cancer's symbol
43 Reds' Rose
45 2:1, e.g.
46 "A-one and __"
47 "I smell __"
48 TV pitchman Merlin
49 "A Christmas Carol" boy
51 Study of optometry?
53 Edinburgh dwellers
56 Aloe __ (lotion ingredient)
57 Retirement kitty, for short
60 Evangeline, e.g.
62 Last-place finisher, so it's said
65 Unyielding
66 Fence in
67 Reneges
68 Quotes poetry

DOWN

1 Frontierward
2 Chester Arthur's middle name
3 Monthly due
4 %: Abbr.
5 __ loss for words
6 Belief
7 Edith + Holly
8 Hideous
9 Black-eyed one, perhaps
10 Farmer, in the spring
11 Billy + Lucille
12 "Rock of __"
13 Italian bread
14 Word before come and go
21 Car for test-driving
23 Alexander + Timothy
24 Abominable Snowman
25 Tennis's Arthur
26 Islamic center
27 Bring to bear
28 Steven Bochco TV drama
30 Patti + Lana
32 Boxing matches
33 Borden bovine
34 Instructions to Macduff
39 Lunch meat
41 "Star Trek" counselor
44 Record
50 Basketball's Thomas
52 "Common Sense" author
53 "Saint Joan" playwright
54 Sign over
55 Reverend Roberts
56 Animal docs
57 "__ You Babe"
58 Misleading move
59 Senate votes
61 SSW's reverse
63 New Deal grp.
64 Yale player

ACROSS

1 Kindergarten instruction
5 Onetime La Scala tenor
11 Shake up
14 Brook
15 Unlocked
16 Hollywood's Thurman
17 Star of "The Invisible Man"
19 Hoover, for one
20 Zeus or Jupiter, e.g.
21 School grp.
22 Wood-shaping tool
23 Fleur-de-__
25 Mr. Sondheim
27 Not left in the lurch
32 "The Time Machine" people
33 Speckled horse
34 Poet Wilfred
36 Meanies
39 Religious offshoot
40 Pay by mail
42 Onetime Texaco rival
43 Not on the level
45 Talkative Barrett
46 Prefix with plasm
47 Not cleric
49 Two-pointer, the hard way
51 Comes out
54 Kin of calypso music
55 Beats it
56 Piggie
58 Orientals, e.g.
63 Belief
64 Star of "The Vanishing" (1993 version)
66 Bedlam site
67 Spoke from the soapbox
68 Pull off a coup
69 Author Beattie
70 Choir voices
71 Minus

DOWN

1 Electrical paths
2 Gyp
3 Ali, once
4 Coin that's not a coin
5 One who shares a masthead billing
6 __ financing (car ad phrase)
7 Sow's opposite
8 Rightmost column
9 A century in Washington
10 __ bodkins
11 Star of "Without a Trace"
12 Flabbergast
13 Japanese noodle soup
18 Kewpie
22 Orbiting points
24 Betsy Ross, e.g.
26 "Don't Bring Me Down" rock band
27 Nocturnal bear?
28 They might be heard a thousand times
29 Star of "Missing"
30 All broken up
31 Disband, postwar
35 Hirschfeld hides them
37 This, in Madrid
38 Chimney grit
41 Ale mugs
44 Barrister's headgear
48 The "c" in etc.
50 Actress Lemmons
51 "My Fair Lady" lady
52 Stoneworker
53 Divans
57 Newts
59 False god
60 Dickensian chill
61 Eerie loch
62 Concorde et al.
64 Book after Esther
65 A stingy fellow?

ACROSS

1 Clicker that might be used on a trawler?
9 London elevator
13 Tibetan V.I.P.
14 Plume source
16 Starter at an Italian restaurant
17 Quick on one's toes
18 Shoshonean
19 Health resort
20 Department store employee
21 Behan's "__ Boy"
23 George Sand, e.g.
24 Gene Kelly's "__ Girls"
25 Loving touches
26 German coal region
28 Propelled a punt
29 Amtrak listing: Abbr.
30 One of the Astors
31 Is interested
32 Caddies carry them
33 Bank account amt.
34 Vatican City dwellers
35 Jetty
36 It causes a reaction
38 Great noise
39 Sparta was its capital
40 Have the chair
44 Resounding, as a canyon
45 TV knob abbr.
46 Statehouse V.I.P.
47 Left the chair
48 Cheese at an Italian restaurant
51 "Put up your __!"
53 Élan
54 Solemn hymn

DOWN

1 Piece of a poem
2 Change, as hems
3 Capuchin monkey
4 Racetrack informant
5 Confirmation slaps
6 Twangy
7 Ambulance attendant: Abbr.
8 Philosopher's universal
9 Scholarly
10 Eliza's 'enry
11 Chicken dish
12 Distance gauge
13 Paint unskillfully
15 Brewer and Wright
20 Parisian papas
22 Kill, as a dragon
23 Turns white
25 Meltdown areas
26 City south of Palo Alto
27 Salad ingredient
28 __ New Guinea
30 Throw off the scent
31 Some lose sleep over it
32 Baking pans
34 Most runtlike
35 Polish dumpling
37 Yankee great Skowron et al.
38 Herds
40 Call up
41 Jim Croce's "__ Name"
42 Gift getter
43 Holiday nights
48 Cushion
49 Baseball hitter's stat
50 Household god, in Roman myth

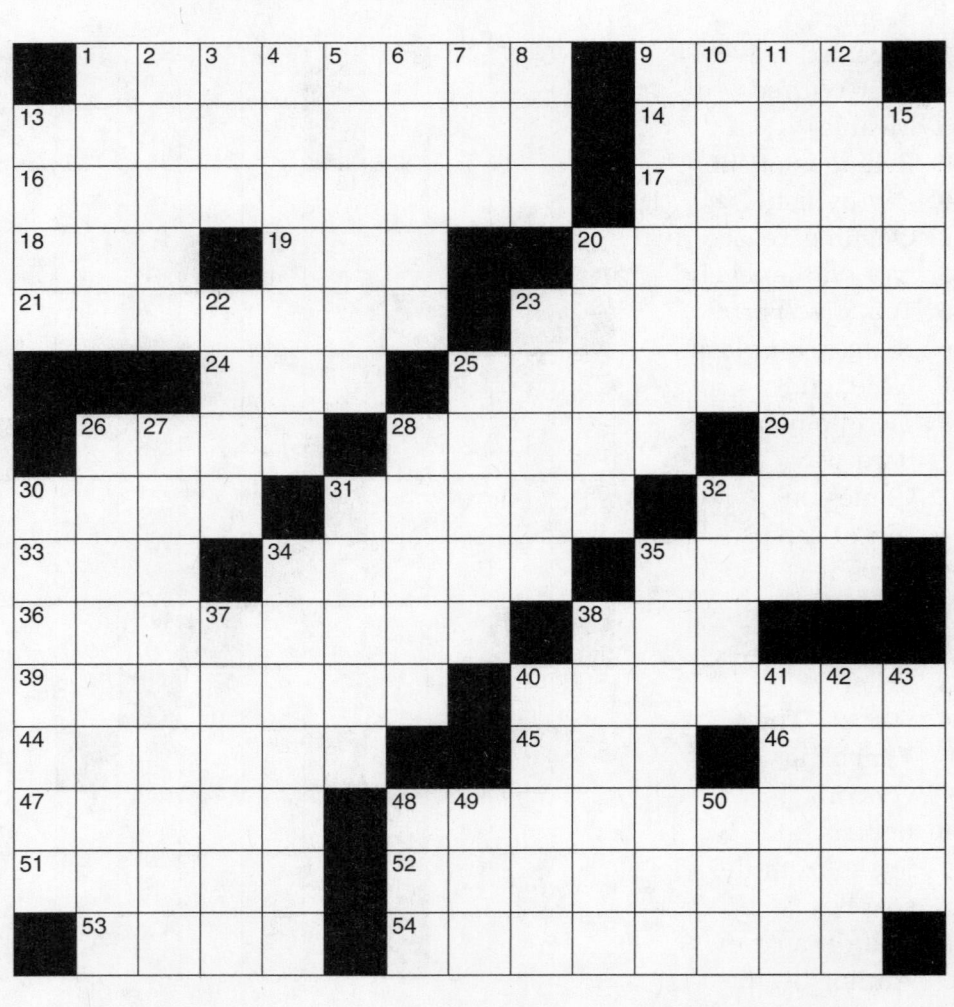

ACROSS

1 Twain character
7 To the extent that
14 Lacking nothing
15 Closet
16 Blinker
17 Art of arguing
19 Traditional areas of knowledge
20 Defraud
21 High-paying easy job
22 Geraint's love
23 "__ Johnny!"
24 Part of an equine family tree
25 Room with an easy chair
26 Become entrenched
27 __ Aviv
28 Football team
30 Part of elopement plans
32 Egg on
33 Fuzzy fruit
35 Holds back
38 Accolade
40 Conflict
41 Negotiations
42 D.C. summer time
45 Flag
47 Wall decoration
48 Blackthorn fruit
49 Derive (from)
50 Thin
51 Sign of life
52 Table
54 Rodeo rope
55 One on a walkout
56 Repay
57 Hobo's garb
58 Business news

DOWN

1 Prepared potatoes
2 "Who'll volunteer?"
3 Of the same mother
4 Stacked
5 Goddess of discord
6 Danger signal
7 Unlined tablet
8 Hot
9 Kith and kin
10 Live
11 On/off routes
12 Nimbleness
13 Ties down
18 Refine
20 Procreate
23 Busy place
26 Socialist Eugene
29 Amateur
30 Terrible __
31 Fit out
33 Czar-era bourgeois
34 Sorts
35 Food that's hole-some?
36 Most acidic
37 Short melody
38 Breadwinners
39 Commotion
41 Merchant
43 Medicinal amount
44 Be indecisive
46 Brainy
47 Much the same
48 More confident
51 Blacktop
53 Be in session
54 Escape

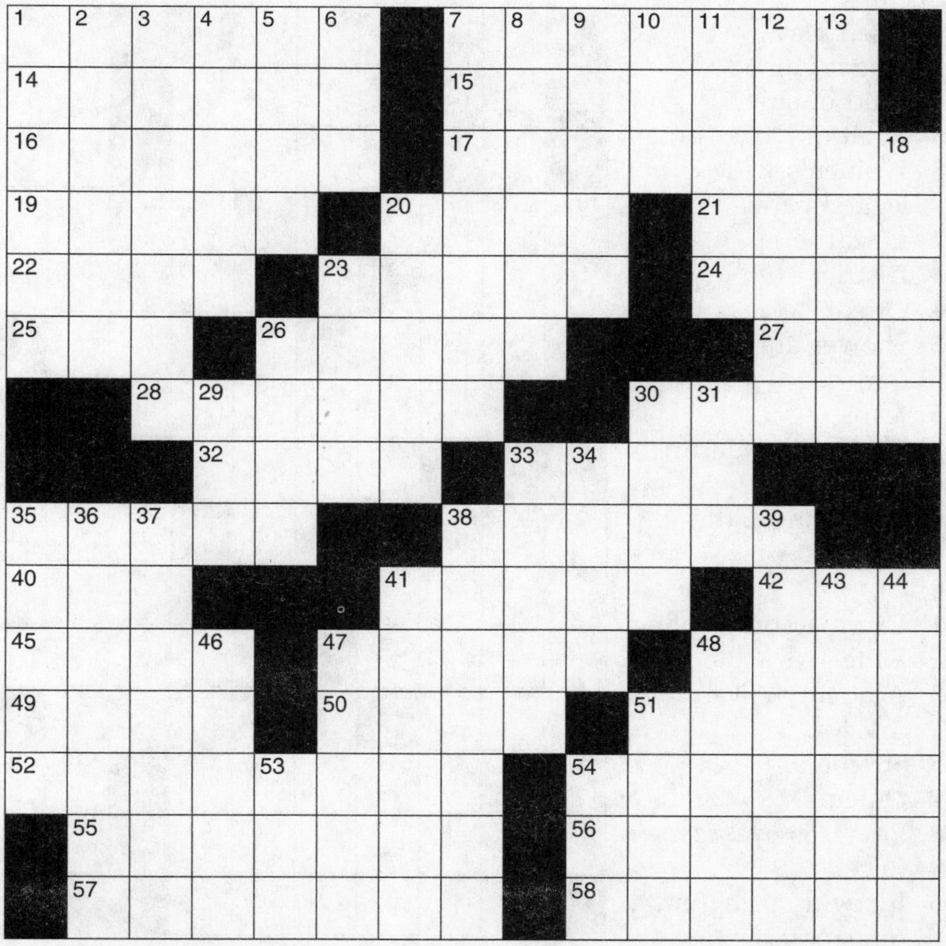

294 *by Arthur S. Verdesca*

ACROSS

1 Entertain from house to house
6 Sirs' counterparts
12 Horse show locales
14 Slow musical pieces
16 Kind of license or justice
17 Measles variety
18 W.W. II German bomber
19 "From the __ of Montezuma"
21 Pascal's law
22 Part of H.R.H.
23 Fixed, as a gauge
25 Reposed
26 Iris's place
28 Chichi
29 Place for belt-tightening
30 Flooring of marble chips
32 Ibsen play
33 Singer Laine
34 Kind of suit
35 Strait of Dover port
38 Women's wide-legged pants
42 __-garde
43 District
44 Orient
45 Shower attention (on)
46 Jeans
48 Third-millennium year
49 "__ Along Little Dogies"
50 Gist
51 Drum accompanying a fife
53 Academy Award category
55 Strainers
57 Quietus
58 Pluck, as eyebrows
59 Juicer
60 Iris with a fragrant rootstock

DOWN

1 Prisoner
2 Alarm, e.g.
3 Stink
4 Like some beer
5 My __, Vietnam
6 "A Christmas Carol" specter
7 Not for kiddies
8 Small flatfishes
9 Questionnaire info
10 "Pizarro Seizing the Inca of Peru" artist
11 Recital singer
13 Sonata's third movement, often
15 Louisiana 11
18 Folded up
20 Respecting
24 Demolishes
25 Founder of Taoism
27 Esoteric
29 Avast, on land
31 Got off
32 Robot, in Jewish legend
34 Most like the Marx Brothers
35 Sponged
36 Dodger
37 Trellis
38 Singer Lily
39 Africa's fourth-longest river
40 Seeps
41 Pen
43 Early American publisher Peter
46 Stupid
47 Beef cattle
50 Where Anna Leonowens taught
52 Affirm
54 Japanese drink
56 W.W. II battle site, for short

ACROSS

1 Garden tool
6 "Gimme Shelter" band, with "the"
12 Explain visually
14 Brecht's "Mother —"
15 With 16 Across, Canadian speech
16 Anagram of 15 Across
17 Kind of fingerprinting, nowadays
18 Pollen holder
20 By way of
21 Left-fielder Ron
23 "For" words
24 Screen __
25 Dubai royalty
27 Lush
28 Suffix with kitchen
29 Reminisce
31 Siege site
34 Midafternoon on a sundial
35 Suffix with sonnet
36 Make no change
41 Iced dessert
45 Heavy reading?
46 One for the road
48 La Scala locale
49 Banned apple spray
50 Error's partner
52 Druggie's nemesis
53 Ukr. neighbor
54 Land of ancient Smyrna
55 Earl Grey, e.g.
56 With 58 Across, hires recording artists again
58 Anagram of 56 Across
61 __ list
62 Enrage
63 Satrap
64 Ad signs

DOWN

1 Like Rushdie's verses
2 Tour org.
3 T.W.A. info
4 Kind of wheel
5 Hams it up
6 Boils
7 Malaysian gent's title
8 Table scrap
9 Ingénue's trait
10 Self-ish folks
11 Upper chambers
12 Ebbets Field player
13 __ only
14 Regain consciousness
19 Beginning (then)
22 With 24 Down, instructor's turf
24 Anagram of 22 Down
26 Coasted
30 Back talk
32 Person in stripes
33 Four years, for a President
36 Headlined
37 The second T in TNT
38 Accumulates
39 Puzzle direction
40 Follow
42 Typewriter rollers
43 Price cutters, in a sense
44 Box up
47 __ bran
50 Believe it
51 Singer Frankie
54 Currency premium
57 Rascal
59 Enlisted V.I.P.
60 A superior of 59 Down

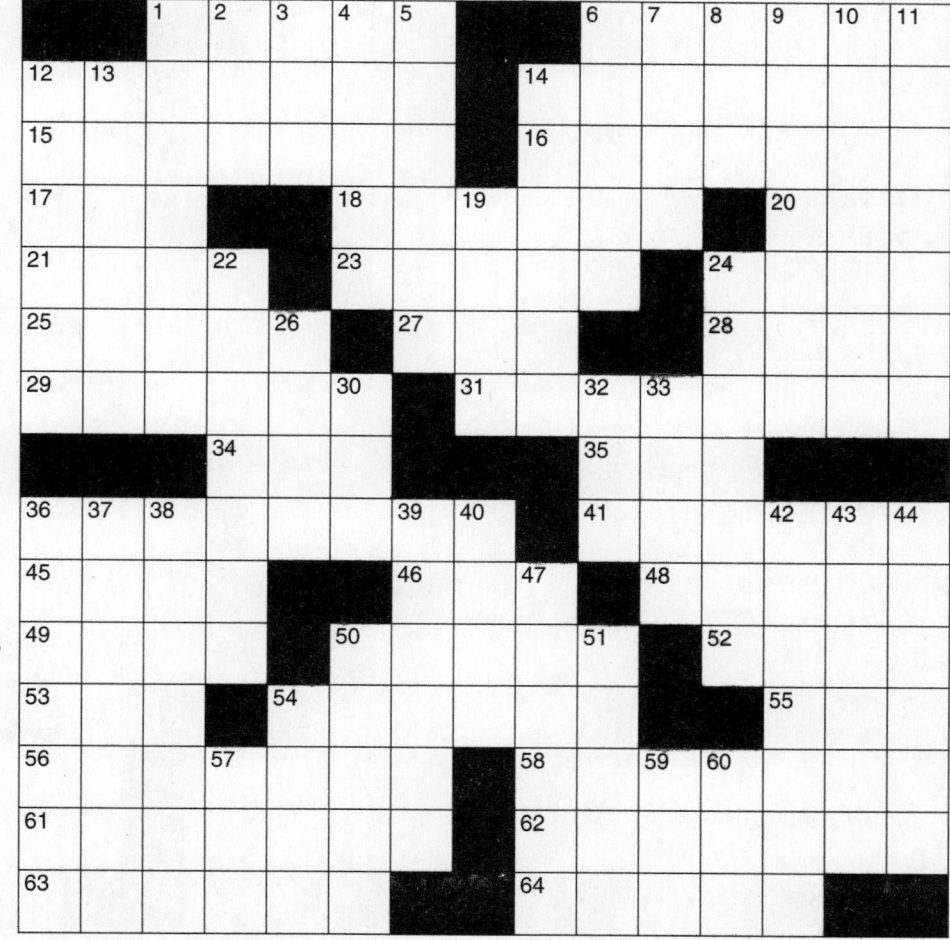

ACROSS

1 "Star Wars" group
7 __ card (wallet item)
13 "Walk on the Wild Side" singer
15 Puget Sound city
17 Feeler
18 "L'École des Femmes" writer
19 Retard
20 "Make __ double!"
22 Introvert
23 Sticky strip
24 Static __
26 Thurmond of hoops
27 __ flash
28 Hang on the line
30 Medicine amounts: Abbr.
31 Some shooters
33 Singer Kitt
35 Subject of the book "Perjury"
36 Open-weave fabric
37 Examine again
40 We're all in this together
44 Addison's "__ to Creation"
45 Leathernecks
47 __ anemone
48 High time?
50 Tar from the Thames
51 Italian bread
52 __ Park, Colo.
54 Masc. alternative
55 Niamey's country
56 Lucky, like sesame seeds?
58 Shiite leader
60 Loose
61 Double negative follower
62 Not worn out
63 Ran the show

DOWN

1 Adjustable
2 Four-time Super Bowl QB
3 Housed in
4 "The Forsyte Saga" lady
5 Overhead expense
6 Poet's adverb
7 On __ (when wanted)
8 Ab __ (from the start)
9 Dudley Do-Right's love
10 M-G-M or TriStar rival
11 Show historically
12 Seventh-inning activity
14 Newspapers
16 Mother of Calcutta
21 Advice
24 Glassware
25 Grant's opponent, 1872
28 Jeffersonian belief
29 1979 Richard Gere film
32 Any miss
34 Artist Lichtenstein
36 Center, for one
37 Beaus
38 Six-time Emmy-winning actor
39 With a will
40 Quiet, expressive one
41 Pioneer pilots
42 Golden
43 Long in the past
46 Rummaged in an arsenal?
49 Vassals
51 Digs
53 Alphabetize
55 Second starter
57 Majors in acting
59 Chew the fat

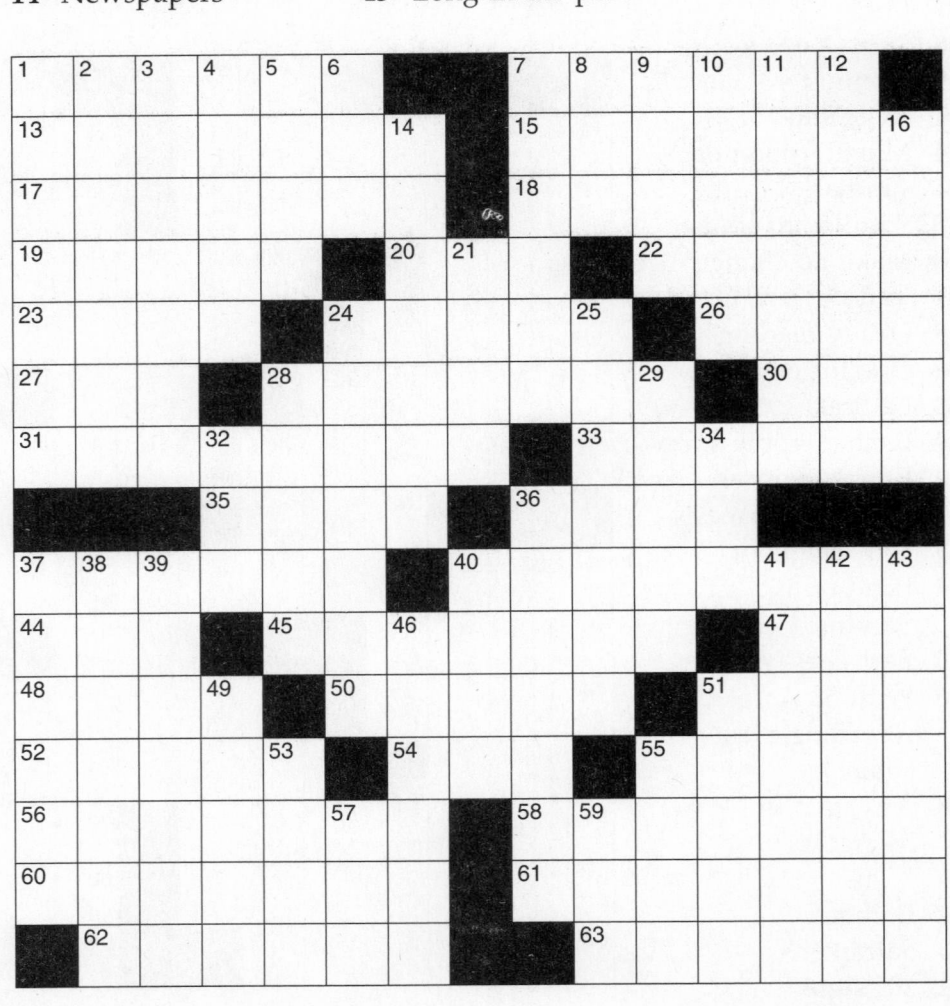

by Harvey Estes

297

ACROSS

1 Espresso
7 Pocketbook material, maybe
14 Opens
16 Make too many eggs?
17 More than dull
18 Juicy morsels
19 Cabbies
20 Valuable deposits
22 Gymnast's need
23 Ticks off
24 Tea type
25 Deft
26 Zip
27 Point count bidding pioneer
28 Amaze
29 Flips out
31 Undiluted
33 Cycle starter
34 Crowd noise
35 Squirrels' sustenance
38 Game fad of the 50's
42 Shade of white
43 Pull strings
45 Preschooler
46 Standard
47 Religious devotion
48 "Star Trek" Klingon
49 Sphere opening
50 "Hans Brinker" author
51 "Madonna With Saints" artist
52 Comic Dick
54 Parasite
56 Activist actor
57 Clothing, informally
58 Lineups
59 Idi Amin, e.g.

DOWN

1 Former Boston cardinal Richard

2 Least great Great Lake
3 Spot for Howdy Dowdy
4 Y's
5 Crimson rivals
6 Expansion wing
7 They're up for discussion
8 Just like ewe?
9 Bolsheviks
10 Ball
11 Invitation to ride
12 Piece of junk mail
13 Kind of bar
15 Stern
21 __ out (just manage)
24 Visit unexpectedly
25 Islands welcome
27 Game-show host Moore
28 Blunt
30 Gale of "Oh! Susanna"
32 Cartoon crime-fighter
35 It surrounds a pit
36 Popular cigars
37 Eight-footers
38 Most adorable
39 Makeshift
40 One cursed by Farragut
41 Initially
42 "Well, __!"
44 Stocking stuffer
47 Logroller, in a way
48 Cellar contents

50 Unit of force
51 Wives' tales
53 Clock-resetting abbr.
55 Degree of distinction

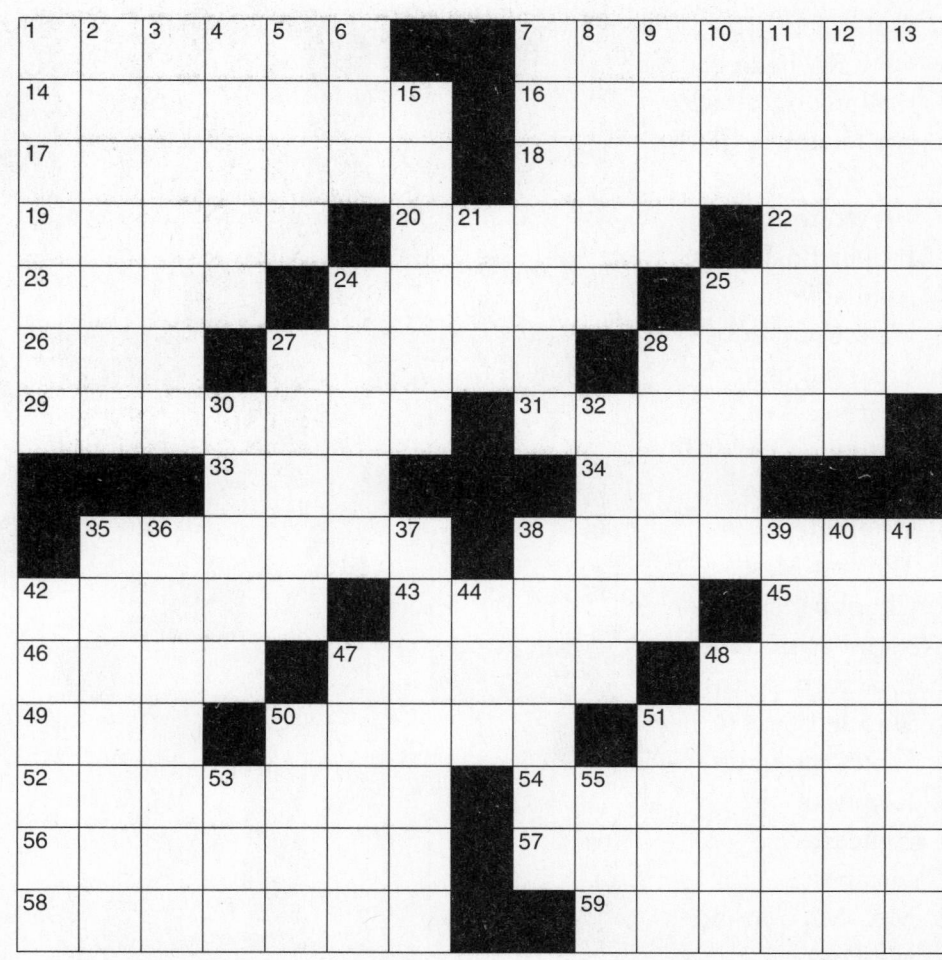

298 *by Mel Taub*

ACROSS

1 He wrote "The Bronx? No, thonx!"
5 Cramped Mother Goose dwelling
9 Renaissance beauty Isabella __
14 Anent
15 Follow the game
16 Send packing
17 "Dark Lady" singer
18 Tallinn native
19 Actor Keach
20 Hollywood palmist?
23 Make cherished
24 Ump's purview
25 Roget's entry: Abbr.
27 Percussion at a powwow
31 Actor Davis
35 Well-oiled grp.
38 New Rochelle college
39 Hollywood quack?
42 For takeout
43 Ex of 17-Across
44 He wrote "The Proper Bostonians"
45 Available for
47 West Point subject
49 Yield slightly
52 Sports jacket
57 Hollywood's leading undertaker?
60 Originated
61 The last Mrs. Chaplin
62 Member of 35-Across
63 In accord (with)
64 Skidded
65 Scottish tongue
66 Heavy of old comedies
67 Location
68 M-G-M co-founder Marcus

DOWN

1 Mother-of-pearl
2 Pale-faced
3 Bed frame
4 Genghis Khan's mass
5 Jerez product
6 Silence
7 Ready if needed
8 Word on old gas pumps
9 Mississippi discoverer
10 Ultra credo
11 Minor dispute
12 Georgia __
13 TV Tarzan Ron
21 Canvas prop
22 Do guard duty
26 Say __ (refuse)
28 Kansas pooch
29 "__ about . . ."
30 Lots and lots
31 Tetra × 2
32 The Old Curiosity, e.g.
33 Nestor
34 Unyielding
36 Review a flop
37 Adequate, way back
40 Domicile
41 Confederate general Jubal
46 Dempsey's nemesis
48 Scrape
50 Luster
51 Carlo Levi's "Christ Stopped at __"
53 Swiss diarist Henri Frédéric __
54 Man in a mask
55 Get rid of
56 Freshen
57 "__ smile be . . ."
58 Borodin's prince
59 Singleton
60 "Phooey!"

ACROSS

1 Dries (off)
7 The color of honey
12 Wining and dining place
13 Bob of reggae
15 The "thee" of "Of Thee I Sing"
16 Teases
18 __ soda
19 Napoli night
21 Least big
22 Football no-no
24 Prefix equivalent to -ish
26 Way on or off
27 He told a hare racing story
29 Outlets
31 Hemingway novel setting
32 Furniture trim
34 Property restriction
36 Site of a Lewis and Clark stop, 1804
38 Inevitable
41 Up, in a way
44 Glaciate
45 Arises (from)
47 "It's __ never"
49 "Stuffed Shirts" author
51 Blithe
53 Find, with "out"
54 Wassail flavor enhancer
56 Penicillin target, for short
58 Sermon subject
59 Semisoft Danish cheese
61 Approved
63 Modern phone option
64 Dürer and others
65 Oboelike in sound
66 Rest-less, perhaps

DOWN

1 Wrapped food
2 Giant stele
3 Disturber of the peace
4 Hibernia
5 Rimsky-Korsakov opera opener
6 Park art
7 Definitely not a know-it-all
8 Fannie __
9 Steep
10 Venerable one
11 Legal O.K.
12 Abettor of Brutus
14 Rubber stamps
17 March honoree (with an aptly numbered clue)
20 Free of duties
23 Balance
25 "__the bag!"
28 Fussbudgets
30 "Dragonwyck" author
33 Nail's companion
35 "Discus Thrower" sculptor of ancient Greece
37 With worry
38 Rip off
39 Eyepiece, in jargon
40 Bounce back
42 Ballroom dance
43 Nylons
46 Toots
48 Pulls apart
50 Get around
52 Streisand title role
55 Detroit River's destination
57 Runners try to pick it up
60 Just a bit
62 Amigo of Fidel

300 *by Manny Nosowsky*

ACROSS

1 Book of the Apocrypha
7 Apse setting
15 Catchall phrase
16 Esthete
17 Uncompromising
18 Swain song
19 Doctrinal holding
20 French assembly
21 Teachers' grp.
22 They have namesakes: Abbr.
23 Grammy-winning country group
25 Results of conks
26 Farm building
30 Guarding mobilely
34 Its fruit is monkey bread
36 It's played at the 7-Down
38 Rose's home
39 Without concern for the future
40 Baron in "Der Rosenkavalier"
41 Wistful one
42 Epcot neighbor
44 Computer add-on?
47 G. & S. princess
50 Embarrass
51 Strauss's "Ariadne auf __"
53 Transportation Secretary Pena
55 Theater's Willy, Linda, Happy and Biff
56 St. Louis arch designer
57 Charlotte __ Virgin Islands
58 Printed, as a quote
59 Way with words?

DOWN

1 One-liners
2 Complete
3 Fills in a hole
4 Tennis hothead
5 XXX activity
6 Derby
7 36-Across's site
8 Circus locales
9 Sportscaster Hank
10 "__ song go . . ."
11 Mr. Chaney
12 A Karamazov
13 Part with
14 Purlieu
20 Southernmost U.S. point
24 Michaels of "Saturday Night Live"
26 __ speak (as it were)
27 Footnote abbr.
28 Literally, superior one
29 Be loyal to
30 Knowing
31 Pusher's nemesis
32 Chief god of Memphis
33 Afflicts
34 Howled
35 Copernican concern
37 Lustrous velvet
41 Kind of mining
42 Umpire for the duel in "Hamlet"
43 Zoo critter
44 Rate highly
45 Artist Delaunay
46 Car of the 20's
47 Conditional words
48 College leader
49 Month after Shevat
52 "__ for All Seasons"
54 Prior to
55 Scale notes

ACROSS

1 Like Ike
5 Like most colleges today
9 One 39 Across
13 "I cannot tell __"
14 Heraldic band
15 Sandbags, maybe
16 Holds up
17 Café additive
18 Chemically nonreactive
19 Chiffonier
21 One 39 Across
23 One 39 Across
25 Verboten: Var.
26 Cantankerous
32 Rep.'s rival
35 "__ be a cold day in Hell . . ."
38 Ancient region of Asia Minor
39 Each of eight in this puzzle
43 Like measles
44 Elliptical
45 Compass dir.
46 Home to Denali National Park
48 Teases
51 One 39 Across
56 One 39 Across
60 Stay informed
62 Island group near Fiji
63 Periodical of haute couture
65 Small dog breed, for short
66 One 39 Across
67 Plaintiff
68 Get ready
69 Fusses
70 Orly birds?
71 Lighten up

DOWN

1 Fishhook part
2 One way to read
3 Sign of autumn's beginning
4 Go AWOL
5 One 39 Across
6 __ pro nobis
7 Statesman Root
8 Coup __
9 Transportation Secretary Federico __
10 Penultimate fairy tale word
11 Wonk, maybe
12 Pocket
15 Actress Ullmann
20 One–time link
22 Symbol for density
24 Expenditure
27 Singer Ocasek of the Cars
28 Classic drama of Japan
29 Seth's son
30 Ocho __, Jamaica
31 One 39 Across
32 1982 movie thriller
33 Iniquitous
34 Pianist Hess
36 Broadway comedy of 1964
37 Live's partner
40 __ Palmas (Canary Islands seaport)
41 Benevolent guy
42 Macs
47 King Kong, e.g.
49 Quilt-making gathering
50 Treeless plain
52 Like the Boston-accented pronunciation of many words
53 Card catalogue abbr.
54 Where the fat lady sings
55 Zaps
56 Ask to produce proof of age
57 Melville novel
58 Participates in a regatta, perhaps
59 One of the Bobbsey twins
61 __ Le Pew
62 Loan-granting Fed. agcy.
64 Fill a flat?

302 *by Sidney L. Robbins*

ACROSS

1 Gore's "__ in the Balance"
6 One who's "agin" it
10 Train unit
13 "__ Without Windows" ('64 song)
14 Supermarket meat label
15 Territory
16 Major Bowes updated?
18 Fat
19 Home on the range
20 Kind of signal
21 Part of SEATO
22 Mail HQ
23 Breakfast order
25 Lift up
29 Woodworker's choice
32 Belgian airline
34 Bests
38 Hemingway opus
41 Dub again
42 Took ten
43 Ingenious
45 Shows remorse
46 Up
50 Marinaro and others
52 Slough
53 Reckon
56 Bosom companions
60 "Remember the neediest," e.g.
61 Olympia Dukakis film
63 Fast time
64 Capri, for one
65 Misrepresent
66 Pupil's place
67 African lake
68 Volvo worker

DOWN

1 Bridge seat
2 Comic Johnson
3 Imitation morocco
4 Civil wrong
5 __ Pinafore
6 Cottonwoods
7 Grammy-winning pianist
8 Yacht heading
9 Person of will
10 1929 event
11 High nest
12 "M*A*S*H" character
15 "Too bad"
17 Parapsychology study
22 Authentic
24 Singing sisters
25 D.C. zone
26 Comic Bert
27 Have __ in one's bonnet
28 Probe
30 Flat sign?
31 Vienna is its cap.
33 In opposition to one another
35 River to the Seine
36 Town near Padua
37 Osmose
39 Melmackian of TV
40 60's org.
44 Craved
46 With room to spare
47 "Little Orphant Annie" poet
48 Goodnight girl
49 Pants part
51 __ Plaines
54 Deluxe
55 Southeast Kansas town
56 Witch's __
57 Golden, e.g.
58 Tart
59 __ Ball (arcade game)
62 Kitchen meas.

ACROSS

1 Former Mississippi Senator Cochran
5 Nutty
9 Gangbusters at the box office
14 River to the Rhine
15 Lena of recent films
16 Like the skies in "Ulalume"
17 Sorts
18 Carty of baseball
19 Oh, so many moons
20 Go astray
23 Stack-blowing feeling
24 Countdown start
25 Tak's opposite
26 Alphabetical run
27 As a whole
31 Bit
33 Mezzo-soprano Marilyn
34 Santa Fe Trail town
35 Pickle
38 Red of firefighting fame
39 Words of wonderment
40 With respect to
41 "Whip It" rock group
42 Drawing card
43 The Divine Miss M
44 Play the siren
46 Smelt, e.g.
47 Aquarium oddity
49 Cry of delight
50 It has its point
51 Harvest goddess
52 Not yet in full bloom
58 Tubby the Tuba creator Paul
60 Reed of note
61 Light-footed
62 Hint
63 An order of the court
64 W.W. I German admiral
65 Pond covering
66 Silent O.K.'s
67 With defects and all

DOWN

1 Shadow
2 Christmas play prop
3 Synagogue cabinets
4 Not dose
5 World's third-largest island
6 '79 sci-fi thriller
7 Muscle spasms
8 Bird that summers in the Arctic
9 Agree
10 Sugary suffix
11 Many skiers use these when they (see diagonal)
12 Writers Jean and Walter
13 Assault
21 Mink's relative
22 Pretension
27 '64 musical "___ a Ball"
28 Leaf's starting point
29 Getting across
30 Stew ingredient
31 Skier Phil
32 Original Jed Clampett
34 Score for Barry Sanders
36 Observe
37 Great Scott of 1857
40 Sound as ___
42 Animal that sleeps with its eyes open
45 Noodle topper
46 Candy
47 Must, slangily
48 Part of an Argentine autumn
50 Steer clear of
53 River of Spain
54 Greek peak
55 Third addendum to a letter
56 "... ___ saw Elba"
57 Shoemakers' bottles
59 Trevino's org.

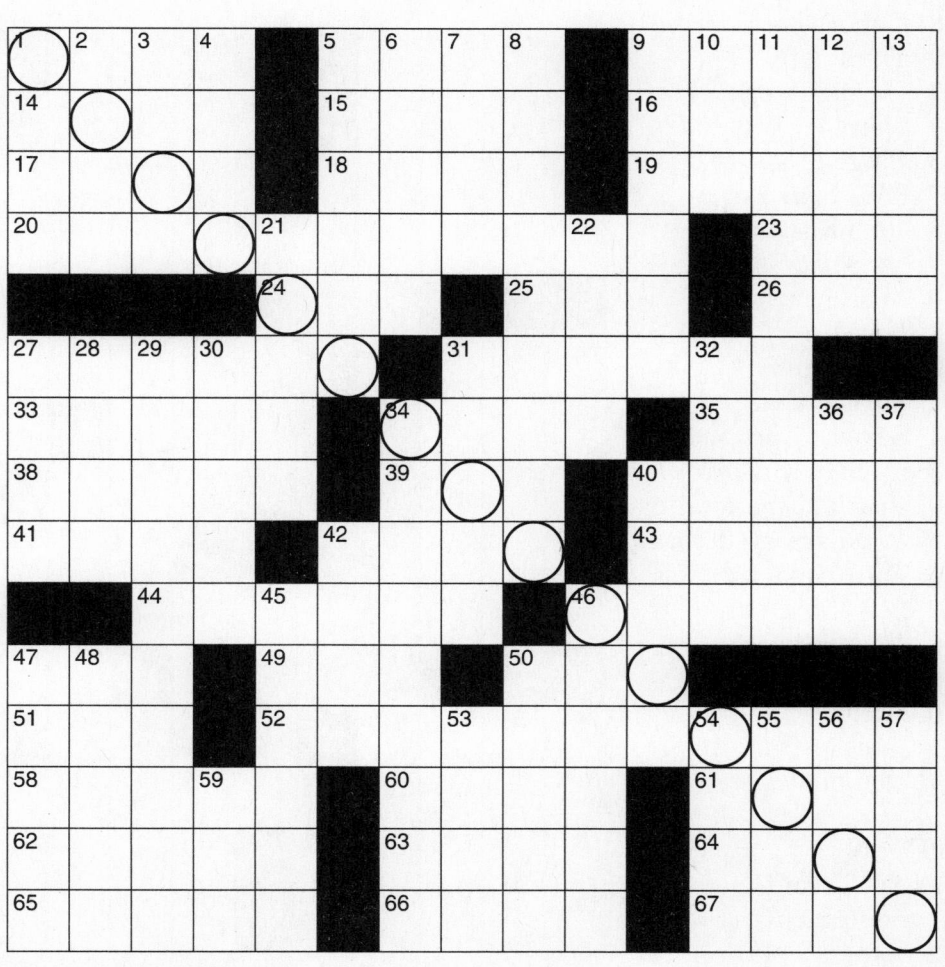

304 *by Janie Lyons*

ACROSS

1 Dog star
5 Gull's cousin
9 Eyeball bender
14 Ground grain
15 Mini revelation
16 Red-eyed bird
17 Haitian despot
20 Cordwood measure
21 Israeli dance
22 Out's opposite
23 Vidal's Breckinridge
25 Actor Young of TV's 67 Across
27 Is grief-stricken
30 Book subtitled "His Songs and His Sayings"
35 Supped
36 Relative of a Bap. or Presb.
37 Balkan capital
38 Gabor sister
40 Thimbleful
42 Dryden work
43 Help get situated
45 Plugs of a sort
47 Saturn's wife
48 1956 Rosalind Russell role
50 "For __ us a child is born"
51 Headlight?
52 Survey chart
54 Seaweed product
57 __ fixe
59 Reached the total of
63 Popular psychologist
66 Paul Anka hit
67 See 25 Across
68 Deep blue
69 Throat malady
70 Achy
71 James Mason sci-fi role of 1954

DOWN

1 Rock band equipment
2 Usher
3 Mend, in a way
4 Alternatives to The Club
5 Round stopper
6 Delights
7 Change the décor
8 Kind of network
9 Roman breakfast?
10 Light beers
11 "Jewel Song," e.g.
12 Mariner's peril
13 Raced
18 She played Grace Van Owen on "L.A. Law"
19 Passepartout, to Phileas Fogg
24 Strongly scented plant
26 Stellar Ram
27 Fiji neighbor
28 City in northern Japan
29 Set in motion
31 Dinnerware
32 Building contractor
33 Not suitable
34 Final authority
36 Madness
39 Oust
41 Nurse, maybe
44 Directed toward a goal
46 Hair fixative
49 Office connections?
50 Donny Osmond, e.g.
53 Record-holding N.F.L. receiver __ Monk
54 Postfixes
55 Sandpaper surface
56 Opened a crack
58 Catalonian river
60 Hawaiian hen
61 In shape
62 Kon-Tiki Museum site
64 Shrill bark
65 Lyric poem

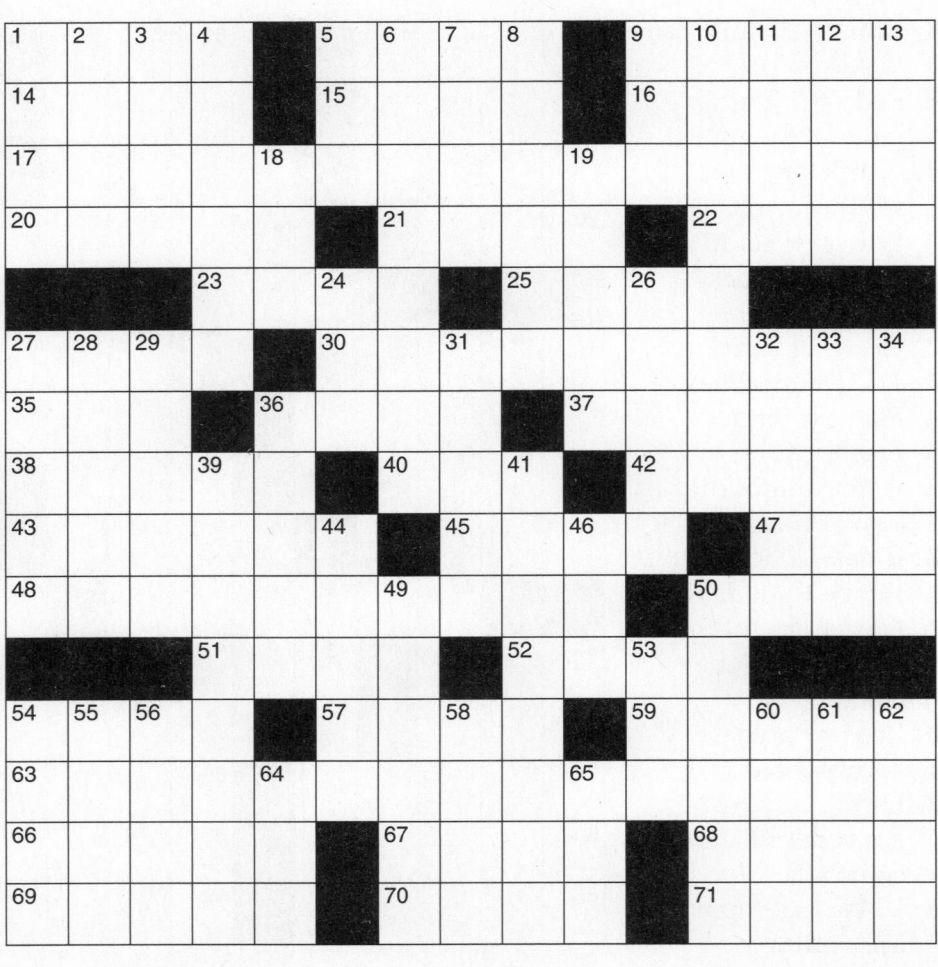

ACROSS

1 Crocus bulb
5 "Son of the Sun"
9 Set-to
14 Pastiche
15 Score in pinochle
16 "A house is not __"
17 Restaurant request
18 Vessel for Jill
19 "Anticipation" singer
20 Song by 11 Down
23 Vinegary
24 Scottish hillside
25 Westernmost Aleutian
27 A clef
32 Unsettle?
35 Scruff
38 "Aeneid" locale
39 Musical or song by 11 Down
42 Nobelist Wiesel
43 Rows before P
44 Gorky's "The __ Depths"
45 Had a hunch
47 Carol
49 Daffy Duck talk
52 Bedtime annoyances
56 Song by 11 Down
61 Mercutio's friend
62 Cigar's end
63 Prefix with China
64 An acid
65 Alert
66 Ending with gang or mob
67 Guided a raft
68 Kane's Rosebud
69 Libel, e.g.

DOWN

1 Pause sign
2 Relating to $C_{18}H_{34}O_2$
3 Dyeing instruction
4 Some handlebars
5 Collision
6 Circa
7 Mountaineer
8 Psychiatrist Alfred
9 Tennessee Senator Jim
10 I.O.U.
11 Late, great composer
12 Mine: Fr.
13 "State of Grace" star
21 Thurber's Walter
22 Informal goodbye
26 Word on a coin
28 Student of animal behavior
29 Make coffee
30 Knowledge
31 Spectator
32 Farm mothers
33 Base
34 "The doctor __"
36 Barley beard
37 Exploited worker
40 It may be golden
41 Actress Verdugo
46 Friend of Harvey the rabbit
48 Belgian port
50 Mergansers' kin
51 Perfumery bit
53 Showed allegiance, in a way
54 Downy bird
55 Stable sound
56 Envelop
57 Our genus
58 Biographer Ludwig
59 Hawaiian honker
60 To be, to Henri

306 *by Norma Steinberg*

ACROSS

1 Outlet center?
5 Wheat __ (crackers)
10 Stick around
14 The last Mrs. Chaplin
15 Storyteller of old Greece
16 Opening for a sweat bead
17 Ballerina's skirt
18 Strainer
19 Novelist Murdoch
20 Colonist's command
23 "Piggies"
24 Have a hunch
25 Like crazy
28 Waikiki dances
31 Dungeons & Dragons beast
32 Row, e.g.
34 School grp.
37 Judy Garland's command
40 Embroider
41 Bowling lanes
42 The hunted
43 Feeds the flame
44 __ Haute, Ind.
45 Thursday's eponym
47 In a mo
49 February command
55 Invitation word
56 Heretofore mentioned
57 House nickname
59 __ even keel
60 Basic belief
61 Ballooned
62 Took off
63 Shorthand, for short
64 Fair to middlin'

DOWN

1 Kitty
2 Musical forte?
3 Golden Rule word
4 Knight's glove
5 Discrimination

6 Will-reading attendees
7 "Um-hmm"
8 Award-winning scienc show
9 Expedited
10 Places for titles
11 "The Velvet Fog"
12 "The Little Mermaid"
13 Sandburg's "The People, __"
21 1982 Pryor film, with "The"
22 Best __
25 May honorees
26 "Let Us Now Praise Famous Men" author
27 Columnist Pearson
28 Sharpens

29 __ daisy
30 O.K.'s
32 Athlete from Tres Coracoes, Brazil
33 Brooklet
34 Good engine sound
35 Level
36 "__ sow . . ."
38 TV host Povich
39 Job vacancies
43 Incite
44 Candidate for day care
45 Butcher's cut
46 Rambo, e.g.
47 Early evening
48 __ a customer
50 Winery fixtures
51 Drive the get-away car, maybe
52 Sole

53 Claudius's adopted son
54 Sheepcote matriarchs
55 Intimidate
58 Brace

ACROSS

1 Noodlehead
5 Dagger handles
10 Silver-tongued
14 Eminently draftable
15 He has "99 beautiful names"
16 San __, Italy
17 "Murder in the Cathedral" setting
19 Faux pas follower
20 Auto part
21 Abe's "The Woman in the __"
22 Bohea, e.g.
25 Caddies carry them
27 In fairness
28 Boulevard
30 Genteel
32 Aquarium fish
33 Humble toiler
34 Pick
37 Training-room complaint
38 Robbery
39 National Enquirer rival
40 66, e.g.: Abbr.
41 Like "Hee Haw" humor
42 Italian Renaissance poet
43 Two-time A.L. M.V.P
45 Lecture
46 Reserve supply
48 Promise word
50 Beat one's gums
51 Brook
52 Writer Angelou
54 Eaglelike, perhaps
55 Perambulates
61 Plains Indian
62 Regarding
63 Xenia's home
64 First-rate
65 Violet relative
66 Arctic native

DOWN

1 Baseball's Gooden
2 __ roll
3 Actor Cariou
4 "So long"
5 Yamaha rival
6 Noted absurdist
7 Kind of shot
8 Tobacco figure
9 Like a wallflower
10 Ptarmigan
11 Assassin's victim, 8/20/40
12 Spur
13 Imperious
18 Lagniappe
21 Con
22 Golden Horde member
23 Upright
24 Miss Marple film "Murder __"
26 Upholstery concern
27 Stun
29 Up to
31 Cheerful
33 Persian sprite
35 Fettuccelle, e.g.
36 Scout group
38 __ de combat
39 "They called her frivolous __"
41 Tobacco wad
42 Singer Tucker
44 Deteriorates
45 Nice and warm
46 Work shoe
47 "Symposium" man
49 Sibyl subjects
53 Baseless?
55 Kind of dance
56 Cultural collection
57 Writer Auletta
58 "Great idea!"
59 Sass
60 Keystone fellow

308 *by Joy L. Wouk*

ACROSS

1 Snake with a nasty bite
4 Snide
9 Doggone pest?
13 Rung
15 Sap sucker
16 Galley propellers
17 Tight closure
18 Bulls and Bears, e.g.
19 Abdul-Jabbar's alma mater
20 Slippery
21 "Cubist" Rubik
22 Nixon's infamous '72 org.
23 Aftershock
25 Poisonous Asian snake
27 Some General Motors cars
29 Flower named for a Swedish botanist
33 Freighters' delays
37 Sea bird
38 Friendship
39 Disencumber
40 Oncoming
41 Well-off
42 "And *then* . . ." stories
44 "Light" ammunition?
46 ". . . bombs bursting —"
47 — a million
49 Nag
53 Easily split rock
56 Eye
58 Unsavory bar
59 It can be a stretch
60 Witch's home
61 First name in cookies
62 Astronaut Shepard
63 Radio hostess Hansen
64 Harness fitting
65 Award for "Kiss of the Spider Woman"

66 Hen, perhaps
67 Just in

DOWN

1 Figure in black?
2 Guide
3 Painter Charles Willson —
4 Party provider
5 Mimic
6 November 25, some years
7 Indonesian island
8 Football gains: Abbr.
9 Date for 6 Down
10 Doily material
11 First name in detective fiction
12 Immediately
14 Site of the first 6 Down

22 O.S.S. successor
24 Grand Ole —
26 Plugs, of a sort
28 Hog fat
30 Lecherous look
31 "Dies —"
32 No ifs, —. . .
33 Bull's-eye hitter
34 Abu Dhabi V.I.P.
35 Isinglass
36 Churchill successor
40 End in — (draw)
42 "We — not amused"
43 Officer in charge of the king's table linen
45 Wind dir.
48 Ancient land on the Aegean
50 "— of Athens"
51 Bring out

52 Fix stitching
53 Louver
54 Hawaiian port
55 "That's one small step for — . . ."
57 Solitary
60 Building wing

ACROSS

1 Iron-pumper's pride
5 Washerful
9 Make pigtails
14 Columbia athlete
15 Oppositionist
16 Diploma word
17 Rattles
19 Comatose
20 Came upon the maharajah?
22 F or G, for example, but not H
23 "__ Cane" (1963 movie)
24 Lead ore
27 Forming opinions
31 Hugo or Tony
32 Neighbor of Chad
34 Easter preceder
35 Gives no stars
36 Got a new address
37 Sneaky guy?
38 Scratch (out)
39 High numbers?
40 Oscar-winning film of 1955
41 Dislike to the max
43 Puts in the scrapbook
44 An Astaire
46 Destiny
47 Intrepid Eric?
54 Form-related
55 Double-crossers
56 Muscat resident
57 Point at the table
58 Mountain sign abbr.
59 Star's small role
60 Slaughter in Cooperstown
61 Decline

DOWN

1 Deep purple
2 German article
3 Overhead
4 Gym shoes
5 One of the Jacksons
6 One's partner
7 First-stringers
8 Ousts
9 Stupid error
10 Hit-or-miss
11 Autobahn auto
12 Creative input
13 "Jurassic Park" actress
18 The way things are going
21 "You're All __ to Get By"
24 Goggled
25 Up and about
26 Strike locations
28 Still
29 Night, in Napoli
30 Lady Jane and Zane
32 Long short story
33 "__ Got My Eyes on You"
36 Silas Marner, e.g.
37 Hobbies
39 Beethoven opera
40 Aucklander, maybe
42 16th-century dance
43 China, perhaps
45 Word maven Newman
47 Coll. hotshot
48 It's on the Tevere
49 "Paradise Lost" character
50 Stereo precursor
51 Dudley Do-Right's love
52 ". . . __ saw Elba"
53 Invitation letters

310

by Lois Sidway

ACROSS

1 Old actress Anna May
5 Kiwi soldier
10 It follows the Gospels
14 On __ with
15 Goddess of fate
16 Miss Loughlin of "Full House"
17 "I'm off to bed," said Tom __
19 Live wire
20 Obliterate
21 Disillusioned by
23 Takes in
26 Desert of dinosaur finds
27 Vicuña relative
29 Wear away
32 Fella
35 Ornery sort
37 Packed straw
38 Nest egg, for short
39 "I get a company car," said Tom __
41 Dillydally
42 Peace Corps kin
44 Chunks in a Greek salad
45 Unit of force
46 It sounds like B flat
48 He's hard to find
50 "__ Dinka Doo"
51 Berate
54 Sheltered, in a way
58 Chair-back part
60 Impulse
61 "I sat in some poison ivy," said Tom __
64 Cubbyhole
65 "Lunch Poems" poet
66 Macintosh sign
67 A final blow
68 __ situation
69 Endangered goose

DOWN

1 Forks and spoons
2 "Lakmé," e.g.
3 Horoscope-related
4 You can chew on this awhile
5 Jack Horner's last words
6 Parisian vote
7 Sidesteps
8 Mr. Guthrie
9 An Iroquois
10 Search for the unknown?
11 "I'll have a curaçao," said Tom __
12 The Bee Gees, e.g.
13 Speak with one's hands
18 Film short
22 Actor Benson
24 Tear
25 Blue fellow
28 Cockeyed
30 1934 baseball M.V.P.
31 Advantage
32 Met #1?
33 "The Haj" author
34 "Gotta run," said Tom __
36 Lute's kin
39 Skiwear
40 Carol syllables
43 Fruit created circa 1904
45 Aquarium star
47 __ Weems
49 Harrow blade
52 Author Walker
53 Avian preening aid
54 Twain hero
55 'Hood
56 Mimic
57 Gunslinger's command
59 One of the Dalys
62 Jackie's second
63 Famous Amy

ACROSS

1 David Bowie's model wife
5 Famed Dublin theater
10 Terrier of fiction
14 Canceled
15 Pen
16 Paul of "CBS This Morning"
17 Burgeon
18 "Read my lips" declaration
20 Never
22 Actress Graff of "Mr. Belvedere"
23 It's forbidden
24 It may be blind
26 Veteran sailor
29 Polite refusal
33 Montreal street sign
34 Indian craft
35 Suffix with diet or planet
36 Bush Attorney General William
37 Become misty
38 Computer symbol
39 "How was ___ know?"
40 Buy a round
41 Cultural: Prefix
42 1987 Costner thriller
44 Carried on
45 PC operator
46 Country ballroom?
47 Alamogordo's county
50 "Jack Sprat could ___"
54 Straight from the shoulder
57 Bear up?
58 Kuwaiti ruler
59 Get ___ of one's own medicine
60 Go smoothly
61 Actress Thompson
62 Kind of situation
63 Noted Ferrara family

DOWN

1 Swenson of "Benson"
2 Satirist Sahl
3 Attic contest
4 "I'm not surprised!"
5 Storefront sight
6 Headache easer, for short
7 Twining stem
8 Riviera season
9 Material for archers' bows
10 Rhododendron
11 ___-Coburg (former duchy)
12 "___ He Kissed Me" (1963 hit)
13 Addie's husband in "As I Lay Dying"
19 Church gift
21 Drinking binge
24 Dunking item
25 Over
26 Polio fighter
27 Lyrist of myth
28 "This way" sign
29 Complain relentlessly to
30 Strauss's "Eine ___ in Venedig"
31 Jockey Julie
32 Religious council
34 ___ d'Alene, Idaho
37 Splitting tool
38 "I can't go on!"
40 Spinks defeater, 1988
41 Deserve
43 Roman Eos
44 Mediterranean vessel
46 Ezio Pinza and others
47 Singles
48 Tony Musante TV series
49 Novelist Bagnold
50 Sufficient, once
51 Lippo Lippi et al.
52 Didion's "Play It ___ Lays"
53 Chaucer piece
55 Antonio or Juan
56 Conductor de Waart

312 *by Sidney L. Robbins*

ACROSS

1 Brazilian dance
6 Teen woe
10 Loot
14 "The Tempest" sprite
15 Avoid
16 Sherwood Anderson's "Winesburg, —"
17 Letter turner
19 Home for some crocodiles
20 Crimson foes
21 Ones who brood
22 Sees socially
23 Artist Magritte
24 Measured (out)
25 Sir Isaac
29 Teeter
31 Singer Merman
32 Beauty's companion
33 Oklahoma city
36 Comedian Jerry
38 Neck artery
40 Tit for —
41 Destroy for fun
43 Tip over
44 Storied Plaza girl
46 Alarms
47 Square, e.g.
48 Help in mischief
50 Makes a mess
51 Off base, maybe
52 Use a letter opener
56 Papal name
57 "Perils of Pauline" star
59 Otherwise
60 First name in mysteries
61 Movado rival
62 Not natural
63 Olympian's quest
64 You'll get a rise out of this

DOWN

1 Pack rat's motto
2 Asia's — Sea
3 60's fashion
4 Writer Hecht and others
5 Pie — mode
6 Wan
7 One-fifth of humankind
8 Goofy
9 Opposite WSW
10 "Moonlight," e.g.
11 Arkansas location
12 Felt below par
13 "Here —!"
18 Invitation info
22 Ruin
23 Stylish desks
24 Tableland
25 Egg container
26 Ms. Kett of old comics
27 Executive branch
28 Part of ITT: Abbr.
30 Per
32 Women's support group?
34 Eat well
35 Puts two and two together
37 Admiral Perry victory site
39 W.W. II agcy.
42 Beach protector
45 Like an unpaid policy
46 Wall Street order
47 In a foxy way
49 Yawning?
50 Raced
51 Space prefix
52 Tree locale
53 Valentino co-star — Lee
54 Residents: Suffix
55 Not pictures
57 "— o' My Heart"
58 Kind of humor

ACROSS

1 Battle of 1836
6 Snoozes
10 Read, as bar codes
14 Actress Linda
15 Song for one
16 Tropical food plant
17 "Great!"
18 Shaker contents
19 __-European
20 Rarely
23 Zero
24 They use lassos
25 Product with Ammonia-D
29 Ineptly
31 Counterpart of Mars
32 Jai __
33 Kind of cow, dog or horse
36 Hercule Poirot's pride
41 Feminizing suffix
42 The last word?
43 Seamstress Betsy
44 Cons
45 TV secretary
47 New York's __ Island
50 Wide's partner
51 Surrenders
58 Double-reed woodwind
59 "The Wind in the Willows" character
60 Something to fall back on?
61 Stir up
62 Toledo's lake
63 Heavy reading
64 Lump
65 Auction off
66 Baker's need

DOWN

1 In addition
2 White House area
3 With: Fr.
4 Roger Bannister's distance
5 Connected to the information superhighway
6 Twang type
7 Show horse
8 Tablet
9 Sinatra's "__ Night"
10 Part of a 90's TV duo
11 Transport for Hiawatha
12 Zeal
13 Middays
21 Overrule
22 Windblown
25 Cloth texture
26 Showy flower
27 Snares
28 Summer hrs.
29 Owls' hangouts
30 Pub draught
33 __ gin fizz
34 Otherwise
35 Like some profs.
37 Intertwines
38 Flows forth
39 Small wonder
40 Blunder
44 Addison contemporary Richard
45 Plopped (down)
46 Peace maker
47 Like some enemies
48 No-no
49 Eschew
50 Cuba's Castro
52 Had on
53 "__, Caesar!"
54 Ice chunk
55 South American capital
56 "Honest" one and namesakes
57 Essence

314 *by Sidney L. Robbins*

ACROSS

1 Extreme point in an orbit
6 "Hogan's Heroes" extra
10 Cole ___
14 Hayes's predecessor
15 Arabian sultanate
16 ___ colada
17 Cecil B. DeMille epic with "The"
20 Prohibition oasis?
21 Pilgrim John
22 What a ring lacks
23 "Finally!"
24 On ship
28 Plate scrapings
29 In a moment
30 Peculiar
32 Fast plane
35 English-French conflict beginning 1337
39 Greek vowel
40 Bay window
41 Prefix with pilot
42 "Scram!"
43 Went in a hurry
45 South American plains
48 Shock
50 ___ acid
51 Jerk
56 What 17 Across had
58 Tooth pain
59 Los Angeles 11
60 Skater's figure
61 "The ___ the limit"
62 Relative of the heckelphone
63 Teacher's charge

DOWN

1 10-percenters: Abbr.
2 Get ready, informally
3 Of sound mind
4 Native Peruvian
5 "Dracula" author Bram
6 Wanderer
7 Gather
8 Wacky
9 Neither Rep. nor Dem.
10 Takes part in a bee
11 One of the McCartneys
12 Opening bets
13 Jimmy Dorsey's "___ It You?"
18 Repair
19 Make a difference
23 Sills song
24 Late tennis V.I.P.
25 Title ___
26 Mrs. Chaplin
27 Also
28 Pitcher Hershiser
30 Revise copy
31 Potato feature
32 Done laps
33 Surfeit
34 Trampled
36 Florid
37 Times to write about
38 ___ Paulo, Brazil
42 Treats with malice
43 Bantu people
44 "Just a moment . . ."
45 Drug-yielding plants
46 "Alas and ___"
47 Netted
48 Sad sack
49 The ones over there
51 Knife
52 Drop in a letter box
53 Actress Swenson
54 Old English letters
55 Beach-storming vessels: Abbr.
57 To and ___

ACROSS

1 Greatly impressed
5 Chairman __
8 Poet Mandelstam
12 Charming
15 Viper
16 Moore of "A Few Good Men"
17 Sagan's "__ Brain"
18 40 Across's beloved 11
20 Shifty shoe?
22 African nation since 1993
23 Danger
25 Reps.
26 Close, as friends
29 Musician's job
31 Composer of "Socrate"
34 National park in Maine
36 Shem's father
38 Getting on
39 Indian writer Santha Rama __
40 Theme of this puzzle
42 End up ahead
43 Frank Baum's initial initial
44 Angel's headgear
45 California's motto
47 Hebrew master
49 Dutch airline
51 Spinners, e.g.
52 Brain tests, for short
54 Essentials
56 Common speech
59 Bureau
63 Locale of 40 Across
65 Mourn
66 Prolific "author"
67 __ pro nobis
68 Plains Indians
69 Items in a code
70 __ Luthor
71 Boss Tweed lampooner

DOWN

1 Liturgical robes
2 Eroded
3 Bacchanalian cry
4 Crab, e.g.
5 Small rug
6 Late tennis great
7 It may be seria or buffa
8 Single-named folk singer
9 40 Across landmark
10 Hungary's Nagy
11 Galileo's home
13 40 Across's eastern border
14 Belgian river
19 Feature of 40 Across, according to Sandburg
21 Get-up
24 1860 nominee in 40 Across
26 Less cluttered
27 Florida city
28 1976 Nobel Prize winner from 40 Across
30 Indian district
32 "__ Ike" (50's slogan)
33 Millay and Ferber
35 Cry of discovery
37 Ripen
41 Kind
46 Type of roulette
48 Sets sail
50 Avg.
53 Pub perch
55 Therefore
56 Perfume holder
57 Humerus neighbor
58 Mary Robinson's land
60 Nintendo rival
61 Impending times
62 "Give it a __"
64 Wailing instrument

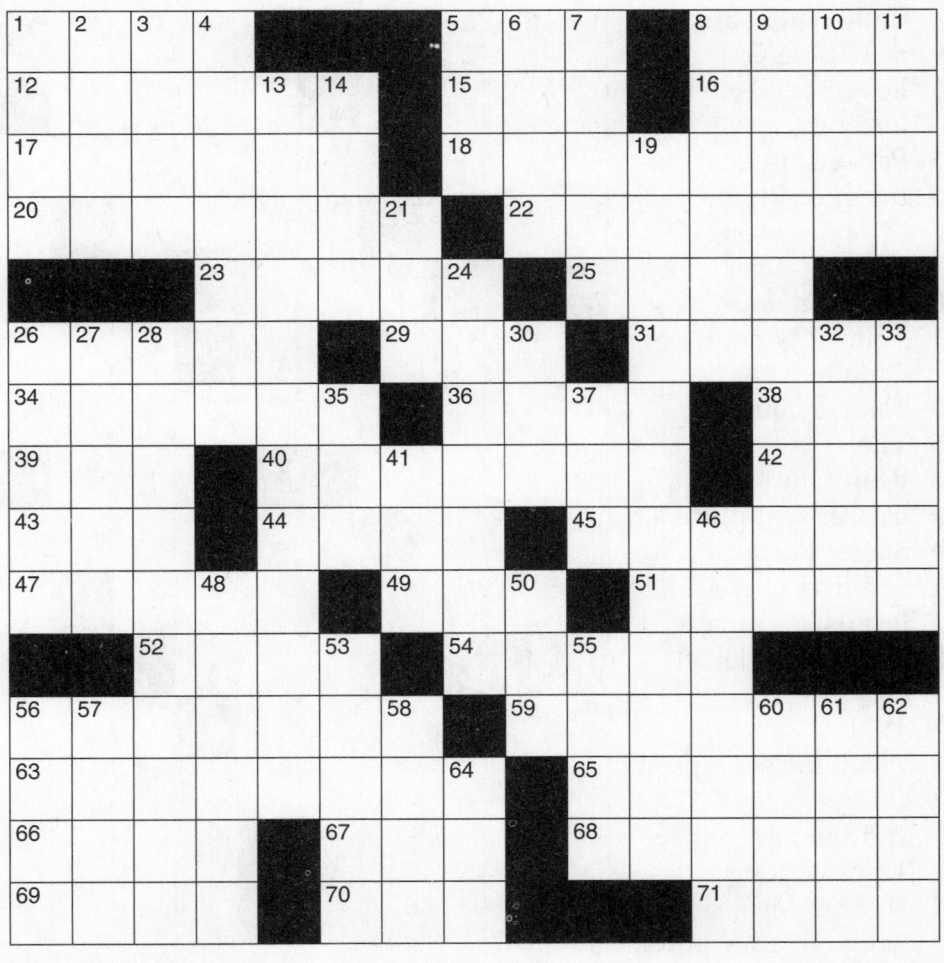

316 *by Janet R. Bender*

ACROSS

1 Not fully shut
5 Penalty
9 Ragu competitor
14 Richness
15 Irish Rose lover
16 Prepared potatoes, in a way
17 POUND
20 Denials
21 Computer insert
22 Discharges
23 Earring site
24 "Ain't She Sweet?" composer
25 Guarantee
28 Scottish Highlander
32 RAND
34 Knock the socks off
35 Away from the wind
36 Sorority character
37 Muslim officers
38 Calif. neighbor
39 SCHILLING
43 Love-lies-bleeding, for one
45 Parsons' places
46 Inventor Rubik
47 "The Sweetest Taboo" singer
48 Timmy's dog
51 Pulitzer winner Quindlen
52 Take to court
55 YEN
58 Really hurt
59 Iron or foot preceder
60 Singer Pinza
61 Servings of ale
62 Profits, informally
63 Antiprohibitionists

DOWN

1 Wyoming's Simpson
2 O'Casey play "___ and the Paycock"
3 Turning point
4 "Losing My Religion" rock group
5 Bullet size
6 More than flabby
7 Swim's alternative
8 Gumshoe
9 Offspring
10 Stairway parts
11 Old French coins
12 Goldfinger portrayer Frobe
13 Lyric poems
18 Think the world of
19 Permitted
23 Time co-founder
24 To whom a caliph prays
25 Turkish city
26 Western capital
27 1983 Indy winner Tom
28 Work behind the plate
29 Biblical gift bearer
30 Cognizant
31 Hornets' homes
33 Fistfight
37 Bad marks?
39 Rinds
40 English novelist Hammond ___
41 Flow forth
42 Detection device
44 Take offense at
47 Move stealthily
48 Speech impediment
49 Prefix with skid
50 Throw for a loop
51 Jean Auel heroine
52 Capacity
53 Military group
54 Selves
56 Newt
57 Unused

by Joan Yanofsky

ACROSS

1 Petite or jumbo
5 Gobs
9 Final Four rounds
14 Composer Satie
15 __ avail
16 Gather into folds
17 Fashionable African land?
19 Chain of hills
20 Till compartment
21 Tartarus captive, in myth
22 Military encounter
25 __ projection (map system)
27 Escargots
28 Embarrassment
30 Accede (to)
31 Places of refuge
32 Neither's partner
34 "The Twilight of the __"
35 Unites
36 Deal (out)
37 __ Lanka
38 Birdie beater
39 "Give My Regards to Broadway" composer
40 Meeting musts
42 "Canterbury Tales" inn
43 Gabriel, e.g.
44 Curmudgeon-like
45 Composer Duparc
47 Courts
48 "__ Cowboy"
49 Fashionable state?
54 Enact
55 Zone
56 Arched recess
57 "Flowers for Algernon" author Daniel
58 ". . . leave no __ unstoned"
59 Haydn's "Nelson," for one

DOWN

1 Wine description
2 George's lyricist brother
3 Address part
4 __ out a living
5 Some temps
6 "Two Women" Oscar winner
7 Remnants
8 Tale of __
9 Naiads' homes
10 Donizetti's "The __ of Love"
11 Fashionable Canadian city?
12 "Othello" villain
13 Actress Anna
18 Curtain fabric
22 Silky-haired cat
23 Fashionable Welsh body of water?
24 Bonds
25 Scold
26 Rest on one's __
27 Is weary
28 Summons
29 Person with a seal
31 Kind of tender
33 Rip
35 1977 Wimbledon champ
36 Crowds around
38 Turbojet and others
39 Movement
41 Infuriate
42 Paris or Hector
44 Cringe
45 Corn covering
46 Russian-born designer
47 "__ off to see . . ."
49 King Cole
50 Computer capacity, for short
51 Site of rejuvenation
52 Double twist
53 "You bet!"

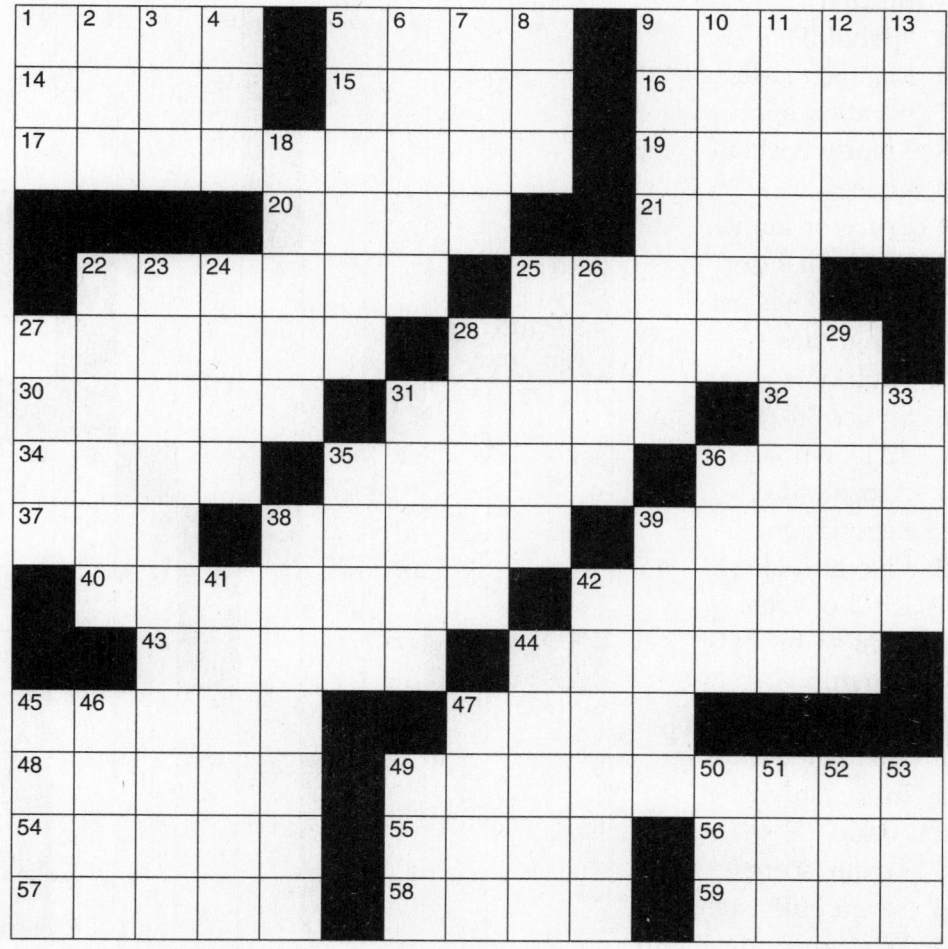

318 *by Christopher Hurt*

ACROSS
1 Author Bret
6 Oberon's imp
10 Not vivid
14 "Goodbye, mon ami"
15 King Harald's capital
16 Cameo stone
17 "__ to Belong to You" (1939 song)
18 McKern and Carroll
19 "Auld Lang __"
20 Tough toy
21 Apollo, Aphrodite, etc.
23 Without exception
25 Scrap
26 Interstate haulers
27 What's sweet about parting
31 Discouraging word
34 Burden
35 "Behold!"
36 Massachusetts vacation spot
38 Brandy cocktail
40 Loose
41 Bruce or Laura
42 Elephant's org.
43 Offering vistas
45 Long tales
47 High note
48 Site of 36 Across and 22 Down
51 Accept, after negotiation
55 Like a mouse
57 Kind of arch
58 1986 #1 hit by Starship
59 "La Gioconda," e.g.
60 Taximeter reading
61 In __ (stuck)
62 Alate
63 Tennis score
64 Seven Hills site
65 What roll calls count

DOWN
1 Reagan pal Al
2 Extemporize
3 Spanish wine
4 Domingo and others
5 1936 Literature Nobelist
6 Victim of Hamlet
7 Vain
8 Become tiresome
9 Greek universe
10 Physics particle
11 Author Seton
12 Actress Redgrave
13 Alimony getters
22 __ Players (theater group)
24 Atlanta sports site, with "The"
28 Diana of "The Avengers"
29 Ersatz butter
30 Twist
31 So
32 Lip-__
33 Model Moss
37 Sophomore's age, maybe
38 Divide
39 Stumble
41 Propriety
44 Onetime chief of 64 Across
46 Opponent of Hannibal
49 Foreshadowings
50 Lament for the dead
51 It can hide a bed
52 "Oh, my!"
53 Garr of "Tootsie"
54 Casino game
56 Calendar pages

ACROSS

1 Horoscope
6 Pachacuti was one
10 Safety specifications
14 Personal care workers
15 Dickensian orphan
16 Stormy greeting?
17 Fat City dwelling?
20 Loudness unit
21 Jots
22 Actor Davis
23 Gatsby portrayer, with 36 Across
25 Just those of Juan things?
27 Outwit, in Fat City?
33 Was a busybody
34 Gibbons
35 Common Market money
36 See 23 Across
37 Warp
39 Parts of matches
40 Unstop, poetically
41 Germany's __ Mountains
42 Munchkins
43 Fat City office attire?
47 Bearing
48 Inspector
49 Sphere, e.g.
52 Paraphernalia
54 Final words
58 Be insincere, in Fat City?
61 Crow's-nest cry
62 "Little Sheba" playwright
63 Yellow-fever mosquito
64 "Ladders" in hose
65 Turned gray
66 Take by force

DOWN

1 1983 Tony musical
2 "Farmer in the Dell" syllables
3 Arabian Peninsula port
4 Prepared leftovers
5 General on Chinese menus
6 Bonkers
7 Requisite
8 Zoom-lens shots
9 Actor-director Kjellin
10 Ballroom glide
11 Boating couple
12 Actress Conn of "Benson"
13 Besides
18 Bountiful's state
19 Despoils
24 Old Ford
26 Printer's mark
27 Plot mathematically
28 Place to get down from
29 Fabric akin to felt
30 Chaucer pilgrim
31 Eightsome
32 Ado
33 Novelist's concern
37 Race's end
38 Using extortion
39 Barely mention
41 Johanna Spyri classic
42 Canton finish
44 Dickinson and Brontë
45 Halted
46 Rochester's beloved
49 Practice à la Marciano
50 Kauai neighbor
51 Where the Rhone meets the Saône
53 Sidle
55 Remain
56 Finishes the cake
57 Examine
59 __ mater (brain membrane)
60 Like sashimi

320 *by Ernie Furtado*

ACROSS

1 Luggage
5 Sneaking suspicion
9 Waist material
13 Broadway aunt
15 "The Old Curiosity Shop" heroine
16 Words of enlightenment
17 Everybody's opposite
18 Brickbat
19 Bear head, once
20 Sgt. Friday's comment at the office equipment store?
23 Check-cashing needs
24 Insubstantial
25 Biblical initials
26 Lend a hand
27 Tour grp.
28 "Mighty __ a Rose"
31 Big salmon order for a security firm?
36 Unvarnished
38 "Don't tell me!"
39 Goes it alone
41 __-European
42 __ the iceberg
44 Part of the cost of floor covering?
46 __ Canals
47 Comic Philips
49 High dudgeon
50 "__ tell"
52 Clock part
54 Emulate
57 Musical instrument that throws Troy Aikman for a loss?
60 "__ never fly"
61 Nobel chemist Harold
62 Championship
63 Clock part
64 Clears (of)
65 Have the helm
66 Grand Ole __

67 Crime battler of 60's TV
68 Once, once

DOWN

1 Movie pooch
2 Not sotto voce
3 Shine
4 Wired
5 Actress Stevens
6 More than ennoble
7 Exile site
8 Writer de Tocqueville
9 Eastern lute
10 Bushwhacker
11 Where ends meet
12 That ship
14 Kind of price
21 Squirrels away
22 Alphabet quartet
26 Peek ending
27 Wife, to Caesar
29 Verdi's slave girl
30 Landon's running mate, 1936
31 Pointillist's marks
32 Wheeling's river
33 Out of style
34 Bats
35 Suffix with pay
37 Lo-cal
40 Star in Virgo
43 Misgiving
45 Pitches, in a way
48 1989 Nancy Reagan book
51 Comeback
52 Bandleader Waring et al.
53 Gaping hole

54 Sunflower, in furniture decoration
55 Loses color
56 Wield
57 Ear spear
58 Albany-to-Buffalo route
59 Tom of golf
60 Words before a kiss?

ACROSS

1 Beelike
6 Longtime record label
9 Funny Anne
14 Popovich or Gagarin, e.g.
16 Michaelmas daisy
17 Sandwich devotees?
19 Greek vowels
20 Expressed wonder
21 Singapore's Kuan Yew __
22 Cube with 21 spots
23 Passeport info
25 Du Maurier's "Jamaica __"
26 Year in the reign of Pius I
28 Perfect
31 Sum of one's virtues, to the Greeks
33 Palmer of "Twin Peaks"
35 Stravinsky and others
36 Sandwich fit for royalty?
38 British P.M., 1970–74
39 "Aminta" poet
40 Is left undecided
41 Hemingway moniker
42 In __ (following)
45 Shaver
46 One vote
48 Grosbeak's beak
50 Fred Astaire's daughter
51 Laundromat appliance
55 To __
56 Chicken sandwich?
60 Mounted lancer
61 Synthetic rubber
62 Hypothesize
63 Lion's __
64 They're more than rare

DOWN

1 Hurt
2 Graceful, in a way
3 Acre's acres?
4 Freeman Gosden radio role
5 "Move it!"
6 __ avis
7 Astrological point
8 Villa Albani statue in Rome
9 Plan
10 It's psychic
11 Painting locales
12 Sublets
13 Lupin of detective fiction
15 Eggy quaff
18 Familiar vow
24 Balthazar, e.g.
27 Work translated by Chapman
28 The "H" of W. H. Auden
29 Spanish Main cargo
30 Issue of 1993
32 Obedient helper
34 Nervous
35 Ingrid in "Casablanca"
36 Actresses Kay and Suzy
37 Shako, for one
38 Final throw
40 Emphasize
41 Diagrammed
43 Punctual
44 Freud, e.g.
47 Relative of Geo. or Chas.
49 Parts of boilermakers
52 Kind of tide
53 Statesman of 3 Down
54 Want ad abbr.
55 Elvis __ Presley
57 My __
58 Minn. neighbor
59 From __ izzard

322 *by Bryant White*

ACROSS

1 Chew the fat
4 Feature of Doyle's "The Adventure of the Dancing Men"
8 Faceup card in faro
12 Fraternal one
13 Region in NW Greece
15 Don Juan's mother
16 Mr. Potato Head accessory
17 Poser
19 Lab tube
21 Busy
22 Lobster claw
24 Kind of acid
25 Poser
30 Golden statuette
31 Jejune
32 Humbug?
35 Drink of old
36 Incite a hen?
38 Farm baby
39 Prince Valiant's son
40 Approach
41 Physics particle
42 Poser
45 Wooden shoe
48 Louis XVI's wife
49 Air-raid warnings
51 Angry
55 Poser
58 __ Ben Canaan of "Exodus"
59 Soprano Moffo
60 Reduces
61 Slate-cutting tool
62 Spotted
63 Boris Godunov, e.g.
64 TV Tarzan

DOWN

1 Vehicle since 1940
2 Jai __
3 Cincinnati letters
4 Tyson of "Sounder"
5 Two-time Smythe Trophy winner
6 Couple in Rome
7 This: Sp.
8 Use a heliograph
9 Best Supporting Actress, 1973
10 Tooth: Prefix
11 Montezuma, e.g.
13 Old Testament book
14 Gunn with a gun
18 Partner of dangerous
20 Outward
23 Coasters for Socrates, e.g.
25 Site for a Cézanne: Abbr.
26 W.W. I battle site
27 Scrutinize
28 El Dorado loot
29 Sauterne, e.g.
32 Ruth's husband
33 Manor head, maybe
34 Actress Sommer
36 Some doctor's reading: Abbr.
37 Empty talk
38 Large-headed match
40 Capone's chief enforcer
41 Counterpanes
42 River in an old spiritual
43 Football's pop
44 Poet Matthew
45 "Heimskringla" et al.
46 Solo
47 European capital
50 Save, with "away"
52 Stupefy
53 Caspian feeder
54 Folklore figure
56 Vetoes
57 __Zulu (South African region)

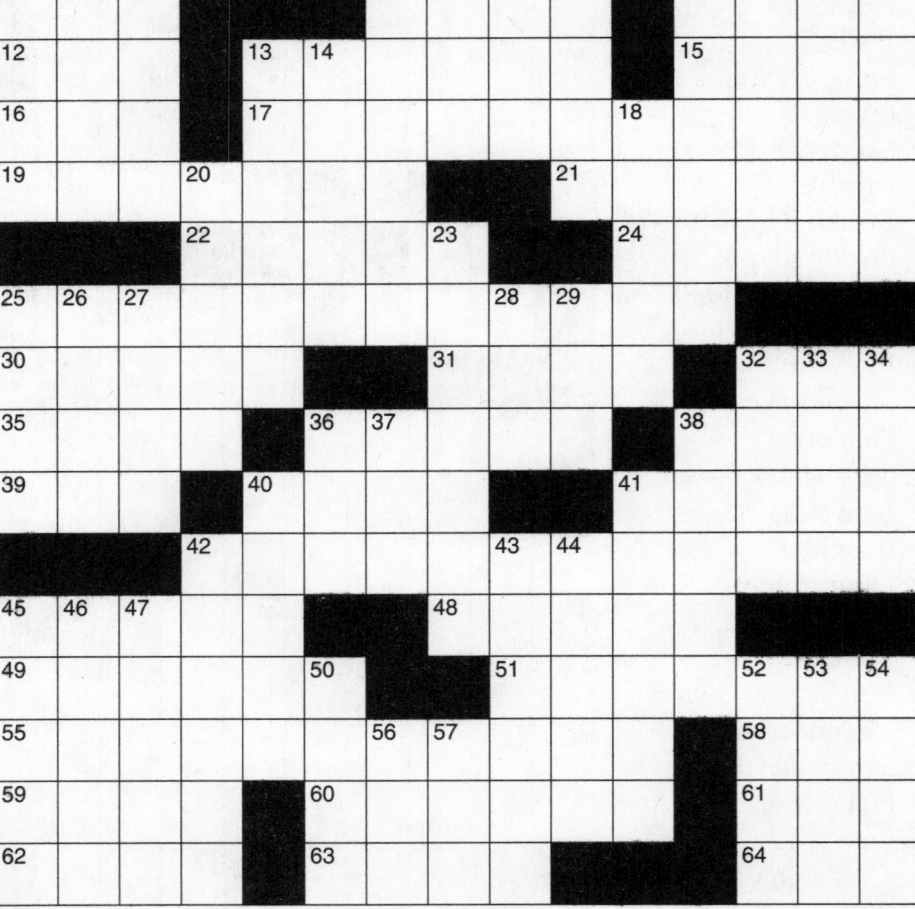

ACROSS

1 He reached his peak in 1806
5 Wahine's welcome
10 Steep
14 "__ close to schedule"
15 Screened over
16 "__ Ever Need Is You"
17 Overpriced insects?
20 "Naughty, naughty!"
21 Three minutes in the ring
22 Kosher
23 O.R.'s locale
24 Party cheese
26 __ oneself (go)
29 Aussie's hello
30 Mortgage agcy.
33 Skylit courts
34 Hoodlum
35 Oscar role in "The Killing Fields"
36 Where to buy Maid Marian mums?
39 Goes out with
40 Filthy lucre
41 "I Love Trouble" star
42 Pre-Columbian
43 Like falling off a log
44 Climbed up
45 40's White House name
46 Fraud
47 March honoree, for short
50 Express alternative
52 Kicker
55 Scans departure screens?
58 Science magazine
59 "Cookery is become __": Burton
60 Film
61 Look
62 Looks at
63 Tabloid topics

DOWN

1 Spender, for one
2 "New Sensation" rock group
3 Crackpot
4 Go wrong
5 Tuneful
6 Abate
7 "The Plague" setting
8 Relinquished, as a football
9 Farm critter
10 Western capital
11 First name in fashion
12 Jai __
13 Star-__ tuna
18 Rather rival
19 Castigate
23 Components of locks
25 Part of Boone's signature
26 He sings low
27 Mrs. Mertz
28 Cornered
29 Devout
30 Something extra
31 Expeditiousness
32 Chipped in
34 Agrees
35 Tournament type
37 Shade of gray
38 Available for duty
43 Grub
44 Treats treacherously
45 Hindu ascetic
46 Alarm
47 Hog food
48 Considerable volume
49 Corn product
51 Kind of tradition
52 End-of-week exclamation
53 "This can't be!"
54 Vous __ (you are): Fr.
56 Toy merchant Schwarz
57 Emer. locale

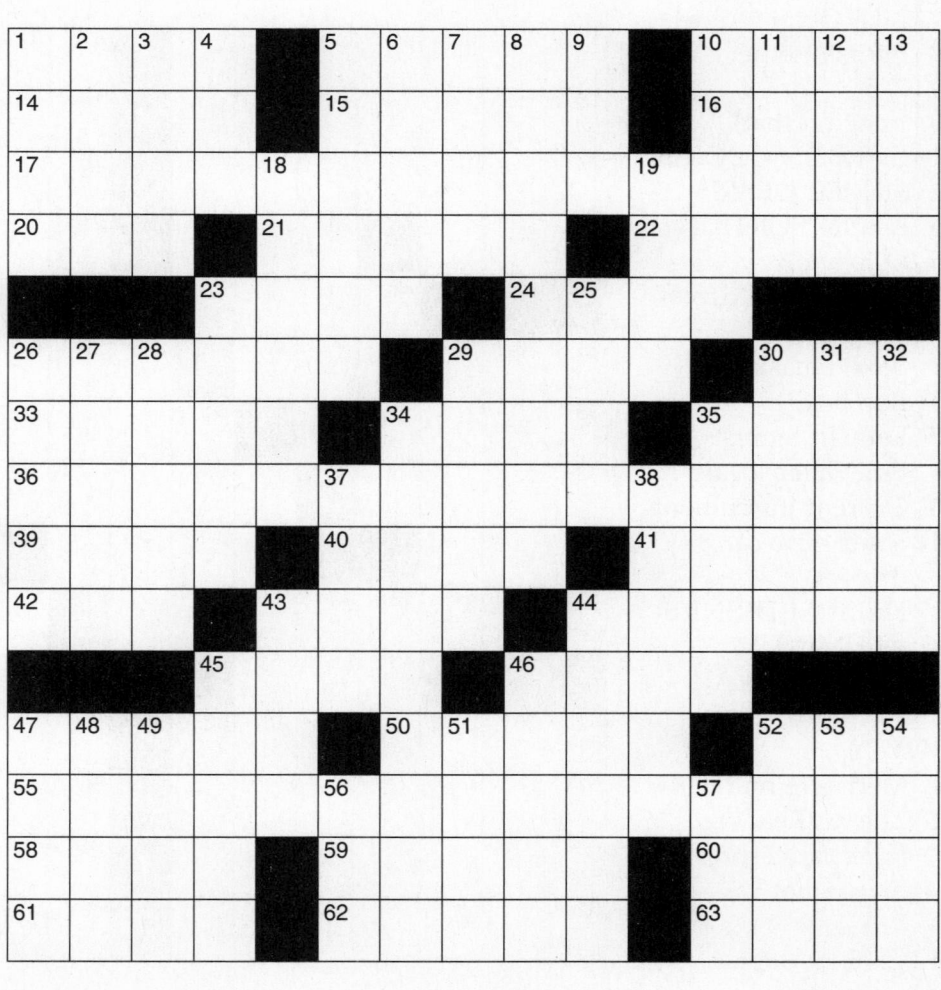

324 *by Randolph Ross*

ACROSS

1 COPPER CHARGES
8 MERCURY WATER SOURCES
15 Furniture piece
16 Glee
17 Competitor
18 "O, where is __?": Shakespeare
19 Hemingway novel setting
20 Bygone auto
21 Quarantine
22 Ship officers
24 Of oneself: Lat.
25 GOLDEN GALE
28 POTASSIUM PORTIONS
33 TIN SOURCE
34 HYDROGEN GAS
35 Auction offering
36 Mauritanian, e.g.
37 Like Oscar Wilde
38 Flintstone pet
39 Zip
40 Imagine that!
41 CARBON COOKER
42 SILVER DEBRIS
45 NEON PORTAL
46 O.T. book
47 Recreational drives
49 Grants
53 Take measures
54 Boz boy
57 Lets, in tennis
58 Bug River locale
60 Current instrument
61 Some new-car drivers
62 HELIUM DRINKS
63 ALUMINUM FISHING GEAR

DOWN

1 Mediocre marks
2 The __ Reader (alternative press magazine)
3 Pro __
4 Cabinet dept.
5 Scented blossom
6 He went to camp in a 1987 movie
7 __ Hall
8 Port opening
9 Back-of-the-book section
10 Rad
11 Latin list extender
12 Actress Kedrova
13 Senator from Mississippi
14 Backwater
22 Bedroom community, for short
23 Kerrigan and company
25 Yoga position
26 Take apart
27 Strive mightily, with "out"
29 U.S. poet laureate __ Dove
30 Former Twin batting champ
31 Largish singing group
32 Attack in a way
34 Bury
37 Recalled
38 Follows hostilely
41 Indispensable
43 __ one's head
44 Slightly tapered
45 Monticello site
48 Comic Poundstone
49 Esau's wife
50 Approach
51 Search
52 Lith. and Lat., once
54 Deck
55 Memo words
56 Dining hall
59 Tempe sch.

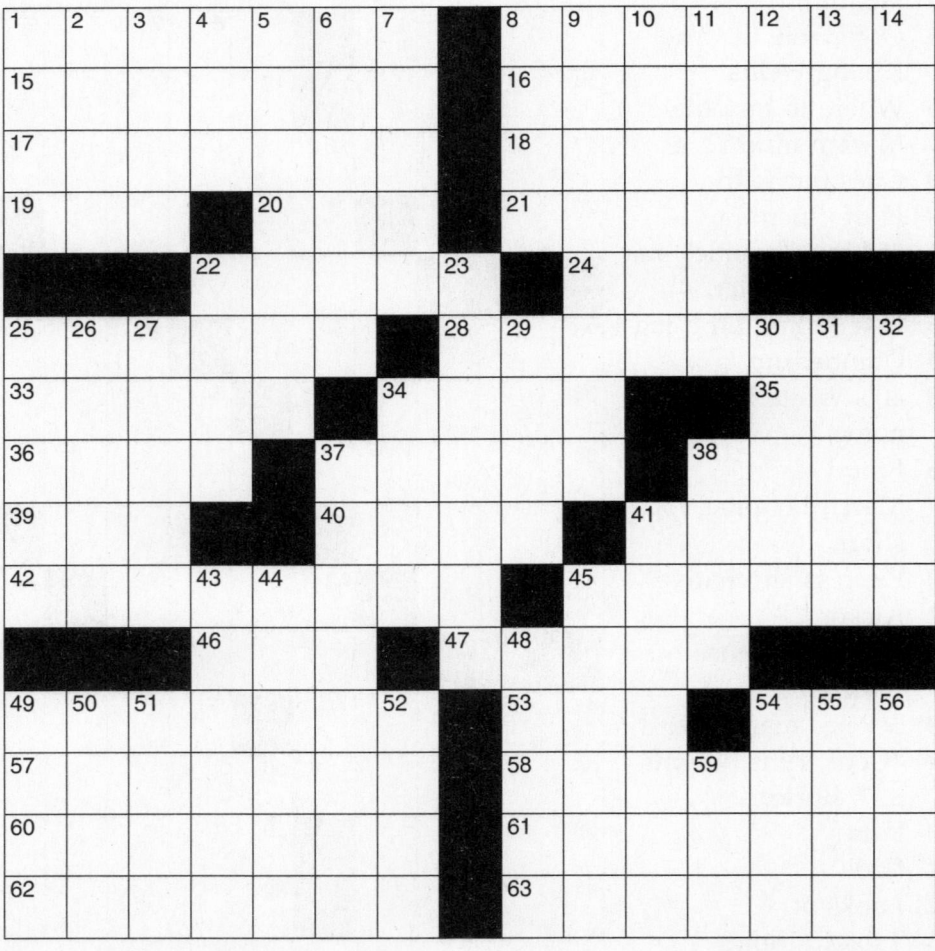

by Daniel R. Stark

ACROSS

1 Kind of sleeve
7 In the cards
15 Symphony written for Napoleon
16 Furniture polish ingredient
17 Spreads the news
18 With no exceptions
19 Poet's contraction
20 One who's squeezed in
22 Mauna __
23 Rough it
25 Seating areas
26 Say truly
27 Up a __
29 Kittenish response
30 Fiery dance
31 Team originally called the Colt .45s
33 Guard
35 Not clerical
37 Split
38 Founder of Detroit
42 Smith of sorts
46 Prince Valiant's wife
47 Fanatic
49 Succinct
50 Scream and shout
51 Traveling aids
53 Business letter encl.
54 Actor Vigoda
55 Quiescent
57 Poison __
58 Nymph changed into a bear
60 Like Don Juan
62 Added up
63 Drill
64 Stonecutter
65 Less muscle-bound

DOWN

1 Daphne du Maurier novel
2 In __ (behind)
3 Bon vivant
4 Year in Claudius's reign
5 Romans preceder
6 Countryish, in a way
7 Made a toast
8 Critic
9 A shaman uses them
10 Dull fellow
11 Jane Fonda farce "__ Wednesday"
12 Library item
13 Family tree
14 __ of Aquitaine
21 Computer capacity, for short
24 Plant growth medium
26 Cloaks
28 Zoo critter
30 Adoxy
32 Part of R.S.V.P.
34 Small number
36 Kitchen container
38 Cat with tufted ears
39 Creek Indian land
40 Unfold
41 Charge
43 Wall hanging
44 Gist
45 Join again
48 Mai __
51 Goddess of the hearth
52 Herbal alcoholic drink
55 Part that's thrown away
56 Catch hold of
59 Him, in Marseilles
61 Inspector Van __ Valk (literary detective)

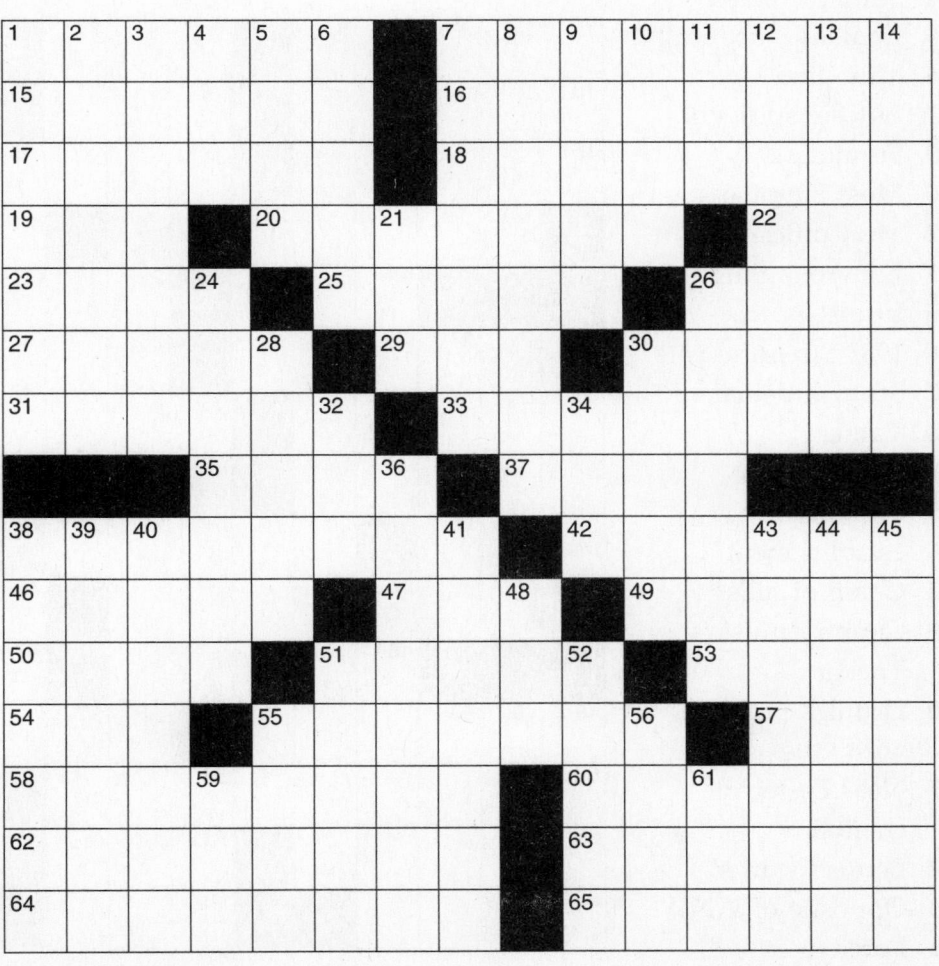

326 *by Martin Schneider*

ACROSS

1 Expire, as a membership
6 Show hosts, for short
9 Fill
13 Secretary of State Root
14 Dadaist Hans
15 Like Old King Cole
16 Baseball bigwig Bud
17 Assurance
19 Not brand-name
21 Spring blooms
22 Wildebeest
23 Entomological stage
25 Less original
28 Monks and nuns
32 Apartment sign
33 Lebanese symbol
34 Soup container
35 Immense, poetically
36 Mine find
37 Lift the spirits of
39 From __ Z
40 Most Egyptians
42 Meet official
43 Louvre highlight
45 Insult
46 1983 Streisand role
47 Scottish denial
48 Value
51 Lethargy
55 Prohibition establishment
57 Chain of hills
59 Country music's Tucker
60 Drunk's problem, with "the"
61 Near Eastern chieftain
62 Bettor's starter
63 Opposite of WNW
64 Pores over

DOWN

1 Broadway's "__ Miz"
2 Words after shake or break
3 Mass
4 Roof worker
5 Noted name in puzzling
6 Biblical trio
7 Fancy term for 5 Down and 15 Down
8 Vacation destination
9 Grad-to-be
10 Liberal __
11 Corner
12 Potato features
15 Noted name in puzzling
18 Lasso
20 Capek play
24 Styles
25 It may come in a head
26 Kemo Sabe's companion
27 Crazy as __
29 "__, I saw . . ."
30 Eroded
31 Dummy Mortimer
33 Slide
38 Cable choice
41 Washer cycle
44 "Roger," at sea
45 __ for the books
48 Film dog
49 Breadth
50 Faxed
52 Wall Street abbr.
53 Brainstorm
54 Like some cheeses
56 Suffix added to fruit names
58 Speech stumbles

ACROSS

1 Play opening
5 Ran
9 Shawl or afghan
14 Forsaken
15 Yellow brick, e.g.
16 Moonshine
17 Unencumbered
19 Composed
20 Follower of 21 Across?
21 Follower of 20 Across?
22 Small: Suffix
23 Ripped
24 Dems. opposition
27 Proverbial distancer
32 Sleepy Hollow schoolmaster
34 Ampersand
35 Firpo of the ring
36 Folk tales
37 Ship's officers
39 ___ time (never)
40 Upshots
41 Morning hrs.
42 Waffle topping
43 Kind of disease, facetiously
47 Hook shape
48 Alphabet quartet
49 Unmixed, as a drink
51 Character actor George
54 Starts
58 In the thick of
59 Be afraid to offend
60 Hope of Hollywood
61 Manhattan campus
62 Gamblers' game
63 Boorish
64 Some combos
65 Sharp put-down

DOWN

1 ___ Romeo (automobile)
2 Hip
3 De ___ (too much)
4 Words before "red" or "running"
5 Literary sister
6 Give some slack
7 Maneuver slowly
8 White House monogram
9 Block
10 Fun and games
11 Kind of beer
12 Eight, in combinations
13 A question of time
18 Singer Lenya
21 Merchandise
23 Manner of speaking
24 Staff leader
25 University of Maine site
26 TV announcer Don
28 1980 DeLuise movie
29 Bizarre
30 "Peanuts" character
31 Stock plans providing worker ownership: Abbr.
33 Young 'uns
37 Horace and Thomas
38 BB's
42 Disreputable
44 Some are spitting
45 World cultural agcy.
46 Flirts
50 Stylish Brits
51 Baby powder
52 Poet Khayyám
53 ___ fide
54 Where humuhu-munuku-nukuapuaa might be served
55 Filly or colt
56 Roman marketplaces
57 Quit
59 Abbr. in a mail-order ad

328 *by Robert Zimmerman*

ACROSS

1 Rig
5 Big dos
10 At a distance
14 Ur locale
15 New York's — Tully Hall
16 Berg opera
17 M
20 Kicker's aid
21 Names in a Saudi phone book
22 Bury
23 Cut and run
24 Yearn
26 Talk radio guest
29 Playwright O'Casey
30 Army rank, for short
33 African lily
34 Brazzaville's river
35 Through
36 H
40 Fabergé objet
41 Collection
42 Candied items
43 1969 Three Dog Night hit
44 Pup's complaints
45 Lively wit
47 Some heirs
48 Time founder
49 "Orlando" author
52 Forum fashion
53 Quarry
56 Y
60 Organ setting
61 Type style
62 Eros
63 Ruptured
64 Tell's target
65 Currycomb target

DOWN

1 Investigate, in a way
2 Tribe whose name means "cat people"
3 Old gray animal?
4 Some ratings
5 Newgate guard
6 1966 Caine role
7 Wagons —
8 German cry
9 Bishop's domain
10 Solo
11 Candid cameraman
12 Der — (Adenauer)
13 Krupp family home
18 Tall writing?
19 Tiny swimmer
23 Took off
24 Director Marshall
25 "Othello" plotter
26 Literary sketch
27 Collimate
28 Moose, e.g.
29 Divans
30 Opera prop
31 Pioneer atom splitter
32 Kingfisher's coif
34 — de ballet
37 Opposite of hire
38 St. Patrick's home
39 Publicity
45 Conductor Ormandy
46 Analyze verse
47 Skier's site
48 Dietary
49 — Point
50 "— victory!"
51 Stink
52 Substitute
53 Cougar
54 Caddie's offering
55 Home of Jezebel
57 —-la-la
58 School dance
59 Scottish cap

ACROSS

1 Break down grammatically
6 Items in a still life
11 Braincase
13 "__ Fables"
15 Considers bond values again
16 Reduce to ashes
18 Fred's sister
19 __ Speedwagon
20 Not give __
21 Mediocre
22 Argued
24 Loudonville, N.Y., campus
25 Classical name in medicine
27 Sprinted
28 "__ Believer" (Monkees hit)
31 Barn topper
32 Football squad
36 Court ruling
37 Hint to solving the eight italicized clues
39 __ Jima
40 Ignite
42 Plane or dynamic preceder
43 Actress Ryan
44 Deteriorate
45 Curses
47 Sprockets linker
50 Reps. counterparts
51 Riding whip
55 Natural gait
56 Emily, to Charlotte
57 Madrid attraction
58 Kind of lot
60 Zebralike
62 March laboriously
63 Paired nuclides
64 Catch suddenly
65 Harvests

DOWN

1 *Trims*
2 Kind of recording
3 Passage ceremony
4 Cash's "A Boy Named __"
5 Printers' widths
6 Set the standard for
7 Architect Saarinen
8 Chemical suffix
9 Lettuce variety
10 *Bowling score*
11 Tomorrow: Lat.
12 Try again
14 Laurel or Musial
17 Wetlands watchdog
19 Deserters
22 Venus, for one
23 River to the Laptev Sea
24 Game fish
26 50's singer Frankie
27 Supplies with better weapons
28 Kind
29 __ tai (cocktail)
30 Cereal bristle
33 Robust energy
34 Pronoun in a cote?
35 Norfolk ale
38 20 quires
41 Evaporated
46 Act niggardly
47 Actor Gulager
48 Emcee
49 *Copycats*
50 More extreme
52 *Mustard plants*
53 Baltic Sea feeder
54 Pea places
56 Long account
57 Swift sailing boat
59 B–F connection
60 Salutation for Edmund Hillary
61 Half a fly

330 *by Mark Danna*

ACROSS

1 Actress Winger
6 Park, in Monopoly
11 "Honest" fellow
14 Where Gauguin visited van Gogh
15 Funnyman O'Brien
16 Bloodshot
17 "Cheers!" in Cherbourg?
19 Chang's Siamese twin
20 Brand of lemon-flavored drink
21 Daydream
23 Koch and Wynn
24 Pampering, for short
26 It's heard in a herd
27 Garibaldi in Genoa?
33 Pickle
36 Paparazzi prey
37 Avaricious one
38 October gem
40 Beam fastener
42 1963 Oscar winner
43 Arose
45 Danger
47 Hang in the breeze
48 Madrid's equivalent of a Texas university?
50 Performance
51 Had lunch
52 Montana and Moon, in brief
55 Gladstone rival
60 Real
62 "Poppycock!"
63 Pre-photo pronouncement in Geneva?
65 Some
66 Skirmish
67 "Dallas" Miss
68 Simonize
69 Classic theater name
70 4 Down again

DOWN

1 Peri opera
2 Made a boner
3 Post-sneeze word
4 Take money for a spare room
5 Loner
6 Agt.'s share
7 Creator of Lorelei Lee
8 Med. subj.
9 Winter melon
10 Competitor
11 Vicinity
12 Early German carmaker
13 Barely beat, with "out"
18 Woman's top
22 Cartoonist Wilson
25 Islamic leader
28 Crowbar
29 Portugal and its neighbor
30 Barely managed, with "out"
31 Raise
32 Alternative to Charles de Gaulle
33 Clinton's runs
34 Each
35 First name in spying
39 Moon-based
41 Alternative to Certs
44 "Desmoiselles d'Avignon" artist
46 Bloodletting practitioner
49 Potted
52 Put down
53 Count in music
54 Winter weather
55 Extract
56 New Rochelle college
57 Charon's domain
58 Kind of beer
59 Relationship words
61 Prefix with play or scope
64 Favorite relative in politics?

ACROSS

1 Twelve __ ("G.W.T.W." home)
5 Cousin of the cobra
8 Pelt
12 Insomnia causes
14 Sausage, e.g.
16 Having no deferments
17 "__ akbar" (Arab cry)
18 The Sphinx and the Parthenon?
20 Available
22 Speech problem
23 Until
24 Author Murdoch
26 Took the most credit
28 Socks and Millie?
32 Popular Dutch export
33 Zero-shaped
34 Mr. Hulot's portrayer
36 Gossip-column snippet
38 Poe story setting
39 Piers 19 and 20?
41 Tony-winner Caldwell
43 Ending for tip or team
45 The Untouchables
46 Russian sea
47 Goneril's father
49 Two-spot and six-spot?
51 Helter __
54 Problem for Superman
55 Unsafe, in a way
56 1982 Stein/Plimpton biography
58 Subject of Freudian study
61 20 cents?
64 Obloquy
66 Blueprint
67 Bald head
68 Cry from the sick ward
69 Barks
70 Town on Long Island Sound
71 Unclothe

DOWN

1 Seraglio room
2 Singer Guthrie
3 Potter's need
4 Kind of sense
5 Concert hall equipment
6 Bewhiskered animal
7 City of Light
8 __ polloi
9 Light entertainments
10 Farm-gear pioneer
11 Sugar-coated
13 Nattily clad
15 Kind of test
19 Floral spike
21 Attraction at St. Peter's
25 Show alarm
27 Squeal
28 Top 40 music
29 Budget rival
30 Jalopy
31 Notary public's need
35 Exemplar
37 Lows
39 Jabbered
40 "No right __"
42 Turgenev's "On the __"
44 Conger
46 Made sense
48 Gave a room a face lift
50 Hall-of-Fame Brave
51 Excessively sentimental
52 __ Lumpur
53 Inflexibility
57 Prize since 1948
59 River through Leeds
60 Chew (on)
62 Years in 7 Down
63 Date
65 Country singer McDaniel

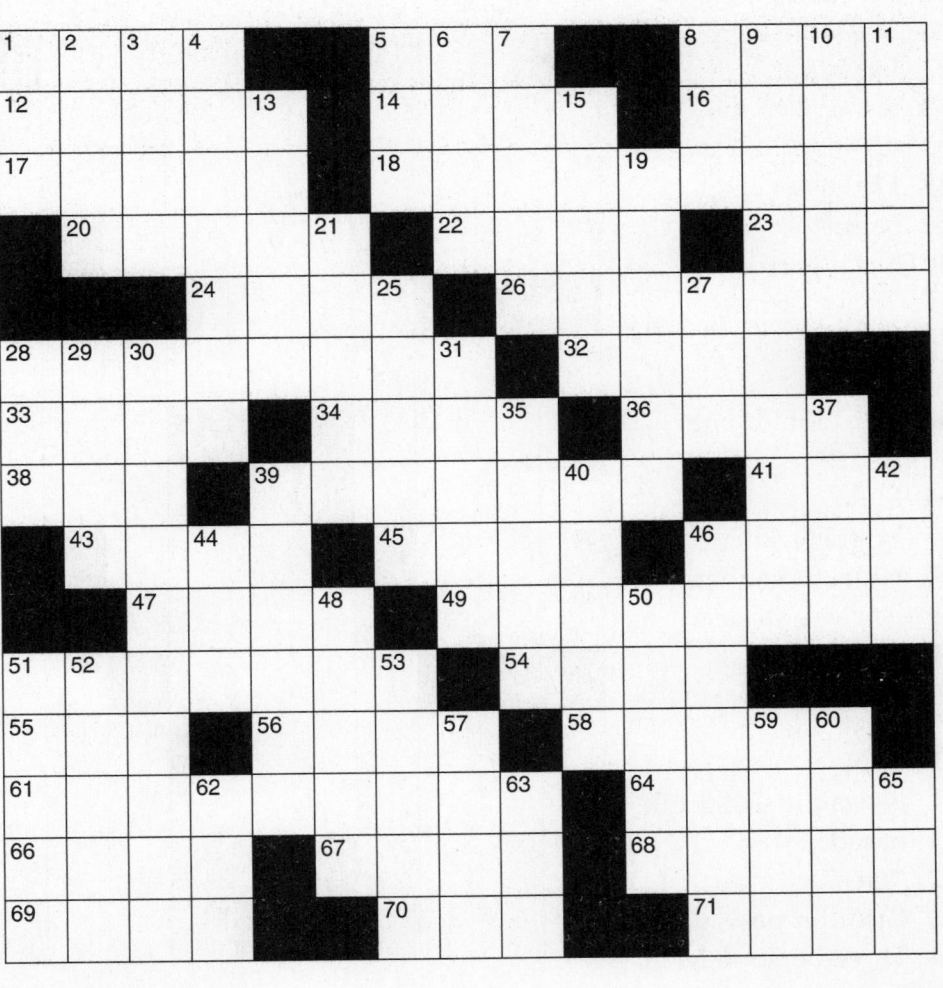

ACROSS

1 G. E. subsidiary
4 Mob member
8 Robotic rock group of the 80's
12 Emphasized, in a way
15 Gov. Bayh of Indiana
16 Mercury
18 "Ich bin __ Berliner"
19 Uses a scope
20 Lipton competitor
21 Snap request?
22 Spread
23 Mars
30 "Pardon me"
31 Successes
32 Hubbub
33 Strings of yore
34 Prevailing mood
36 Stash the bags
37 Jersey call
38 Sea east of the Caspian
39 Down to the __
40 Saturn
45 Stack part
46 "Now __ me down . . ."
47 Knowing
50 Fair-to-middling
51 Ashen
54 Pluto
57 Woody's kid
58 Hidalgo highway
59 Ancient Mexican
60 Parcel (out)
61 Guinness Book suffix

DOWN

1 Nostalgic soft-drink brand
2 "Très __!"
3 Gridiron pos.
4 Three-horse sleigh
5 "U Can't Touch This" rap singer
6 Western Indians
7 "__ a life!"
8 With dexterity
9 Kind of eye
10 Singer Jerry
11 One and __
12 Numbered rd.
13 High-tech memos
14 Diplomats' quest
17 Interprets
21 TV correspondent Brit
22 Wound
23 Majorca seaport
24 "__ Beautiful Doll"
25 Nafta opposer
26 Kind of dog
27 Hand-dyed fabric
28 Love to death
29 Galley drudge
34 Double __ (puzzle type)
35 Etna locations
36 Influence
38 Change
41 "__ customer"
42 "I __ Like That" (60's hit)
43 Comic Bossler
44 Hot cereal name
47 Did the crawl
48 Irene of "Fame"
49 Unfavorably
50 "Don't tread __"
51 Trials
52 One __ (ball game)
53 Flyer's org.
55 Actor Waterston
56 Tram contents

ACROSS

1 "The Nazarene" writer
5 "Elephant Boy" boy
9 __ night
12 Cheer noisily
14 "Am __ Love?"
15 1990 Best Supporting Actress
17 Juárez river
18 Newswoman Compton
19 Twiggy willows
21 Singer James
23 Nurse a drink
25 Conductor Dorati
26 Poverty
27 "Waterlilies" artist
29 __ Z
30 Partying with Eddie Cantor?
34 René or Renée
35 Toymaker
36 Noisy bird
43 Scale notes
44 Lambaste
45 Composition
48 Road from Dawson Creek
51 Kind of hill or lion
52 Feast
53 Canned-tomato style
55 Truckers' watchdog
57 Any ship
58 Nothing to shout about
62 "Xanadu" rock group
63 Noisy festivity
64 Manuel's intro
65 One of a trio in Scandinavian myth
66 Pursue

DOWN

1 ". . . __ Christmas"
2 __ up (film genre)
3 Bill's partner
4 "May I?" step
5 Hires
6 Act of contrition
7 Biblical month
8 Hairstyle that needs hairpins
9 Coordinate
10 Listen in on
11 Unappreciative one
13 Airline to Karachi
15 Songbird
16 Scouting org.
20 Kind of gin
22 Town in a W.W. II novel
24 Notre Dame bench
27 Copycat
28 Heat unit
31 Keystone officer
32 Rock __ (jukebox brand)
33 Land __ (night locale)
36 Package
37 Hair products maker Curtis and others
38 Warring Seminole chief
39 Brady bill opposer
40 Father
41 Become popular
42 Occurrence
46 Loose a bra
47 Filter
49 __ Parker, 1904 candidate for President
50 Mint
54 How the answer to this goes
56 Ceiling
59 Greek letter
60 Typewriting abbr.
61 Start of a bray

334 *by Richard Silvestri*

ACROSS

1 Honeydew kin
7 Fatherless fellow
11 Crow's feat?
14 Slurred over a syllable
15 Ring happening
16 Part of a flick?
17 College study
19 NNW antithesis
20 Gerund maker
21 It's sold in bars
22 Wrangle
23 Screech, for one
25 Bit for Fermi
26 Stories connector
27 Bring in the crops
29 In an evil way
31 Stealthily
33 Flying Peter
34 Carry
35 Type of tiger
38 Religious sch.
39 Reflected on
41 Abandoned
45 Penny or Lois
46 See eye to eye
47 Hertz alternative
48 Lose (to)
49 Way out
50 Slow down from a run
51 Start of the St. Ives riddle
53 Fleur-de-__
54 Trinidad and Tobago's capital
58 Exaggerator's suffix
59 Philharmonic instrument
60 Monopoly card
61 Hog haven
62 Obscene
63 Perfumed, in a way

DOWN

1 Animation frame
2 "Thrilla in Manila" victor
3 Ssspeak like thisss
4 Arabian Sea gulf
5 Glacier Bay sight
6 Orthodontist's org.
7 Seafood order
8 Scale opening
9 Jam ingredient
10 Short range?
11 One of the Magi
12 Lambaste
13 Light rowboat
18 Skin softener
22 Baseball's Old Professor
23 El Dorado treasure
24 Travel
25 "__ Goes By"
26 Kiosk
28 Piece of eight
30 Loses one's balance?
32 Annapolis freshman
35 Fish like a mackerel
36 Spirited steeds
37 Letterman rival
39 Swiveled
40 Drops in the morning
41 Soup scoops
42 Self-centered sort
43 Snowman of song
44 Cultivating tool
50 Option for Hamlet
51 "Off the Court" author
52 Stretch over
54 D.C. figure
55 TV watchdog
56 Rocks in a glass
57 Actor Beatty

ACROSS

1 Section under the mezz.
5 Scuttlebutt
9 Send by parachute
13 Yarborough, et al.
15 Middle name of "The King"
16 One abroad
17 "Utopia" author
19 Earring locale
20 It sounds right
22 Aggrieve
23 Role for Shirley in '63
24 Transport, in a way
25 Christian monogram
26 They dog AWOL's
27 Campaign name of '52
29 __ loss
31 See 26 Down
32 Half and half
33 Jonson's "Sweet Swan of __!"
34 It sounds right
39 Couple's pronoun
40 Make a doily
41 Antonym: Abbr.
42 Contorted
43 __ favor (please)
44 Baden-Powell offshoot org.
45 CNN parent company
48 Start of many a tale
50 Boldly attempt
52 Air
53 It sounds right
56 "Take __"
57 Exactly
58 Bear in the sky
59 Be full
60 Kewpie doll, perhaps
61 Leave in
62 Bo Derek film before "10"
63 "Greystoke" extras

DOWN

1 Sushi bar selection
2 Peppy
3 New Mexico city noted for archaeological finds
4 Cut off from escape
5 Circus people
6 Woolf's "__ of One's Own"
7 Verdun's region
8 Socialized with
9 Street in old TV
10 Wayne–Martin western of 1959
11 Remote control feature
12 Milord
14 Kerouac's Paradise
18 Don
21 Treat a sprain
26 Cocktail, with 31 Across
28 Shale oil product
30 Whatever
31 Troy Aikman stats
32 Calendar abbr.
33 Roadie equipment
34 Bowl over
35 Economic association since 1957
36 Newborn attendant
37 Person who makes beds?
38 Clean air org.
43 Grade school ammo
44 Rodeo mount
45 __ greens
46 Proceed easily
47 Accept a proposal
49 Sole attachment
51 Montezuma II, for one
52 Marketplace
53 Currency for 35 Down
54 Emerald City visitor
55 Forbidden City occupant: Abbr.

336
by Manny Nosowsky

ACROSS

1 Suit
6 Bit of smoke
10 __ scratch
14 Town near Bangor
15 "The __!" (hmmph!)
16 Good enough to eat
17 One __
19 Gray's subj.
20 Disprove
21 Go all-out
23 Washington story, maybe
25 Remembrance of things past
26 Easier to count
29 Turn-of-century Secretary of State
31 Fleece
33 Hurrays
34 U.C.L.A. rival
35 Knocked, in a way
37 She raised Cain
38 One side in an 1862 battle
40 1951 Johnnie Ray hit
41 Disk spinner
43 Exception word?
44 Deliberate
45 Vending machine part
46 Stewed
47 Firedamps
48 Name in robotry
50 "Once __ a midnight . . ."
52 Dinner alfresco
55 Fancy-coiffed bird
59 Nobelist __ von Behring
60 Two __ (dilemma)
62 The L of L-dopa
63 Scads
64 __ up (relented)
65 From the top
66 Popular source of quotes, for short
67 Sans élan

DOWN

1 Beethoven's birthplace
2 Spooky waterway?
3 80-day traveler
4 Gulps
5 Rock
6 Dorothy Parker, e.g.
7 G. & S. princess and others
8 Door stopper?
9 Army chaplain
10 Box label
11 Three __
12 Type of glass
13 Dish (out)
18 Main
22 Worrier's risk, so they say
24 Turkish for "ruler"
26 Oscar-winning film director Zinnemann
27 Runoff site
28 Four __
30 Convenient story
32 In itself
34 Not 100% open
35 Make a memo of
36 Aids in disguises
38 Photo choice
39 Balletic put-on
42 Mr. Average
44 Sports legend of 1920
46 With trumpets ablare
47 Spurred on
49 Symbol of vastness
51 Reward for yrs. of study
52 Gymnastics coach Karolyi
53 "I agree!"
54 Inflatable items
56 Bouquet
57 Heavily damaged city of W.W. II
58 Swirl
61 Somme summer

ACROSS

1 Like some eagles or tires
5 Poker Flat chronicler
10 Price
14 "Now __ me down . . ."
15 Dillies
16 Patron saint of physicians
17 In need
19 "Miss __ Regrets"
20 Former Washington nine
21 Journalists Joseph and Stewart
23 Bog
24 Dutch painter Jan
25 Actor Peter
28 Fleet cats
31 Comic Costello
32 __ incognita
34 Psalms word
35 "Bon" words
37 Appears
39 Flintstones pet
40 Bit of clowning
42 Soup ingredients
44 Cattle call
45 Newborns
47 Shortly
49 End of a tunnel, proverbially
50 Came in horizontally
51 Manhandler
53 Fellow crew member
57 Have an itch for
58 "Fantastic!"
60 1949 hit "__ in Love With Amy"
61 Sky-hued flower
62 Shoe support
63 Glassmaker's oven
64 Broadcasts
65 Asserts

DOWN

1 Invitations
2 A lily
3 Mowing site
4 Ball of fire
5 Feted ones
6 Tennis's Agassi
7 Collectors' cars
8 Robert Morse stage role
9 Subject of a will
10 Shut up
11 In a tenuous position
12 Leave hastily
13 1994 film "Guarding __"
18 Like Pisa's tower
22 Sediment
24 Humiliate
25 Broadway tune "__ River"
26 Ten-__ odds
27 Not with it
28 Northern Indians
29 Vietnam's capital
30 "Darn it!"
33 Rent out again
36 Presaging trouble
38 One-way transporters
41 Zoo fixture
43 Cuts
46 Pulses
48 Owns up to
50 Protected, as the feet
51 Subject to court-martial, maybe
52 Curse
53 Bedaze
54 Taj Mahal site
55 "__ also serve who . . ."
56 Hot times on the Riviera
59 Little: Suffix

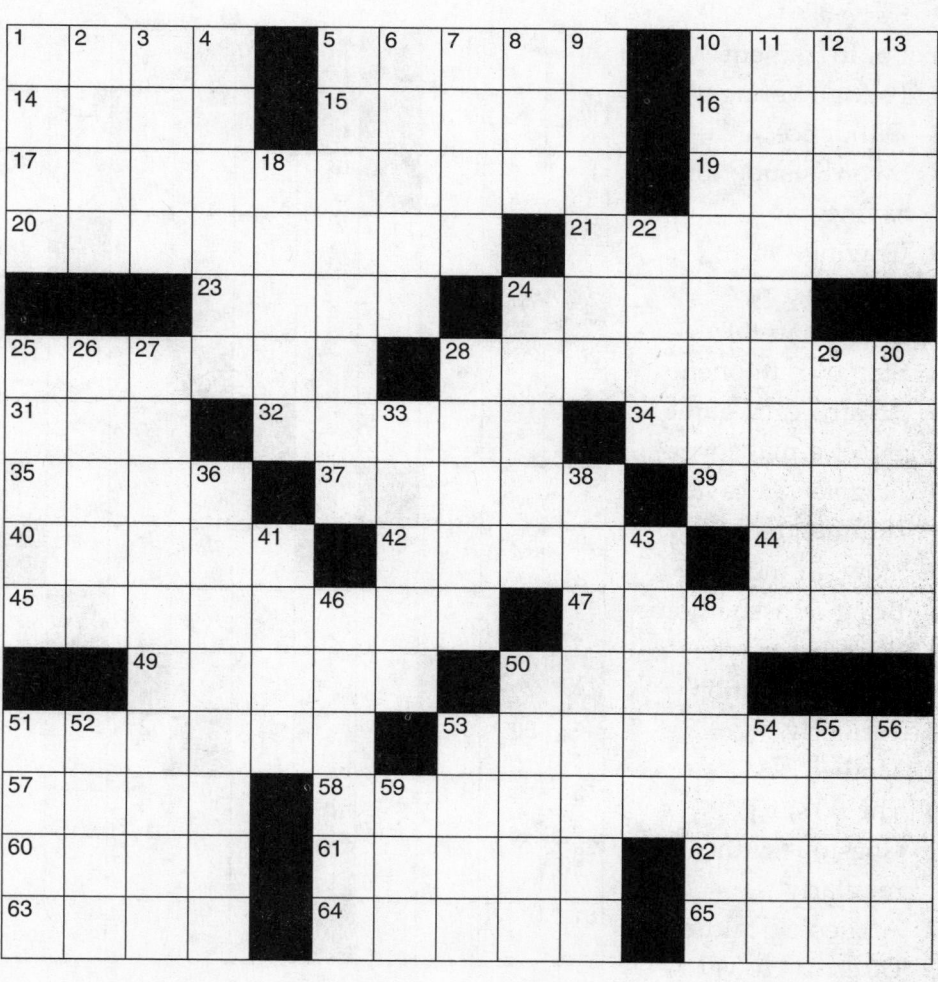

ACROSS

1 Gregory Hines specialty
4 Take for granted
10 Colorless
14 Actress Gardner
15 Stay-at-home
16 Roof overhang
17 House member: Abbr.
18 Interior decorator's hiree
20 Wields the gavel
22 Swear (to)
23 Pinker inside
24 Opponent
25 Greek geometer
27 Premolar
31 Pallid
32 Secrete
33 Poi ingredient
34 Fed. power agcy.
35 Diffidence
38 Sword's superior, in saying
39 Craving
41 Ends' partner
42 More than fat
44 Stereo components
46 32-card card game
47 Effect a makeover
48 Napoleon's cavalry commander
49 Slow, in music
52 Bring an issue home
55 Pet rock, maybe
57 Hair application
58 Formerly
59 Mother —
60 The 90's, e.g.
61 Goes out with regularly
62 Archeological finds
63 Director Howard

DOWN

1 Canvas cover
2 Declare positively
3 Houseman TV series, with "The"
4 Two are often prescribed
5 Under the elms
6 "Great!"
7 Salt Lake City team
8 Russian for "peace"
9 Makes more valuable
10 Person who's feeling down in the mouth?
11 Fad
12 Lexington and Madison: Abbr.
13 Lahr or Parks
19 One of the Aleutians
21 Shopper's lure
24 Adjutants
25 Noblemen
26 Exhaust
27 Ties
28 Toothless threat
29 "__ my case"
30 Gift recipient
32 Kind of power
36 Barn dances
37 Legendary hemlock drinker
40 Sidewinder lock-ons
43 False god
45 Actor Dullea
46 A form of 46-Across
48 Tycoon
49 Primates
50 Madonna's "Truth or __"
51 Church area
52 Lo-cal
53 Mr. Mostel
54 Flair
56 Chow down

ACROSS

1 Room between rooms
5 Handouts
9 Farm building
13 Opera solos
15 West Virginia resource
16 Sack starter
17 1970 Tommy Roe hit
20 Spain's locale
21 Leslie Caron role
22 Hesitation sounds
23 Writer Bombeck
25 Swindle
26 Sweet treat
30 "Fiddler on the Roof" fellow
35 Literary collection
36 Weep loudly
37 Arctic, for one
38 Recurring theme
41 French denial
43 Lisboa's sister city
44 1985 Kate Nelligan title role
45 Big shot
47 Calendar ender: Abbr.
48 Anglo's partner
49 Tentacled sea creature
52 Ostrich's cousin
54 Author Bellow
55 Lemon drink
58 Meadow bird
60 Drinkers' toasts
64 "Black Bottom Stomp" performer
67 Came down
68 Christmas centerpiece
69 The elder Judd
70 Critic Rex
71 Cruising
72 Tiff

DOWN

1 Pilgrim to Mecca
2 Pilgrim to Mecca
3 Citrus flavor
4 Emblem of victory
5 Item up the sleeve
6 Take it easy
7 Slander
8 With cunning
9 Visit Vail, perhaps
10 "Come Back, Little Sheba" playwright
11 Cowardly Lion portrayer
12 Chooses
14 Helical
18 Doorway parts
19 Perfect
24 Long, long time
26 Caan or Cagney
27 _ Gay
28 Type of rubber
29 Superior to
31 Author Umberto
32 "Rigoletto" composer
33 Film director Peter
34 Tennyson's "_ Arden"
39 Odysseus's rescuer, in myth
40 Exquisitely
42 Guitarist Lofgren
46 Ecto or proto ending
49 Panel of 12
50 Alaskan river
51 Groups of indigenous plants
53 "I Remember Mama" mama
55 Partly open
56 Take out of print
57 Nobelist Wiesel
59 "Red Balloon" painter
61 On
62 _ Linda, Calif.
63 Fit of anger
65 Former Ford
66 _ & Perrins

340 *by Roger H. Courtney*

ACROSS

1 Cremona violinmaker
6 Henri's squeeze
10 Tennis units
14 Quarrel
15 Stadium protests
16 Wynken, Blynken and Nod, e.g.
17 Criticize a prizefight?
19 Small brook
20 Transgression
21 Blackmailed
22 Cold stick
24 Le Sage's "Gil __"
25 One way to run
26 Instruments for Rostropovich
29 Economic hostility
33 Poet T. S.
34 Trumpeter Al
35 __ morgana (mirage)
36 Highway caution
37 Skater Sonja
38 Late king of Norway
39 "I __ Got Nobody" (20's hit)
40 Mare's feed
41 Jacques, in song
42 Rings loudly
44 Bell's signal
45 Itineraries: Abbr.
46 Handed-down stories
47 Expensive
50 Bit
51 Word with date or process
54 Imitator Little
55 Boxing commission?
58 Medicinal plant
59 Killer whale
60 "Happy Birthday" medium
61 Cravings
62 Shade of blue
63 Cup of thé

DOWN

1 Clumsy boats
2 Actor Paul
3 Ever and __
4 Idiosyncrasy
5 Imagination tester
6 French clergymen
7 "__ Indigo"
8 Chit
9 Guesswork
10 How hard Riddick Bowe can hit?
11 Rock star Clapton
12 Cash drawer
13 Fileted fish
18 "What a pity!"
23 Delivery letters
24 Items used in "light" boxing?
25 "Mrs. __ Goes to Paris"
26 Actor Romero
27 "Dallas" matriarch Miss __
28 Detroit footballers
29 Hues
30 Charles's princedom
31 Old name in game arcades
32 "Nevermore" quoter
34 Call at a coin flip
37 Winnie-the-Pooh receptacle
41 Awhile
43 Shoshonean
44 Humorist Lazlo
46 Not an express
47 Devoutly wish
48 Annoy
49 Religious image
50 Peruvian Indian
51 Speaker's spot
52 Coffee dispensers
53 Fisher's "Postcards From the __"
56 Suffix with fail
57 Wood sorrel

ACROSS

1 Whip end
5 Mystery writer's award
10 Sassy young 'un
14 "__ silly question . . ."
15 Painter Andrea del __
16 Portnoy's creator
17 Hmm?
20 __ Dame
21 Packwood, for one
22 Curse
25 Purse fastener
26 Jeweler's weight
28 Some of the Brady bunch
31 Eat like a chicken
34 Blend
36 Utah's Hatch
37 D.D.E.'s command
38 Hmm . . .
40 Volga tributary
41 Writer Terkel
43 Requisite
44 Porch adjunct
45 Arab capital
46 Ignoramus
48 South African statesman Jan
51 Gospel singer Jackson
55 Many TV shows
57 Cathedral displays
58 Hmm!
61 Mitch Miller's instrument
62 Mountain nymph
63 Electricity carrier
64 District
65 Don Knotts won five
66 Actress Young

DOWN

1 Suburban greenery
2 Seeing __ (since)
3 Do figure eights
4 Where to hang your chapeau
5 Biblical verb ending
6 "Zip-a-Dee-Doo-__"
7 Alum
8 Relics collect here
9 The "R'" in H.R.H.
10 Pugilistic muscleman
11 Famous debater
12 Rat chaser?
13 Talese's "Honor __ Father"
18 Word repeated after "Que"
19 Speaker
23 In a line
24 Eagle's nail
27 Like Neptune's trident
29 Adidas rival
30 Break sharply
31 Annoyance
32 Famous last words
33 Camp V.I.P.
35 Concert hall
38 Debate subjects
39 Irish novelist O'Brien
42 Like a golf ball
44 Manatees
47 Word sung twice before "cheree"
49 Lake near Carson City
50 Drang's partner
52 DeVito's "Taxi" role
53 Venous opening
54 Gray
55 Ms. McEntire
56 Cherry leftover
58 "Far out!"
59 Spring time
60 Lots of ft.

342

by David Ellis Dickerson

ACROSS

1 Masquerades
6 "Fe, fi, fo, __!"
9 Batman foe, with "The"
14 Native Alaskan
15 Prince Hirobumi
16 Sheeplike
17 Irving's "A Prayer for Owen __"
18 The lambada, once
19 Grand mountain
20 Dr. Seuss title
23 Actress Skye
24 Ho Chi __
25 Car job
28 __ Bingle (Crosby)
30 God Almighty
34 A year in Mexico
35 Put to the grindstone
37 Studio prop
38 Dr. Seuss title
41 Plant seeds again
42 __-scarum
43 Coach Parseghian
44 Shakespearean oath
46 Smidgen
47 Love of Greece?
48 Dance or hairstyle
50 Calf's meat
52 Dr. Seuss title
59 One-__ (short play)
60 Crystal ball, e.g.
61 Keep busy
62 Violinist Isaac
63 Part of R.S.V.P.
64 Wrestling's __ the Giant
65 Western film title of '75 and '93
66 Golf peg
67 Relaxes

DOWN

1 Like venison
2 Out of the wind
3 Carroll contemporary
4 Em, e.g.
5 Pen, for Pierre
6 About mid-month, with "the"
7 Brigham Young's home
8 Computer-phone link
9 Norse land of giants
10 Make out at a party?
11 Songstress Eartha
12 Organic compound
13 Philosopher Descartes
21 Conclude with
22 Small bird
25 Dens
26 Hungry
27 Idaho city
29 Betty Ford program
31 1991 Stallone comedy
32 Brain surgeon's prefix
33 Columnist Maxwell et al.
35 Author from Salem, Mass.
36 Inferable
39 Dinner chickens
40 More like Shirley Temple
45 __ Solo of "Star Wars"
47 Sir Galahad's mother
49 Popular word game
51 "__ Is Born"
52 Fastener
53 VIII, to Virgil
54 Blvds. and rds.
55 Toledo's vista
56 Hitches
57 William of "The Doctor"
58 Unlocks, in a sonnet

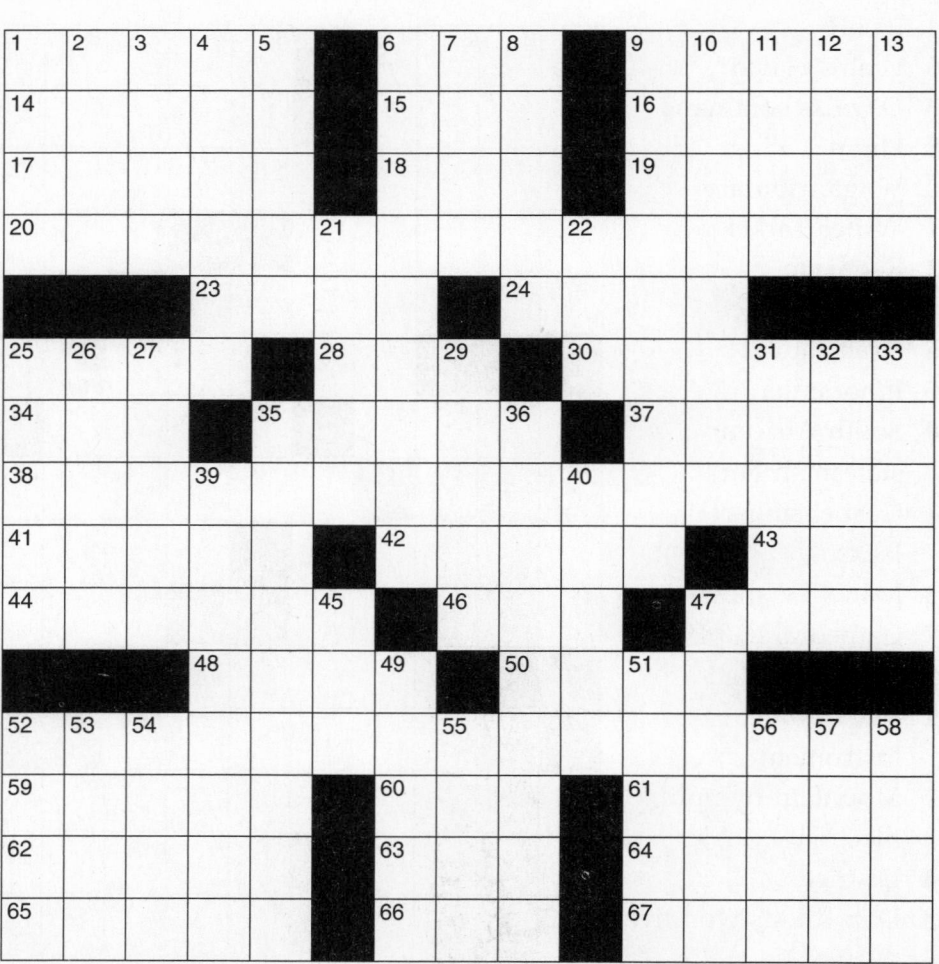

ACROSS

1 Rustic lodging, informally
6 The Fighting Tigers: Abbr.
9 Bust
14 Make __ out of (contradict)
15 Rustic lodging
16 "... partridge in __ tree"
17 "Alone" composer Brown
18 To catch a thief
19 Yo-Yo string?
20 With 53-Across, 1940 Reagan film
23 Reagan TV series
27 Singer Tucker and others
28 Language suffix
29 On the Baltic
30 Opposite of nord
31 Courage
33 Ultrasound is one
34 Part of NASA: Abbr.
35 __ homo
38 Part of The Shadow's attire
41 Yellowish red
43 Old hand
46 Colorado Indians
47 TV frequency
48 Used a blender
50 Much-maligned Reagan flick
53 See 20-Across
54 Contradict
56 Certain savings, for short
57 Oil-well capper Red __
60 With no letup
61 French seasoning
62 One of the Fab Four
63 Piece of pie
64 N.F.L. scores
65 __ Hall (South Orange school)

DOWN

1 Prohibit
2 __ carte
3 __ Nora Charles ("Thin Man" pair)
4 Delicate
5 Uproar
6 Start of a tax form
7 Angry dog
8 Dim the spirits of
9 Exuding kitsch
10 Scheduling break
11 Dismissal
12 "My gal"
13 Spanish gold
21 Family room piece
22 Middling mark
23 Drunk's affliction
24 __ Claire, Wis.
25 Affirmation
26 Took a load off
32 Scientific charlatan
34 A little bird
36 Isle of song
37 Pullman units
38 __ games (Reagan announcing job)
39 Lunched
40 Biked
42 Put up for sale
43 Kind of race
44 __-de-chaussée
45 Prefix with meter
47 Thurman of "Johnny Be Good"
49 Tour assistant
51 __ France
52 Some exams
54 Arc
55 Opposite of WSW
58 Goodman's "When __ A-Dreamin' "
59 Diminutive Reagan

ACROSS

1 Hang up one's jersey
7 Roll of bills
10 Chi. time zone
13 It ties the score
14 Palatine Hill site
15 Pi follower
16 Less messy
17 Actor Estrada
18 __-hoo
19 Old bandleader Edmundo
20 Keeled over
22 Library censures
24 Eats at the beach
26 They follow morns
27 Common suntanning locale
29 Eager to leave the picnic?
30 Atlanta Hawks arena, with "The"
31 Bites ineffectually
33 "Blech!"
34 Olympics skiing champion Alberto
36 "Car 54, Where Are You?" creator Hiken
37 Tiny mark
40 Nope's opposite
41 Was friends with
43 "My People" author
44 Xerox copy, for short
46 Equestrian competition
48 Director Kazan
49 Plains Indian
51 Woman's bio word
52 Jackie's hats
54 Turndowns
56 Prince Edward, e.g.: Abbr.
57 Sailor's direction
58 Rambo types
61 Classical start
62 Iodine source
63 To whom the Parthenon was dedicated
64 Vane direction
65 Speech pauses
66 Prepare fruit for eating

DOWN

1 Stimpy's pal
2 Adam's apple?
3 Little Anthony and the Imperials hit
4 "__ the Night," 1985 film
5 __ Peanut Butter Cups
6 Drop the ball
7 Not so good
8 Wrong
9 Hockey fake
10 1970 Vincent Price film
11 Huzzahs
12 Foot, in slang
14 Poker-table phrase
20 Nowheresville
21 Hangs like an earring
22 It can be soft or blind
23 __ sapiens
25 18-wheeler
28 Rush Limbaugh target
29 "__ Wiedersehen"
32 Backs
35 G.I.'s address
38 Tweety's home
39 Bender, of a sort
42 Very early
44 Fixes diapers
45 Molière miss and namesakes
47 Group of 100
49 Gondola guide
50 Nancy Kerrigan jumps
53 Shirr
55 Publishing notable Adolph
58 Like the woman of Chaillot
59 "A Chorus Line" showstopper
60 Rueful

by Rich Norris

ACROSS

1 Fitzgerald's forte
5 Inter __
9 W.W. I battle site
14 Science fiction's __ Award
15 Persuade cagily
16 Prime
17 Bon Ami rival
18 Dog command
19 Robert Louis Stevenson home
20 NO RUNS
23 Conservatory site?
24 Prepare to shoot
25 Have a few
28 Takes away (from)
33 Very, to Vivaldi
34 Muscovite, e.g.
35 Ring around the collar
36 NO HITS
40 Actor Wallach
41 1962 Met __ Chacon
42 Backspace, on a computer
43 Lorenz Hart, for one
46 Razzed
47 Music hall tune
48 Linkletter subjects
49 NO ERRORS
57 Reddish equines
58 Baker
59 Vitamin D source
60 "... the better __ you with"
61 Memphis's locale
62 __ vera
63 Flag features
64 Without much thought
65 TV's "__ Blue"

DOWN

1 Ayatollah preceder
2 King work
3 Mideast potentates
4 E.P.A. concern
5 Mount up
6 Slack
7 Sonnet part
8 Kerrigan feat
9 "You bet!"
10 Sci-fi energy source
11 The Apostle of the Franks
12 Coll. course
13 Buck
21 Be pushy
22 Corrode
25 Drive
26 Tart-tongued writer __ Ivins
27 Washington's __ House
28 One, for one
29 Cavern phenomenon
30 Exonerate
31 Coquette
32 Fathered
34 Thickness units
37 Be lordly
38 Beginnings
39 Pledge, probably
44 One whose work is decreasing?
45 Reasons why
46 Bus
48 Sound at sundown
49 Some are liberal
50 Geezer
51 __ Grande, Ariz.
52 Grammy winner Braxton
53 More than willing
54 Too glib
55 Sit (down)
56 Managed, with "out"

346 *by Jim Page*

ACROSS

1 Swit co-star
5 Record label abbr.
8 __ E. Coyote
12 Foreman
14 Superdome and Silverdome, e.g.
16 Nursery rhyme listeners
18 Dig it!
19 Puzzlement
20 Kind of badge
22 "The Counterfeiters" author
23 __ hound
24 Mail client
27 Model Carol
28 Corn chip topping
30 Lacoste and others
32 Karl Malone's team
34 Pleases
36 Large number
37 Pave over
39 Heroic story
41 Actress Farrow
42 More retiring
44 Outshines
46 ". . . __ saw Elba"
47 Eniwetok, e.g.
48 Brooklyn Bridge designer
52 Early TV's Denise
53 Pretty Maid's nursery rhyme declaration
58 Former Philly mayor Wilson et al.
59 Fiddle-faddle
60 Toshiba rival
61 Band's booking
62 Campaign

DOWN

1 Just dandy
2 Year in Nero's reign
3 Reading room
4 Zeals
5 Certain firearms
6 Actress Ryan
7 Modern site of ancient Kish
8 1962 Dion hit, with "The"
9 "The very __!"
10 Line to the Hamptons, for short
11 "Don't overdo it"
13 Subway __
14 Conservative
15 Like grade-A meat
17 Lively tots
20 Soda jerk's drink
21 Property
23 "Ironside" actress Elizabeth
24 Basketry twig
25 Kind of paint
26 Another round
29 Coasting at Lillehammer
31 Union and others: Abbr.
33 Opposite of 8-Down
35 Thievery
38 1970 Ossie Davis musical
40 Lauds
43 Holds one's horses?
45 First-rate joke
48 Fixes
49 Novel set on Tahiti
50 Designer von Furstenberg
51 The Daltons, e.g.
54 Miss Piggy word
55 __ flash
56 Wash. advisory grp.
57 Command to a plow horse

ACROSS

1 Rear
6 Edible rodent
10 Address abbr.
13 Historic earldom
14 Jambalaya locale
15 Perrier, par exemple
16 Smog?
18 More than aloofness
19 Yves's eve
20 Write off
22 Belly laugh
25 Like Desmond Tutu
28 Synge's "__ Island"
29 Fred Harman's comics cowboy
32 Of ecological stages
34 Athlete's foot
35 Hack
36 Ownership
37 U.N. arm
38 Firms (up)
40 Bambi's aunt
41 Rings
43 Mountain capital
44 Freedom
46 Head overseas
47 Showed indecision
50 Sound of a live wire
51 Belle and others
53 Appear ahead
55 Comics interjection
56 How a young lady succeeds?
62 Sign
63 Goodbye
64 __ Fountain
65 Dance step
66 Almost up
67 Indians whose name means "lovers of sexual pleasure"

DOWN

1 Actor Stephen
2 "Do __ say!"
3 Medit. nation
4 At some times of the year
5 Fair
6 Something to be up to
7 One vote
8 Tell secretly
9 Overlords
10 Inaugural balls?
11 Confront
12 "Parigi, o cara," in "La Traviata"
14 Old dance site
17 Airline to Karachi
21 Bit of light
22 Low-priced lodging
23 __ million
24 Results of deer hunting?
26 Cross-examiner
27 Jay and family
30 Uses force
31 Has a second meeting with
33 Ed Sullivan Theater host
34 Cañon feature
39 Hornswoggle
42 Diamond call
45 Comparative suffix
48 Tennyson's "doves in immemorial __"
49 __ good turn
51 She at sea
52 One of the Sinatras
54 Aware of
57 MNO, on a phone
58 Tippler
59 Storm producer
60 Time before
61 Family member

348

by Timothy S. Lewis

ACROSS

1 Lowly homes
5 One of the Simpsons
9 Abundantly supplied
13 Dairy section purchase
14 Overly sentimental
15 60's singer Sands
16 Knitting loop
17 Crude transportation?
18 House cat
19 House shader
20 Baseball's Canseco
21 "On Golden Pond" Oscar winner
22 With 34-Across and 48-Across, Wordsworth lines on Lucy
26 Fur type
27 Otto I's domain: Abbr.
28 Dig this
29 Sax, for one
30 "Take the __"
33 Road hazard
34 See 22-Across
37 N.Y.C. subway
40 "__ Restaurant"
41 "Amo, __, I love a lass . . ."
45 Sweep at sea
46 Japanese discipline
47 Pennsylvania folks
48 See 22-Across
53 Site of the Cambrian Mountains
54 Turkish bread
55 __ Palmas, Canary Islands
56 Model Macpherson
57 Equatorial capital
59 Huff and puff
60 Dissembled
61 Shark's line
62 Source of sake
63 "The __ doth protest . . ."
64 High point
65 German border river

DOWN

1 Desire
2 Wail
3 It can eat you out of house and home
4 La preceder
5 Verdi's "__ Miller"
6 Jersey and Guernsey
7 "__ walks in beauty . . ."
8 Burns's birthplace
9 Cut again
10 Rowena's inamorato
11 Grate expectations?
12 Six-carbon molecules
14 Farm sounds
20 Bump
21 Diva Mirella
23 Make over
24 Banquo, e.g.
25 Astronomical butter
30 "Anthony Adverse" author
31 Making bows
32 Transportation for Sinbad
35 Nuremberg defendants
36 Aforementioned
37 Dr. Johnson's biographer
38 First name in gospel
39 Warbled
42 Lost
43 Obliquely
44 Not one to trust
47 Sleuth's cry
49 Strapped
50 Home of the Trojans
51 KNO_3
52 Home of the Trojans
57 Sine __ non
58 Home of the Trojans
59 Old hand

by Mel Taub

ACROSS

1 Ezio Pinza, e.g.
6 Leak
10 Mention publicly
14 Mythological figure
15 It's found on the end of a string
16 Hogarth depiction
17 Texas A & M student
18 Untimely arrival
20 National anthem?
22 907 kilograms
23 Sip
27 Houston, for one
28 "To __" (with 44 Across, tune to which U.S. anthem was set)
31 Belli's bailiwick
34 Gold Cup Day site
36 "Holy cow!"
37 Cross to bear
39 Not by a long shot
40 Lay by
41 Straight prefix
42 Yemeni's neighbor
43 Took the van
44 See 28-Across
46 Pourboire
49 Direct
50 Obsolescent occupation
53 National anthem?
58 Whoop it up
61 Nick of "Cape Fear"
62 Impersonator
63 Hold overseas
64 Grenoble's river
65 Shadows
66 More than cheerfulness
67 Relinquished

DOWN

1 Whilom airline inits.
2 About 1% of the atmosphere
3 Transition
4 Louis and Paul, e.g.
5 Folk singer from Birmingham
6 Most populous N.Y.C. boro
7 Former Irish Prime Minister Cosgrave
8 Alaskan wildlife refuge site
9 Killer __
10 Gains
11 Beat it
12 Maui strings
13 Neighbor of Pol.
19 U.S. Pres., militarily
21 Peter I, II or III
24 Splendid
25 Italian white wine
26 Ran its course
28 Israelite stoned for stealing at Jericho
29 Twelve
30 Moving jerkily
31 Bulgarian king, 1918–43
32 As to
33 Pleated trimming
35 A number of
38 Four-time Super Bowl champs
45 Ancient Syria
47 Peaceful
48 Hirsute
50 Distinctive manner
51 In bundles
52 Among: Fr.
54 Burglar
55 Rigorous test
56 Cleaving tool
57 Actual performance
58 Touched
59 Mail abbr.
60 Tapster's unit

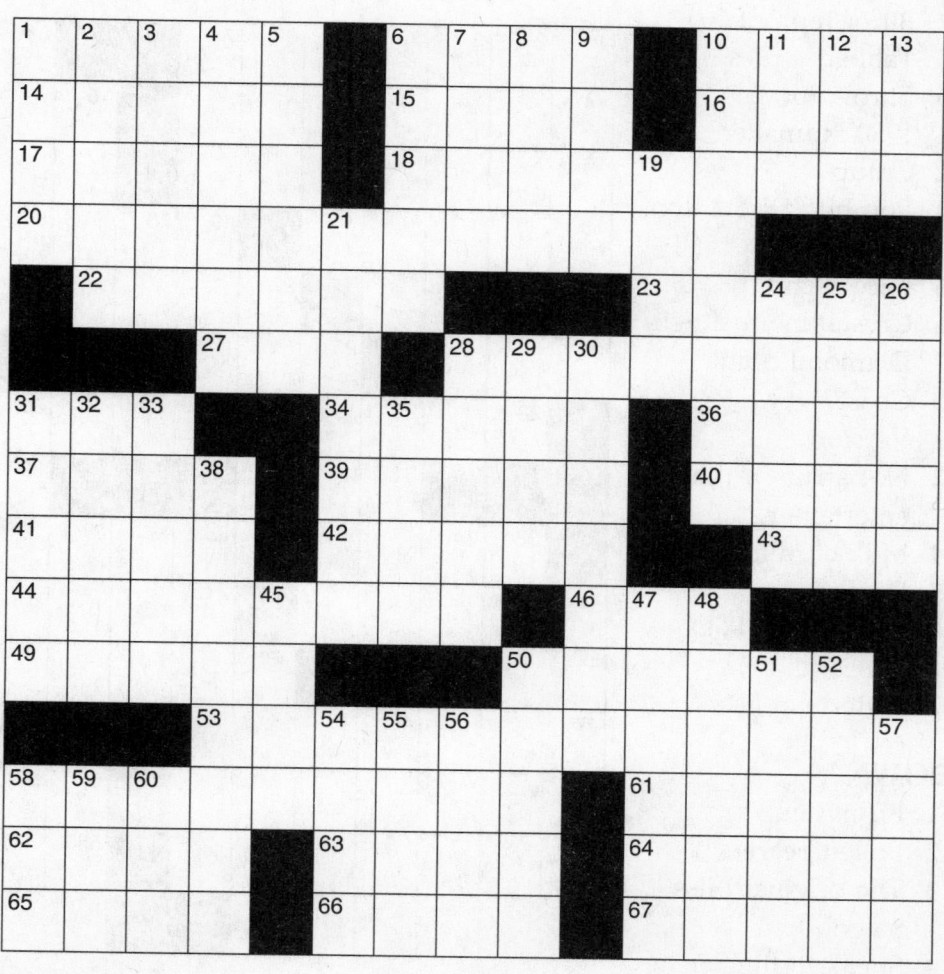

350 *by Randolph Ross*

ACROSS

1 __ temple
8 Grippers
14 Like the White Rabbit
15 Unrefined metal
16 Hawk's home
17 Benedictine, e.g.
18 Bar servings
19 December 31 event
21 Biblical writing on the wall
22 Seasons
23 Diamond girl
24 Uru. neighbor
25 __ Lama
26 Supports
28 Cable alternative
31 "Double Fantasy" singer
32 Bit of reproof
33 Tabloid topics
40 Throw for __
41 1980 fadmaker
42 Cutup
44 Pop hit "Da __ Ron Ron"
45 Nice nights
46 Crystalline rock
47 Diamond point
50 Coast
51 Version
52 Not a run-of-the-mill entertainer
54 Milk-curdling agents
55 Dock
56 Awards for P. D. James
57 Letterman lists

DOWN

1 Effluvium
2 Pollen bearers
3 The original Miss Saigon
4 Speak to the Senate
5 They have their orders
6 Practitioner's suffix
7 "12 Tribes" painter
8 TV transmitter in space
9 Cause of gray hair
10 Extension
11 Camden Yards ennead
12 Against
13 Tackle box items
15 N.B.A. Hall of Famer Bob
20 Kyrgyz range
22 Permanent place?
25 Patron saint of France
26 "Wanna buy __?" (old radio comedy line)
27 Snack
29 Robin Williams film
30 Notions holders
33 Overwhelmed
34 On the horizon
35 Sounds of strain
36 Prove acceptable to
37 Bow to bow, perhaps
38 Comeback
39 Polish, with "up"
40 Stick
43 Acts foppish
45 Vegas equipment
46 Top
48 Lab vessel
49 Landing
50 Red's signification
53 Sorority letter

ACROSS

1 Canyon sound
5 Cross-legged exercises
9 August forecast
14 Bumbler
15 50-50
16 Mohawk Valley city
17 Kitchen fat
18 Shea Stadium nine
19 Pressed one's luck
20 Big-eared animal
21 Vacation locale
23 In — (ready for release)
25 Sign of summer
26 Cordage
29 It will be printed tomorrow
34 Gerald Ford's birthplace
36 Banned apple spray
38 By way of
39 Vacation locale
42 Declare
43 Speaker Gingrich
44 Solemn procedures
45 "— forget"
47 1959 Fiestas song
49 Comic Charlotte
51 Outcome
54 Vacation locale
60 Have a tab
61 Like gold
62 On-the-cob treat
63 Ilsa of "Casablanca"
64 Wrist movement
65 Tale starter
66 Pre-owned
67 Army vehicles (You're welcome)
68 Blue-green
69 Jolly, to the British

DOWN

1 Brilliance
2 Sharply disagree
3 Monmouth Park events
4 — man out
5 Sana native
6 "Back to you"
7 Fetches
8 Photographer Adams
9 Rock of Hollywood
10 Jazz locale
11 Muralist Joan
12 Cake decorator
13 Janet Reno's home county
21 Lacquer
22 Pine
24 Associate
27 Put the finger on
28 Is brilliant
30 Painter's mishaps
31 Russian parliament building
32 Sea swooper
33 "Broom Hilda" creator Myers
34 Whitish gem
35 Military command?
37 "Wheels"
40 Late-late show hour
41 Vacation events
46 Violent downfalls
48 Tornado part
50 Orlando attraction
52 Shareholder
53 Sleepwear item
54 —-Hartley Act
55 Hip-shaking in Kauai
56 Actress Moran
57 Rube
58 TV knob
59 Whale of a movie
63 Broadway hit of 1964–65

352 *by Randolph Ross*

ACROSS

1 Like Job
8 Bob or beehive
14 Leisurely musical pieces
15 Decrees
17 Pentagon advocate?
19 Parlor piece
20 Ex-Knick coach Jackson
21 Author of "Life in London"
22 Heart of France
24 Part
25 Visit Robert Reich?
31 Medical apprentice
32 Ease
37 Blue "Yellow Submarine" characters
38 Revised
40 Ancient beginning
41 Off course
42 Foggy Bottom boat?
46 Narc's collar
50 "Since __ Have You"
51 Not for
52 Juan's uncle
53 Pescadores neighbor
59 Reno's piano practice?
62 Tympanic membrane
63 Guides, in a way
64 Brews tea
65 Menu listings

DOWN

1 Falsifies accounts
2 Chick ender
3 White House heavyweight
4 Beach Boys' __ Around"
5 "__ kleine Nachtmusik"
6 Titan tip
7 Poetic monogram
8 Spa installation
9 Maestro Toscanini
10 Words often exchanged
11 Twice as unlikely
12 Down Under dog
13 "Love Story" star
16 January 1 song ending
18 Riding the waves
23 Bullfight cries
25 Walk with difficulty
26 Unwanted classification, once
27 Printing style: Abbr.
28 Hawaiian state bird
29 Kingston and others
30 Fee schedule
33 Friend of Ernie
34 Sills solo
35 Caterpillar construction
36 Advantage
38 Calling company
39 Intersection maneuver
43 Asks for a loan
44 They trip up foreigners
45 Magician's sound effect
46 First or home, e.g.
47 Last of the Mohicans
48 Genesis
49 Spanish squiggle
54 __ were (so to speak)
55 Ovid's way
56 Oenologist's interest
57 Entr'__
58 Costner character
60 Prior, to Prior
61 G.I. __

by Joel Davajan

ACROSS

1 Rolling stone's deficiency
5 Anchor position
10 Complain
14 Aleutian island
15 __ Loa
16 Literally "high wood"
17 Obstinate
20 Royal spouses
21 Be on the brink
22 Professional bean counters
23 Designer Christian
24 Hardy's pal
27 Describe
28 Org. founded in 1948
31 Bandleader Shaw
32 Imparted
33 Sondheim's "__ the Woods"
34 Elusive
37 Branch Davidians, e.g.
38 Speaker's platform
39 Worker's wish
40 Off __ tangent
41 Curb, with "in"
42 Daredevil acts
43 Actor Sean
44 Lady in an apron
45 "Yessir," e.g.
48 Moon of Jupiter
52 In the altogether
54 Final notice
55 Teach one-on-one
56 Lion's den
57 Like 52 Across
58 Atlanta university
59 Thompson of "Howards End"

DOWN

1 Opposite of fem.
2 Mr. Preminger
3 Daze
4 Like the 2 in B_2
5 Not knowing right from wrong
6 Small pies
7 Hosiery snags
8 Actress Claire
9 Diversions
10 Future star
11 Border on
12 Actor's part
13 Look with squinty eyes
18 Sheepish lass
19 A long time
23 Prima donnas
24 Rope a dogie
25 Senator Specter
26 City east of Syracuse
27 Store up
28 __ a million
29 Alamogordo event, 7/16/45
30 Shoe bottoms
32 Rye or corn
33 Silent, or almost so
35 Toothless
36 With pretentiousness
41 Tear
42 Compensation
43 Pro golfer Calvin
44 TV's "__ Dad"
45 Presently
46 "Elephant Boy" star, 1937
47 Have brake problems
48 Roman statesman and censor
49 Thailand, once
50 Adjust the sails
51 Polish border river
53 Add

354 by Ronald C. Hirschfeld

ACROSS

1 They're plucked
6 Busy as __
10 Lake formed by Hoover Dam
14 Bye
15 Druid, e.g.
16 Presque __, Me.
17 Close behind
20 Chair plan
21 Setter or retriever
22 "Fables in Slang" author
24 Part of a bridal bio
25 Words after "The last time I saw Paris"
34 Buck follower
35 Muddies the water
36 "The Company"
37 Bara and Negri
39 Years in Paris
40 Mole
42 Native: Suffix
43 Comedienne Fields
45 Hebrides language
46 Completely unperturbed
50 Olympian: Abbr.
51 Knock-knock joke, e.g.
52 Sounds the hour
56 1967–70 war site
61 Discourage
63 Japanese aboriginal
64 Assassinate
65 Put up
66 Cuff
67 Cod relative
68 Drinks with straws

DOWN

1 It's a laugh
2 1985 film "My Life as __"
3 __ of passage
4 Drudge
5 Dairy bar order
6 Otto's "oh!"
7 English channel, with "the"

8 Like many textbook publishers
9 Adjective for Rome
10 Cellar growth
11 Old gas brand
12 Sleep like __
13 Excellent, in slang
18 Cry of achievement
19 Ancient capital of Macedonian kings
23 Corrigenda
25 June in Hollywood
26 Sister of Thalia
27 Alfa __
28 Sock __
29 Quinine water
30 Smarten
31 Lip-puckering
32 Hair-coloring solution

33 __ et Magistra (1961 encyclical)
38 It causes sparks
41 Lapidarist's object of study
44 City on Lake Winnebago
47 Tar
48 Actor Gooding
49 Glues
52 Earth
53 Bluefin
54 Scat cat
55 It's north of Neb.
57 Flying: Prefix
58 TV exec Friendly
59 Cape __ (westernmost point in continental Europe)

60 Colonists
61 __ de deux
62 Fork

ACROSS

1 College digs
5 Haggadah-reading time
10 Coarse hominy
14 Piedmont city
15 Cuisine type
16 The Magi, e.g.
17 Railbird's passion
20 Certain wind
21 Check
22 Opposite of "yippee!"
23 Buyer caveat
24 Bottoms
27 Darlings
28 Railroad abbr.
31 Old toy company
32 Trim
33 It's not a dime a dozen
34 Bettor's bible
37 Grocery buy
38 Sword of sport
39 Archaic "prior"
40 Political abbr.
41 Cutting reminder
42 Didn't quite rain
43 Broadcasts
44 Baptism, e.g.
45 Corner piece?
48 Some legal documents
52 Across-the-board bet
54 Mont. neighbor
55 Mercantilism
56 Mrs. Chaplin
57 Curaçao ingredient
58 Downy duck
59 Snoopy

DOWN

1 Desert dessert
2 Agcy. founded in 1970
3 Hwys.
4 Results of some errors
5 Summer wear
6 Some House of Lords members
7 Word before free or calls
8 Ike's command, for short
9 Double-check the seat belts
10 Muddles
11 "Judith" composer
12 Cold-war fighters
13 Starting gate
18 Like some gates
19 A Kringle
23 Penthouse home?
24 Pheasant broods
25 Words to live by
26 Stoop
27 Race-track runner
28 Snob
29 Notre planète
30 1947 Horse of the Year
32 "__ Got a Brand New Bag"
33 Track hiatus time
35 Have fun
36 Like trotters, e.g.
41 Dust collector?
42 Actor Martin
43 Dismay
44 "The Cloister and the Hearth" author
45 Switch
46 Roofing item
47 Chip in
48 Interpret
49 "Git!"
50 Geologists' times
51 Waffle
53 Dernier __

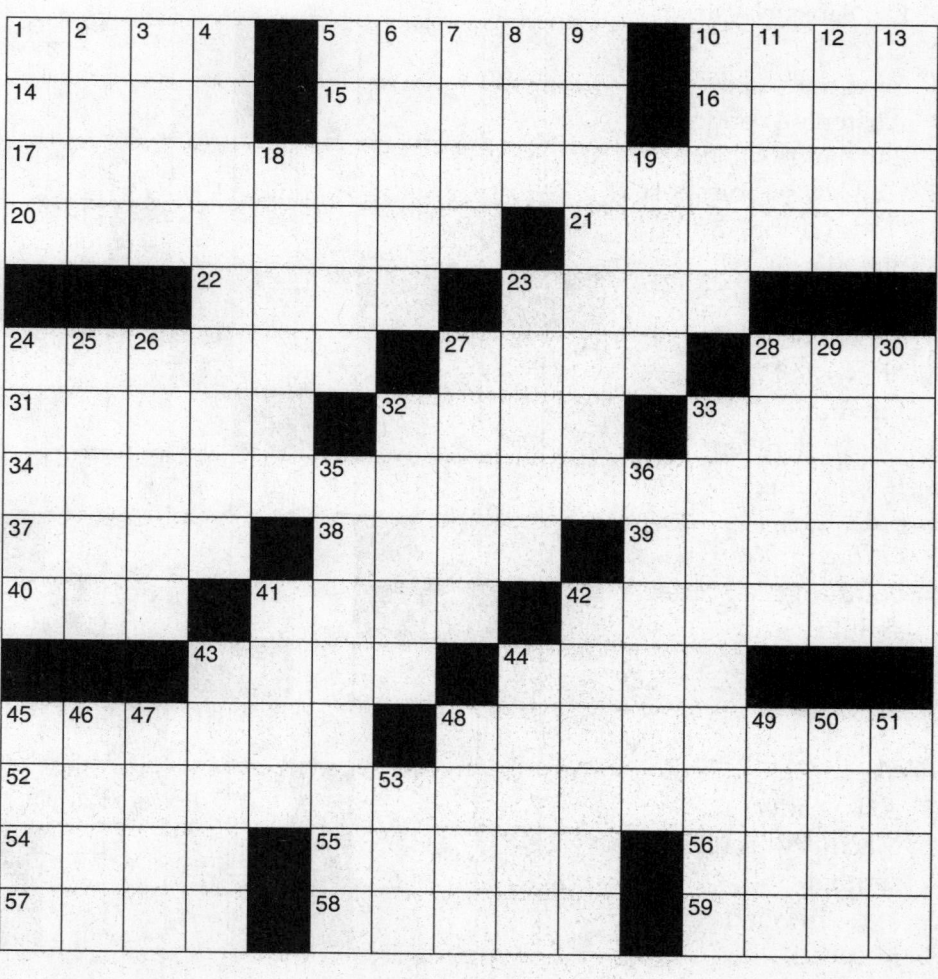

356 *by Fred Piscop*

ACROSS

1 Like Caspar Milquetoast
6 Yodeling locale
10 Quantities: Abbr.
14 City south of Gainesville
15 Chip's partner
16 Attack of the flu
17 Hook's flag
19 Florence's river
20 Like some shopping
21 Just say no?
23 Grp. founded in 1960
25 Present, for one
26 Antiknock number
30 __ and hounds
33 Calhoun of "The Texan"
34 Swiss mathematician
35 Son–gun link
38 Dr. Seuss classic
42 Da or ja
43 Onetime pupa
44 Austen's Woodhouse
45 Duchamp subject
46 Gym class, for short
48 "Siddhartha" author
52 Stat starter
54 Craftsperson
57 Short vocal solo
62 "Jurassic Park" beast, for short
63 Ocean denizen
65 It's nothing
66 Split __
67 Ottoman: Prefix
68 South-of-the-border shouts
69 Catch some Z's
70 Torpedoes

DOWN

1 Axis leader
2 Macintosh screen symbol
3 Type of bonding?
4 Miseries
5 Wright brothers' home
6 See 18 Down
7 Jet follower
8 No contest, e.g.
9 Belgrade resident
10 Cut down
11 Notorious Bugs
12 City near the ruins of Carthage
13 "JFK" director
18 With 6 Down, Ali maneuver
22 "Private Parts" author
24 Locomotive, perhaps
26 Overindulgence
27 Roy Innis's org.
28 Very, in Versailles
29 Parliament vote
31 What's more
32 Davidson's "The Crying Game" costar
34 "Holy cow!"
35 Resistance figures
36 Celebrity
37 Make __ dash for
39 Dress to the __
40 Cassowary kin
41 Susan of "L.A. Law"
46 Saucy
47 Block and tackle et al.
48 Little Iodine creator
49 "My Wicked, Wicked Ways" author Flynn
50 Eydie's partner
51 Boxcars
53 Medieval guild
55 Like some cheeses
56 El __ (ocean current)
58 Lateral lead-in
59 Go sour
60 __ off (anger)
61 Commotions
64 Cooper's tool

ACROSS

1 Smelling things?
6 Howard and Brown
10 Hill-climber of rhyme
14 Well-nigh
15 Hand-cream additive
16 Writer Wiesel
17 "__ Davis Eyes"
18 1982 Beineix thriller
19 Flat amount?
20 Subject of this puzzle
22 Designer Gernreich
23 Opulence
24 __ Islands
26 Hamilton of the Carter White House
30 "Topper" pooch
31 Tom Joad, e.g.
32 Bond
35 Fixed-up building
39 Accord signer of '78
41 G.I. address
42 Tool for bending cold metal
43 Laugher?
44 Bumper blemish
46 Noted name in lithography
47 TV palomino
49 Maintain
51 Promised Land
54 Bumpkin
56 Barbra's costar in '68
57 Noted performers on 20 Across's show
63 Falling-out
64 "__ Man" (Estevez flick)
65 Kind of cannon
66 Opposed
67 Geometry datum
68 Wipe out
69 It may generate interest
70 Clobber
71 Jinni

DOWN

1 Kemo __
2 Sacked out
3 A good deal
4 1984 Nobelist
5 "__ by Starlight"
6 Base of a number system
7 "Thimble Theater" name
8 Smoked salmon
9 Rap session?
10 Performer on 20 Across's debut show
11 Alimentary canal part
12 Yorba __
13 Admit
21 Bronchiole locale
25 Snobbery
26 Playwright Logan
27 Rubber-stamp
28 The Cyclone, e.g.
29 Performer on 20 Across's debut show
30 Light gas
33 Alan or Cheryl
34 News org. founded in 1958
36 Wealthy person
37 Ripening agent
38 Insurance writer A.M. __
40 Georgia home
45 Mr. Kaplan
48 Draw in
50 Used wax, perhaps
51 __ Sea (W.W. II site)
52 __ acid
53 Gore/Perot debate topic
54 Beat the offense
55 Lusitania sinker
58 "You are __"
59 Ran like mad
60 Rich soil
61 Former Sinclair competitor
62 Examined

358 *by Richard Silvestri*

ACROSS

1 Obsolete
6 Serpent song
10 Up to snuff
14 Type type
15 Put a stake on the table
16 Mr. Kadiddlehopper
17 Campaign-poster word
18 Night light
19 Litter littlest
20 Marquis de Sade's favorite side dish?
23 Before, to bards
24 Grandiose poetry
25 Wound reminder
28 Lingerie buy
31 Undiminished
35 Start of M-G-M's motto
36 Pop singer Abdul
38 Seven-time N.L. homer champ
39 Marquis de Sade's favorite entree?
42 Start of the año
43 Begin, as winds
44 Morn's opposite
45 Wanted-poster word
47 Snitch
48 Shelley output
49 Lab bottle
51 Former Mideast monogram
53 Marquis de Sade's favorite vegetable?
60 Ambition
61 At the summit of
62 More than manly
63 Move like the Blob
64 A little
65 Cultural characteristics
66 Ran in the laundry
67 Had no doubt
68 Ocean areas

DOWN

1 Regard
2 __ breve (2/2 time)
3 Dad's Day gifts
4 Whistler was one
5 Dissuade
6 Fastening device
7 '85 film, "__ the Night"
8 Washington, e.g.
9 Ranchero's wrap
10 Verse with a message?
11 In a funk
12 Brownie's eye?
13 CPR specialist
21 Interdict
22 Hanoi's region
25 Fencing weapon
26 Brom Bones's prey
27 In __ (agitated)
29 Has misgivings about
30 Birch kin
32 Readied the press
33 Christopher of the screen
34 Crossword birds
36 "Will it play in __?"
37 Official records
40 Made a basketball boo-boo
41 Ask for a loan
46 Upholstery fabric
48 Baroque
50 Admit
52 Aligned the cross hairs
53 Air-conditioned
54 Bulldoze
55 Igloo shape
56 Gush forth
57 Need a backrub
58 Karate motion
59 Ponderosa name
60 Lump

ACROSS

1 Ace depository
7 Peter Lorre typecast
13 In no hurry to buy
15 Inexpensive
16 Table spread
17 Humiliate
18 Twice-told
19 Fairy tale kid
22 Hoodwink
26 Mosaic piece
28 __-per-view
29 University of Maine town
31 Jazz star, with 36 Down
34 Dialing for dollars?
37 Slums Mother
38 Heavy bundles
39 Einstein's birthplace
40 Indy 500 occurrence
44 Humdrum
46 Vodka cocktail
49 Coach Holtz of Notre Dame
50 "All systems __"
52 Survey
53 Spying on who's buying?
59 Alternatives to malls
60 "Marriage is __": Cervantes
61 Saint-Tropez is one

DOWN

1 Makes confetti
2 Company trademark
3 Clean water agcy.
4 Prefix with glottis or gram
5 Pinot ou Chardonnay
6 Downstairs: Fr.
7 For beginners
8 Armored god
9 Like many football stadiums
10 Scheduled
11 Reception site
12 N.Y. summer time
13 Chambre
14 Kotter of 70's TV
15 Start, as a computer
19 Start of a toast
20 Spray, perhaps
21 Grandma
23 Knowing about
24 Bit of distress
25 Goggle
27 Fish entree
30 Sun or moon
31 Bear riot
32 "This is only __"
33 Not discounted
34 __ off (scold)
35 Anecdotal Bombeck
36 See 31 Across
37 Butter container
41 Writer at Orchard House
42 Guffaws
43 __ out (ignore)
45 "It __ Be You" (Kahn-Jones hit)
46 Romance or sci-fi, e.g.
47 Pop music's __ Pop
48 Drive
51 Bravo and Grande
52 Ending with spin or speed
53 Art deg.
54 Golfer Woosnam
55 Sgt., for one
56 Color
57 U.F.O. occupants
58 __-mo (replay technique)

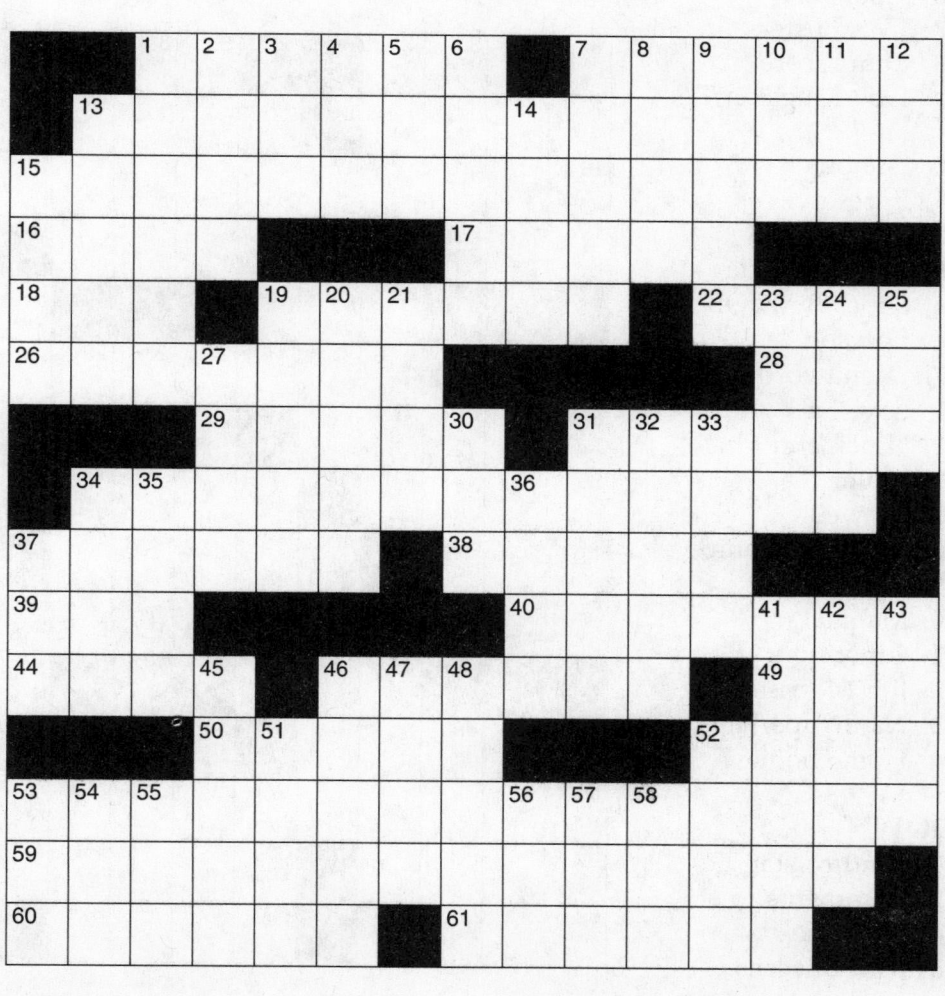

360 *by Betty Jorgensen*

ACROSS

1 Beckoned
5 Arroyo
9 Edith Evans, e.g.
13 Travel writer Thollander
14 Arrangement containers
15 Enthralled
16 Start of a quip
19 "__ was saying . . ."
20 "Women Who Run With the Wolves" author
21 Appearance
22 Stipple
23 Rent out
24 Quip, part 2
33 Punts, e.g.
34 Out of place
35 "Bleak House" girl
36 Moons
37 TV adjusters
38 Court score
39 1959 Kingston Trio hit
40 __ nous
41 In reserve
42 Quip, part 3
45 Stable particle
46 Super Bowl QB Dawson
47 "Kenilworth" novelist
50 "Luck and Pluck" writer
53 As well
56 End of the quip
59 A Guthrie
60 Marshal
61 Other
62 Jim Morrison, e.g.
63 Nanny, perhaps
64 Home bodies?

DOWN

1 Kind of star
2 Comments to a doctor
3 Half of sechs
4 High ways?
5 Bulb measure
6 Court V.I.P. Arthur
7 Tunisian rulers, once
8 Theory
9 Lennon's last home, with "The"
10 Exchange premium
11 One of Chaucer's travelers
12 Hash-house order
14 Horizon, maybe
17 Persian cries
18 Bright-eyed and bushy-tailed
22 Silent-spring causers
23 More than snips
24 Frightful force
25 It comes from the heart
26 Capital on the Bou Regreg river
27 Reach in total
28 Vast, in the past
29 Name on a pencil
30 Point of greatest despair
31 Order
32 Decreases
37 Puzzle
38 Betimes
40 Woman with a lyre
41 "Siegfried," e.g.
43 Lusting after
44 Thomas Gray piece
47 A herring
48 Mackerellike fish
49 Ibsen's home
50 Farming prefix
51 Turkish money
52 Backbiter?
53 Prefix with port or play
54 Drying oven
55 Hugo works
57 Piano tune
58 Up on

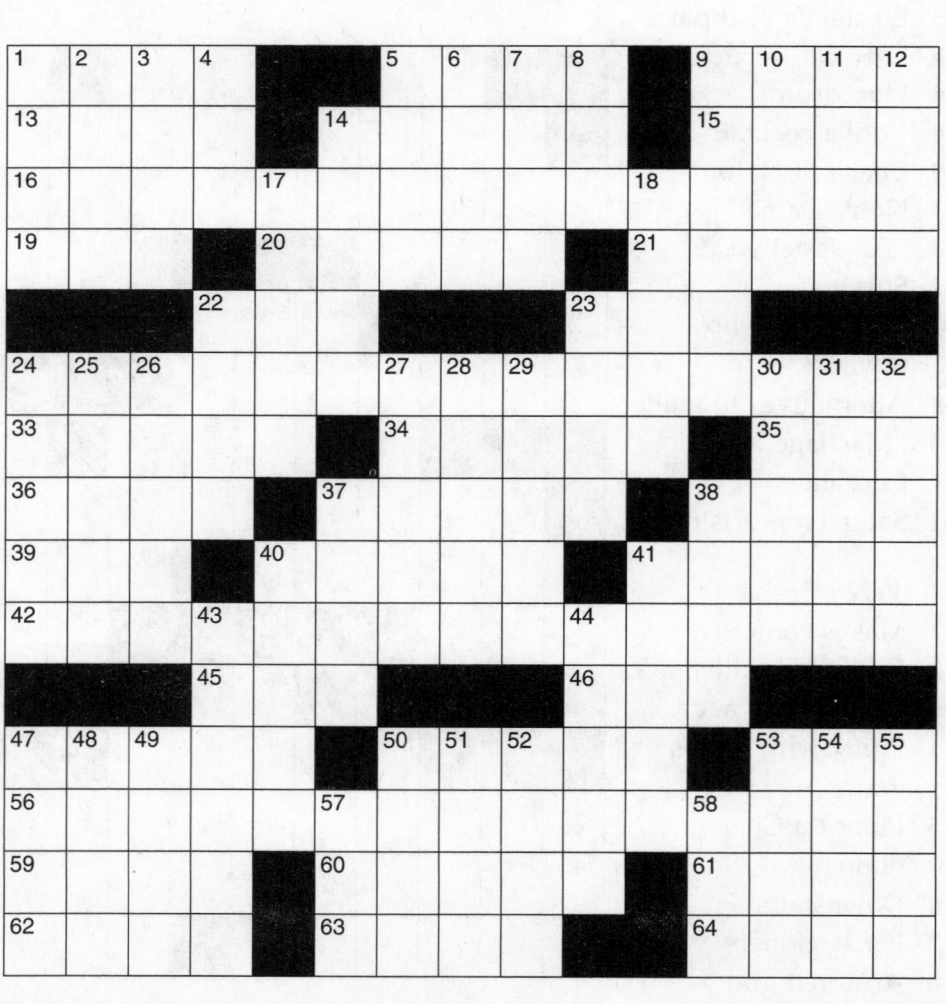

by James Neal

ACROSS

1. Food critic Sheraton
5. In the van
10. __ law (rule of electricity)
14. Green acres?
15. Brendan Byrne, e.g.
16. Muumuu accessories
17. Tilt
18. Jabbered
19. Alternative word
20. Massachusetts musical ensemble
23. Othello's nemesis
24. Louvre annex architect
25. Soviet space station
27. Brussels __
31. Fill driveway holes
33. In back
35. Somme summers
36. Parental substitutes, emotionally
40. Swamp
41. Hairsplitter
42. Wore away
45. Chapel next to St. Peter's
48. It's often seen ringside
49. Carpet down
51. Get __ the ground floor
52. Harvestman
57. French novelist Pierre
58. Skiing mecca
59. Grammatical subject
61. Sponsorship
62. Shiny fur
63. Mrs. Dithers
64. Yiddish writer Sholem __
65. Western "justice"
66. Genesis locale

DOWN

1. Actor Brooks
2. Eye malady
3. Bad luck
4. Kind of circuit
5. Vegas game
6. Retirement nest eggs
7. Flat payment
8. Person with a big nose?
9. "The Resurrection of Lazarus" painter
10. Backdrop for a TV scene
11. Spouse
12. Letters
13. Compass dir.
21. Salvation Army founder
22. Eskimo __
26. Latin thing
28. Suffix with press or moist
29. Maryland athlete
30. They're sometimes cracked
32. Aptness
34. "__ Pagliaccio"
36. Andirons
37. Sweet-smelling
38. Fill-up filler
39. "__ Tomorrow" (Sammy Kaye hit)
40. Columnist Greenfield
43. Windup
44. Wright-Patterson base site
46. Worthless
47. Nail down
50. Greek Academy founder
53. Gossip
54. "__ be in England . . ."
55. Turndowns
56. "Sommersby" star
57. __ & Perrins
60. Bert Bobbsey's twin

362 *by Sidney L. Robbins*

ACROSS

1 Day in Hollywood
6 Like a V.P.
10 Hula hoops, mood rings, etc.
14 Live
15 Talk drunkenly
16 Revise
17 Like Macaulay Culkin, in a 1990 movie
19 Mr. Mostel
20 Diner signs
21 The Boston __
23 Sense of self
24 __ Moines
26 One of the Greats
28 Loathed
33 Zilch
34 Egyptian deity
35 Jeanne d'Arc and others: Abbr.
37 Asp
41 Straddler's spot
44 Ordinary talk
45 Roman "fiddler"
46 Composer Thomas
47 Western Indian
49 Hair curls
51 Cheerleader's prop
54 Kind of nut or brain
55 Live
56 Verne captain
59 Cut in a hurry
63 Poses
65 Intersection concern
68 Mound
69 Tickled-pink feeling
70 Declaim
71 Confederate
72 Paradise
73 Big books

DOWN

1 N.J. neighbor
2 Plow pullers
3 Abundant
4 Ratio words
5 Bleachers
6 Mary Kay of cosmetics
7 Hog filler?
8 Certain wrestler
9 Boring tool
10 Turk topper
11 Run like __
12 Somber tune
13 Remained firm
18 Trypanosome carrier
22 Divide the pie
25 __ fire (ignite)
27 Certain wallpaper design
28 Dewy
29 Eastern V.I.P.
30 Fuss
31 Finishes
32 Postpone
36 Not a one-panel cartoon
38 Yawn inducer
39 Go into hysterics
40 Soft drinks
42 Pretend
43 "I'm telling the truth!"
48 Appear
50 Awkward bloke
51 Bygone title
52 Bay window
53 Kind of detector
57 Fine, temperaturewise
58 Convex/concave molding
60 Dated hairdo
61 Did laps in the pool
62 Abhor
64 Mata Hari, e.g.
66 Hatcher
67 Favorable vote

ACROSS

1 High rung on the evolutionary ladder
6 Alternative to a shower
10 Quatrain rhyme scheme
14 Like __ from the blue
15 Environs
16 Wise guy
17 Popular chocolate snack
19 On the level
20 River through Florence
21 Mother __
22 Help in crime
23 Quad number
24 Lock
25 Torah readers
29 Forgiving one
32 Oscar, e.g.
33 Prefix with cycle
34 Draft org.
37 March events?
40 Lolita
42 Phony prefix
43 Fond du __, Wis.
44 New Zealand native
45 Where Spain and Portugal are
48 Seasoning
49 Afterward
51 Kind of show
53 Singer Minnelli
54 Kick locale
56 Dumb __
60 Paid promotion: Abbr.
61 Give up hard drink?
63 Vegetarian's no-no
64 Sheltered
65 Similar
66 Wan
67 Lease
68 Little ones

DOWN

1 It's a laugh
2 "Deutschland __ Alles"
3 Daybreak
4 What's more
5 To the __ degree
6 Louisiana waterway
7 Bowers
8 Socials
9 Tortoise's competitor
10 Glaring
11 Place to have one's head examined
12 Bouts of chills
13 Borscht ingredients
18 Selves
23 Hoedown musician
24 Shortened
25 Criticizes
26 Not at home
27 Coming-of-age event
28 Cross-one's-heart garment
30 Play on words
31 Some
35 Dried
36 Agitate
38 Unit of corn
39 Phys. or chem.
41 Baby food
46 "Reds" star
47 Out of bed
48 Bygone
49 Andean animal
50 Gofers
52 Commencement
54 Box lightly
55 Patriot Nathan
56 It's full of baloney
57 Final notice
58 Roué
59 War deity
62 Hardly an underperformer

364 *by Wayne Robert Williams*

ACROSS

1 Impudent youngster
6 Salesmen, briefly
10 Impudent talk
14 Cheapskate
15 Beasts of burden
16 Baseball's __ brothers
17 1994 film role for Jim Carrey
19 Movers' trucks
20 More like winter sidewalks
21 Singer Estefan
23 Inge play
26 Closet spook
28 Nabokov novel
29 Clique
31 Norse deity
32 Film maker Wertmuller
34 Window surrounding
36 Fiery gems
41 Photographer's instruction
44 Rob
45 Neophyte
46 Paradise
47 Wedding vow
49 Soak (up)
51 Actor Tognazzi
52 By airmail from France
57 Dealer in cloth
59 "__ Twist"
60 England's Scilly __
62 Call to the phone
63 Happy camper?
68 Kuwaiti honcho
69 Nile queen, for short
70 Neutral shade
71 Does lawnwork
72 Bakery bite
73 Of the eyes

DOWN

1 New Deal grp.
2 Sot's interjection
3 Just manage, with "out"
4 Writer Ira of "Sliver"
5 Concise summary
6 Old-fashioned learning method
7 Long-distance commuter's home
8 For each
9 Full of obstacles
10 "Stompin' at the __"
11 Wake-up noise
12 Actress Braga
13 "Black-eyed" girl
18 Most hospitable
22 "Vive __!" (old Parisian cry)
23 Becomes tiresome
24 Ninny
25 Tippy transportation
27 Those not mentioned
30 Arm art
33 Letters before an alias
35 Not outgoing
37 Leading prefix
38 Make sense
39 Feudal lord
40 Man of the casa
42 __ and kicking
43 Bribe money
48 Straightforward
50 Magician's word
52 Vatican leaders
53 Texas shrine
54 Strict
55 Declares
56 Neighbor of Chad
58 Songwriters' grp.
61 Tab's target
64 Pie __ mode
65 No longer chic
66 Wire service
67 Old-time gumshoe

ACROSS

1 Son of Abraham
6 RR stops
10 Ill-considered
14 Hajj destination
15 Justice Black
16 ". . . and to — good night"
17 Whittles down
18 The sun, to the skin
19 Hera's husband
20 Noted baseball announcer
22 Give the boot to
23 Actor Ray
24 Lustily robust
26 Cervantes's — Panza
30 Improvise
32 Mountain of central Russia
33 Defense acronym
35 Actress Christine
39 Fixed shoes
41 Emancipates
43 Borgnine's "From Here to Eternity" role
44 Pronounced
46 Abstract artist Paul
47 Clear, as a tape
49 Loco
51 Quarterback, often
54 Misplace
56 Compassion
57 All worked up
62 Concept
63 Tastes
64 "— of Athens"
66 First name in casino ownership
67 Option word
68 Gentry
69 Educator Sullivan
70 Noticed
71 Acted grandmotherly

DOWN

1 Mischief-maker
2 Cook quickly
3 Caldwell's "God's Little —"
4 Scored on a serve
5 Algiers quarter
6 Archeologist's fragment
7 Harbor helper
8 Author James
9 Horse color
10 Clinton's home team
11 Certain Alaskan
12 Kind of fund
13 Cursory
21 By oneself
25 Is sickly
26 Malibu sight
27 Neighborhood
28 Cartoonist Thomas
29 Near miss
31 Celebrated Freud case
34 Hubbubs
36 Dance performed in a grass skirt
37 High schooler
38 Sinking-in phrase
40 Knowledge
42 "Aeneid" queen
45 Setback
48 Gets up
50 Cleared
51 Jazz trumpeter Louis
52 "The Age of Anxiety" poet
53 Shock jock Howard
55 Novelist Tillie
58 Cairo's river
59 Hawaiian seaport
60 Spew forth
61 Dull routine
65 Pulp penman Buntline

366 *by Arthur S. Verdesca*

ACROSS

1 Yin's partner
5 Toy gun ammo
9 Rift
14 __ patriae (patriotism)
15 Together, in music
16 "It __ Be You"
17 Parisian entree
18 Vatican City monetary unit
19 Down Under soldier
20 1954 Hitchcock hit
23 Bonny one
24 Singer Acuff
25 Beautify
28 Barley bristle
30 Buddy
34 Spanish wave
35 Passage
37 Cain's nephew
38 Behave
42 Clam supper
43 Sacred song
44 Onetime medicinal herb
45 German donkey
46 Élan
47 Charitable foundations, e.g.
49 Chinese ideal
51 Part of a wagon train
52 Merit award
59 Use
60 Candy brand
61 Paint unskillfully
62 Mesa __ National Park
63 Felipe, Jesus or Matty
64 Former Mormon chief __ Taft Benson
65 Shipping amount
66 Desires
67 __ Bien Phu (1954 battle site)

DOWN

1 Croquet locale
2 French call for help
3 __ cloud in the sky
4 Edsel feature
5 Soft leather
6 Farewell
7 Result of tummy rubbing?
8 Ore layer
9 Maria Rosario Pilar Martinez
10 Jacks-of-all-trades
11 Wood trimmer
12 Weekly World News rival
13 Beaded shoe, for short
21 Chinese-Portuguese enclave
22 Coffee server
25 Ice cream mold
26 Biblical prophet
27 Thanks, in Thüringen
28 Journalist Joseph
29 Grieved
31 "My Dinner With __"
32 Brimless hat
33 Test car maneuvers
36 18-wheeler
39 Iron pumper's pride
40 Diligent
41 Lagoon former
46 Actress Caldwell
48 Lacked
50 Locale in van Gogh paintings
51 Breakfast fruit
52 At any time
53 Betting game
54 Kind of vision
55 Fiddlers' king
56 "Schindler's List" extra
57 Fix
58 Israeli diplomat
59 Dow Jones fig.

ACROSS

1 First name in Solidarity
5 Festive
9 Philatelist's item
14 Jai __
15 Mideast gulf
16 Eunomia, Dike and Irene
17 Partner of pieces
18 Schindler's request
19 Kind of orange
20 Feminine suffix
21 1928 A.L. batting champ
23 Correspondence
25 "It's a sin to tell __"
26 Alias of Romain de Tirtoff
27 Substitutes
31 Tupelo's favorite son
33 Impersonators
34 Nosh
35 Fizzles out
36 "__ Jacques"
37 Carol syllables
38 Ex-governor Richards
39 Kind of table, informally
40 She played Lady L in "Lady L"
41 Singer Jim and others
43 Novi Sad native
44 "Diary of __ Housewife"
45 Parched
48 CNN newsman
52 Thou, today
53 Poet's almost
54 Frown
55 Bulkhead
56 Terrify
57 Folk follower
58 Hazzard County officer, on TV
59 Risk
60 Butterine
61 1169 erupter

DOWN

1 Stick-on
2 Molière girl
3 "Peace Train" singer
4 Towel word
5 Aplenty
6 Felipe's farewell
7 Minus
8 U.C.-Irvine's nickname
9 Easy winners
10 Type of salad
11 Uzbekistan's __ Sea
12 Crèche figures
13 Hammer part
21 "Smoke __ in Your Eyes"
22 Tinted windows prevent it
24 Cleveland's Speaker
27 Scharnhorst commander et al.
28 Crimson Tide coach
29 Buckley's "God and Man at __"
30 Cartoonist Drake
31 Cheese town
32 Part of a fishing trio
33 Sticky-tongued critter
36 Newspaper edition
37 Actress Loughlin
39 Tambourine
40 Comic Lew
42 Expedition in Kenya
43 Mono's successor
45 Sky-blue
46 Athenian statesman
47 Oral Roberts University site
48 Big stinger
49 Formerly
50 Limerick man
51 Wrench, e.g.
55 Tiny

368 *by Richard Thomas*

ACROSS

1 By the side
6 In the back
10 Hoarded
14 1936 Leslie Howard role
15 Nose (out)
16 Actress Nazimova
17 Foes at Gaugamela
20 Mythological lineup
21 Whomps
22 __ Claire
23 Loyal
24 Foes at the falls of Reichenbach
31 Topple
32 Leisure
33 Card
35 June honoree, for short
36 Taxable income
38 Philippine island
39 Plaintive
40 Out of business
41 Camera carriage
42 Foes at Troy
46 Fix, artwise
47 "Flying Down to __"
48 Bundle barley
51 Cosmetic items
56 Foes at Tenochtitlán
58 Mayberry moppet
59 Simulacrum
60 Ferber title
61 Level
62 Not stifling
63 Levels off

DOWN

1 Not give __
2 "Damn Yankees" role
3 Sign from on high
4 Barber's call
5 Green light
6 Pilot's vision problem
7 Nirvana
8 Cabinet dept.
9 Group based in Geneva
10 First name in the N.B.A.
11 Literary pseudonym
12 Jack Horner's surprise
13 Itar-__ (news agency)
18 Circa
19 As __ (generally)
23 "Take __!"
24 Tankard's kin
25 Rival of Sally
26 "The Cloister and the Hearth" author
27 N.Y.C. subway line
28 Busybody
29 Reb general Richard
30 Dear pelt
34 Fellows
36 Colonial African land
37 Prefix with Disney
38 Mil. rank
40 Caniff's "__ Canyon"
41 Bishop's bailiwick
43 Oregon's __ Lake
44 Narrow opening
45 "Hey you!" sound
48 Dundee denizen
49 Original Arizonan
50 Gannon University home
51 Marston __ (1644 battle site)
52 Don River's outlet
53 Hayseed
54 Ugandan exile
55 Needs a facelift
57 AT&T alternative

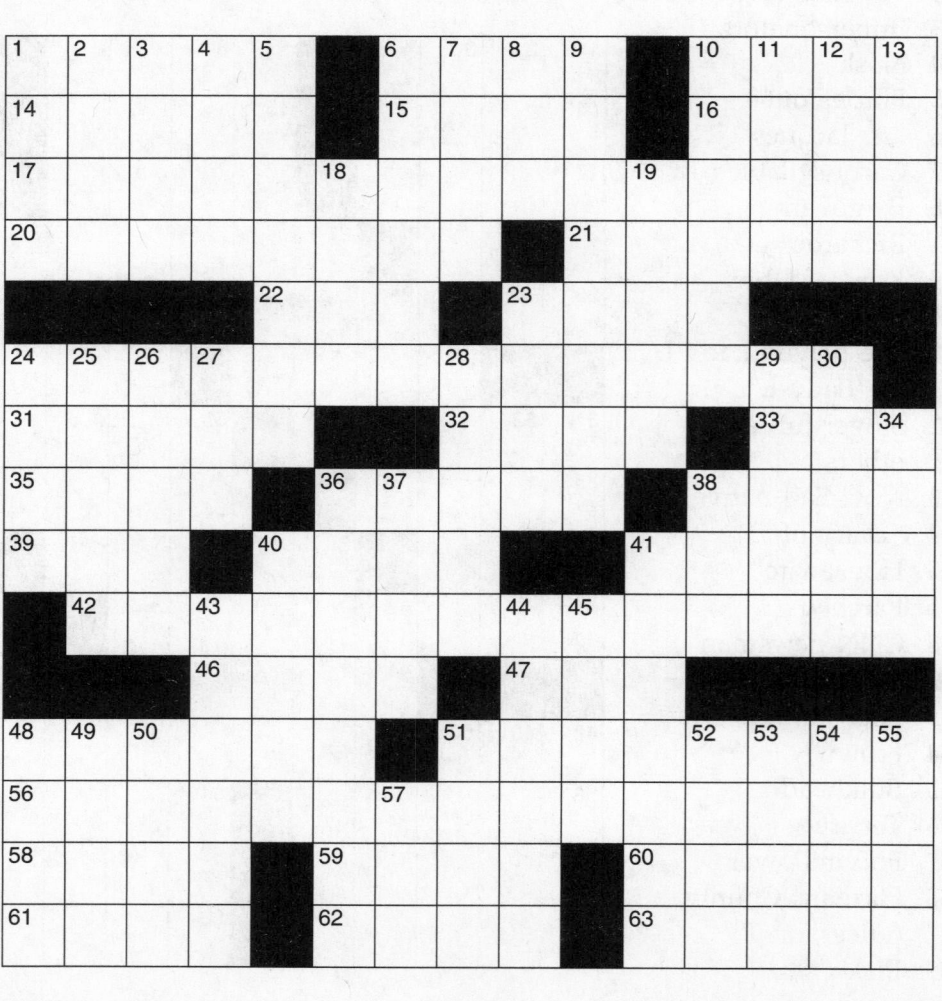

ACROSS

1 Be a party to
5 Breakfast strip
10 "__ corny as Kansas . . ."
14 Judd Hirsch sitcom
15 Jagged
16 __ me tangere
17 First place
18 Spry
19 Future flower
20 Start of an old proverb
23 Gran Paradiso, e.g.
25 Mideast export
26 Russian co-op
27 Part 2 of the proverb
32 Ancient city on the Gulf of Aqaba
33 Reduce
34 Muralist José
35 Irritable
37 Give the eye
41 Don Corleone
42 Circa
43 Part 3 of the proverb
47 Birchbark
49 One may be high at 5:00
50 __ Plaines, Ill.
51 End of the proverb
56 __ supra (see above)
57 Understand
58 Mr. Saarinen
61 Graph start
62 École attender
63 Leave shore
64 Apollo craft
65 Playwright Rice
66 Stepped

DOWN

1 Downed
2 Michael Jackson album
3 Archetype
4 A Turner
5 Grin's partner
6 Historic county in Scotland
7 Hairdo
8 Frogner Park locale
9 At no time, to poets
10 Natural
11 Nelson Eddy in "Rose Marie"
12 French avenue
13 Fortuneteller
21 "Goodbye, Columbus" author
22 Lion's pride
23 Iowa university town
24 Singer Lovett
28 Communications conglomerate
29 __ Downs
30 Took a chair
31 Rossini's "Count __"
35 Spasm
36 Ordinal ender
37 Gram. case
38 Firestone rival
39 Darth Vader's son
40 Vacation times abroad
41 Opinion
42 Wise __ owl
43 Garland
44 Loggers' tourneys
45 When some local news is "live"
46 Render impotent
47 Kind of service
48 Stage comment
52 Business exec William
53 Cheerleader's routine
54 Watch part
55 Hatching post?
59 John Wayne's "__ Lobo"
60 Used

370 *by Jonathan Schmalzbach*

ACROSS

1 Symbol of suburbia
5 Author Grey et al.
10 Joyful cries
14 Hand cream additive
15 Sommelier's stock
16 Crow's-nest spot
17 Storage spot in a Brooklyn home
19 Word with sound or dog
20 Jargon suffix
21 Hurry
22 Petrol amount
23 What a Brooklyn guy blames today's problems on
27 It's stuck on Brooklyn theater floors
30 Place that Lot fled
31 Eager
32 What Brooklyn students hate to take
36 Half of Mork's sign-off
37 Serra's title
39 Ages
41 What a Brooklynite catches at J.F.K.
43 Creeper
44 Too-too
46 Where a Brooklynite tipples
47 Body that busted a Brooklyn gangster
52 Anchor position
53 Three, to Gina
54 Job's lot
57 Role for Oland
58 Laundry chore in Brooklyn
62 Annoyed interjection
63 Liver, e.g.
64 Conception
65 Clumsy craft
66 Author Zora ___ Hurston
67 Shore flier

DOWN

1 Forced (to)
2 Pub brews
3 Hoop's locale, perhaps
4 Pastoral spot
5 Austrian-born writer Stefan
6 Anouk et al.
7 Wind dir.
8 Bard's twilight
9 Jet set's jet
10 Sphere of operation
11 Cole Porter's "Katie Went to ___"
12 Type of turf
13 Dutch artist Jan
18 Noah's eldest
22 Hamstrung
23 Unearthed
24 Sleepy ones
25 Fulda feeder
26 Repetition
27 Comic Aykroyd
28 "Heavens!"
29 Missing
33 Little Foys number
34 Newspaper nickname
35 Mens ___ in corpore sano
37 ___ Springs
38 One against
40 Sunday speech: Abbr.
42 Unit of sugar or coal
45 Star-shaped
46 Bunnies' mummies
47 Russian villa
48 Old anesthetic
49 China flaw
50 Sty sounds
51 "Forsyte Saga" heroine
54 Broad
55 Singular person
56 Actor Eddie
58 Slip into
59 Before, to Burns
60 Links grp.
61 Dog command

ACROSS

1 1980 Olympics host
5 Writer __ Louise Huxtable
8 Setting
13 Computer list
14 Outfielders' throws
16 Sleeping problem
17 One-legged ballet pose
19 "Swan Lake" wardrobe
20 Ballet spin
22 Fernando of "The French Connection"
23 __ Grande, Ariz.
24 Café cup
26 Bull in Chihuahua
29 New Mexico artists' town
31 Spots on the face
34 Drinkers' heavens
37 1935 Astaire/Rogers musical
39 "Great Expectations" boy
40 Helpmate of sorts
42 Oil-rich __ Dhabi
43 "In" site, in a phrase
45 Took hold again, as a plant
47 Riga resident
48 Old Syria
50 Latin life
51 "If __ Hammer"
53 Where Cuzco is
56 Took it easy
58 Hopping step, in ballet
61 Plié spots
63 Anna Pavlova, e.g.
66 Accustom
67 Garfield pal
68 Desirous Greek god
69 __ incognita (old map notation)
70 D.C. lawmaker
71 Writer Kantor

DOWN

1 Thurman of "Henry & June"
2 Eccl. talk
3 Lose it
4 Limiting line
5 Lhasa __ (hairy terriers)
6 Pas __ (dance for four)
7 The shivers
8 Contents
9 Computer's heart, for short
10 Ballet leaps
11 Opposite of alte
12 Smooth
15 Begin in earnest
18 Time of importance
21 Sampler
25 Weaken
26 "Fiddler" actor
27 Express a view
28 Ballet coach
30 Ad __ per Aspera (Kansas's motto)
32 Local theaters
33 Old music magazine
35 Cote sound
36 Rub
38 Cortés's quest
41 Series of connected ballet movements
44 Biblical verb ending
46 Artists' lifeworks
49 Stallone role
52 Voyaging
54 Stephen Foster's "__ Bayne"
55 Female ruff
56 Theatrical bit
57 Murray of song
59 Softens
60 Aer Lingus land
62 Be wrong
64 "__ a chance!"
65 Oar wood

372 *by Manny Nosowsky*

ACROSS

1 Bombay V.I.P.
6 Hacienda part
10 Money grp.
13 With 16 Across, financially O.K.
14 By its very nature
16 See 13 Across
17 Lab containers
18 Hemmed
20 James Murray work: Abbr.
21 Air hero
24 Pro __
25 Kind of violet
29 Hawaiian verandas
31 Cousin of a mlle.
32 Inseparable
33 Lake __ (Mississippi's source)
34 German "I"
35 Musical ending
36 Composer with a clavier
37 Mississippi waterway
39 Gland finale?
40 Der __ (Adenauer)
41 Coll. srs. exam
42 Sophisticated
44 Scare word
45 Jungle squeezers
46 California team
47 Approve
49 The nth degree?
50 Festival time
51 Postal abbr.
52 Soviet workers' cooperative
54 Robin's transport
58 See 63 Across
62 Cost containment measure
63 With 58 Across, blockaded
64 Firecracker's path
65 Fun-house cries
66 Pretender

DOWN

1 Green
2 "The __ Daba Honeymoon"
3 Write a bit
4 Former ova
5 Abélard, e.g.
6 Rushed
7 Balaam's beast
8 See 9 Down
9 With 8 Down, a reply's start
10 Banned chemical compound
11 Had a little lamb
12 Lettuce variety
14 Agenda listing
15 German import
19 See 45 Down
21 Legendary Arabian hero
22 Make a list
23 Doer
25 With a bow, musically
26 Radiator fluid
27 Faster than adagio
28 Least remote
30 Late apartheid opponent
31 Appraises, with "up"
35 Sierra Maestra country
38 Flaherty's "Man of __"
43 Takes the elevator, perhaps
45 With 19 Down, predeparture words
48 Author Bombeck
49 Make ready, informally
52 "Poor pitiful me!"
53 Prefix with type
54 Merit badge grp.
55 Swiss river
56 Hosp. attention
57 Word of disgust
59 Both Begleys
60 "Huh!"
61 Sin

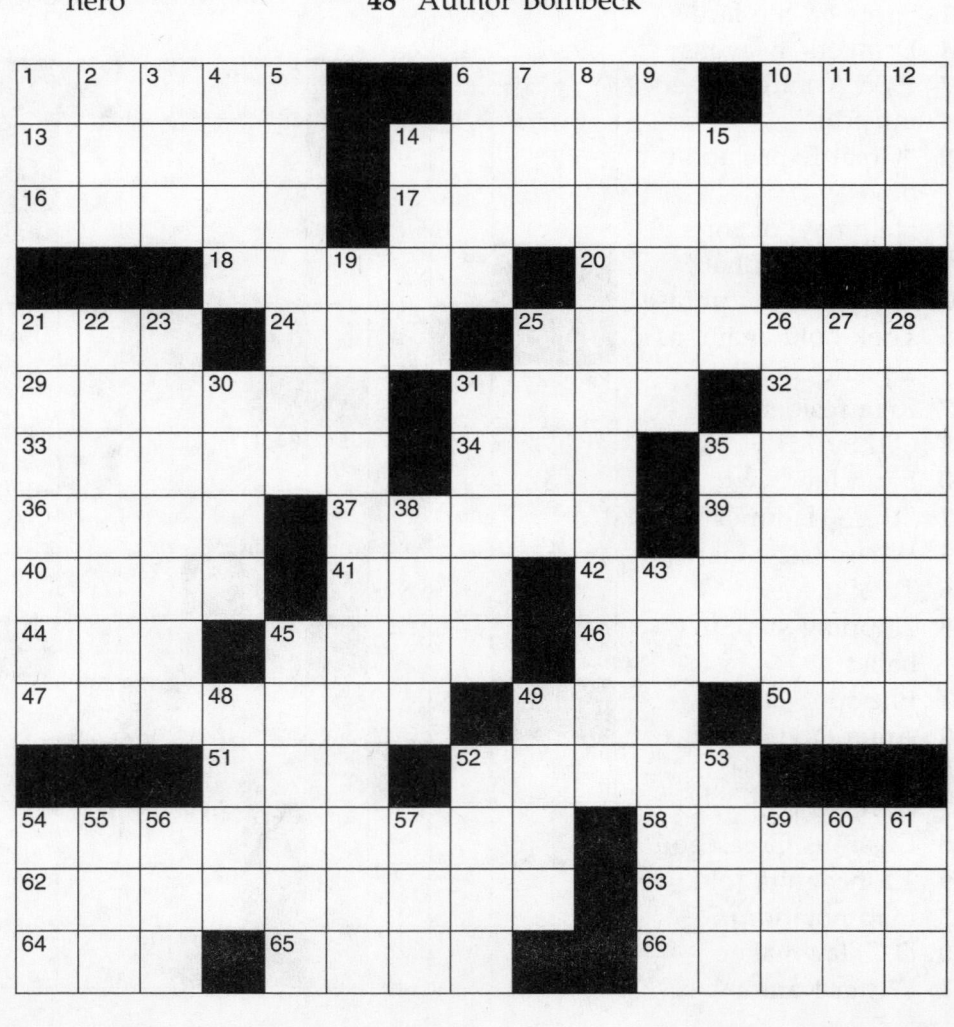

ACROSS

1 Gutter site
5 Insomnia cause?
9 Marmon __ (first auto to win the Indy 500)
13 Sick as __
14 Onetime Aegean land
16 Actress Chase
17 Start of a quotation by 9 Down
20 Neighbor of Braz.
21 Popular machine
22 Detroit products
23 Kind of code
25 25, e.g.
28 Runway
30 __ daisy
31 Signal since 1912
34 Indulgent
35 Sister of Selene
36 Straddling
37 Middle of quote
41 All __ (attentive)
42 Zinger
43 Acht, __, zehn
44 1994 U.S. Open golf champion
45 Star of "Mon Oncle"
46 Tidy up
48 Poznan's location
50 Seats, slangily
52 Peacock "eyes"
55 Addition
57 Suffix with insist
58 End of quote
62 "__ boy!"
63 Ruth's mother-in-law
64 Western star Richard
65 Admit, with "up"
66 Girlie show props
67 Certain investor's agreement, for short

DOWN

1 Gobble
2 More than appreciates
3 1985 Tom Hanks comedy
4 Kind of maniac
5 Losing proposition
6 Offspring of 7 Down
7 Rest stop
8 Noisy bird
9 See 17 Across
10 __ Romeo
11 Potato part
12 Mountain route
15 1991 Sondheim show
18 Bag
19 Like a haunted house
24 Hamas adherents
26 San __
27 Savvy about
29 Galatea's sculptor, in myth
31 Salisbury Plain attraction
32 Comic strip reaction
33 Aix-les-Bains, e.g.
36 Chills
37 One of 18
38 Movie computer
39 Bit
40 __, Minn. (1862 Sioux uprising site)
45 Highway robbery?
47 Ballpoint part
48 Guilty and others
49 Stuffed deli delicacy
51 Dictator's aide
52 One of five Norse kings
53 Île de la __
54 Salamanders
56 Ad exec George __
59 Capture
60 Gunk
61 __ Lingus

374 by Norman S. Wizer

ACROSS

1 Irrational art
5 One of the Huxtables
10 Summer getaway
14 Not on the level
15 Radio-related
16 __-Altaic (language group)
17 Start of a quote by Will Durant
20 Isaac or Howard
21 Put into difficulties
22 Old spy grp.
24 "On Golden Pond" playwright Thompson
25 Quote continued
31 Prefix with valence
32 Jabir al-Sabah, e.g.
33 Take forcibly
38 Local life
40 Storm heading
41 Pang
42 Mount
43 Pedal pushers?
45 Greek peak
46 Quote continued
49 Shaver
53 Pricing word
54 Touch a chord
57 Racket
61 End of the quote
64 Crosses
65 In heraldry, having small projections in the upper corners
66 Distribute
67 Glamour rival
68 Assemblies
69 Kind of money

DOWN

1 Judo levels
2 Much
3 Fawn
4 Choice of Paris
5 Preserve
6 Blockhead
7 The blue of baby blues
8 Opposite of gormandize
9 Small posy
10 Show rudeness in traffic
11 Glacial formation
12 Shocks of a sort
13 Spy of a sort
18 Split sec.
19 "Groovy"
23 1967 Monkees song
25 Yaks
26 Drop
27 Reed
28 John Ciardi's "__ Man"
29 Curtain fabric
30 Esurience

34 Places for displaying wares
35 Constellation name
36 Optimistic
37 They're sometimes split
39 Arithmetic figure
44 Easy mark
47 Stumped
48 Advanced
49 Babble
50 Kind of eagle
51 Nary __
52 Constrictor
55 Language akin to Shan
56 Site of Galway Bay
58 Noncommittal response
59 Give a bellyful
60 Surveyed
62 Bottom line
63 Mdse.

ACROSS

1 1965 disturbance site
6 Reserved
14 Flog
15 Booker T. Washington, e.g.
16 Fallaci of "If the Sun Dies"
17 Overshadow
18 Half man, half goat of myth
20 Got together
21 Part of 46 Across: Abbr.
22 Rhapsodic
26 Itinerary word
27 Hag's cry
29 Zilch
30 J.F.K. portraitist
34 Spike
35 Eagerly expectant
36 Variety
37 J.F.K. biographer
40 Group shop
41 __ Fail (ancient Irish stone)
42 British actress Bartok
43 Where runs are made
46 "Sweet 16" org.
48 Cow
49 Decking out
53 In the background
57 "G.W.T.W." role
58 Permit
59 Beijing belief
60 Followers
61 Driving hazard

DOWN

1 Guarded
2 Seed covering
3 Drudgery
4 Deli order
5 Bestrides
6 Cold-war forces
7 Conductor de Waart
8 Breadbasket
9 Less hospitable
10 Bar
11 Correlation ratio symbol in statistics
12 Nullifier
13 Trevi coin count
14 __ Alamitos, Calif.
19 One way to get the blame
22 Sinister part?
23 Heads of ancient Rome
24 Designer Simpson
25 Escapade
26 Red-eyed birds
28 J.F.K. Library architect
30 Rodeo yell
31 Marquis Hirobumi __
32 Average name
33 Trial
34 Delineate
38 Anodynes
39 Son of Cedric the Saxon
44 William __ Gladstone
45 Grand
47 Overlays
49 Lime finishes
50 Opponent of Jimmy and Arthur
51 Vespiary
52 Campus facility
53 Actress Hagen
54 Ice cream __
55 Traffic caution
56 Time abroad

376 *by Harvey Estes*

ACROSS

1 Insertion mark
6 Rock layers
12 Kojak portrayer
14 It frequently finds itself in hot water
16 Cracker Jack prize
17 Peter Finch movie "Raid on __"
18 Saw
19 Chicken __ king
21 Standing near home, maybe
22 Communion or baptism
23 SALT concern
25 China: Prefix
26 Path for Confucians
27 Language from which "sarong" comes
29 Article in Der Spiegel
30 Hollered
32 Kon-Tiki wood
34 Cool, as coffee
35 Computer unit
36 Idiot box
38 Cash reserves
42 Loan org.
43 Beatty's co-star in "Bonnie and Clyde"
45 Paul's singing partner
46 Watermelon waste
48 To __ mildly
49 Actor John
50 Word with jack or label
52 "I __ You Babe"
53 Prize money
54 Sugar type
56 Gym exercises
58 Enters helter-skelter
59 Works a deal on
60 Least done
61 Founded

DOWN

1 Of the heart
2 Amelia Earhart, e.g.
3 Roundup site
4 Actress Sommer
5 __ kwon do
6 X-rated
7 Countdown beginning
8 Pro follower
9 Aids and __
10 House cats
11 Balkan country
12 Fits' companion
13 Quarterback Ken
15 Divulge
20 Put ammo in
23 Hot-dog
24 Tended tots
27 Became hitched
28 Coopers __ Bumppo
31 Superman symbol
33 Grant opponent
35 Enchant like Samantha
36 Where things vanish
37 Absolutely bland
38 Group with HQ in Brussels
39 Debate stifler
40 Understood
41 Underline
42 Dowdy person
44 Guitarist Ted
47 Spoiler
49 Em and Bee
51 Schnozzola
53 Tilting-tower town
55 Mom's girl
57 Spokes' intersection

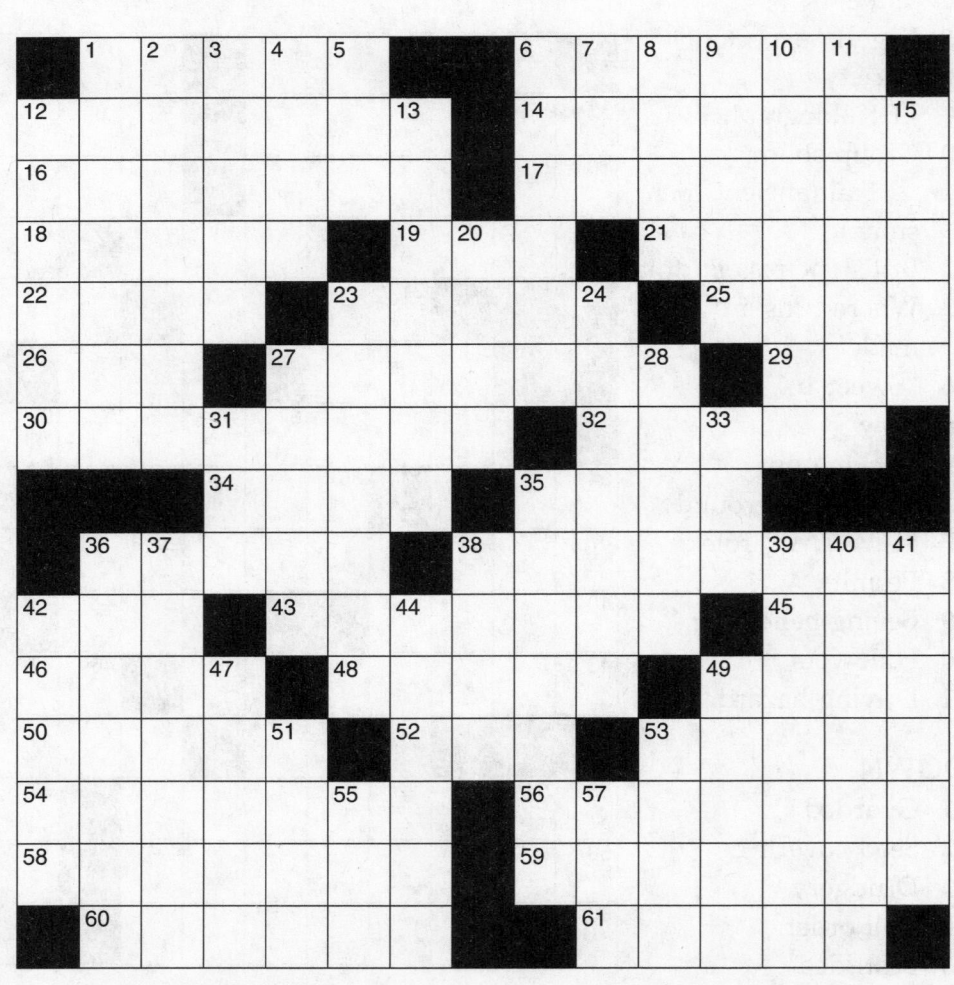

ACROSS

1 Bakery byproduct
6 Went by plane
10 Copied
14 Arizona features
15 Scottish isle
16 Lemon's partner
17 With 36 Across and 55 Across, a sales pitch disclaimer
20 Baden-Baden and others
21 Shea team
22 Eastern V.I.P.
23 Mr. Caesar
24 Ship to __
25 "Swan Lake," e.g.
29 Tiny bit
31 Not native
32 Printer's employee
33 Printer's measures
36 See 17 Across
39 His wife took a turn for the worse
40 Obsolescent piano key material
41 Bellini opera
42 Hoarder's cry
43 Telescopist's sighting
44 Strength
47 Opponent
48 Xerox competitor
49 "When I was __ . . ."
51 In __ of (instead)
55 See 17 Across
58 Person 'twixt 12 and 20
59 "The King and I" setting
60 Singer Cara
61 Misses the mark
62 Paddles
63 Waco locale

DOWN

1 Concert hall equipment
2 Harvest
3 Greek mountain
4 Wrestlers' needs
5 Type of cobra
6 Shot
7 Artist's pad?
8 Son of Seth
9 Revolutionary, e.g.
10 "Remember the __"
11 Heartbroken swain
12 Leno, for one
13 Bucks and does
18 Give forth
19 Indian noblewoman
23 Feeling
24 Suffix with tip or dump
25 Get-out-of-jail money
26 In addition
27 Bit of fluff
28 Mr. Durocher
29 Harden
30 "Sure, why not?"
32 Borodin's "Prince __"
33 To be, in Paree
34 Secretarial work
35 Burn
37 Confess
38 "__ on your life!"
43 Fashion
44 "60 Minutes" regular
45 Reason out
46 Sentence subjects
47 Country homes
48 Pigeon coop
49 __ da capo
50 Noted James Earl Jones stage role
51 Entice
52 The holm oak
53 Erupter of 1669
54 Applications
56 G.I. entertainers
57 Command to Fido

378 *by Peter (Lefty) Gordon*

ACROSS

1 Spirogyra or frog spit
5 Impression
9 Diamond protector
13 Burpee bit
14 Conclude, as negotiations
16 See 31 Across
17 Lefty, celebrity relative
20 Turkish title
21 Customary practice
22 Strengthens, with "up"
23 Tugs
25 "Babes in Toyland" star, 1960
28 Head of the costume department?
30 Leonard and Charles
31 With 16 Across, former Phillies manager
34 "Queen ___ Day" (old game show)
35 Corporate abbr.
36 Have a hunch
37 Lefty artist
41 Shows one's humanity?
42 Bud
43 ___ Fein
44 Voted
45 Great
46 Overwhelms with humor
48 Catch in a net
50 Pipe type
52 Highest point in Sicily
55 Course for a newcomer to the U.S.: Abbr.
57 Lament
58 Lefty actor
62 French 101 word
63 Copy of a sort
64 Noted rap artist
65 Gloomy

66 Overdecorated
67 Danson, et al.

DOWN

1 Composers' org.
2 Three miles, roughly
3 Lefty President
4 Foofaraw
5 Horus's mother
6 Star in Cygnus
7 Baa maid?
8 Razor-billed bird
9 Kind of sax
10 Publican's offerings
11 Ridicule persistently
12 Is worthwhile
15 Lefty actress
18 Five-year periods
19 Refusals
24 Pontiac Silverdome team

26 Camden Yards team
27 Polaroid inventor
29 Lefty comedian
31 Lefty comedian
32 ECU issuer
33 Lawyer in both "Civil Wars" and "L.A. Law"
36 Student's worry
37 Roman law
38 Before, to Byron
39 Jutlander, e.g.
40 In a despicable way
45 Writer Quindlen
47 Blotto
48 Oldtime knockout
49 Subs
51 Bridge seats
52 Horse that made sense?
53 One of the Jackson 5

54 Tannish color
56 Hot
59 Chaperoned girl
60 Actress Joanne
61 Paroxysm

ACROSS

1 Trounce
8 "My gal" of song
11 Castleberry of "Alice"
14 Have coming
15 Soldier's fare
17 Traveled militarily
18 Catch-22 situation
19 Black and white, e.g.
21 U.S.N. rank
22 Ireland
23 Cosmo and People, e.g.
26 I, to Claudius
27 "___ Lisa"
31 Shower mo.
32 Scruggs of bluegrass
34 Epithet for a tyrant
36 Not a warm welcome
39 Flower child
40 A big blow
41 De Maupassant's "___ Vie"
42 Some of Wordsworth's words
43 Legendary Hollywood monogram
44 Ed of "Daniel Boone"
45 Roller coaster cry
47 "Society's Child" singer Janis ___
49 Sang-froid
56 In progress
57 Vegetarian's no-no
59 Alley of "Look Who's Talking"
60 Rodeo ropes
61 Ship's heading
62 Always, poetically
63 Majority's choice

DOWN

1 S. & L. offerings
2 Lover's ___
3 Christiania, today
4 Scarlett and others
5 Bear Piccolo
6 Civil rights leader Medgar
7 Change the decor
8 Punic War general
9 Knight's attire
10 Slip-up
11 Fight sight
12 Mislay
13 Washington bills
16 Mai ___
20 Like Captain Ahab
23 Like a he-man
24 Sap sucker
25 Bellyache
26 Be off the mark
27 Denver summer time: Abbr.
28 Disgrace
29 Nary a person
30 Saint whose feast day is January 21
32 Biblical judge
33 Word of support
34 Bugs' voice
35 Hairy ancestor
37 Obsolescent disks
38 Engine part
43 Like slim pickings
44 Lacking iron, maybe
45 Essayist E.B.
46 Three-time skating gold medalist
47 Model
48 Novelist Malraux
49 Furnace fuel
50 Getting ___ years
51 Bogeyman
52 Pop music's ___ Lobos
53 Gardner of mysteries
54 Backside
55 Overindulge
58 Chairman's heart?

380 *by Harvey Estes*

ACROSS

1 Zubin with a baton
6 Old streetlight
13 Daley and others
14 Gravel-voiced actress
15 Iron shortage
16 Commit
17 Just the highlights
18 Slammin' Sam
19 Trendy
20 Getting better, as wine: Var.
22 Up to now
24 Size up
26 Paints amateurishly
28 Almost shut
32 Kind of symbol: Abbr.
33 One whom Jesus healed
34 Rodeo rope
35 Dashboard reading, for short
36 Leave the pier
38 Acquire
39 Ask on one's knees
41 Had
42 Short lunch order
43 Belgrade dweller
44 In abeyance
45 Sciences' partner
46 Tooth
48 Comfort
50 Probe
53 Some pads
55 Accident mementos
58 Serves a sentence
60 Byrnes of "77 Sunset Strip"
61 Brown paint, e.g.
62 Six-footer?
63 Resort locale
64 Newspaper section

DOWN

1 Lion's pride?
2 It's hard to miss
3 Respect

4 Nonsense
5 Simile center
6 Comic Kaplan
7 Assuages
8 Picture with its own frame
9 Wheel bolt holder
10 King of comedy
11 Part of a pair
12 Sound of relief
13 Scuff up
14 It's hard to say
18 Fastens with a pop
21 "I have no __!"
23 __ chi ch'uan
24 Tail ends
25 Temptation for Atalanta
27 1991 American Conference champs

29 It's hard
30 Listing
31 Sounds off
33 Digital-watch readout: Abbr.
34 Postal letters
37 Have a hunch
40 1970 Jackson 5 hit
44 Looking while lusting
45 Waylay
47 Time and again
49 In unison
50 Tots up
51 Afternoon TV fare
52 Lifetime achievement Oscar winner Deborah
54 Mingo portrayer
56 Puerto __

57 Play place
59 Take part in a biathlon
60 Kipling novel

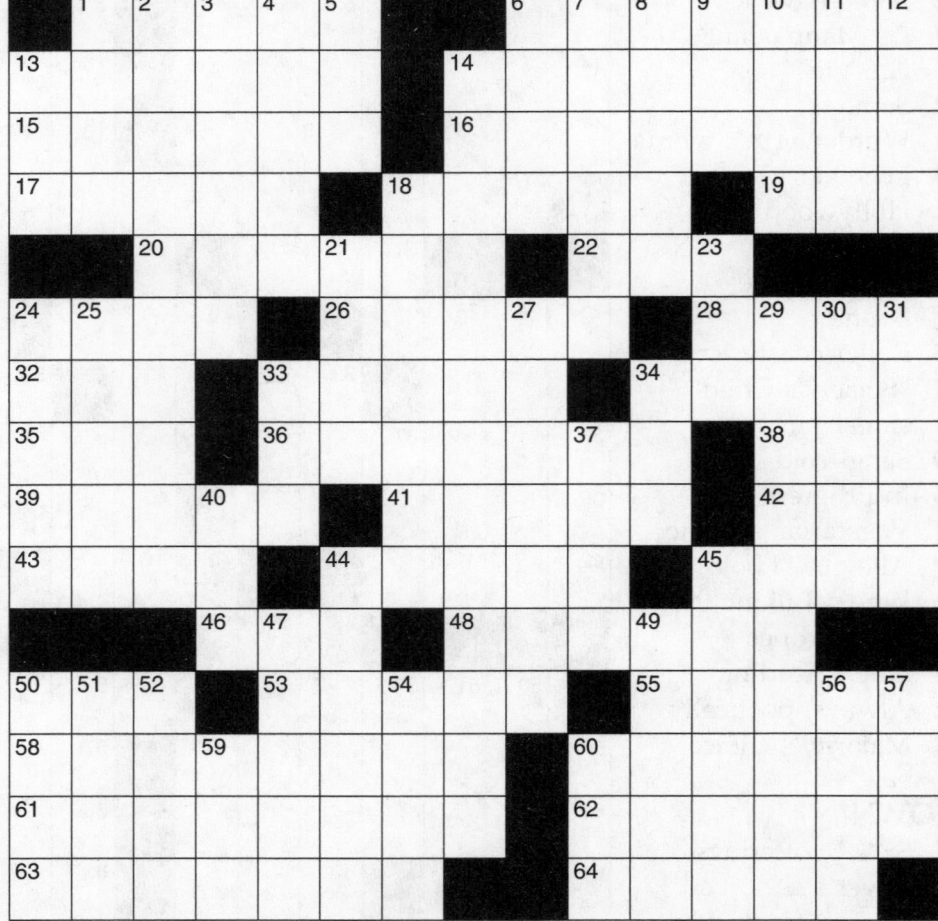

by Joel Davajan

ACROSS

1 Give tit for tat
5 Pillow covers
10 Bunco
14 It debuted in Cairo, Dec. 24, 1871
15 Video screen dot
16 So long
17 What's my line: #1
20 Guard
21 They make colorful displays
22 Transcending
23 Have trouble on the ice
24 Gas, in Greenwich
27 Wine casks
28 Cleopatra biter
31 The A in "CAT scan"
32 Cartoonist Peter
33 Utah ski center
34 What's my line: #2
37 Nautical direction
38 Danza of "Who's the Boss?"
39 Refine, as 53 Down
40 Old Ford model
41 Dickey fastener
42 Thinks out loud
43 Level
44 Amatory writing
45 Brutality
48 Ghostly
52 What's my line: #3
54 First name in fashion
55 Prefix with figure or form
56 G.P.A., in slang
57 "Not my __"
58 Intelligence
59 Mr. Culbertson and others

DOWN

1 Easy marks
2 Telegraph
3 Mideast gulf
4 Rural-themed opera
5 Crystalline gemstone
6 Stowaway
7 Leaf angle
8 One of Alcott's Little Women
9 Boy Scout tie
10 Reserved
11 Musical with the song "Memory"
12 __ smasher
13 Viking touchdown site
18 Villa d'Este locale
19 Speaker at Cooperstown
23 Cheerful
24 Of the Vatican
25 Glorify
26 "Dead"
27 Vogue
28 Green-card applicant
29 Hackneyed
30 Cords, e.g.
32 Love, in Le Havre
33 Signature event
35 Goes for
36 Phase
41 Acapulco assent
42 Danish city
43 Bit of color
44 Certain tournaments
45 Difficult position
46 Confederate
47 Philosophical
48 Comics publisher Lee
49 Actor Julia
50 "Go __!"
51 Cleaning agents
53 Ferriferous rock

382 *by Cathy Millhauser*

ACROSS

1 Slates
6 Provinces
11 Part of a footnote abbr.
14 Way of speaking
15 Slacken
16 Paul's "Exodus" role
17 Kind of scout
18 River to the Missouri
19 Charles S. Dutton sitcom
20 Performed a Herculean feat #1
23 Fray
25 Preliminary figure: Abbr.
26 "A Letter for __" (1945 movie)
27 Manipulate
28 Crony
30 Uncle Sam poster words
31 Performed a Herculean feat #2
36 Ile-de-France river
37 Tart apples, informally
38 Performed a Herculean feat #3
44 __ Bornes (classic card game)
45 "Hey, you!"
46 Bravo, e.g.
47 Heraldic band
48 Treaty org. since 1948
50 Painter Hopper
53 Performed a Herculean feat #4
56 List ender
57 Bad, bad Brown of song
58 Appoggiaturas
61 Hilo souvenir
62 Honeymoon follower
63 Pauperized
64 Fast wings, for short
65 Save up
66 Attach an ell

DOWN

1 Become prone
2 TV's Mrs. Morgenstern
3 Aimed
4 Rental sign
5 Suggest, with "of"
6 Baseball's Moises
7 Change "potatoe" to "potato", e.g.
8 Our 50, to Francois
9 Zero
10 Admiral sunk with the Scharnhorst
11 Truck: lorry:: trailer: __
12 Type of board
13 Summons
21 Unseat
22 ". . . consider her ways, and __": Proverbs
23 Baby bloomer?
24 "Do __ say!"
29 Made fun of, in a way
30 Yen
32 Column bases, in architecture
33 Nature outing
34 Mischief-makers
35 More substantial
38 1979 World Series champs
39 Backdoor
40 Results
41 Precision-made
42 Tell the world
43 Staff
44 Mushrooms
48 Concert site
49 Skylit courts
51 Secretary Shalala
52 Wined and dined, perhaps
54 Wagner heroine
55 Regards
59 Tokyo, once
60 Dict. listing

ACROSS

1 Alias of Margaretha Zelle
9 Finish of the 50's
15 Sweet potatoes
16 Trucked
17 Au natural
19 Hoosier humorist
20 With whom Jacob contracted to marry Rachel
21 Cardinal sin
22 One of a vaudeville seven
24 Lip
26 Seven on the Mohs' scale
29 Civil War buffs favorite actress?
34 New news
35 At such a time that
36 At the summit of
37 Summer cooler
38 Two-striper
43 Bar drink, at times
45 Connector of song
46 Sirens
47 Just a bit
48 Golfer Alcott
49 Gulf in 1991 news
53 You can be slapped with these
55 Genes material
58 Just what we need
62 Revisionist?
63 Coffee shop freebies
64 They build up spirits
65 Added as an afterthought

DOWN

1 "The Best Little Whorehouse in Texas" lady
2 Mil. school
3 Receipts
4 Live
5 Kept out of sight
6 Take apart
7 Tabula __
8 Largest of the Galápagos islands
9 They make a difference
10 What "that" ain't
11 Hick
12 Giant chemicals company
13 First name in TV talk
14 Nelson of 30's musicals
18 Tires
22 Fountain order
23 Master Melvin
25 Roman I
26 Mountebank
27 Author Sinclair
28 Dig for squares?
30 Kind of bead
31 Win by __
32 Raider's chief
33 Peter and others
39 Sash
40 Top workers?
41 Lark
42 Most economical in business
43 Word in many tournament names
44 Proceed smoothly
49 Be loyal to
50 Whipped up
51 Solo
52 Meadowlands team
54 This señora
55 Fizzled
56 Poppaea's husband
57 Org.
59 Contrary indication
60 Bother
61 A crowd in Torino?

384
by Lois Sidway

ACROSS

1 Agcy. vigilant about vittles
4 Make or break, e.g.
8 Two-fisted
13 Abbr. for an old soldier
14 Energy choice
15 Playwright Fugard
16 Gifted
17 Didja ever see a __?
19 "I don't think so"
20 Mine, to Marcel
21 Parenthetical comments
22 Staff
24 Many a hip-hop poet
26 Didja ever see a __?
29 Imprint
33 Jai __
34 Team in an annual all-star game
37 Color
38 Didja ever see a __?
41 Didja ever see a __?
43 Bowl over
44 Thick slice
46 Newsy bit
47 Plight
49 Didja ever see a __?
53 Some like it hot
56 Poet Teasdale
57 They get squirreled away
60 Lenin's police org.
63 Go vroom, vroom
64 Didja ever see a __?
66 Sundial number
67 Antipasto goody
68 Plow man
69 Presidential monogram
70 Devonshire dad
71 Hairdresser, sometimes
72 Grin's stopping point

DOWN

1 Garçon's pourboire
2 Split
3 Where touts tout
4 "Va-va-va-__!"
5 Barcelona bull
6 Project glowingly
7 Buddy
8 Bit of poolroom finesse
9 Garb
10 Nigerian border lake
11 Grind, in a way
12 Ford contemporary
14 __ Na Na
18 Breach
23 Constitutional
25 Child's ammo
27 Wails from baby
28 Bass __
30 Hitch
31 Word on a diploma
32 Drill sergeant's call
35 Black & Decker competitor
36 Famous marshal
38 Certain missile
39 Be in the red
40 Sunscreen ingredient
42 Super Bowl III champs
45 Hogwash
48 Tried hard
50 Simon of fiction
51 French fries brand
52 Cincinnati university
54 Tick off
55 Controversial food additive
57 On
58 Some kind of a nut
59 Last writes?: Abbr.
61 Rumble of contentment
62 French article
65 Tack on

by Fred Piscop

ACROSS

1 __ Islands (Pacific group)
9 Pink end
15 Type of music
16 Generic
17 Whenever
18 VCR user's need
19 Props (up)
20 Faith
22 N.B.A.'s Archibald
23 Kind of crazy
24 Tennis score
25 Perplexed
26 Arch site
27 Complaint
28 Chemical salt
31 Postal abbr.
32 Monte __
35 Marshaled
37 Apollo component
38 Having rectangular cells, as a ceiling
42 Hue and cry
44 Wyoming's Simpson
45 Lose it
49 Early stock speculator Russell
50 Common side order
51 "See you"
52 In __ (doubled up)
54 Serve
56 Moolah
57 Heartfelt
59 Park, e.g.
60 Kind of exam
61 A day ago, dialectally
62 Stopped

DOWN

1 Name in aviation
2 Hello and goodbye
3 VCR user's need
4 Gets stuffed
5 Word repeated before "show"
6 The Beatles' "Yes __"
7 Info on a French passport
8 Big name in small construction
9 On the ocean: Fr.
10 Word with block or test
11 Temper
12 Lori of "Petticoat Junction"
13 Make thin
14 Yielded
21 Singer Coolidge
23 Dipsomaniac
26 Throat problem?
27 Bushed
29 "Up and __!"
30 Govt. investigator
32 Graduates' celebration time
33 Correspondent
34 Conjures up
36 Auden verses
39 Big blow
40 Hugged
41 Eddie Murphy flick
43 Something remembered
46 Floating
47 Forthwith
48 Respired, dog-style
50 Clydesdale outfitter
53 Rock music's Mötley __
54 Some live by them
55 Culture starter
58 Small note

386 *by Bob Lubbers*

ACROSS

1 Kind of file
7 Dupe
11 Vacation spot
14 Razz
15 Speed
16 Total cost
17 Dear ones
18 Come before
20 Psychiatrist?
22 Mirror image?
23 Pain of a sort
24 Express
25 Cookout fare
28 Bus starter
30 Actor Jannings
34 Canter
35 Re-election runners
36 "__ to Psyche"
37 In a managerial position to
38 Self-diagnosis?
40 Fancy
41 It's bleu on maps
42 "Steve Allen Show" veteran
43 Detach, in a way
44 Hyde Park sight
46 "The Last Time I Saw Paris" composer
48 Oxygenators
49 Sci-fi objects
51 Shopper's helper
53 Where one is in the stadium?
56 Personal revelation?
59 Stove stuffing
61 Land, as a fish
63 Back
64 To be, abroad
65 Kind of kick
66 Of course
67 U.S. Army medals
68 Camera-shy critter?

DOWN

1 Forbes competition
2 Nostalgic soft drink name
3 Boy Scout's act
4 One who makes personal plugs?
5 "__ Restaurant"
6 Condor condos
7 Tangle (with)
8 Ax
9 Demonstrator's doctrine
10 "With Reagan; The Inside Story" author
11 Dateless
12 Orbit
13 Help
19 Urgent
21 Native Nebraskan
24 Sigmund's daughter
25 Tiptoe's opposite
26 Fly like a flying saucer
27 Works
29 Party
31 Display
32 Standard
33 Is attracted
38 Section in a psychological test
39 This puzzle's punning theme
40 Self-defense testifier?
45 Make a proposal
47 Sergeant major: Abbr.
48 "Brighton Rock" novelist
50 Say "I do" again
52 Splatter safeguard
53 Questionable
54 Cassino cash
55 Romance symbol
56 Time in "Julius Caesar"
57 Boola-boola cheerers
58 "__, Pagliaccio"
60 Killer of the deep
62 Formerly

by Sidney L. Robbins

ACROSS

1 Mosque tops
6 Lone Ranger attire
10 Strike caller
13 Dynamic
14 "I cannot tell __"
15 Mimic
16 Chinese principles
18 Lavish party
19 Tosspot
20 Worships
21 Freshly
22 Life, for one
23 Enlarge
24 Soup dipper
28 Six-stanza poem
31 Lily
32 Does, for example
33 Knot of hair
36 Procrastinator
40 Relative of the buttercup
42 Moral no-no
43 Tentmaker of fame
45 Kind of camera focus
46 Modified
49 Mount
50 Sighed (for)
52 Playboy pic
54 Took a taxi
55 Sound choice?
57 Busy person around Apr. 15
60 Smidgen that's smashed
61 Occasionally
63 Greek letters
64 Kurdish home
65 Throw out
66 N.Y. winter time
67 Trapper's trophy
68 Fires

DOWN

1 TV's "__ of Our Lives"
2 Hodgepodge
3 Money maker
4 "Uncle Tom's Cabin" girl
5 Spot for 100
6 Giuliani and others
7 Equipped with a theft protector
8 Trig function
9 Barrels
10 No longer bedridden
11 Fracas
12 Shrimp
15 Once more
17 Successor to H.S.T.
23 Telegram
24 Lassies' partners
25 Jai __
26 Homeless
27 Conducted
29 Melville novel setting
30 Countdown start
34 "Render therefore __ Caesar . . ."
35 It's a gas
37 Trucker's amount
38 Holy Roman, e.g.: Abbr.
39 Squealer
41 Alluring West
44 License extension
47 Considers
48 "The Story of Civilization" author
49 Hollow stones
50 Jabber
51 Specks
53 Bear's abode
55 Quick cut
56 Ripped
57 In high style
58 Captain Ahab of film
59 Busy ones
62 Initials of 1933

388 by Wayne Robert Williams

ACROSS
1 Interlaced
6 Canadian tree
11 Unit of chewing tobacco
14 Idiotic
15 Relieve
16 One of Frank's exes
17 Motion picture award
19 __ Kippur
20 __ ex machina
21 Red Square figure
23 Spacecraft sections
27 Tentative forays
29 Gone from the program
30 Shoulders-to-hips areas
31 "__ Irish Rose"
32 Paper purchases
33 Once existed
36 Guitarist Lofgren
37 See 30-Down
38 __ fide
39 Farm enclosure
40 Crude characters
41 Gershwin hero
42 Jai alai ball
44 "Ode to __ Joe"
45 Votes
47 Hamlet, at times
48 Shrine to remember
49 Spotted
50 Reunion-goers
51 Nature personified
58 First lady
59 "Middlemarch" author
60 Inventor Howe
61 Matched grouping
62 Tears
63 Show shock, e.g.

DOWN
1 Store-bought hair
2 Musician Yoko
3 Actor Kilmer
4 Football lineman
5 Tries to rile
6 John Fowles novel, with "The"
7 "__ Well That Ends Well"
8 Hebron grp.
9 Big, friendly dog, for short
10 Huxley's "__ in Gaza"
11 Teen film hit of 1992
12 To have, to Héloïse
13 Curses
18 Require
22 "Xanadu" musical grp.
23 Signifies
24 Pluto's path
25 Perry's paper
26 Functions
27 Bubble masses
28 Columnist Bombeck
30 With 37-Across, the ground
32 Wild times
34 1973 Rolling Stones hit
35 Word with nay or sooth
37 Bit of poetry
38 Manila machete
40 Early feminist
41 Avant-gardist
43 Slippery __
44 Rabbit's title
45 Hardens, as clay
46 Breathing
47 Borscht ingredients
49 Bullet-riddled
52 Cheer
53 Malleable metal
54 Pale or Newcastle brown
55 Narrow inlet
56 Middle X or O
57 Presidential initials

by Nancy Joline

ACROSS

1 Tops of wine bottles
6 Wreak havoc upon
12 Gorge
13 Undergoes again, as an experience
14 Fund-raiser
15 Requiring immediate action
16 Postprandial drinks
18 Dessert pastry
19 __ hurrah
20 Actor Jannings
22 Chest rattle
23 Brightened
25 Burghoff role on "M*A*S*H"
27 Columbia, vis-à-vis the ocean
28 Entraps
30 Nullifies
32 Hash house sign
34 Info
35 Reduces
38 Glass ingredient
42 Tex-__ (hot cuisine)
43 DeMille films
45 Exorcist's adversary
46 Elderly
48 Angry to-do
49 Cable TV's C-__
50 Scuttlebutt
52 Take to court
55 Burst inward
57 Aficionado
58 It stretches across a tennis court
59 Bellyached
60 They may be liquid
61 Tried to catch a conger

DOWN

1 Variety of rummy
2 William Tell and others
3 Prevalent
4 Make a sweater
5 Hunting dog
6 Tyrannosaurus __
7 Parted company with a horse
8 Good physical health
9 Nothing special
10 Calms
11 Hold in high regard
12 Stay
13 Sojourned
14 Strike alternatives
17 Muscat is its capital
21 Former capital of Nigeria
24 "__-porridge hot . . ."
26 Word before fire or transit
29 Hitchcock's "The Thirty-Nine __"
31 Hubble, e.g.
33 Cut, as roses
35 Peanuts, e.g.
36 Frees from liability
37 Disfigure
39 Ascribed
40 Like nuts at a chocolatier's
41 French year
42 Boater's haven
44 Plodding person
47 Fellini's "La __ Vita"
51 Cheer (for)
53 Devoid of moisture
54 The dark force
56 O.R. personnel

390 *by Arthur S. Ash*

ACROSS

1 Razor sharpener
6 Health resort
9 More than a mere success
14 Mussolini's notorious son-in-law
15 Assist
16 With uneven gait
17 Mink's poor cousin
18 Ushered
19 Truism
20 Item to cut for dessert
23 Late-night star
24 President Manuel, ousted by Franco
25 TV rooms
26 New Rochelle institution
28 Game show sound
30 Princess Diana's family name
33 Bedecked
37 Mea __
38 Get repeated value from
39 Replaceable shoe parts
42 Agrees
44 Carry on
45 30's and 40's actress Anna
46 Porcine cry
49 Kind of system
51 Weakens
55 Popular poultry entree
58 __ hilt (fully)
59 "Le veau __" ("Faust" aria)
60 Roomy dress cut
61 Chef's attire
62 Consume
63 American statesman Cyrus
64 Oceans, to Longfellow

65 Season on the Riviera
66 Lawn tool

DOWN

1 "Bad mood" look
2 Small obligation
3 Snitch about
4 Entree for a solitary diner
5 Scrutinize, with "over"
6 Marathoner Alberto
7 Michelangelo work
8 Afterthoughts
9 Bridge desideratum
10 Dieter's dish
11 A miss's equivalent
12 Dish's companion in flight
13 Songs of glory

21 Diminish
22 Foray
27 Florida city
29 Like Eric the Red
30 H.S. subject
31 So-called "lowest form of wit"
32 Bygone trains
34 Sally Field TV role
35 Erhard's training
36 __ Plaines, Ill.
40 Prefer follower
41 Latecomer to a theater, maybe
42 Ancient fertility goddess.
43 Suffix with young or old
46 Santa's reindeer, e.g.
47 "__ you're happy!"
48 Potassium salt

50 Summer ermine
52 Geriatric process
53 __ de León
54 Lip curl
56 Understands
57 Pan's opposite

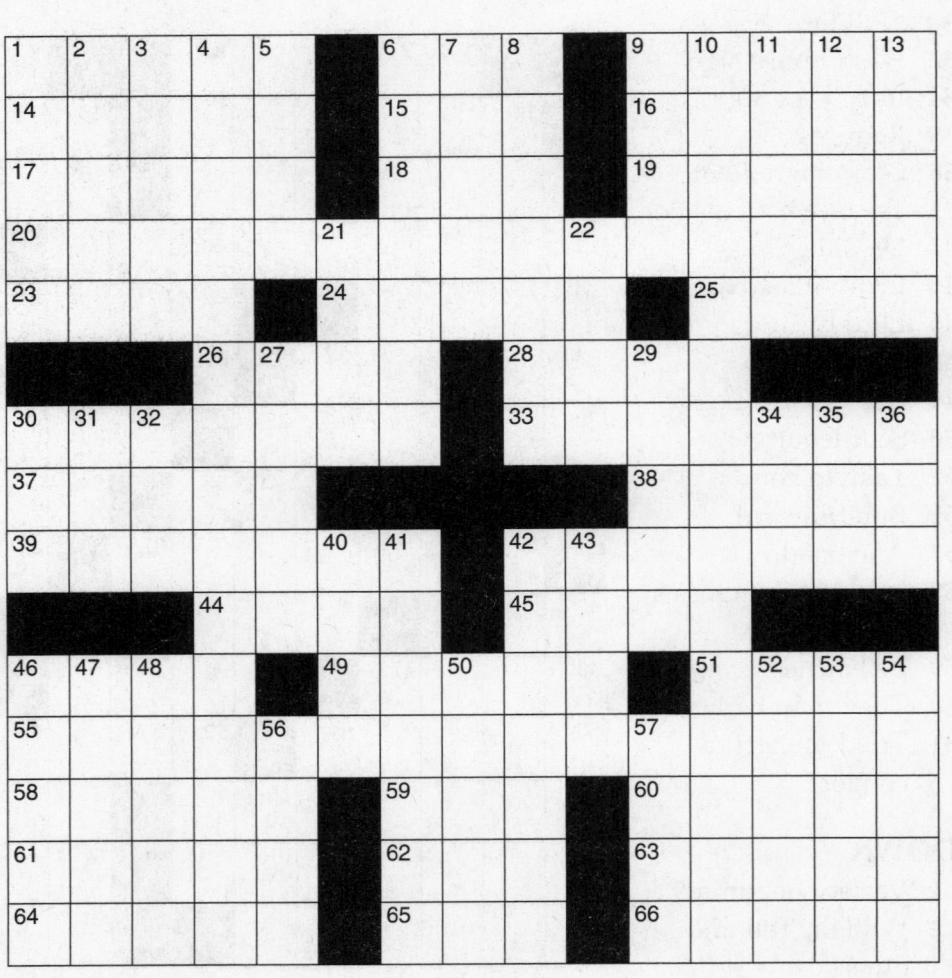

ACROSS

1 Incarcerate
5 Wife, in Madrid
11 U.S./U.K. divider
14 Wearer of an aiguillette
15 Warehouse charge
17 Start of a quip
19 Slippery swimmer
20 Axis end
21 Lift, as ice or oysters
22 Ilk
23 Enormous
26 Stress
29 "McSorley's Bar" painter John
30 Good earth
31 New Zealand native
32 Family V.I.P.'s
35 Middle of the quip
39 Pigpen
40 Brainy group
41 Something to cop
42 Mork's gal
43 Like schlock
45 Extra leaves
48 Ireland's __ Islands
49 Spread for a spread
50 Manchurian border river
51 Sunny day production
54 End of the quip
59 Starlet's hope
60 Lackawanna's partner in railroads
61 Draft agcy.
62 Dallas's __ Plaza
63 Become tiresome

DOWN

1 Rib
2 Yorkshire river
3 Worshiped one
4 Rock's __ Zeppelin
5 Police accompaniment
6 Clown's prop
7 Corn bread
8 Assn.
9 Writer Rohmer
10 Farming: Abbr.
11 "Flow gently, sweet __": Burns
12 Coming-of-age period
13 Shelf
16 Consumed
18 "__ the Roof" (1963 hit)
22 It's good for the long haul
23 Actress Massey
24 Filipino
25 Hotel housekeeper
26 Pauper's cry
27 Old feller
28 Guinea pig
29 Impertinent
31 Obeys
32 House slipper
33 Lincoln and Vigoda
34 Dog command
36 Head of Abu Dhabi
37 Shipped
38 Unguarded, as a receiver
42 Reagan Attorney General
43 Like a curmudgeon
44 Mata __
45 Bridge declaration
46 D.E.A. workers
47 Swizzles
48 Provide divertissement
50 Soviet spy Rudolf
51 Now's partner
52 Siberia's site
53 River of Flanders
55 Proof's ending
56 Half of deux
57 Seventh Greek letter
58 Like a crescent moon

392 *by Ernie Furtado*

ACROSS

1 Swiss city on the Rhine
6 "Jake's Thing" author
10 Nice shindigs
14 Allan-__ (Robin Hood cohort)
15 Carry on
16 "__ Fire" (Springsteen hit)
17 *Paris site*
18 "__ partridge in a . . ."
19 Kind of fountain
20 Runaway, of a sort
22 Runway, of a sort
24 Book-lined rooms
25 *London site*
27 Cartoonist Bushmiller
29 Twofold
32 Game award, for short
35 Make a pot
36 Skin layer
38 *Rome site*
40 *Amsterdam site*
41 Drop out
42 Seat for two or more
43 "You don't __!"
44 __-tiller
45 They beat deuces
47 *Florence site*
50 Not on land
54 Upset-minded teams
57 Positions
59 Big 10's __ State
60 Letter encl.
62 *Moscow site*
63 Derby
64 Ended
65 Off
66 River to the North Sea
67 Corn bread
68 Having an irregular edge

DOWN

1 With __ breath
2 One of the Astaires
3 Dresden dweller
4 Slip by
5 __ majesty
6 Mr. Parseghian
7 Sea cow
8 Kipling story locale
9 Legendary Packers QB
10 Surgical knife
11 Love, Spanish-style
12 Italian town, site of a 1796 Napoleon victory
13 Fastener
21 N.F.L. standout Lott
23 Not a main route
26 Naldi of silents
28 1964 Four Seasons hit
30 "__ 'n' Andy"
31 Trevi Fountain coin
32 Classic sports cars
33 Turn sharply
34 Somewhat, in music
36 Loss
37 High overhead?
39 Money for Mason
40 "Cheers" role
42 Harold of politics
46 Pianist Gyorgy
48 Noted children's writer
49 An encouraging word
51 Defunct treaty org.
52 Group character
53 Unanimously
54 Nimble
55 Birds Eye product
56 __ over
58 "__ kleine Nachtmusik"
61 Afore

by *Thomas W. Schier*

ACROSS

1 Jerk
6 Netman Kriek
11 Peek
12 Even (with)
14 Bristles
15 Symbol of somberness, in poetry
17 Passbook amt.
18 Not a winner
20 Tell (on)
21 Fishes by dangling the bait on the water
23 Meadowlands hockey player
24 Lasso
25 "___ or lose it!"
27 June honoree
28 Farm worker
29 Xerxes ruled here
31 Directional sign
33 Bank burglars
35 Packaging material
36 Informational sign
39 Topped
42 Take ___ at
43 Düsseldorf dessert
45 White House resignee of 1988
46 Team finisher
47 Stenos' output
49 Dully colored
50 Author Kesey
51 Indiana town near South Bend
53 French city where Henry IV was born
54 Diane and Ruth
56 Portray, as historical events
58 Outbuilding
59 More ___
60 "Following the Equator" author
61 Bridge seats

DOWN

1 Cautionary sign
2 Not in France
3 Theater org.
4 Burn
5 Interfered (with)
6 Spur-of-the moment trips
7 Basketball's Shaquille
8 "Bird on a Wire" actress
9 Meet
10 Cautionary sign
11 Bribe, informally
13 "Grim" one
14 Make sense
16 Forever, to Keats
19 Race track
22 "Yes, sir," in Seville
24 Switched according to plan
26 Packed closely
28 Pluck a uke
30 Muslim honorific
32 ___ Schwarz
34 Thinks over
36 Difficult matters
37 Bony
38 Prom night transport
40 Stern and Newton
41 Coming out
44 Juliet's was "sweet"
47 Cuban patriot José
48 Metric measure
51 Yakutsk's river
52 Sigmoid swimmers
55 Go off course
57 End up with

394 *by Fred Piscop*

ACROSS

1 __ and hounds (outdoor game)
5 Section of the brain
9 Palindromic name in pop music
13 Mideast carrier
14 Flower part
15 Regrets
16 MANTLE
19 Bars
20 Kind of bed
21 Hubbub
22 Olympus queen
23 RUTH
30 Indian princess
31 Offended
32 Street sign abbr.
33 "Ars Amatoria" author
34 Manages, as for oneself
35 Signaled
36 Command to Rover
37 Absorbed by
38 Prefix with dollars
39 AARON
43 With eyes and ears open
44 Antipollution grp.
45 St. Francis's home
48 Confirming
53 JACKSON
55 British P.M. __ Douglas-Home
56 Jerks' works
57 Westernmost Aleutian
58 Ritzy
59 Word repeated before "1, 2, 3"
60 Nikita's no

DOWN

1 Fab Four flick
2 Controversial orchard spray
3 Zany Martha
4 Dignified
5 Hightailed it
6 __ out (withdraws)
7 Cry from Scrooge
8 Euclid's grand work
9 Ark's terminus
10 Pat baby on the back
11 One of Alcott's little women
12 Sickly, as a complexion
14 "__ a gun!"
17 Color anew
18 Prefix with dollars
22 __ hearing
23 One of a road crew
24 Architect Jones
25 Pioneer of the twist
26 Reach in total
27 __ couture
28 Tinker–Chance link
29 Second draft, informally
30 L.B.J. son-in-law
34 Most passionate
35 __ section
38 Easy catch
40 Jerk
41 Greasy-spoon fare
42 Southwestern formations
45 P.D.Q.
46 One-man band
47 Courts
48 No ifs, __ or buts
49 Command to Tabby
50 __-bitty
51 N.B.A's Thurmond
52 Flood
54 Ebbets Field's Preacher

ACROSS

1 Monopoly purchase
6 __ of office
10 Singing Beatle
14 Maytag rival
15 German numeral
16 Shade of red
17 Kind of dressing
18 Boccaccio work, with "The"
20 Actress Swenson
21 GLASGOW: __
22 E. B. White piece
24 Put on __
25 Toulouse tams
27 Art __ (master keyboardist)
29 Get up
30 1987 Wimbledon winner
31 Actor Jannings
35 __ Tin Tin
36 From Novi Sad
39 "__ No Hooks"
40 Boat's backbone
42 Geissler tube illuminant
43 Winding paths
45 Fall flower
47 Long-legged shorebird
48 Actress June
50 Memorable shrine
51 MONACO: __
54 Satan's doing
57 LEM driver
58 Ballerina Shearer
59 Spanish province or capital
60 Andrews Sisters, e.g.
61 Shenanigan
62 Quiet street
63 Drains of stamina
64 Ninnies

DOWN

1 Mata __
2 Arabian sultanate
3 TANGIER: __
4 Sheathes
5 __-di-dah
6 Strange to say
7 Kind of rug
8 Gumshoes
9 Son of the West Wind
10 Before kickoff
11 Goldfinger's first name
12 Convoy chaser
13 Boston suburb
19 Waiter's handout
21 Tums target
23 Fr. holy women
25 Sergeant's voice
26 Canal opened in 1825
27 Olden drum
28 "It's __ to tell a lie"
30 Manitoba Indian
32 MOSCOW: __
33 "Oh, that's what you mean!"
34 Paris's Gare de __
37 Contest responders
38 St. Petersburg's river
41 Shotz Brewery worker of 70's TV
44 Gershwin's "__ to Watch Over Me"
46 Utah's state flower
47 Tankard tipple
48 Hebrew prophet
49 Writer Chekhov
50 Detroit output
51 Shopping center
52 __ Delano (F.D.R.'s mother)
53 Witticism
55 Spring flower
56 Teddy material
58 People or GQ

ACROSS

1 Gather
6 Radar gun reading: Abbr.
9 Bend
14 Collector's items
15 France's __ d'Yeu
16 Throng
17 Lewis's Gantry
18 "The Beggar's Opera" author
19 Yeate's __ Theatre
20 Singing sister of old Hollywood
23 American skiing medalist at Lillehammer
27 Cry of disgust
30 Twerp
31 Gross-weight deduction
32 "A miss is as good as __"
34 Toddler
35 Where Zeno taught
36 Filmdom's Sam Spade
38 What's-his-name
40 Annealing oven
41 High school problem
45 In abeyance
46 Over, in Essen
47 __ et quarante (betting game)
49 Posthumous duettist of 1991
50 "The Big Chill" actress
53 "Cheers" star
57 Shortcoming
60 Telephone button
61 Actor Reeves
62 Spy
63 "Gimme __!" (end of a Yale cheer)

64 Patti LuPone role
65 Kind of bag
66 Writer Deighton
67 Attack

DOWN

1 Maintain
2 Venus's home
3 Weaponry
4 Expensive
5 Thinker
6 __ worker
7 Magazine since 1953
8 "Lo!" modern-style
9 Music of the Benedictine monks
10 Noted televangelist
11 Sun, e.g.
12 Hafiz work
13 Pivotal

21 Alas, to Helmut
22 Sideways
24 Sups at home
25 Beethoven's Third
26 Reception china
27 Trite ideas
28 Microscopy subject
29 More costly
33 CNN personality
37 Mongol
39 Cornmeal concoctions
42 Stemware
43 Voyager II subject
44 Animate
48 __ kwon do (Korean karate)
51 Pot
52 Student abroad

54 Café au __
55 Within: Prefix
56 China's dollar
57 Parent
58 Personal pride
59 Importune

by Randy Sowell

397

ACROSS

1 Instance
5 Kind of metabolism
10 Loading site
14 ". . . __forgive our debtors"
15 Get the lead out?
16 "The Cherry Orchard" miss
17 18th-century poet (whose name shares a feature with 36 and 56 Across)
20 Sweetheart
21 February 14 figure
22 Major-league transaction
23 It may be proper
24 Opera composer Nikolai
26 Highlight
29 Relieved
32 Narrative Byron poem
33 Room to __
34 Support
36 17th-century dramatist
40 United
41 Navratilova rival
42 Boston athlete
43 Natural habitat
45 "Martha" et al.
47 Isolated
48 TV sheriff Tupper
49 Plus
52 Onetime labor chief
53 Good name for a cook?
56 20th-century writer
60 Old song "__ She Sweet?"
61 Get __ on
62 Churchill prop
63 Hwys.
64 "John Brown's Body" poet
65 Linemen

DOWN

1 Daisy Mae's drawer
2 "Days of Grace" author
3 "M*A*S*H" actress
4 That's a moray
5 Rough posting for a foreign correspondent
6 Illegal firing
7 Processes lumber
8 Quiet color
9 Dracula actor Christopher
10 Traverse a beat
11 "To Live and Die __"
12 Looked at
13 Comic Martha
18 Ancient land of Spain
19 Leader of '45
23 Around
24 Eye-cue tests?
25 Ocean flier
26 Ken-L-Ration competitor
27 Queeg's command
28 Fish basket
29 Wear
30 "Oklahoma!" aunt
31 Singer Reese
33 Vista
35 Realizes
37 Not hands-on
38 Tied
39 Low-fat desserts
44 Picks
45 Spanish __
46 Charles's game
48 Mightier than
49 Partly open
50 "__ was you!" (mystery denouement)
51 Nostalgic song ending
52 Middle name in Memphis
53 Mr. Musial
54 Take care of
55 Spends
57 Rainy day rarity
58 Soul, in Soissons
59 Virtuoso

398 *by Richard Silvestri*

ACROSS

1 Symbol of stiffness
7 Brewing ingredient
11 Leave it to beavers
14 Julia, on "Seinfeld"
15 Mayberry moppet
16 Mistress Braun
17 "Wait 'Til My Bobby Gets Home" singer
19 Marshy area
20 Dockworkers' org.
21 Four laps, sometimes
22 A Sesame Streeter
23 X rating?
25 Sticker
27 Come to a halt
28 Patron saint of Norway
30 Co-star of "The Producers"
32 Government health program
34 "Hail, Caesar!"
35 Forge materials
36 Where Naxos is
39 Hard water?
40 Contest entry, perhaps
42 The Babe Ruth of Japan
46 Science writer Gernsback
47 Ease up
48 Hymn accompaniment
50 Record
51 Site of the 1960 Olympics
52 Ad writer's honor
53 Lend a hand
55 Cousin of Fortran
56 Former E Street Band member
60 Baseball throw
61 Working away
62 Bar perches
63 Journal addendum
64 Coolers
65 Lake Huron port

DOWN

1 It's seen in anger
2 According to
3 Tenderizing sauce
4 Brook
5 Hoopster Shaquille
6 Place to relax
7 "The Misanthrope" author
8 Harlem theater
9 As it occurs
10 Driving need
11 Trounce
12 Disinclined
13 Place for trophies
18 Barbecue leftovers
22 Implore
23 Tabby's mate
24 Kind of sch.
26 Rhododendron relative
27 Break the 10th Commandment
29 Impair
31 Warfield of "Night Court"
33 Secret supply
36 10^{100}
37 Witch's vessel
38 Therefore
40 They go by the book
41 Cerberus or Argus, e.g.
42 Ranchero's wrap
43 Homes
44 Vandalize
45 Arrive at last
49 1993 treaty
52 Give as a reference
54 Dr. Frankenstein's assistant
56 Shut-eye
57 C.I.A. forerunner
58 "Boola Boola" singer
59 Hush-hush D.C. grp.

ACROSS

1 Spring weather forecast
5 Grey and others
10 Docs
13 Personal prefix
14 "Simon Boccanegra," e.g.
15 Defense mechanism
16 Tramp
17 Motherly type
18 Seep
19 Plant holder
21 Quickened pace
23 Coin on the Spanish Main
24 Can
25 1995, 2005 and 2003, in China
30 Vowel sounds in "melee"
31 Wheel part
32 Cry out
34 Released felon
35 Spoon
36 High-minded
37 Adolescent
38 Multitude
39 Dresden's location
40 1996, 2001 and 2002, in China
43 Road to Roma
44 Lee or Teasdale
45 Elastic cord
48 Used a pony
52 Parrier's equipment
53 Its capital is Kinshasa
56 Western necktie
57 Fighter of 1899–1902
58 Dreaded computer word
59 Nation on the Strait of Hormuz
60 Remnant
61 Slumgullion and pepper pot
62 Decimal system

DOWN

1 Spray
2 Lay off
3 Important person
4 1994, 2000 and 1998, in China
5 They have many signs
6 "Rocky" villain __ Creed
7 Bottom line
8 Before, before
9 Unbecoming wit
10 Debatable
11 Stun
12 Road ending
15 2004, 1997 and 1999, in China
20 Encored, in a way
22 "__ du lieber!"
24 Blackout
25 Onetime Chinese rebel
26 __ year (annually)
27 Haunted house sound
28 Saarinen namesakes
29 Nonelectric shaver
30 Court call
33 Layer
35 Seckel or Anjou
36 Austronesian language
38 Blessed events?
39 Philanthropists
41 Geneviève, e.g.: Abbr.
42 Place in trust
45 Actress Daniels of the silents
46 Over
47 Shortfall
49 Endured
50 Panache
51 Grandees
54 High school class
55 Sharp feeling

400 *by A. J. Santora*

ACROSS

1 Hopeless
6 Where the tiller is
9 Zingers
13 Free
14 Colorado skiing mecca
16 Not right
17 How natives communicate
20 Type of mail
21 Mighty mite
22 __ Rabbit
23 Rebuffs
25 Sort of
29 Droll 1993 best seller
32 "The proof of the pudding __ . . ."
34 Foofaraw
35 Seed
36 Dressing-down
41 Actor Holm
42 Old B'way sign
43 Latch __
44 Not the secretive sort
49 Innumerable
50 Yearbook classmates: Abbr.
51 To live, to Livy
55 Richard Harris movie of 1977
57 Hornless
59 Communicating (with)
63 Mr. Hulot's creator
64 Cabal
65 "__ e Core" (1954 pop song)
66 On __ (freelancer's terms)
67 Mamie Eisenhower, __ Doud
68 Wanderer

DOWN

1 MacLaine's "Out on __"
2 Individualist
3 Soprano Lehmann
4 Heralds
5 Look searchingly
6 Photographer Richard
7 Kind of cry
8 Actress Louise
9 Tribesmen in the film "Simba"
10 Wise one
11 Singing syllable
12 Neighbor of Leb.
15 Hispanic community
18 "I came," to Caesar
19 Reps. and Sens.
24 Lillehammer events
26 "Rome __ built in a day"
27 Part of old discothèque names
28 Hedge shrub
30 H.S. course
31 Palindromic lady
32 Three-time World Cup winner
33 Sub detector
37 It's sold in lots
38 Bungle
39 On a roll
40 Native
41 Computer co.
45 Spike Lee's "Malcolm X," e.g.
46 Uncover
47 Old English royal house
48 New London grp.
52 More bruised
53 Diploma word
54 New Republic piece
56 Related
58 Greek letters
59 Military sch.
60 Rest
61 Geneviève, e.g.
62 Bach's "Partita __ Minor"

BLANKET STATEMENTS by Nancy Salomon

ACROSS

1. Volcano flow
5. Kind of drum or fiddle
9. Halloween disguises
14. Passing notice
15. Get sore
16. Tatum or Ryan
17. Makeup brand
19. Join forces
20. French farewell
21. March of __
23. Nada
24. Ran first
25. Accountant's software
28. Porterhouse or T-bone
29. Many a Melville setting, with "the"
30. They may be served with a twist
33. Pork cut
37. Like some pre-Columbian culture
38. Golden attribute?
41. Filmdom's Joel or Ethan
42. Removes gently
43. Home of the Bears and the Bulls: Abbr.
46. Exhibit annoying satisfaction
47. Silky-haired dog
51. Pvt.'s boss
54. Little piggy?
55. Skater Hamilton
56. Wedding seater
58. Full of chutzpah
60. End-of-filming gala
62. See eye to eye
63. Bit of Italian bread?
64. Verne's captain
65. Exams
66. 1974 Sutherland/Gould spoof
67. Broadway star Verdon

DOWN

1. The slo-o-o-ow train
2. Dwelling
3. Lively, as an imagination
4. Suit to __
5. Grocery tote
6. Harmful precipitation
7. Screams
8. Alabama march city
9. Puddinglike dessert
10. __ Arbor, Mich.
11. Take by force
12. Couric of "Today"
13. "George Washington __ here"
18. Rural
22. Asner and Begley
26. Baseball's Tony or Alejandro
27. Most hearty
28. Horrid smell
30. Computer that doesn't use Windows
31. __ dye (chemical coloring)
32. Way to go: Abbr.
34. Mrs. Lennon
35. Hosp. section
36. After-tax amount
38. Healthful
39. "Time __ My Side" (Stones hit)
40. Precede, with "to"
42. Swellhead's journey?
44. Corned beef dishes
45. Co. abbr.
47. Chance for a hit
48. Smithy
49. First, second, reverse, etc.
50. Bays, in a way
51. Chronic nag
52. "__ to the Church on Time"
53. Don at the tailor's
57. Crooned
59. Put in rollers
61. Mas' mates

402 PRIZED by Gilbert H. Ludwig

ACROSS

1. Green stuff
6. On __ (without assurance of payment)
10. Fivesome on a five
14. Kind of committee
15. Spanish snack
16. Org. protecting workers
17. "Some Like It Hot" co-star
19. Innocent
20. Like a hit B'way show
21. Mex. neighbor
22. Filler of holes
24. Make __ for it
25. Mrs. Addams, to Gomez
26. 1990's boxing champion
31. Fairly
32. Actor Cariou
33. Little worker
35. Worker's demand
36. Bro's kin
37. Housing unit
39. Extra-play periods: Abbr.
40. Essen exclamation
41. TV cop Chris
42. Country star who sang "Roses in the Snow"
46. "Othello" role
47. Commedia dell'__
48. Level, in taxes
51. Columnist Marilyn __ Savant
52. Triangular sail
55. Music genre since the 50's
56. Onetime winner of all the awards in this puzzle's theme
59. Raison d'__

60. Privy to
61. Intensely hot
62. Treat for Little Miss Muffet
63. Taj Mahal city
64. Ruffled

DOWN

1. They may be left at one's doorstep
2. Whiff
3. "Curses!"
4. Actress Myrna
5. On target
6. Leave high and dry
7. Frisk, with "down"
8. Formal correspondence
9. Sea north of Iran
10. Blanket wrap
11. Writer Dinesen
12. Rizzuto or Collins
13. Protected
18. Great deal of interest
23. Blonde shade
24. Takes steps
26. Take to the soapbox
27. Earthquake
28. Friend of Job
29. One-named New Age musician
30. Aconcagua and environs
31. Old hand
34. Trifle
36. Darting

37. Hauls away
38. Grimm figure
40. Camus's birthplace
41. Rebound shot
43. It's a knockout
44. Jabber
45. Castro's capital
48. Suds
49. "Portnoy's Complaint" author
50. Bit of a spread
52. Minced oath
53. Start of a legal memo
54. "Cheers" bartender Woody __
57. Rocky peak
58. Estuary

ACROSS

1. Part of P.T.A.: Abbr.
5. Make sense
10. St. Thomas or St. Martin
14. It's hard for some people to carry
15. Dough
16. N.Y. Met or L.A. Dodger, e.g.
17. White's dessert?
19. Fly high
20. Ho hello
21. Dried up
22. There's no free ride on these hwys.
23. Key task?
25. Fable fellow
27. "Row, Row, Row Your Boat" and others
30. Check for fit
33. Prepare for a rainy day
36. Bud's buddy
37. Disco spinner
38. Prop in slapstick
39. Carrey's snack food?
41. Mine find
42. Shows flexibility, in a way
44. Hit like Holyfield
45. Numero uno
46. Free-for-all
47. Western howler
49. Blender maker
51. Like Joe Average
55. From pillar to __
57. Televises
60. Bid the bed adieu
61. __ in a blue moon
62. Sawyer's beef?
64. Sharif of "Doctor Zhivago"
65. Leg bone
66. Life-or-death matter: Abbr.
67. The lady's
68. Like snakeskin
69. Madams' men

DOWN

1. Trip to the plate
2. Rude and sullen
3. Be a busybody
4. Recently employed worker
5. Diplomat: Abbr.
6. Bucks' mates
7. Fuss over, with "on"
8. Extremists
9. Check casher
10. Coming up
11. Pesci's sandwich?
12. Faucet failure
13. Screws up
18. Billionth: Prefix
24. Patsies
26. Stern's opposite
28. "__ won't be afraid" ("Stand by Me" lyric)
29. Flying elephant
31. They fit in locks
32. Nikita's "no"
33. Junk E-mail
34. Glorified gofer
35. Wilde's entree?
37. Popular pencil brand
39. Let it be, editorially
40. Newborn child, for one
43. Bothers à la baby brother
45. They may be black and blue
47. Siskel or Ebert
48. Warty-skinned critter
50. Bridge positions
52. Home of the N.B.A. Heat
53. "Lou Grant" star
54. Salacious looks
55. Christopher Robin's pal
56. Treater's words
58. Singer McEntire
59. Go yachting
63. Mary __ of cosmetics

(404) "YOO HOO!" *by Thomas W. Schier*

ACROSS

1. Flashlight's projection
5. Bus. get-together
8. Adjust on the timeline
14. With 2-Down, "My People" author
15. Pacific battle site, in brief
16. Fromm and Remarque
17. Australian ranch hand
19. Lunatics
20. Pyrenees nation
21. Pretty marble
22. Showy parrot
24. Chinese food additive
27. Dali or Corot
28. Mass robe
31. Needed liniment
33. Tot's game
36. Braincases
38. Connect via phone
39. Leaping marsupial
42. Pacific island nation
43. Workout facility
44. Tax on imports
47. Certain M.I.T. grads
48. Cowboy
50. In its entirety
53. Austrian Alpine pass
58. Where 26-Down is
59. Algonquian Indian
60. Donut coatings
61. Drink on draft
62. Peru's capital
63. "Murder Must Advertise" writer Dorothy

64. Tripper's turn-on
65. Like some drinks

DOWN

1. Mexicali locale, for short
2. See 14-Across
3. Alphabetical start
4. Shark variety
5. Medicine chest door, usually
6. Having one intermission
7. Baby syllable
8. Did a framer's job
9. Sappho's Muse
10. Child's reply to a taunt
11. Highest point
12. Unnamed ones
13. Feudal worker
18. Los Angeles suburb
21. Job for Holmes
23. Laotian money
24. Baseball's Connie and others
25. Dump into a Dumpster
26. Lake Volta's country
28. Once in __ moon
29. River through Tours
30. Year-end check, maybe
32. Our lang.
34. Relations
35. Motorists' org.
37. Where nudes may be sketched

40. Tasting like certain wood
41. Man-mouse connector
45. Certain letter-shaped tracks
46. Involuntary, as a landing
48. Pool table fabric
49. Gastric woe
50. Makes "it"
51. "Man __ Mancha"
52. Caterer's carrier
54. "Road" picture destination
55. Colossal
56. City on seven hills
57. Prod
59. __ Kan (pet food brand)

ROYAL *by Elizabeth C. Gorski*

ACROSS

1. Supreme Diana
5. Distiller Walker
10. Shade of blue
14. 1975 Wimbledon winner
15. Solo
16. Plunks (down)
17. Summer resort off the coast of Massachusetts
19. Bring in
20. Elixirs
21. Saviors
23. Ward of "Sisters"
25. D'Amato and others
26. The "S" of R.S.V.P.
29. Elvis's home
33. "At Seventeen" singer Janis
36. Hut material
38. Two socks
39. On a single occasion
40. Scented pouches
43. Quaker's "you"
44. Mine extracts
45. Balance sheet item
46. Make soaking wet
47. Sound systems
49. 60's radicals: Abbr.
50. Surgery sites, for short
52. Jugglery
54. Make king
59. Regal headwear
63. Henry __
64. 1984 Prince hit
66. Have __ good authority
67. Cream
68. Book after II Chronicles
69. Late-night regular
70. Athletic shoe feature
71. Hard to fathom

DOWN

1. Undivided
2. Norse capital
3. Blackball
4. Common carriers
5. Pain in the neck
6. Hurting
7. Wander
8. Author Rice
9. Club __ (resorts)
10. Blooming time
11. Funny feeling
12. Neighbor of 27-Down
13. Nile creatures
18. Old-time deliverers
22. Carrier to Stockholm
24. Current name
26. Smelling __
27. The Oregon Trail crossed it
28. Aphrodisiac
30. Cutter
31. Many a snake
32. Recipient of annual contributions
34. Didn't dillydally
35. Hatching places
37. Spell-off
39. Sounds of surprise
41. Precise moment
42. "A Chorus Line" girl
47. Ukr., once
48. Means of release
51. Safari sight
53. Dog-__ (well-worn)
54. Fiendish
55. Evening, in adspeak
56. Intl. acronym since 1960
57. Not valid
58. Toledo's lake
60. Bring the house down
61. Billion follower
62. Ginger cookie
65. Org. looking after kids

ACROSS

1. Disney's deer
6. With 16-Across, a famed diarist
11. "Am ___ believe . . . ?"
14. 'Hoods
15. Get a new tenant for
16. See 6-Across
17. Mighty Cardinal
19. ___ Cruces, N.M.
20. ". . . sting like ___"
21. "Oh wow!"
22. Broken-down motorist's signal
24. Nickname of 17-Across hero Babe Ruth
28. On the train
31. Unbending
32. Gets really steamed
33. Suffix with gang
34. Massachusetts' Cape ___
37. Turn loose
39. Official reproach
42. N.F.L. scores
43. Cooperate with a shooter
45. Playful animal
46. Lamb Chop's mentor
48. Had relevance to
49. Call after a hit by 17-Across
53. Minxes
54. "Cara ___" (1965 hit)
55. Diva's big moment
59. State next to Miss.
60. Title for 17-Across
64. ". . . ___ a lender be"
65. Clear the board
66. Contradict
67. Little scurrier
68. Sees socially
69. Where Minos ruled

DOWN

1. Crimson Tide, briefly
2. Show horse
3. Nothing more than
4. Popular fundraiser
5. Credo
6. Vernacular
7. 1980's sitcom with two Darryls
8. The Greatest
9. Suffix with cash
10. Opponent for Martina or Monica
11. Nonblood relative
12. Princess topper
13. Beginning
18. Common ailment
23. Hallucination cause
25. Constellation bear
26. One in the family
27. Very nasty sort
28. Border on
29. 007
30. Squelches a squeak
33. Pint-sized
34. Like a button
35. After-lunch sandwich
36. Actor Bruce
38. Bit of a tiff
40. American-born Queen of Jordan
41. Runner in the raw
44. Kind of cat
46. Pacifier
47. Quite quiet
48. Bridges of Hollywood
49. The Donald's first ex
50. Eagle's gripper
51. Bright
52. Takes on
56. Get to, so to speak
57. "What's ___ for me?"
58. Onetime Time film critic James
61. Man-mouse link
62. Welcome ___
63. "ER" network

KEEPING IN CONTACT *by Fred Piscop*

ACROSS
1. "Peanuts" boy
6. Exile of 1979
10. Carry on, as a campaign
14. Take for one's own
15. Shells, e.g.
16. Allege as fact
17. With one's fingers in a lake?
20. Grand larceny, e.g.
21. "__ Darlin' " (jazz standard)
22. Sugary drink
23. "Relax, private!"
26. Longed (for)
28. Adorns unnecessarily
31. Toiletries holder
33. Brouhaha
34. A.T.M. necessity
35. Wagnerian heroine
39. With one's fingers in a skyscraper?
43. Like last year's styles
44. Part of U.C.L.A.
45. KLM competitor
46. Echo, e.g.
48. An ex of Xavier
50. Bob Cousy's team, for short
53. Duds
55. "Bravo!"
56. Wax producer
58. Latino lady
62. With one's fingers in a socket?
66. Bering Sea island
67. At no time, to poets
68. Ceramists' needs
69. Element #10
70. City to which Helen was abducted
71. Kind of shooting

DOWN
1. Joke response, informally
2. __ fixe (obsession)
3. December air
4. Send to a mainframe
5. Is miserly
6. Decline in value
7. Seagoing inits.
8. Evil repeller
9. Pueblo dweller
10. Kind of chest or paint
11. For the birds?
12. Hollow rock
13. Blew it
18. "The Science Guy" on TV
19. Ciudad Juárez neighbor
24. Similar
25. Marathoner's shirt
27. Borodin's prince
28. Meower, in Madrid
29. Matinee hero
30. Blaring
32. 0's and 1's, to a programmer
34. Absolute worst, with "the"
36. One of the Simpsons
37. Cherished
38. Sinclair rival
40. Cyberspace conversation
41. Grimm youngster
42. Launderer's step
47. __ Brothers
48. Haunted house sounds
49. Playwright Ibsen
50. "Over There" composer
51. Make jubilant
52. Slowly, on a score
54. Approximation suffix
57. "__ Too Proud to Beg" (1966 hit)
59. Look at flirtatiously
60. Tennis's Lacoste
61. Like some profs.
63. Pester for payment
64. Prefix with logical
65. Have a bawl

(408) SPACED OUT *by Peter Gordon*

ACROSS
1. Wings
5. Rick's love in "Casablanca"
9. Carry's partner
13. One of 39-Across
14. On toast, in diner slang
15. Commedia dell'__
16. Intended
17. Illuminated sign
18. MTV's "The __ World"
19. One of 39-Across
21. One of 39-Across
23. Shoebox marking
24. Sex researcher Hite
25. "Welcome" site
28. Europe's highest active volcano
30. Took care of
34. Labor Dept. division
36. Troubles
38. Practice piece
39. Theme of this puzzle
42. Monopoly piece
43. Jazz singer James
44. Jonathan Larson musical
45. Unwanted noise
47. Simplicity
49. Lao-__
50. Tackle box contents
52. Neighbor of Wyo.
54. One of 39-Across
57. One of 39-Across
61. Part of 36-24-36
62. Whitish
64. Ab strengthener
65. Bridge position
66. Uniform
67. What your nose knows

68. Lover of Aphrodite
69. Actress Russo
70. Info

DOWN
1. One of the Baldwins
2. Rachel's sister, in the Bible
3. "Bull Durham" character
4. Main course
5. Brainstorm
6. Bagel topper
7. Sound of a basket
8. Part of a pregame ceremony
9. One of 39-Across

10. Calculus calculation
11. Symbol on a Cowboy's helmet
12. Remained fast
13. Baseball V.I.P.'s
20. Fix a road
22. Some native New Yorkers
24. Greets the general
25. Naphthalene repels them
26. "__ in the Dark"
27. Angle symbol
29. "Good going!"
31. Comforter
32. Perfect places
33. Al __
35. February stones

37. Mlle., in Spain
40. Untouchable Ness
41. Mr. Arafat
46. One of 39-Across
48. Town in central New Jersey
51. Jack
53. Casual comment
54. It erupted on October 27, 1986
55. When repeated, a 1997 Jim Carrey comedy
56. Church part
57. Kind of pool
58. Put away
59. Not theirs
60. Brit. legislators
63. Novelist Deighton

NOT AS MUCH *by Ed Early*

ACROSS

1. Pile
5. Alternative to plastic at a supermarket
10. Winter transport
14. Stewpot
15. Where Sun Valley is
16. Fashioned
17. Crockett or Jones
18. Static
19. Mideast bigwig
20. Lose it
21. Vessel in an alcove
22. Society's 400
23. It's a waste of time
27. Thespian
30. Lily plants
31. Vehicles with booms
33. Bread for a stew, e.g.
34. Missile berth
38. Inner city structure
41. Some sheep
42. Terhune title character
43. Cram into the hold
44. Warner Brothers' __ J. Fudd
46. Antique shop item
47. 1967 Agatha Christie thriller
52. Jeopardy
53. Nicotine's partner
54. Inventor Elias
58. Chapters in world history
59. Well-coordinated
61. Privy to
62. Malicious
63. Butter up?
64. Hardly Mr. Cool
65. New Year's Eve song word

66. Hold for later, as big news
67. Legs, to a zoot suiter

DOWN

1. Bricklayers carry them
2. Flair
3. Thomas __ Edison
4. Corner conveniences
5. Betty Grable's photo, for one
6. Idolizes
7. Modern driller?
8. Remarks requesting elucidation
9. Fish eggs
10. Food fish
11. Female vampire
12. Tweaks a manuscript
13. Rock's __ and the Dominos
22. Serpentine curve
24. City SSW of Moscow
25. Subjects of clashes
26. Second-year students, for short
27. Yearn
28. Brag
29. Domesticated
32. Convinces of
34. Nero Wolfe's activity

35. Roman road
36. __ Strauss & Co.
37. Hydrox rival
39. Menaces for warplanes
40. Inscribe for good
44. Slippery one
45. Commercial center in Venice
47. Olympians' blades
48. Having chutzpah
49. Bathtub part
50. Knit goods thread
51. In leaf
55. Draft classification
56. Apple spoiler
57. Winds up
59. Stomach muscles, for short
60. Toujours __

410 I/O SWITCH by Diane C. Baldwin

ACROSS

1. 1977 George Burns film
6. Stays idle
10. Sentry's cry
14. Bottom of a suit
15. Blue-pencil
16. Rose's fellow
17. Bad
18. Learning method
19. "__ Lisa"
20. Backs of 45's having a sudden change in direction?
23. "Ah, me!"
24. Moon goddess
25. Operatic soprano Geraldine
28. Gush forth
30. Alfonso XIII's queen
31. Tall footwear for rappers?
36. Bank adjuncts
38. It may be lent
39. Writer Ephron
40. Trackside aid that can't be beat?
45. Buddhism sect
46. Playwright Clifford
47. Certain steak
49. Chatterbox
52. Taj Mahal site
53. Portable writing surface for an equestrian?
57. Inlet
58. Verve
59. Boring fellows
62. Singular fellow
63. Full-fledged
64. Weird
65. Hankerings
66. Skyrocket
67. Dozed

DOWN

1. Harem room
2. Chop
3. Malarkey
4. Eyepiece
5. Old Testament temptress
6. Feudal underlings
7. Hero
8. Former Yugoslav chief
9. Accelerates
10. Burr's duel victim
11. Domicile
12. Kind of cabinet
13. Josh
21. __-mutuel
22. Albanian foe
25. Exploit
26. Against
27. Highway exit
28. Iranian royalty
29. A sweater uses it
32. Annoyance
33. Seep
34. It's just over 14-Across
35. All there
37. Plugs
41. Like Pindar's works
42. Kitchen gadgets
43. Therefore
44. Diatribes
48. Race (along)
49. Hatfield's foe
50. "Leave me __!"
51. Starting point in decision making
52. Baseball's Doubleday
54. Hodgepodge
55. One of the Three Bears
56. Serious
60. Lulu
61. Established

ACROSS

1. Carried on
6. "Think Fast, Mr. __" (1937 mystery)
10. Dour
14. Single-handedly
15. ". . . and make it snappy!"
16. Field of work
17. Poles, e.g.
18. Fingerprint or dropped handkerchief, say
19. Kimono sashes
20. Oppose
23. Some ancient writings
25. Exploit
26. Just-passing grade
27. Gone by
28. Mournful cries
31. Drudges
33. Dinner at boot camp
35. The Baltic, e.g.
36. Home on the farm
37. Wall Street fixture
42. Exclamations of regret
43. Bud's pal
44. Empty, in math
46. "Amerika" author
49. Film critic Jeffrey
51. The Greatest
52. Lofty lyric
53. Utter
55. Asian capital
57. Like some tenors
61. Mean one
62. Compote fruit
63. Fine suit material
66. Property claim
67. Island dance
68. Bequeath
69. Lavish affection (on)
70. Site of Iowa State
71. Bud Grace comic strip

DOWN

1. Is no longer
2. "Is that __?"
3. Kicker's target
4. Accredited diplomat
5. Catch sight of
6. Jet speed measure
7. Capital near the 60th parallel
8. Ford debut of 1988
9. Makes the first bid
10. Gentle firelight
11. Psychic energy, to Freud
12. Married
13. Interlocks
21. Newsstands
22. Nasal partitions
23. Tennis's Shriver
24. Census data
29. Teeny
30. Without strict oversight
32. Boston suburb
34. Overcharge, slangily
36. Railroad switches
38. Many a climactic movie scene
39. Dove's cry
40. Protector
41. Raines of 40's–50's film
45. Author __ Yutang
46. German goblin
47. Slow ballet dance
48. Animal that drives rabbits from their burrows
49. Lecture hall
50. Not demand everything one wants
54. Beginning
56. Tree cutter
58. Actor Auberjonois
59. Sound in body
60. Times to live through
64. 56, to Flavius
65. Grant's opposite

412 YER OUT by Jeremy Thomas Paine

ACROSS

1. Some fathers: Abbr.
4. Winter Palace ruler
8. Big name in hotels
14. Private eye, for short
15. $75/night, e.g.
16. Microscopic creature
17. Like: Suffix
18. Picnic raiders
19. Maritime hazard in W.W. II
20. Richard Benjamin's film debut, 1969
23. Stubborn beasts
24. Hospital cry
25. Enzyme ending
26. __-Israeli relations
27. Dangerous date for Caesar
28. Ripening agent
29. Vamoosed
31. E.M.T.'s procedure
33. With 34-Across, 1996 action film sequel
34. See 33-Across
37. "Rubber Soul," "Revolver" and others
38. Only so far
40. Apple or pear
43. Disavow
44. "Leave __ Beaver"
45. Article in Arles
46. Quake locale
48. Tempestuous spirit?
49. Cage/Shue picture of 1995
52. Clapboards, e.g.
53. Locale

54. Inits. in long distance
55. Beloved of Aphrodite
56. __ about (approximately)
57. New: Prefix
58. Least cooked
59. Politician Gingrich
60. "Don't give up!"

DOWN

1. Marks of shame
2. Backup help
3. Academic types
4. Shore dinner entree
5. Off-the-wall
6. One who shows up
7. Saved
8. Carries
9. Permeate
10. Weaver's apparatus
11. It may land in hot water
12. Hardly brainy
13. Sadat's predecessor
21. Disastrous collapse
22. Surg. areas
27. Little devils
28. Large wardrobe
30. Navigator's need
31. Supercomputer name
32. Bad sound for a balloonist

34. Actress Joan of "Rebecca"
35. Plaintiff or defendant
36. Aardvark
38. Runs to mom about
39. "Anna Karenina" author
40. Astronomical object
41. Iroquoian tribe
42. Field
43. Grooved on
46. The end
47. Dread
48. Turn aside
50. Morning glory, e.g.
51. Put away

RATED XXX *by Stephanie Spadaccini*

ACROSS

1. Skiing mecca
5. Dogs and cats, e.g.
9. Hidden room's secret opening
14. Comic Sahl
15. "Dies __"
16. Idolize
17. Vulgarian
18. Seagoing: Abbr.
19. Have a feeling about
20. X
23. Old-time entertainer __ Tucker
24. Morse code component
25. Quiche, e.g.
26. The Emerald Isle
28. Hairpiece
31. 60's protest
34. "Time __ My Side" (Rolling Stones hit)
35. Demonstrate
36. X
39. Music synthesizer
40. Malarial fever
41. The Phantom's instrument
42. Switch positions
43. Quaker's "you"
44. Prefix with nuptial
45. __ Paulo, Brazil
46. Italian cheese
49. X
54. Slow mover
55. __ Orange, N.J.
56. Hollow response
57. Pancake syrup flavor
58. Friend, to Françoise
59. Actress Perlman
60. Like some stomachs
61. Look closely
62. Burn quickly

DOWN

1. Prefix with dexterity
2. Makes off with illegally
3. TV teaser
4. Big and strong
5. Finger that curls
6. Rub out
7. Tight as a drum
8. Clockmaker Thomas
9. Die, euphemistically
10. Highly skilled
11. Forbidden thing
12. Once, once
13. Attorney F. __ Bailey
21. Zoo beast
22. Patsy's pal on "Absolutely Fabulous"
26. In the style of: Suffix
27. Debaucher
28. Supporter of the American Revolution
29. Little bit
30. 17th-century actress Nell
31. Japanese wrestling
32. Get __ the ground floor
33. W.B.A. calls
34. "Come Back, Little Sheba" playwright
35. Naked runners
37. "Yippee!"
38. Designer Kamali
43. Writing pad
44. Baggage handler
45. "Look happy!"
46. First name in TV talk
47. Hiding spot
48. Milo or Tessie
49. Ginger cookie
50. Blabs
51. Spring
52. Renown
53. Fly like an eagle
54. Texas Mustangs, for short

414 CLOWN AROUND *by Frances Hansen*

ACROSS

1. Polish border river
5. Lazy girl?
10. It's uplifting
13. Comic's missiles
14. Strangle
15. Stimpy's TV pal
16. Character created by 58-Across
18. F. D. R. measure
19. Spiral-horned sheep
20. "Ready, ___ . . . !"
21. Tiny stream
22. Employers of 58-Across
25. Greek H
26. Army cops
27. Frozen desserts
28. German spa
30. Claiborne or Smith
32. West Pointer
33. 1951 film featuring 58-Across
37. Patrick of "Marat/Sade"
40. Ernie Els's org.
41. Comic DeLuise
44. Patti of opera lore
47. Under the weather
49. Caviar
51. Where 58-Across died, 1979
54. Bandy words
55. Burgle
56. Parrots, in a way
57. SST's fly over it: Abbr.
58. Memorable Big Top star born 12/8/1898
60. King of Kings

61. Drops in the letter box
62. Ciardi's "___ a Man"
63. Leandro's love
64. "I give up!"
65. So-called monster's home

DOWN

1. Surgeon's decision
2. You're working on one
3. Showed on TV again
4. Sanctuary
5. ___-fi
6. Old Polish lancer
7. Pyramid and cube
8. Like some arms
9. Society page word
10. Grilled
11. Satiated
12. Wall Street worker
16. ". . . gimble in the ___": Carroll
17. Nun's headdress
21. Decorative strip of fabric
23. "Oh, you wish!"
24. Medieval chest
29. Of a stone pillar
31. Nuke
34. "Who does he think ___!"
35. End-of-week cry
36. Xylophone tool
37. Knead
38. Converting device: Var.
39. First name in TV talk
42. Gregg Olson and others
43. Early assembly-line cars
45. Bates of "Psycho"
46. Extremely tiny
48. Commit unalterably
50. "Duck soup"
52. Clear as ___
53. Part of a sentence, in linguistics
58. Cassowary's cousin
59. Mao ___-tung

CHILD'S PLAY *by Patrick Jordan*

ACROSS

1. Garden crasher
5. Gather up
10. Mary __ cosmetics
13. Less inept
15. Futuristic slave
16. "__ Gotta Be Me"
17. Addition to the family
19. Replayed tennis shot
20. Recent hires
21. New Zealand tribesman
23. Hog heaven?
24. Ques. counterpart
25. Rolling Stone Richards
27. Colloquialism for 17-Across
31. Shattered pane piece
34. Individuals
35. "Blame It on __" (Caine comedy)
36. Game with mallets
37. Religious law
39. "__ never fly!"
40. "Sure thing, skipper!"
41. German car
42. Disconcerted
43. Colloquialism for 17-Across
47. Fool (around)
48. Jerusalem is its cap.
49. Quiz
52. Crockett's last stand
54. Poshness
56. Square dance partner
57. Colloquialism for 17-Across
60. Adam's madam
61. Public persona
62. Ten __ (long odds)
63. When it's light
64. Behind bars
65. Like many a mistake

DOWN

1. Desires
2. Thumbs up/thumbs down critic
3. Broncos QB John
4. Figure skater Thomas
5. Marshal Dillon's portrayer
6. Unruly crowds
7. Lawyer's org.
8. Blubber
9. Thwarts
10. Unit of frequency
11. Declare firmly
12. Himalayan legend
14. George's predecessor
18. Russo of "Get Shorty"
22. Versatile transport, for short
25. Bingo relative
26. Utopia
27. Sis's sib
28. Kind of boom
29. Aswan Dam locale
30. Narrated
31. Bickering
32. Boxer Oscar De La __
33. "Roots" writer
37. Cows' mouthfuls
38. Together, in music
39. Author Fleming
41. Like some exercises
42. Drew a blank
44. __ Perignon
45. Worked the soil
46. "Gotcha"
49. Pear variety
50. Teatime treat
51. Tensed, with "up"
52. Not young
53. Volcanic flow
54. Cutting part
55. Get an __ effort
58. Actress Thurman
59. Broken-down 47-Across

416 AA BATTERY *by Adam Cohen*

ACROSS

1. "In"
5. Faint flicker
10. Hits with a ray gun
14. Author — Neale Hurston
15. "Amazing" magician
16. Together, musically
17. Protein components
19. — Strip
20. Paraphrased
21. Latter-day Saint
23. Nature goddess
24. Fruit of the Loom competitor
25. Openings
28. Information accessed on a computer
31. Water sources
32. Assumed
33. 1968 hit "Harper Valley —"
34. Hangover?
35. Roebuck's partner
36. Mimic
37. Ryan's "Love Story" co-star
38. Observe Yom Kippur
39. Speck of land in the sea
40. Deserter
42. Coat of many colors wearer
43. Coeur d'—, Idaho
44. "Stand By Me" singer — King
45. Beefed
47. Xylophone-like instruments
51. Singer Falana
52. East African capital
54. Takes advantage of
55. "Good Times" actress Esther
56. Stew ingredient
57. Deli jarful
58. Symbol of freshness
59. Art Deco artist

DOWN

1. Ivan the Terrible, e.g.
2. "Where the heart is"
3. Eye part
4. Biblical hymn
5. Without charge
6. Shoestrings
7. Writer Bagnold
8. Put a wing (on)
9. Slips up, as a dating service
10. Croatian capital
11. It might bob up in conversation
12. "The Godfather" author
13. Penn name
18. Filling stations?
22. "Chestnuts roasting — open fire"
24. Le —, France
25. Take an oath
26. Positive thinking proponent
27. American Dance Theater founder
28. Steak —
29. Pricey
30. Our planet
32. Crystal rock
35. Run of the mill
36. Come together
38. Pulitzer-winning writer James
39. Ancient part of Asia Minor
41. Rio Grande city
42. It's across the Hudson from New York
44. Jumps (out)
45. Dejected
46. Sub — (secretly)
47. 1551, in monuments
48. 1930's heavyweight champ Max
49. Aid in crime
50. Sushi bar drink
53. — 180 (turn around, in slang)

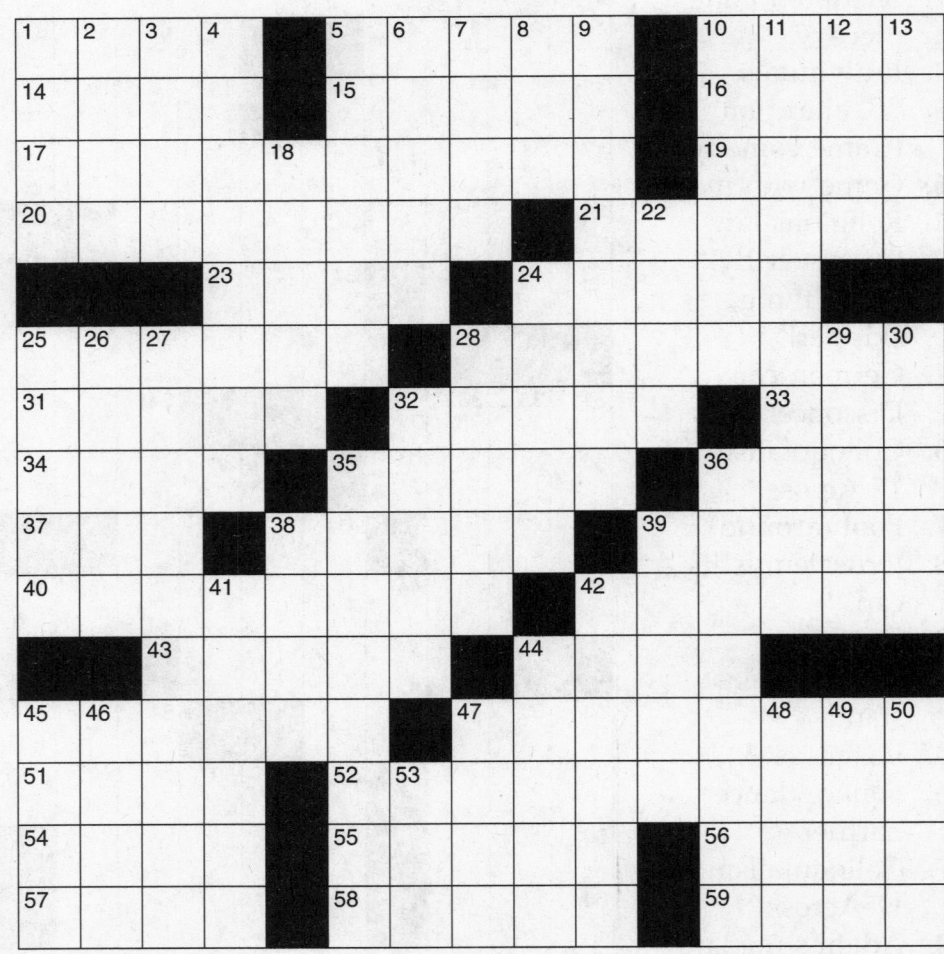

"THAT SOUNDS FISHY" *by Susan Harrington Smith*

ACROSS

1. Shells, for short
5. "Not on __!"
9. Mark left by Zorro?
13. Instrument for an étude
15. Pre-stereo
16. Dramatic entrance announcement
17. Blooper
18. Verve
19. Hertz rival
20. Little guy getting the third degree?
23. Wee, to Burns
25. "Gosh!"
26. Kind of crew
27. Neatly combed curmudgeon?
31. Hunter in the night sky
32. Lamp type
36. Filmmaker Jacques
37. Lesley of "60 Minutes"
39. __ Penh, Cambodia
41. Ropes, as a dogie
43. Cartoon "Mr."
44. Gambling locale for the taciturn?
47. French dramatist Antonin __
51. Sounds from Santa
52. Fishing aid
53. Bright-red unglazed china?
57. They may clash in business
58. Shower
59. Addicts
62. Letter for Gandalf
63. Tied
64. Sign up
65. Caddie's bagful
66. Withhold, as funds
67. Concerning

DOWN

1. Mimic
2. Russian space station
3. Tequila drink
4. __ about (circa)
5. Sauntered
6. Word with crashing or tidal
7. Sir Geraint's wife
8. Like Cinderella's slipper, to her stepsisters
9. Jump involuntarily
10. Quibble
11. ". . . can you spare __?"
12. Grating
14. Beginning
21. Jeans brand
22. Tramp
23. Robert Burns, for one
24. Subway artwork
28. Louis-Philippe and others
29. Gulf
30. "Yay, team!"
33. 3.7 and 4.0, e.g.
34. Train V.I.P.'s
35. Nary a soul
37. Fused
38. 4:00 gathering
40. No longer worth discussing
42. Hare's tail
43. Poe's "The __ of the Red Death"
45. Climb, in a way
46. Fortune 500 listings: Abbr.
47. On the qui vive
48. Scamp
49. Dinner leftover for Bowser
50. Donkeys
54. Carry on
55. "Très __!"
56. Annapolis sch.
60. Twaddle
61. __-pitch softball

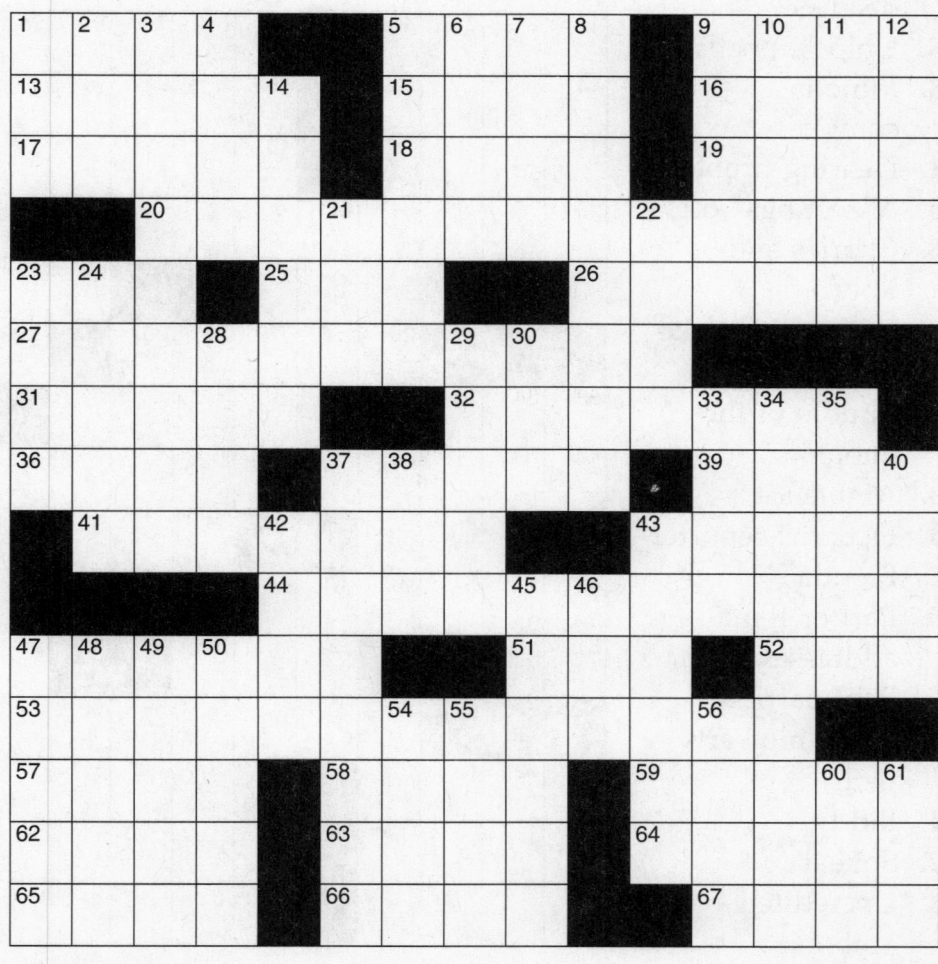

ACROSS

1. Theatrical hit, in slang
5. Wild party
10. Bound along
14. Word with slide or home
15. Ninth-inning excitement, maybe
16. Tel __
17. Antiquing agent
18. How the euphoric walk?
19. Barn accessory
20. Start of a Ralph Waldo Emerson quote
23. Spread about
24. It may be living or dead
25. Unlock, poetically
28. Minolta competitor
31. Hearing problem?
33. "Greetings" org.
36. Charles and Ephron
38. Prefix with nuke or freeze
39. Middle of the quote
43. Ambience
44. Fictional reporter Brenda
45. Part of E-mail addresses
46. Pool parties?
49. Lawn mower's path
51. Biddy
52. Squeal
54. Uncredited authors

58. End of the quote
61. Easing of tensions
64. Sidekick
65. "Blondie" character
66. Flightless bird
67. Take up again
68. Politico Long
69. Foreboding
70. Deck out
71. Reo maker

DOWN

1. Kindergarten disrupters
2. Word of obligation
3. One on the lam
4. Actor Mel or Jose
5. Critter in a kids' rhyme
6. An ex of Artie
7. Winged
8. Playground sight
9. Old Northern Ireland county
10. Soap brand
11. In vitro items
12. Mat coup
13. Adam's rib, so to speak
21. "Dallas" family name
22. Public health org.
25. Held title to
26. Barbecue spot
27. Be real
29. Loads from lodes
30. Quashes
32. Amscrayed
33. Squirrel away
34. "On the Beach" author

35. Lorelei, e.g.
37. Side order at KFC
40. One of the Bobbseys
41. Be a dead weight on
42. Garden products brand
47. Spanish gold
48. 1943 Bogart film
50. Big chief
53. Busted, in a way
55. City near Inchon
56. Bushed
57. Collar stiffeners
58. Like some beds
59. "In __ veritas"
60. Elbe tributary
61. Ref's ruling
62. That guy
63. Wow

"YOU'LL LOVE IT" *by Richard Silvestri*

ACROSS

1. Witty remark
5. Prince of Darkness
10. Loot
14. Sweet sandwich
15. Proclamation
16. Atlantic City game
17. My fodder's place?
18. Needle point?
19. Humerus neighbor
20. "The guy's going to shoot"
22. Set aside
23. Long, long time
24. Mopes
26. One with equal billing
29. Approach stealthily
32. None of the above
33. Fort McHenry sight
35. Bond foe
36. Sault __ Marie
37. Like many martini olives
40. Tag players
41. Put one's cards on the table, maybe
43. "Don't rush into anything!"
44. Banks of diamond fame
46. Maid of __
48. Drawn-out war tactics
49. Time on the job
50. Ambassadorship, e.g.
51. Hurt plenty
53. "This one's on me"
57. Day divider
58. Rot
60. Car bar
61. Social asset
62. Tea party crasher
63. Bat's home
64. Sommer in the cinema
65. Hologram illuminator
66. Revenuer

DOWN

1. Kid
2. Cuyahoga's outlet
3. Order to a broker
4. Not in time
5. Next year's alumnus
6. Grace
7. Get bushed
8. Play piece
9. Unspecified ordinal
10. Lay low
11. "You and I are about to leap"
12. Part of A.D.
13. Barnyard butter
21. Has apprehensions
22. Tankard contents
24. Spine-tingling
25. Inner drive
26. Kramer or Topper
27. Cousin of a mink
28. "The woman will behave outrageously"
30. Loosen
31. Sits for snaps
33. Religious observance
34. Andalusian article
38. Famous Friend
39. Jefferson was one
42. Diplomat's quest
45. Disavow
47. Pitch in
48. Lead-tin alloy
50. Show topper
51. Put up stakes
52. Shade of black
53. Nile wader
54. Makeup __
55. Menlo Park middle name
56. Beavis or Butthead
58. Guy's date
59. Pay stretcher?

420 POSITIVE THINKING by Michael S. Maurer

ACROSS

1. Cross a shallow creek
5. Instituteur's place
10. Not nigh
14. Toward shelter
15. Pyle of Mayberry
16. __ Raton, Fla.
17. Part 1 of a quip
20. __ Schwarz
21. Encumbrances
22. Neuters, as a horse
23. Part of T.G.I.F.
24. Take in
25. Quip, part 2
34. Like a bucket in an old song
35. Dunce
36. River inlet
37. .035 ounce
38. Basketball boo-boos
39. Flight ratio
40. A.B.A. member
41. They may be served with caviar
42. Printing process, briefly
43. Quip, part 3
46. Blow away
47. Morrow of "The Bad News Bears"
48. Valuable violin
51. Like Audubon's interests
54. Scale notes
57. End of the quip
60. Common Market money
61. Biscotto flavoring
62. Sophocles tragedy
63. Chiang Mai native
64. Foofaraws
65. Like microbes

DOWN

1. Stray animal
2. A, in communications
3. Retro art style
4. Bioelectric swimmer
5. Madame Bovary's problem
6. Manage
7. Arabian Sea nation
8. Doesn't disallow
9. Act human
10. Heading on a roll book
11. Stable newcomer
12. Etcher's need
13. X-ray units
18. John of rock
19. Prolonged pain
23. Particular
24. Yellow fleet
25. Hindu disciplines
26. Superman's adopted home
27. Pointy-snouted fish
28. Bubbling
29. Pugilistic period
30. Infant's woe
31. Hold the floor
32. Not, in Nuremberg
33. Whoop
38. Chimney channel
39. Catchall category: Abbr.
41. __ State (Arkansas nickname)
42. "Rawhide" singer
44. 60's dance
45. Skirts
48. Help a hood
49. Kind of engr.
50. __-lung
51. Part of A.D.
52. Empty
53. Assuming that's true
54. South Pacific republic
55. Lawyer Dershowitz
56. Voluptuous
58. Polish off
59. Insurrectionist Turner

ACROSS

1. Difficult position
5. Narc's find
10. Shtick performance
13. Bar order, with "the"
15. Conductor Sir Georg
16. Dug in
17. Sugary drink?
19. Oater affirmative
20. Rachel's sister
21. Elephant's tail?
22. A few
23. Sheepish remark?
25. Brewery?
28. Org. that does investigations
29. ___-Cat (winter vehicle)
30. Not look too lively
31. Paw
33. Dits' partners
36. With 22-Down, cautious statement
40. This puzzle's theme song?
43. Vintage tune
44. "Amscray!"
45. Blowgun ammo
46. Blowgun ammo
48. Sounds of indecision
50. ___ juice (milk)
51. Heavy drinker?
56. B and B
57. Fab Four film of '65
58. Calendar abbr.
59. Palindromic time
61. "Mârouf" baritone
62. Bottles-only drinker?
66. Gun
67. Let up
68. Minimum wage makers, maybe
69. Devon river
70. Mike of "Wayne's World"
71. A.P.O. addressee

DOWN

1. Hero
2. Telepathy and such
3. Beat in a dance marathon
4. 1991 film "Little Man ___"
5. Flat tire sound
6. Namely
7. Coeur d'___, Idaho
8. Pokes drive them
9. Triple, say
10. Louisiana feature
11. Knickknacks
12. Dakota lodging
14. Jetés, e.g.
18. Name in a #1 Beach Boys song
22. See 36-Across
23. Hardly an intellectual
24. Sharon of Israel
26. Has a good, hard laugh
27. Padlock's partner
32. Cause to err
34. Initials for a prince
35. Asian capital
37. Tropical waders
38. Tire center
39. Incriminate
41. Borscht base
42. Loch ___
47. Free-for-all
49. Eagle's descent
51. Cut
52. E-mail forerunner
53. Greenish
54. Obliterate
55. Career officer
60. Lyric poems
62. Brooklynese pronoun
63. Stats accompanying F.G.'s
64. A Siamese twin
65. Alphabet trio

422 COMMAND LINES by Randall J. Hartman

ACROSS

1. Bringing up the rear
5. Message on a work order
9. Bars for guitars
14. Jai __
15. Proven
16. Like acacia leaves
17. Left on a map
18. Cannabis
19. Premarathon food
20. # 1 ("Hogan's Heroes")
22. # 2 (old radio/TV serials)
24. Word said with a salute
25. Burden carrier
26. Woodstock supply
29. Tablecloths and such
31. Month before juin
34. Alert
36. People who aren't what they seem
38. Theme of this puzzle
41. Beat the pants off
42. Onetime Asian Communists
43. Flunky's response
44. Descendants
46. Fannie __
47. More than partial
49. Catchall abbr.
51. # 3 ("Sands of Iwo Jima")
54. # 4 ("F Troop")
58. Jewels site
59. "Cheerio!"
61. Pioneer talk show host
62. Ambassador's inferior
63. Pianist Gilels
64. Twosome
65. Leaves in a hot rod, with "out"
66. Antarctic explorer Sir James
67. Paris's Avenue __ République

DOWN

1. Parts of a code
2. Smart-__
3. Medals locale
4. Book before Philemon
5. Smoke shop stock
6. Egyptian port
7. Tentacle
8. # 5 (Beatles album)
9. Handles hardship
10. "Halt!" to a salt
11. Kind of tense
12. "Beetle Bailey" dog
13. O'Casey or O'Faoláin
21. Order on the court
23. Bit of hope
25. Plague
26. Like some goals
27. Flat replacement
28. Audition tapes
30. Foot, to Flavius
31. About one drop
32. Prudential rival
33. 1979 hit "__ Really Going Out With Him?"
35. Passeport info
36. Begins, as work
37. Popular cooking spray
39. Orinoco, e.g.
40. Battle stars
44. __ Anne de Beaupré
45. # 6 ("Gomer Pyle, U.S.M.C.")
47. Its capital is Innsbruck
48. Rubber-stamps
50. Amorous archer
51. Exercise routine bit
52. Pitchfork prong
53. 90's party
54. Name that has its ups and downs
55. Part of A.P.R.
56. Film critic Pauline
57. Humorist Bombeck
60. Latin series starter

ACROSS

1. Fishhook feature
5. Clogs' cousins
11. File folder feature
14. Siouan speaker
15. Man with all the answers?
16. Cry's companion
17. "Touched by an Angel" star Downey
18. "Fighting" N.C.A.A. team
19. Depression __
20. Fisherman's woe?
22. Fictional pachyderm
24. Indications
25. Come in behind the others
26. Had a TV dinner, say
29. Eyeglass prescription measurement
32. "__ depends . . ."
33. Beaus
36. Cunning
37. Barfly
38. Brushwood
39. Like King George III
40. Triage sites, briefly
41. Like margarita glasses
42. Slalom obstacle
43. Odd occurrence
45. Foul-up
46. "Open __!"
47. Picket line crossers
50. Snake in the grass
52. Lamé wear?
56. Affirmative action
57. Pill bug or wood louse
59. Bad thing to hear at a checkup
60. Copy
61. Better half
62. Hoopla
63. Compose
64. Drew upon
65. Stevenson scoundrel

DOWN

1. Use an auger
2. Positron's place
3. Easy win
4. Gets lost
5. Overcharge
6. "Stormy Weather" songwriter
7. Waist circlers
8. Waist circlers
9. Lacrosse quorum
10. Sun Valley lift?
11. Jimmy the Greek?
12. Nimbus
13. Den denizen
21. Dark half of a Chinese circle
23. Warbucks's henchman, with "the"
25. Like a gridiron
26. Perplexed
27. Brier feature
28. Adam's apple?
29. Sandbag stack, maybe
30. Tickle
31. Golf's __ Cup
33. Oil source
34. Cunning
35. Take steps
38. Russian monarch with lipstick marks on his cheek?
42. Leave for the winter, say
44. One to remember, for short
45. "Fawlty Towers" airer
47. Absorb
48. Intimate
49. Part of V.A.T.
50. Kind of judgment
51. "Forget it!"
52. Sticky stuff
53. Yawl call
54. Sondheim's Sweeney
55. It's about a foot
58. Workout locale

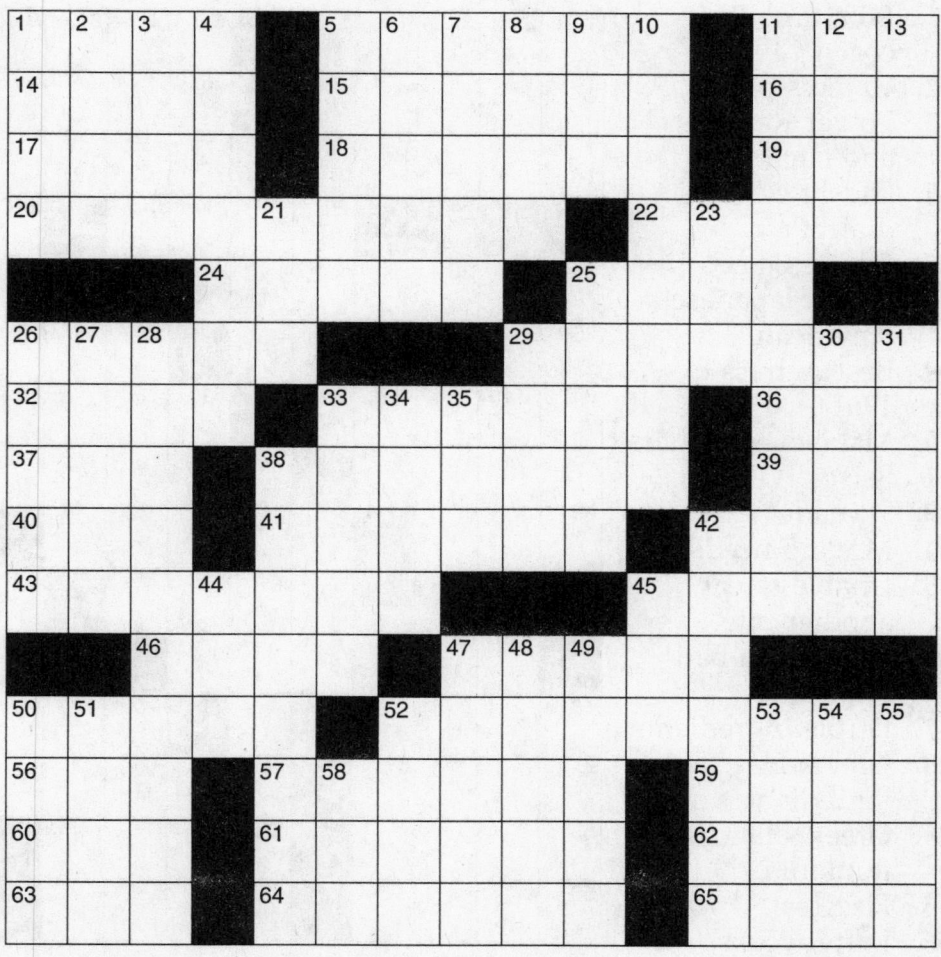

424 IT'S ALL GREEK TO ME *by Matt Gaffney*

ACROSS

1. U. of Maryland athletes
6. Grape place
10. Traditional pooch name
14. Love to death
15. "__ your pardon!"
16. Cold capital
17. Greek metropolis?
19. Tool for a prisoner's escape, maybe
20. Goes head-to-head
21. Local lingo
23. O.K.'s from city hall
27. Conflict
28. Terry McMillan's "Waiting to __"
29. Tipped individual
30. XX
31. Longtime Bears coach George
32. Green's prefix
35. Power Rangers and such
36. Old English dialect
37. Express glee
38. Noted Japanese-American
39. Best Actress of 1961
40. Make eyes, maybe
41. Seizes
43. Shoulder extension
44. Moving needs
45. Unable to eat another bite
46. Result of a bad bite?
47. Potpie ingredients
48. One-A-Day ingredient
49. Greek's fanciful thinking?
55. Fizzless
56. Lofty works
57. Spooky
58. Nonmuscular parts
59. Ran
60. Narrow vents

DOWN

1. Trig. ratio
2. Part of some E-mail addresses
3. Dale's man
4. Shark, so to speak
5. Humbly yielding
6. Drinking and others
7. Sacred bird of the Nile
8. Make after expenses
9. Like hieroglyphics
10. Pushover
11. Greek's lessening of anxiety?
12. North of Virginia
13. There are five per foot
18. Swallow-tailed bird
22. These may be fine
23. Italian sauce
24. One who no longer has life?
25. Greek's chant on a trireme?
26. Olympus Mons site
27. Where dos get done
29. Shines
31. Heavenly host?
33. Perform a Thanksgiving task
34. Chose
36. Sensitive area
37. Pitch indicator
39. Guitar relative
40. Some good hands
42. Superdome team
43. "ER" command
44. "Cheers" waitress
45. Hearing, say
46. Bit of jazz
47. Dock
50. Phrase of commitment
51. One making twists and turns
52. __ Lanka
53. Mess __
54. Nodded answer

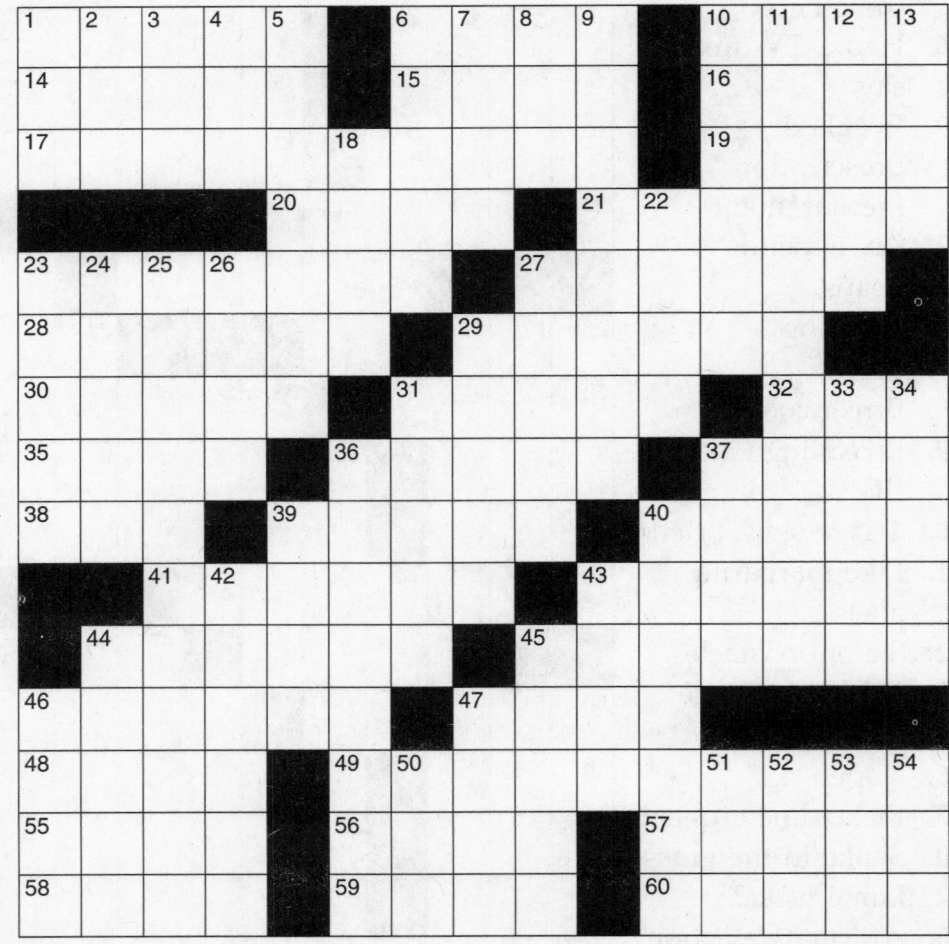

RESERVED ENERGY *by Alan Arbesfeld*

ACROSS

1. Carry on
5. Cut
11. Restorationist's skill, for short
14. Ink's color, to Shakespeare
15. Madame's eager reply
16. Brazilian vacation destination
17. Pest control devices
19. Mideast land: Abbr.
20. Oolong, for one
21. Prefix with laryngology
22. Floor
24. "Urban Cowboy" star, 1980
28. Medical vial
31. Chatter
32. Spacious
33. Traditional
37. Cosby's "I Spy" co-star
38. Strike site
40. Fibster
41. Having honest emotion
43. Fondly remembered "S.N.L." name
44. Midwest hub
45. Hate
46. Improperly altered
50. Ram in the sky
51. Terre Haute sch.
52. Mineral spring
55. Plague
56. Theme of this puzzle
61. Relative of a rhea
62. Camden Yards player
63. "Close"
64. Puff Daddy's music
65. Strange one
66. TV award

DOWN

1. Fabric
2. Up to the task
3. "Naked Maja" artist
4. Dash-dot, dash-dot, dash-dot
5. Hate
6. __ a limb
7. Plum's center
8. "The Bells" writer
9. Land east of the Atl.
10. Repudiate
11. Court event
12. Symphonic poem creator
13. Jazz pianist Chick
18. "__ Bully" (1965 hit)
23. Obelisk, say
24. Double Dutch equipment
25. Sang
26. Act as an arbiter
27. Gump of the comics
28. Chief: Prefix
29. Pout
30. Actress Negri
34. Rub the wrong way
35. Youngsters
36. "Doggone it!"
38. Many miles away
39. Play the siren
42. It must go on
43. Outfit
45. "Fantasia" creator
46. Bring to a point
47. Bouquet
48. Checkroom problem
49. Manipulate
52. Did the butterfly, e.g.
53. Make waves?
54. Host
57. Spleen
58. Early sixth-century date
59. Côte-__, France
60. Have to pay back

ACROSS

1. Basketball Hall-of-Famer from the Celtics
8. A pop
11. About 5/8 of a mi.
14. Some patches
15. Oakland's county
17. Gentle pace
18. Greatly surpassed, with "over"
19. Mornings, for short
20. U.S. retailer since 1902
21. "General Hospital," e.g.
24. Bidding
25. "Trent's Last Case" author
28. Pick-me-up
32. Core
33. Grand achievement
34. Columnist Barrett
35. "Hold On Tight" rock grp.
36. Be in arrears
37. It has springs
40. Bering, e.g.: Abbr.
41. Spoils shares?
43. Lose control of a car
44. Marker
45. Money in the bank, say
47. "Petals in the Wind" author
49. Do a maître d's job
51. Cartoonist Peter
52. "U Can't Touch This" singer, 1990
55. Halloween decoration
57. Tenant farmer
58. Subdivision of a Roman legion
62. Pet carrier feature
63. Ruler's length
64. Jordan has a part in it: Abbr.
65. Reg. version
66. Noted children's book illustrator

DOWN

1. Tease
2. __-Magnon
3. Nudge
4. Recorded
5. "Cheers" regular
6. Slaughter in baseball
7. J.F.K. arrival
8. Like some fog
9. Take flight to unite?
10. Least experienced
11. "Show Boat" composer
12. Notion in Normandy
13. __ Luck
16. Personal counselor
20. Military vehicle
21. Cayuga relative
22. Dome opening, in architecture
23. Ones overseeing monk-y business?
24. Sad
26. Cpl. or sgt.
27. Stranded motorist's need
29. More of a busybody
30. Around, so to speak
31. Old-time Met tenor
37. 32-card game
38. Brooch part
39. Tack on
42. Angel
43. Melee memento
46. Musical speeds
47. Went off at an angle
48. Approve
50. Sensed odors, old-style
52. Thom __ shoe stores
53. Newborn's place
54. Wedding dance
55. Judge's seat
56. Freshly
58. Back-to-work time: Abbr.
59. "The Haunted Palace" poet
60. Auction amount
61. Biblical verb ending

ACROSS

1. Have __ at
4. Pickles
10. Still sleeping
14. 16-year-old's desire
15. Garb
16. Island east of Java
17. Little Bighorn victor
19. Wild plum
20. "__ bitten, twice shy"
21. Sportscaster Merlin
22. Isn't able to
23. Common document requiring signature
25. "The Dark at the Top of the Stairs" writer
26. Garb
27. Eat
30. Leave a mark on
31. "Seinfeld" regular
34. Coagulates
35. Meat-ban cause
39. Be gaga over
40. Chuck of Watergate fame
41. Protection: Var.
42. L. Ron Hubbard's "__ Doc Methuselah"
43. Hauls (off)
48. Collections of anecdotes
49. Warm up before cooking
51. Long-necked instrument
52. Driver's woe

55. "Fernando" group
56. Mideast chief
57. De Niro classic
59. TV ad
60. Intro
61. Charge
62. Tobacco holders
63. Little bloodsucker
64. N.Y.C. highway, with "the"

DOWN

1. International agreement
2. Win
3. Delphi figure
4. Mom's month
5. Spirit of a people
6. Lifted, so to speak
7. "Dear" ones
8. Irish language
9. Surveyed
10. Graph coordinate
11. Bank amounts
12. Stretch
13. They practice girth control
18. A lot of pizzazz?
24. "Hold on __!"
27. Move obliquely
28. Les États-__
29. Cash in Cancún
32. Crazy in Cancún
33. Military truant
35. 1980's TV hit
36. Pilot's field

37. Where to get your last licks in?
38. Suffix with infer
39. Most heartfelt
44. Famed whaler
45. Say no to
46. Put off till another day
47. Less fresh
49. Computer order
50. Descartes and others
52. Cavern, in poetry
53. Swimmer's practice
54. Author James
58. College test, for short

428 FRENCH FOOD *by Stephanie Spadaccini*

ACROSS

1. Game of chance
6. Exit quickly
10. Part of a profit calculation
14. Kind of surgery
15. Red shade
16. 1983 award for David Mamet
17. Indian __
18. Medicinal plant
19. Riviera city
20. French wine made the old-fashioned way?
23. Sphere
24. Rolaids rival
25. Machine part?
28. Birthday-to-birthday span
31. Dom DeLuise sitcom "__ Luck"
34. Mine, in Amiens
36. Newsman Elie
38. Loathsome individuals
40. French delicacy served at McDonald's?
43. Jazzman Shapiro
44. Valley
45. "It __ Necessarily So"
46. Young man
48. Beggar's duds
50. "Hel-l-l-lp!"
51. Plus others
53. Ill. neighbor
55. Low-cal version of a hi-cal French dessert?
61. Pound of literature
63. __ Duro Canyon, Tex.
64. Salinger's "Franny and __"
65. Become frayed
66. What feuding families may get
67. Kind of cycle
68. Whirlpool
69. Moist
70. TV actress Christine

DOWN

1. Group, as of votes
2. Apiece
3. In a muddle
4. "Cool!"
5. Obstinate
6. The lady of the Haus
7. Downtime
8. W.W. II vessel
9. Quite a sight
10. Pioneer's wagon
11. Life sentences?
12. "__ 'em, Rover!"
13. Driving aid?
21. Draw __ on (aim at)
22. Ham it up
25. Family man
26. Bradley and Sharif
27. Get-rich-quick method
29. Not up
30. Hand over (to)
32. Ganges garb
33. "A Bell for __"
35. A going concern?
37. 1970 Kinks hit
39. Some jets
41. Busybody
42. Labor grp. since 1900
47. Went "blah-blah-blah"
49. Be very hot
52. Split
54. 1988 Olympics site
55. Alum
56. Whole bunch
57. Trinitron TV maker
58. "Beloved" author Morrison
59. Genteel affairs
60. Jane who becomes Mrs. Rochester
61. Wool gatherer
62. Brit's finale

GYMNASTICS by Rich Norris

ACROSS

1. Antisubversive grp. until 1975
5. Adagio, for one
10. Edges
14. It broke up in Dec. 1991
15. Available
16. Switch ending
17. Jailed
19. Phone, slangily
20. Kit item
21. Rhythmic ballroom dance
22. Map feature
25. Correct
29. Actor Michael
30. Fixed
31. Kind of fingerprint
32. Disagreeable encounters
34. Extinct kiwi relative
35. Gifts for the betrothed
42. A pop
43. Finnan __ (smoked fish dish)
44. Rap sheet letters
47. Turner and others
49. Throw with effort
50. Mattress alternative?
52. Weatherman Al
53. Fight site
54. Uzbekistan's __ Sea
56. Arrived
57. Tot's riding toy
63. Subj. of state regulation
64. Daughter of William the Conqueror
65. Moola
66. Cainites, e.g.
67. Hunt in Hollywood
68. It may come easily to hand

DOWN

1. Focus
2. Employment
3. Burn residue
4. Standards
5. Bustle
6. As a whole, in Le Havre
7. 1959 Kingston Trio hit
8. Expected result
9. Wife of Saturn
10. Kind of center
11. Pressed
12. 1975–76 National League M.V.P. Joe
13. California wine region
18. Making mention of
21. "Hazel" cartoonist Key
22. Concerning
23. Friend or foe, e.g.
24. Vocalized
26. Figure
27. 1982 sci-fi film
28. Moor
33. Dark brown
36. List
37. Obviously enthusiastic
38. Democracy, for one
39. Sask. neighbor
40. "Had enough?"
41. One in the futures market?
44. Calculator of a kind
45. Dojo activity
46. Lacking vitality
47. Norris Dam project: Abbr.
48. Arab home
51. Genuflected
55. "A Bridge Too Far" author
57. "A likely story!"
58. Shelley work
59. __ canto
60. Popular 20's auto
61. Done with a wink, maybe
62. W.W. II command

430 BODY OF ART? *by Nancy Salomon*

ACROSS
1. Elbowroom
6. One of the 3 B's
10. Kellogg Foods brand
14. Plant in Flanders fields
15. Double-reed woodwind
16. Prod
17. Mac maker
18. Start of a quip
20. I-95, e.g.: Abbr.
21. Fritter away
23. Kind of down
24. "One __ customer"
25. Actress Alicia
26. Two-toned horses
28. Quip, part 2
33. Sighs of distress
34. A lot of a drill sergeant's drill
35. Hoo-ha
36. Take a chance on
39. It may help you "catch up"
40. Fret
41. Shade of blond
42. Modern summons
44. Genetic letters
46. Quip, part 3
52. Boated, maybe
53. Chop down
54. Maiden name preceder
55. Actress Gaynor
57. Matrix
59. How the Des Moines R. flows
60. End of the quip
62. A lot

64. Big __ elephant
65. Result of venting?
66. Part of a spur
67. Five-time Wimbledon champ
68. Session with an M.D.
69. Nuts

DOWN
1. Side in the Peloponnesian War
2. Beer opener
3. Telethon, e.g.
4. Pfc.'s boss
5. Baloney
6. Potted tree
7. Help with the heist
8. Whitewashes
9. Giggling sound
10. Prodding
11. Spot overlooking center court, say
12. Way in
13. Fungus byproduct
19. Brings up
22. Aardvark fare
27. Passé
29. "All systems go"
30. Guys
31. Wordsworth work
32. "Get going!"
36. Wet behind the ears
37. __ Kabibble
38. Have a good day on the links
39. Can't wait to have

40. Word with whip or rip
42. Kind of acid
43. Snake charmee
44. Mother of Hera
45. The Big Apple
47. Lounging around
48. There may be a catch in it
49. Powerful combination
50. Look for again
51. With vigor
55. Ancient kingdom east of the Dead Sea
56. In that case
58. Invitation letters
61. Chicken __ king
63. Rock's __ Fighters

GROUP PROJECT by Alan Arbesfeld

ACROSS

1. Reprimand, with "out"
5. Capital on the Willamette River
10. Full mark
14. Inter __
15. Three-time A.L. batting champ
16. Relax
17. TV series?
20. Made hot?
21. Intertwined
22. City half an hour north of Des Moines
25. Mentally twisted
26. Facial movement
29. Off the job
31. Football squad
35. Mountain in Crete
36. Slumber rumble
38. William Howard Taft's alma mater
39. World Series?
43. Popular restaurant chain, briefly
44. Tear
45. D.C. summer clock setting
46. Spoonful, say
49. Virgin Islands, e.g.: Abbr.
50. __ Plaines, Ill.
51. Mideast hot spot
53. Prescription info
55. Widespread
58. City ESE of Rome
62. Mini-series?
65. Fiend
66. No longer ineffable
67. A party to
68. Unloading site
69. Puts on display, with "out"
70. Guitar accessory

DOWN

1. Word with blue or sea
2. Plenty
3. Bowery denizen
4. Eric Clapton hit with a seemingly endless chorus
5. Assn.
6. Like
7. Many a twist
8. Rogers's partner
9. The Barber of the old Polo Grounds
10. Stigma
11. Angel's delight
12. Big name in menswear
13. Neighbor of Guat.
18. Negligent
19. Table salt
23. Mystery writer Buchanan
24. Vegas equipment
26. Shrinking
27. Potato choice
28. Seasonal song
30. Appear suddenly
32. Like many barns
33. Give the slip
34. Settles down
37. Committed a faux pas
40. Kind of group
41. Detective Wolfe
42. Against
47. Pitcher Hershiser
48. Disney, to ABC
52. Gulf emirate
54. Set of values
55. "Thank Heaven for Little Girls" musical
56. Peut-__ (maybe, in France)
57. Fancy wheels
59. Macbeth's burial place
60. Cut off
61. __ extra cost
62. Cut (off)
63. Take home
64. Gridiron gains: Abbr.

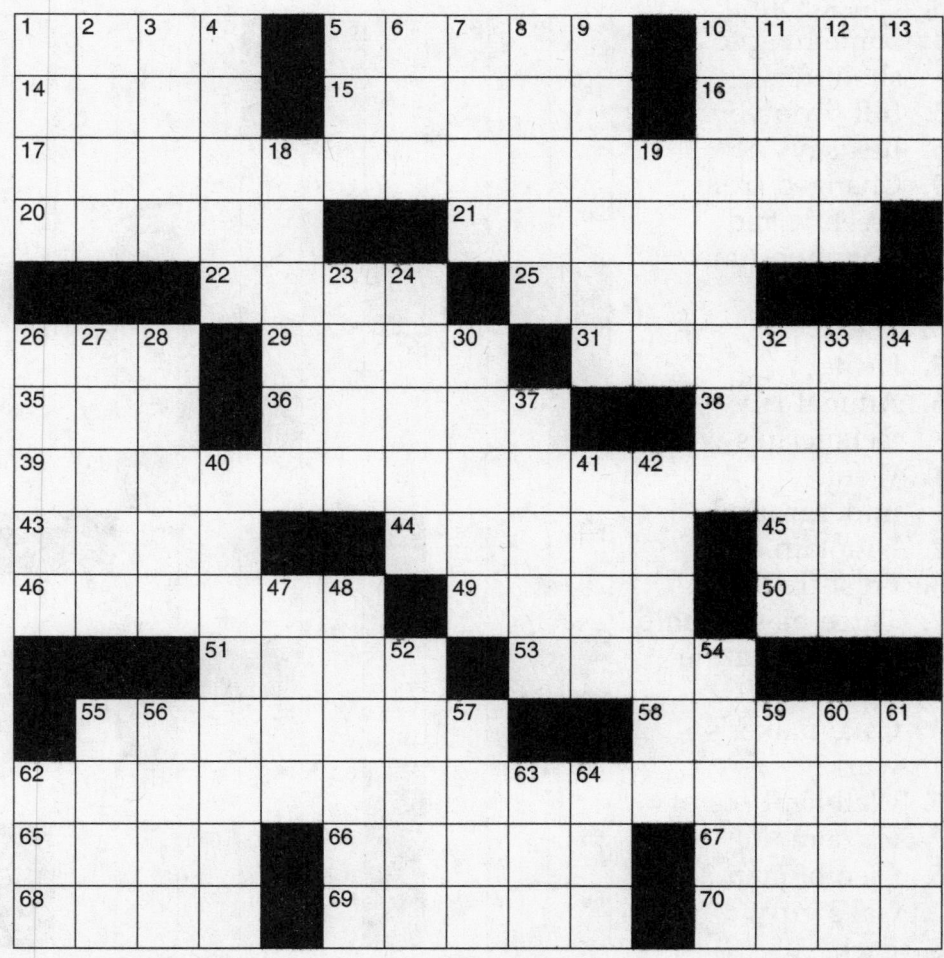

432 "IT'S A LIVING" by Nancy Salomon

ACROSS
1. Compact data holders
6. Do something
11. Highest deg.
14. Work __ (code of the dedicated)
15. Causing goose bumps
16. Bud's buddy
17. Fashion designer's work?
19. Total idiot
20. One way to cook spaghetti
21. Drill master?
23. Wife of Charlie Chaplin
25. A billion years
26. Sequel writer's work?
33. Clock sound
34. Something to shoot for
35. It'll drop your jaw
36. Just says no
39. Changed from green to red
42. Common lunch time
43. "Lid"
45. Heater
46. Animal lab technician's work?
51. Went underground
52. Fountain order
53. Frost-free zone
57. Three-masted ship
62. Wet behind the ears
63. Cake maker's work?
65. Well-kept secret, for some
66. Cleo of jazz
67. Gal's guy
68. Each
69. Wrapped up
70. Span. misses

DOWN
1. Ten, for openers
2. "__ be a cold day . . ."
3. Like Clydesdales
4. Wind instrument?
5. Dopes
6. Forward
7. Electrifying swimmer
8. Rainless
9. Movie theater
10. High schooler
11. Hardly beauty pageant types
12. "Bonanza" brother
13. Run a cloth over
18. Kind of collar
22. Delivery from Santa
24. Nile biter
26. Dictation taker
27. 50's leader
28. 201, classically
29. Black gunk
30. ". . . __ shall die" ("It Must Be Him" lyric)
31. 1936 track gold medalist
32. Night spot
36. Neighbor of Bulg.
37. Crack, so to speak
38. Hero
40. Vatican figures
41. First lady
44. Filling danger
47. One of the buddies of "Bosom Buddies"
48. Safe to consume
49. Like some vows
50. Troubles
53. Green flanker
54. Vogue
55. "The Godfather" co-star
56. Veer out of control
58. Place on piles
59. Bombard
60. Scat artist Fitzgerald
61. Vitamin bottle info
64. Vane dir.

ACROSS

1. __ Damon of "Saving Private Ryan"
5. Site of the oldest church in France
9. Bones
13. Teacher of Heifetz
14. Queens's __ Stadium
15. The whole gamut
16. Supercomputer pioneer
17. Electoral test
19. Hold up
20. Certain playing marble
21. Bout decision
23. One of the Musketeers
25. Long time
26. Prepare, as a hook
27. Old-fashioned wizards
28. Club alternative
29. Man of many words
30. Film feline
31. __ alai
32. Savory fungi
33. It's nowhere
36. Skipped past with a remote
39. Remote targets?
40. Large bulrush
44. With force
45. "Around the World in 72 Days" writer
46. Have food delivered
47. Pew area
48. Charge
49. "Fighting" Big Ten team
50. Pipe connector
51. Firefighter's breathing apparatus

53. Kicker
54. Slacker
56. Author O'Flaherty
57. Like an 8-Down
58. Malarial fever
59. Cornell of Cornell University
60. Vacation-planning aids
61. J.F.K. arrivals
62. Girls in gowns

DOWN

1. Yarn work
2. Dawnlike
3. Brewers' needs
4. Essay
5. Spars
6. City near Padua
7. Storied homebuilders
8. Big fan

9. Late-night name
10. "What was __ think?"
11. Kind of industry
12. "God strengthens" in Hebrew
18. Convert, with "over"
20. Start of a cheer
22. Giant Mel and family
24. Baked entree
26. School for bad lads
28. Many college grads
29. Seoul G.I.
31. Clampett patriarch, in 60's TV
32. Hosts, for short
34. Little red one

35. Arbutus, e.g.
36. Actor Billy of "Tombstone"
37. Mixture
38. St. Petersburg-born ballet star
41. Put to work
42. 3,500-year-old writing deciphered in 1953
43. Mysteries
45. Yankee Yogi and others
46. Caribou kin
48. Taradiddle
49. F.D.R.'s Interior Secretary
51. Comments further
52. __ above the rest
55. Sass
56. Put down the first card

434 ADD A LINE *by Manny Nosowsky*

ACROSS
1. Striplings
5. Storied rabbit
10. "That's __ to me!"
14. Sierra Club concern: Abbr.
15. One barred from a U.N. no-fly zone
16. Say again
17. How Oliver categorized his meals?
20. Smoothly change the subject
21. "__ always say . . ."
22. Say
23. Mets, Jets or Nets
25. California Grenache, e.g.
27. It might bring you up to scratch
30. Wrestling hold for a recluse?
35. __ number on
36. Zola heroine
37. Musically flowing
38. __ Haute, Ind.
40. They precede kicks, for short
42. Colchester's county
43. Ruler with a table
45. Biased type, briefly
47. Catsup catcher?
48. Organized bribery?
50. Full house, e.g.
51. Zone
52. Sticks around a stake
54. Big name in petroleum
57. Second notes
59. Dislike, and then some
63. Soil and soot?
66. Sacramento's __ Arena
67. Poor boy
68. Panache
69. Bolshevik target
70. Contemptible ones
71. Pattern of behavior

DOWN
1. Chair supports
2. Growing room
3. QB Flutie
4. Magnifying glass carrier, maybe
5. "Mamma __!"
6. Bulb, e.g.
7. Walks softly
8. Wiggle
9. The dark side
10. Rainy day reserves
11. Quito's country: Abbr.
12. "Come again?"
13. Step on it!
18. Rebel leader of '61
19. J. P. Morgan founded it
24. "That's it!"
26. Standard product
27. Bird marker, maybe
28. "__ is human"
29. Magna __
31. Spokes
32. Dreadlocks wearer, informally
33. Had a home-cooked meal
34. Went a round
36. Atomic particle
39. Concern for a blood typer
41. Traffic halter
44. Feel bad about
46. One or more
49. Come to the point?
50. Whence the word "golem"
53. Tatter
54. Get __ on the back
55. "The War of the Worlds" base
56. Boat in "Jaws"
58. Actor Morales
60. Hawaii's __ Bay
61. Neighbor of Saudi Arabia
62. Big part of many a family budget
64. Interjections of surprise
65. Bill, the Science Guy

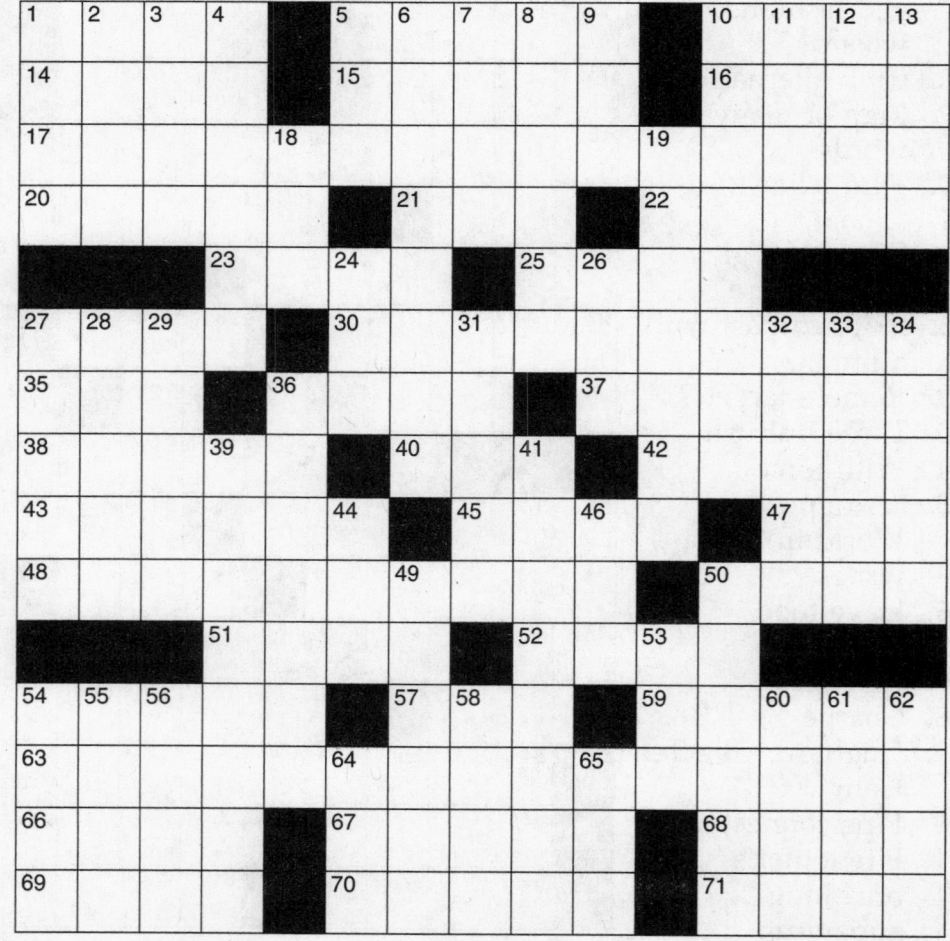

ACROSS

1. In __ (undisturbed)
5. Shindig
9. Acclamation
14. __ impasse
15. Ancestor of the Q'ero Indians
16. Everybody's opposite
17. Anklebones
18. Punkie
19. "Fiddler on the Roof" role
20. Nicolas Cage co-star, 1995
23. Kind of derby
24. Aimless
27. "Hands off!"
28. __ de León, Spain
30. Each
31. Direction at a scene's end
34. Southern dessert
37. Rhône feeder
39. Family card game
40. __ column (building support)
41. Tiny bankroll
44. Animation frames
45. "Nightline" name
46. Bathroom supply
47. Old English letter
49. Icelandic poet __ Sturluson
51. Assassination victim of 1940
55. Sullivan offering, inevitably
58. Long-armed zoo creature
60. Quarter-deck?
61. Playwright Connelly
62. Not solid-colored
63. He sang of Alice
64. Sigmund Freud's daughter
65. "Paradise Lost" character
66. Bill site
67. Capone chaser

DOWN

1. Fills up
2. Prefix with -phile
3. Actress Shire
4. 1964–65 World's Fair centerpiece
5. Major-leaguers
6. Take over
7. "Beat it!"
8. "Thirty days __ November . . ."
9. Captivate
10. Heart of Paris
11. Tomato
12. Whatever
13. Kicker's aid
21. Nancy Hanks's boy
22. Narcissist's love
25. Sam of "The Piano"
26. They're usually not good with tricks
28. Kind of column
29. Procrastinator's promise
31. Dukes
32. Pale
33. Toilette accessory
35. Pitch
36. Aristotle Onassis, notably
38. Gogo, in "Waiting for Godot"
42. Deer's scut
43. Iron-rich tonic
48. Follow
50. __-Wreck
51. Govt. promissory note
52. Fictional gunfighter
53. Typeface extensions
54. Community orgs.
56. Exam for college srs.
57. Cosmonaut Gagarin
58. Photo __
59. Its mouth is its biggest part

436 "THINKING MAN'S PUZZLE" *by Robert H. Wolfe*

ACROSS

1. Unguent
5. A prisoner may enter one
9. Russia's Sea of __
13. Omnium-gatherum
14. __ grudge (harbored resentment)
16. Slayton of Apollo 18
17. Thrashes
18. Perfectionist's aim
19. Progress impeder
20. Fear an English philosopher's family?
23. 40's war agcy.
24. "__ believe it!"
25. 1972 Broadway debut
27. 1965 Peace Prize recipient
30. Showily enthusiastic
32. Seoul soldier
33. Latin conjugation word
35. Gradually remove
38. Peace of mind
41. Anthology
43. Like a sleeping bag
44. Sofer of soaps
46. Suffix with guitar
47. Dundee design
49. Take turns
52. Massage parlor offering
54. Year in Marcus Aurelius's reign
56. Pulitzer-winning writer Akins
57. English philosopher not yet arrived?
62. White chip, often
64. Michael of "Flashdance"
65. Hayworth's royal hubby
66. Convoy components
67. Derby Stakes site
68. Chisholm Trail town
69. C.O.N.T.R.O.L. enemy
70. Eyelid problem
71. Puts on

DOWN

1. Barefaced
2. Banned spray
3. Greenish
4. Subway tunnel art, maybe
5. Communication from an Alexandrian philosopher?
6. Gave false hopes
7. Sophocles subject
8. One of the Aleutians
9. Spots
10. Fear of an ancient Greek philosopher?
11. Rain forest ruminant
12. Non-meat-eater
15. Beth's preceder
21. W.W. II gen.
22. Mythical bird-woman
26. __ passu (equally)
27. Orsk's river
28. "Don't look at me!"
29. Declaration about unhanding a German philosopher?
31. Heaps
34. Hess who was a dame
36. Composition of some clouds
37. Borgia in-law
39. Caboose
40. Tight as __
42. Era of a German philosopher?
45. Overlay, in a way
48. Delmonico alternative
50. Ab __ (from day one)
51. Teed off
52. __ National Forest, Ark.
53. Conquest of Croesus
55. "Quo Vadis?" director Mervyn
58. Cry over spilled milk
59. "That's awful!"
60. Kind of a drag
61. Bounds
63. River's path, possibly

ACROSS

1. See 28-Down
6. "Bleak House" girl and others
10. "A Passage to India" doctor
14. Book of prophecies
15. Heart
16. Oliver's request
17. Garden annual
18. Spanish direction
19. Children's author Blyton
20. Newsman's dramatic cry
23. Mason of "The Goodbye Girl"
24. It precedes 15
25. Greek gulf or city
27. Literary postscript
32. Rock stars' dates
36. Kind of terrier
38. Welcome to paradise?
39. Travolta film, 1989
42. Common trash can site
43. Con
44. A long time in México
45. Overpower
47. Troubadour's dawn song
49. "Grand"
51. Storm's cause, maybe
56. Heed sound advice
60. Incisiveness
61. Early 11th-century date
62. Vitality
63. Wall St. acronym
64. Park director's concern: Abbr.
65. Comb and comb and comb
66. Slightly tainted
67. Naysay
68. No longer in the closet

DOWN

1. Gulf
2. Popular landscaping plant
3. New York's __ Place
4. Oozes
5. Kitt who wrote "A Tart Is Not a Sweet"
6. Humorist/illustrator Jon
7. Is circumspect
8. Player in a dome
9. Stow, as cargo
10. University town west of Cedar Rapids
11. Commercial __
12. Colored part of a ball?
13. British ending
21. Draconian
22. Calyx part
26. Boxing stat
28. With 1-Across, star of Broadway's "The Women," 1936
29. Meat purchase
30. Cousin of "whoops!"
31. Comedian's stock
32. Tickled
33. Heracles' captive maiden
34. Play a round
35. __-Ball (arcade game)
37. Bibliographical abbr.
40. "Easy Rider" biker
41. Color appropriate for 7-Down
46. Like this puzzle
48. Syrian hub
50. In reserve
52. Pacific republic
53. Seagull spot
54. "Long time __"
55. Ceaselessly
56. Stew bean
57. Columnist's squib
58. Like a Playmate
59. Slick
60. Do a supermarket job

(438) LETTER PERFECT *by Manny Nosowsky*

ACROSS

1. Willing spirit?
6. One who may be caught off base
10. Thin veneer
14. Combat zone
15. Wellington resident
16. Concern for 90's investors
17. Stickers
20. U.S./Canada's __ Canals
21. Media attention
22. Skin damager, for short
23. Table-hop
25. Penetrate, with "through"
26. High-grade
33. "Black Orpheus" setting
34. Fill another teacup
35. Bide-__
36. Marty's friend in "Marty"
38. 70's kidnappers
39. Bombing, as a comic
40. World War II weapon
41. De-icer
43. Pants part
44. Artful cover
47. Hot items
48. She played Maid Marian in "Robin Hood," 1991
49. Offend, in a way
52. Promise to pay
54. "Give __ break"
57. Suggestion for solving this puzzle
61. Lotion base
62. Peter, Paul or Mary
63. Scalawag
64. Latest word
65. Spirit
66. Kind of bath or boat

DOWN

1. Dental problem corrected by braces
2. God offended by Daphnis
3. Stout fellow?
4. Tips, e.g.
5. Seine filler
6. Analogous
7. Split second
8. Part of 52-Across
9. Cordial
10. Referees ensure it
11. Mallorca or Menorca, e.g.
12. Emblem of innocence, in art
13. Certain service
18. Mischief-maker
19. Part of the eye
24. Hungarian name equivalent to Amory
25. Bellyache
26. One of a famous trio
27. Doctor-turned-wordsmith
28. Result
29. Grinder
30. "__ not yield" (Macbeth to Macduff, unwisely)
31. It may be held in a church
32. Burglar
33. File
37. Covers
39. Snare, maybe
41. Shaded, like some 50's cars
42. Play with horses?
45. Start of many an exclamation from Robin
46. Kid's rebuttal
49. African model
50. Shade of blue
51. Fall on Pikes Peak?
52. "My Friend" at the movies
53. Out-of-doors
55. Halftime lead, e.g.
56. Prefix with plane
58. American rival: Abbr.
59. MGM motto start
60. Rabbinical sch.

ZIP-A-DEE-DOO-DAH *by Alan Arbesfeld*

ACROSS

1. 95501
9. Smiling, for now
15. Topical
16. Avoidance
17. 97401
18. 16501
19. Tongue's locale
20. Actress Thompson
22. Dict. listing
23. Telephoned
27. Drop shot
29. Rosemary portrayer
32. 54703
37. Odd
39. R. J. Reynolds brand
40. River of Belgium
41. Theme of this puzzle?
44. Lover of fur?
45. Headed off on
47. Very hot
49. 80110
52. Give the once-over
53. Majestic swimmer
54. Case for small scissors
56. Stomach
59. Group
61. __ Nostra
65. 73701
67. 08818
71. Aplenty
72. Madness
73. Go to
74. 79910

DOWN

1. Summers abroad
2. "Nope"
3. __ Park, Queens
4. Arabian title
5. Kal __ Foods, Inc.
6. Put away
7. A.F.L.'s partner
8. Field size, maybe
9. Lack of vitality
10. Actor Rick
11. Prefix with directional
12. Pleads
13. Perceive
14. __ of admissions
21. Year in the reign of Edward VI
24. Atmosphere: Prefix
25. Reputation
26. Southernmost of the Marianas
28. Big name in cheese
29. Wishy-washy reply
30. "The Wild Duck" playwright
31. Lay __ (flop)
33. Mild cigar
34. "Dallas" Miss
35. Pipsqueak
36. Portrait
38. Certain exams
42. French antiseptic
43. Milk: Prefix
46. Recent arrival
48. Trifle
50. Threw four balls at
51. Plastic __ Band
55. They stand for something
56. Prefix with store
57. Sci. course
58. Weaken
60. Transfer
62. Aware of
63. Huffy state
64. Sophocles tragedy
66. Universal John
68. "Runaway" singer __ Shannon
69. Mischievous one
70. Pirate's home, with "the"

(440) ENDLESS SUMMER *by David J. Kahn*

ACROSS

1. 60's accessories
6. Insult
10. Debutantes' affairs
14. "A Room With __"
15. Certain securities deal
16. Release
17. 23-Across hit
19. Subject of many Sanskrit epics
20. Handle-shaped
21. Nantucket resident, maybe
23. 1988 inductees into the Rock and Roll Hall of Fame
25. Where Euboea is
27. Some can dig it
28. Low
29. Stolen loot
32. Pushes
36. Perennial 23-Across concert opener
40. Kind of pad
41. One-word advice
42. Bring into play
43. Angelo or Antonio, e.g.
45. Pointed feature
48. 23-Across hit
53. Volunteer
54. TV western actor
58. Not fully shut
59. 23-Across hit
61. "Coriolanus" setting
62. It may be left in a locker
63. Wild
64. Pair
65. Repeater?
66. Metaphor or irony, e.g.

DOWN

1. Rum-laced cake
2. Author __ S. Connell
3. Put-ons?
4. Campaign event
5. Wrap
6. Mrs., abroad
7. Buy alternative
8. Sleep disorder
9. Gambling mecca
10. Thiamine deficiency woe
11. Brazilian novelist Jorge
12. British salt
13. General's pride
18. Come back again
22. Sign of indifference
24. Lincoln had one
25. Attack
26. Cameo, say
28. Roast leaders
30. Pizzeria __ (fast-food chain)
31. Fast talk
33. Fit of shivering, in dialect
34. Threatening word
35. Moscow-to-Volgograd dir.
37. Heartened
38. Gillette products
39. Like some music
44. Alternative to AOL or CompuServe
46. Wandering
47. Hide seeker?
48. Was informed of
49. Waiter's word
50. Guanaco's cousin
51. "All systems go!"
52. Bird with an S-shaped neck
55. Architect Saarinen
56. Lose it
57. Seafood entree
60. Mouths

ACROSS
1. Quarrel
5. Twenty-one words
10. Warp
14. Cherry __
15. Overthrow, e.g.
16. Capture on video
17. Ouida's "__ of Flanders"
18. Exurb
20. Onion servings
22. Suffix with final or fatal
23. Site of Texas College
24. Atlantic City event
26. "Fat chance!"
28. Fantasize
30. Standing
35. With 45-Across, a 1976 Eagles hit
38. Noggins
39. Footnote note
40. Do schoolwork?
42. What Band-Aids aid
43. Golden Horde member
45. See 35-Across
47. City south of Salem
48. Printing flourish
49. "Princess __" (1884 premiere)
51. Some Fertile Crescent residents
55. Opposer of Cortés
59. Bug killer, briefly
61. Make mischief
62. Madonna's first top 10 song
65. Harassed
66. Washerful
67. Old hull caulking

68. Actress Swenson
69. "Frasier" honor
70. Systems of waist removal?
71. Shrinking

DOWN
1. Line of cliffs
2. Lecterns
3. "Moving right __ . . ."
4. Milieu of the stressed-out
5. Playboy Mansion name
6. Peeve
7. Speaker of note
8. Billing cycle, often
9. Fraction of a joule
10. Command to Fido
11. Auto engineer Benz
12. Foil's heavier cousin
13. Erode
19. Pre-op inhalant, once
21. Hindu outfit
25. Not entirely happy
27. It takes a bow
29. Zoo barriers
31. Trade area of expanding importance
32. Coin word
33. South American monkey
34. Down __ (Maine)

35. Marathoner's stat
36. "__ Ben Adhem"
37. Kind of snake or crab
41. Roasted item
44. In the cooler
46. Turkish money
50. Runner-up to Ike
52. Make amends
53. Elbow
54. Command to Fido
55. Proficient
56. Really move
57. Alpine transport
58. Countercurrent
60. High ground in Dutch lowlands
63. Fishing aid
64. German river

(442) HARD AND SOFT by Cathy Millhauser

ACROSS
1. Wrap
5. Scrap
9. Sparkle
14. Common rhyme scheme
15. Mayor Dinkins's predecessor
16. Coronet
17. Choose one of two gas forms?
20. Connecticut River town
21. __ Maria liqueur
22. Not give __
23. Kind of bay
26. Poker game
28. Grand you earn, old-style?
34. King David's instrument
35. Author Beattie
36. Yale of Yale University
38. Prohibition __
39. Hoffman and Streep, in a 1979 film
42. "Just kidding!"
43. __ Martin cars
45. Airport approximation
46. Mideast capital
47. Part of a Pilgrim's anatomy lesson?
51. Metric prefix
52. Rex's stout detective
53. Let go
56. Noisy trains
58. Caddies' offerings
62. "Do that vowel over, Kojak"?
66. Poster boys, maybe
67. Pitcher Hideo
68. Falsified
69. 1964 Olympics site
70. Times that try parents' souls
71. Geriatric Jedi master

DOWN
1. May in New Jersey, e.g.
2. "The Mikado" attire
3. Basics
4. Occupies
5. Word with water or jet
6. Olla
7. Sieben follower
8. Belief in God
9. Berlioz's "Nuit d'__"
10. It went coed 8/24/96, with "The"
11. Bert who was a Leo, aptly
12. Department
13. Field cover
18. Withdrawal
19. Pro __
24. Flat cleaner
25. Hawaiian coffee
27. Banjos' kin
28. Former ABC sitcom
29. Grating
30. Emulate Cicero
31. Like some goals, sadly
32. Where Moses got the word
33. Flip-flop
37. Its motto is "Industry"
39. Kind of jerk
40. People: Prefix
41. Actress Martha
44. Neat
46. Soon
48. "Body Count" rapper
49. Mum
50. The Fates, e.g.
53. Glassmaking ingredient
54. Overhaul
55. Furry "Star Wars" creature
57. Put in the hold
59. Wheeling's river
60. Financial aid criterion
61. Kind of jerk
63. Prefix with -prene
64. Medical provider grp.
65. Daybreak deity

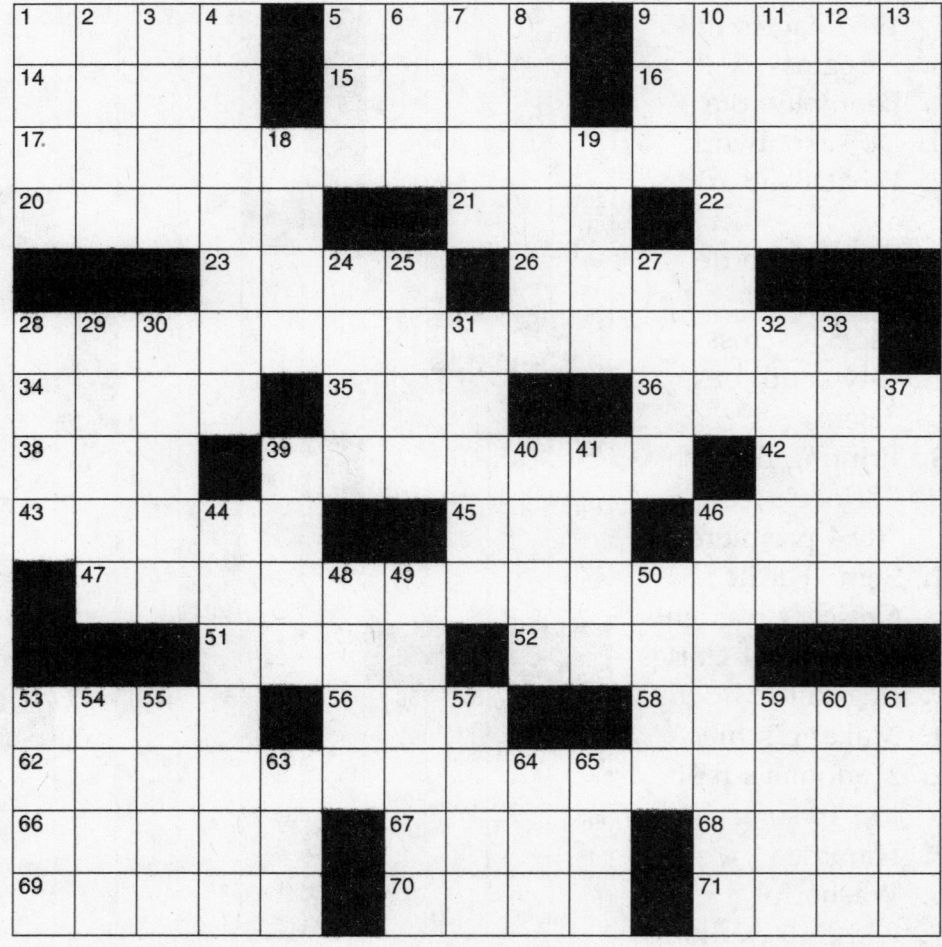

AM I BLUE? *by Nancy Salomon*

ACROSS

1. Sentimental
11. "Diary of __ Housewife"
15. With 37- and 67-Across, a question
16. Hootenanny sight
17. Swords, after conversion
18. Prime the pot
19. Bruise preventers
20. Big night
21. Couric of "Today"
23. Pacific's counterpart in W.W. II: Abbr.
24. Detroit's Joe Louis Sports __
26. Brings up
28. Tried to keep one's seat
30. Unsatisfying outcome
32. Bee chaser?
33. Noise of the lambs
35. Peak seen from the Ionian Sea
36. Well-kept secret, for some
37. See 15-Across
42. Sorority letter
43. Low islands
44. Common girl's middle name
45. See 57-Across
46. Otto I's realm: Abbr.
47. Not robust-looking
51. Wise guy
53. Graph measure
57. With 45-Across, try to get
58. Voting groups
60. Defunct sports org. since 1976
61. Amorous skunk Le Pew
62. It's a wrap

63. Sabotaged, in a way
66. While away the time
67. See 15-Across
68. Western tribe
69. Pilots must pass it

DOWN

1. Not a guzzler
2. Recently
3. Author Dostoyevsky
4. Pulls
5. Child carrier
6. Shade of yellow
7. "__ a dream": King
8. "Two Women" co-star, 1961
9. Scrape (out)
10. PC place
11. Let up
12. More than crazy
13. Bruce Wayne, to Batman
14. Singer Joey with the 60's Starliters
22. Three before seven
24. Lawless
25. "__ way!" ("You go, girl!")
27. Student of palms
29. Aladdin's monkey
31. Like the U.N.
34. Way off
35. Signals to speak up
37. Pound sounds
38. Hot-dog
39. Give a sermon
40. Some electrical junctions
41. Old comic "Out __ Way"
48. Means
49. Driver's switch
50. "You __ bother!"
52. Double agents
54. Dockworker
55. Having a lot to lose
56. Seine city
59. Brewski
61. British P.M., 1783–1801
62. Asian __
64. Excluding
65. High points: Abbr.

444 TWO FIVES *by David J. Kahn*

ACROSS

1. Finish a suit?
7. Steak style
14. Between here and there
16. Floor cover
17. Combination
18. Decorating with crinkled paper
19. Weekly since 1955, with "The"
21. Saison d'—
22. Actor Santoni
23. Washington V.I.P. Jordan
27. Bread and whisky
29. Seventh-century date
31. Naughts-and-crosses failure
32. Sensitivity
35. Fettered
38. Washington Memorial dedicatees
42. Not benched, in hockey
43. Catchall abbr.
44. Realtor's offering
45. Non-P.C. letter opening
47. Frau's spot
51. Blessing precursor
54. Percolate slowly
57. A, in France
58. Flame tender of myth
61. Reception helper
64. Dehydration remedy
65. Lover in dire straits?
66. Sink
67. Five-year periods
68. Tittered

DOWN

1. Three-time Cy Young Award winner
2. Ill will
3. "Rose of —"
4. Sound
5. Longtime Hoosier Senator
6. French level
7. Crunchy dish
8. Pushy upstart
9. Model Gabrielle
10. Candle
11. Jackie's "O"
12. Smuggle
13. Bacon accompanier
15. Touch up
20. Conversely
24. Brunch item
25. Team mates?
26. Some auction bids
28. One of Adam's clan
30. Dvořák's Symphony No. 9 — minor
33. Actress Sue — Langdon
34. Causes trouble, in old-fashioned talk
36. Reason for a do-over?
37. Mischievous
38. Crimson Tide rival
39. Apprised of
40. Suffix with leather
41. Bell Atlantic competitor
46. Advertises
48. Common mineral in rocks
49. Busy
50. Had a hunch
52. Gala, e.g.
53. "The Prisoner of —"
55. Put out
56. Put out
59. Crew on the high seas
60. Babe's name
61. Piz Bernina is one
62. Wedding page word
63. Whip but good

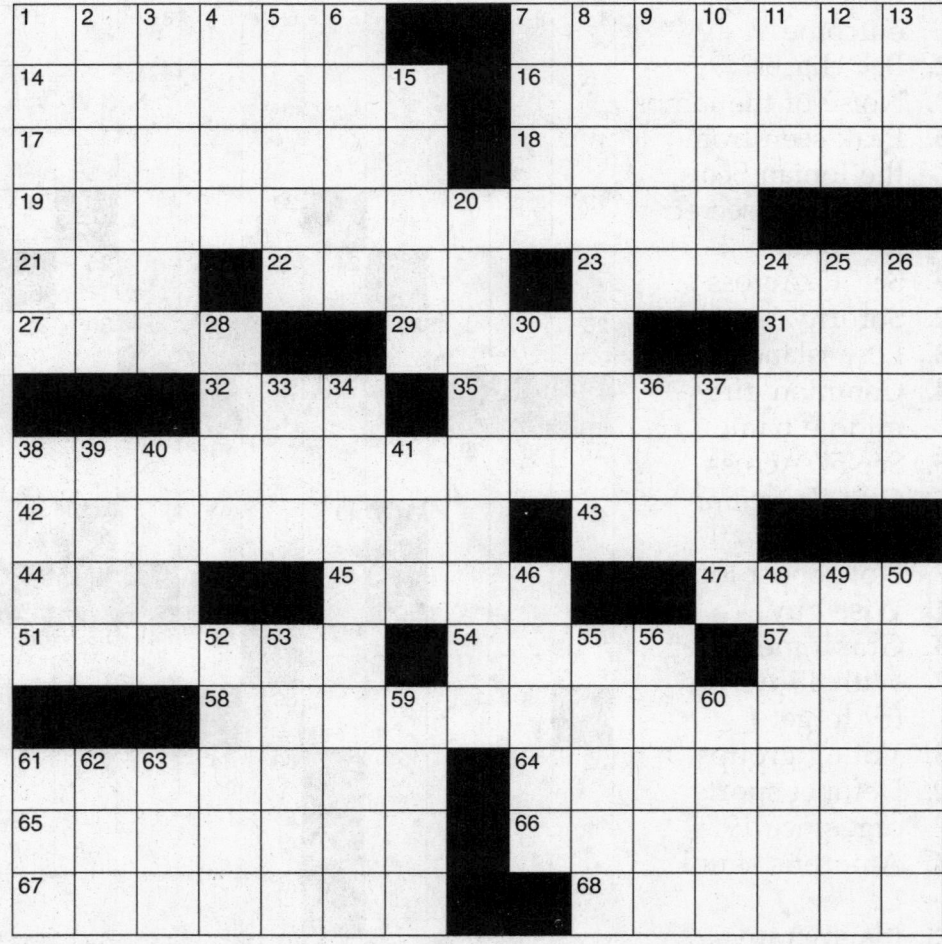

ACROSS

1. Opposite of 61-Across
4. Lunatic, often
9. "The Man Without __" (1993 film)
14. Grp. behind the 1998 Nobel Peace Prize
15. Take the honey and run
16. Spread abroad, as a rumor
17. Harden
18. Definitely no Einstein
19. Prudential rival
20. Always, to a cowboy?
23. Prefix with logical
24. Epitaph beginning
25. Chew the fat
27. Degermed, in a way
31. Sled driver, maybe
33. Car wash machines
36. Piccadilly Circus statue
37. Dickens classic, to a cowboy?
42. Runners
43. Cleverly intricate
44. Crocheted coverlet
47. Perennially popular game books
51. Give a hard time, slangily
52. Stewart's role in "Harvey"
55. Village Voice award
56. Murder mystery setting, to a cowboy?
61. Back
62. Dismal, to Donne
63. Like Gen. Powell
64. Some Strads
65. Kind of element
66. Cap material?
67. Twiddles one's thumbs
68. Vaccinator's supply
69. LL.D. holder

DOWN

1. Heavyweight
2. Major name in frozen foods
3. Auto maker Chrysler
4. Fictional secret agent Williams
5. Baseball family name
6. Maelstrom
7. Eocene, for one
8. Zellweger of "Jerry Maguire"
9. Lets up
10. At no cost, in Germany
11. Helicopter's predecessor
12. Gum flavor
13. Pilot's announcement, for short
21. Poppycock
22. __-1900 (old)
26. Director
28. Paint base
29. Abbr. stamped on a food label
30. Do it!
32. "Lake Wobegon Days" writer
34. TV pioneer
35. Opposite of 61-Across
37. Not reluctant
38. Made new alterations
39. Pale yellowish-white
40. Toothy grp.?
41. Smidge
45. Lady-killer
46. __'wester
48. Gibraltar's locale
49. Split
50. Sonnet ending
53. Board measure
54. Irish port
57. Contemporary of Dashiell
58. Half-moon tide
59. Name often seen above a star
60. Chief exec.
61. Area of coll. study

446 FOR THE BIRDS by David J. Kahn

ACROSS
1. Some caste members
5. Take down __
9. Art drawing
14. Reason for an NC-17 rating
15. It may be braided
16. "Mourning Becomes Electra" brother and namesakes
17. Movie princess
18. Peter, but not the saint
20. Francis, but not the saint
22. Floor-making factory
23. "I'll second that"
24. "Gunsmoke" shower
27. Unproductive
29. Big bill
31. Loose
33. Garth Brooks, notably
34. Christopher, but not the saint
39. 1925 trial name
40. Low grade
41. Take out for the shelves, say
42. One way to stop
48. Smallest Can. province
49. Unfortunate
52. Bryan, for one
53. Stephen, but not the saint
57. John, but not the saint
59. Vivacity
60. How doughnuts are prepared
61. Provide for free, informally
62. Baseball's Brogna

63. Not say directly
64. Cap site
65. Vessel with a load

DOWN
1. Metal tips
2. Sartre classic
3. Not quite a run
4. Attesting official
5. Popular houseplant
6. Clip
7. Admittance
8. Glittery stone
9. Chesterfield, for one
10. The Phantom of the Opera
11. Wreath feature
12. Like Bach's Sonata No. 3 for violin

13. Pale blond
19. Some Monopoly purchases: Abbr.
21. ". . . __ shall die" (1967 lyric)
25. Bingo call
26. Sunday spiel: Abbr.
28. Put away
29. Unnerve
30. And never
32. Marked, as a ballot
33. Device for recording speech
34. Bad marks
35. "Lost in Space" family name
36. U.S.N. rank
37. Witch's work

38. Bill Gates, e.g.: Abbr.
39. Banquet
43. Curved figure
44. Stuntmen
45. Emphatic, in a way
46. Rainier locale
47. Up to this time, once
49. Twinkling of an eye
50. Smart one
51. Popular mustard
54. Ear-related
55. Repellent
56. "__ here"
57. Conrad title character
58. Prefix with vocal

ACROSS

1. Science fiction award
5. Obi-Wan, for one
9. E-mail nuisance
13. Football Hall-of-Famer __ Page
14. Pulls some levers
15. Florence flooder
16. "Alas!" sighed the jean legs, "__."
19. Character actor Wynn
20. Confirm
21. Bonkers
22. Some blues
24. Unkept yard, e.g.
26. Chase scene?
29. Trompe l'__ (art illusion)
31. Minerva's symbol
32. "Big deal," said the pockets, "__."
37. Fabled loser
38. Speak of love
39. Scheme
41. "Oh dear!" cried the waist, "__."
46. Home in space
47. Big video game name
48. Model-turned-actress Carol
49. 1997 Spielberg movie
53. Carrel filler
55. "Far out!"
56. Those of Juan's things
58. Melodic Melba
62. "I hear you!" replied the seat, "__."
65. Like some antibiotics
66. Isabel II, e.g.
67. Irk-aholic?
68. It's under layers
69. Former Orr teammate, familiarly
70. The terrible __

DOWN

1. Peddle
2. 1997 Peter Fonda title role
3. Yielded
4. Uninterruptedly
5. "Mud"
6. 1998 erupter
7. Probe (into)
8. Words after "peekaboo"
9. Blue
10. Look at things to come?
11. Co-Nobelist with Menachem
12. Jacques Cousteau's world
14. Plywood layer
17. Lazy waters
18. Highland pants
23. Because
25. Incline
26. 6-Down output
27. Spicy cuisine
28. TV's Griffin
30. Spinks and others
33. Pours
34. Was sweet (on)
35. Bone under a watch
36. Sweat
40. Demolitionist's supply
42. Flea or gnat
43. Start of a correction
44. "To do" list
45. Countdown deejay Casey
49. Bad lighting?
50. 1984 skiing gold medalist
51. Notions
52. Doctor's orders
54. Stealing: Prefix
57. FedEx, say
59. MGM founder
60. Assuming that
61. Small amphibians
63. Crispy sandwich
64. Rock's Brian

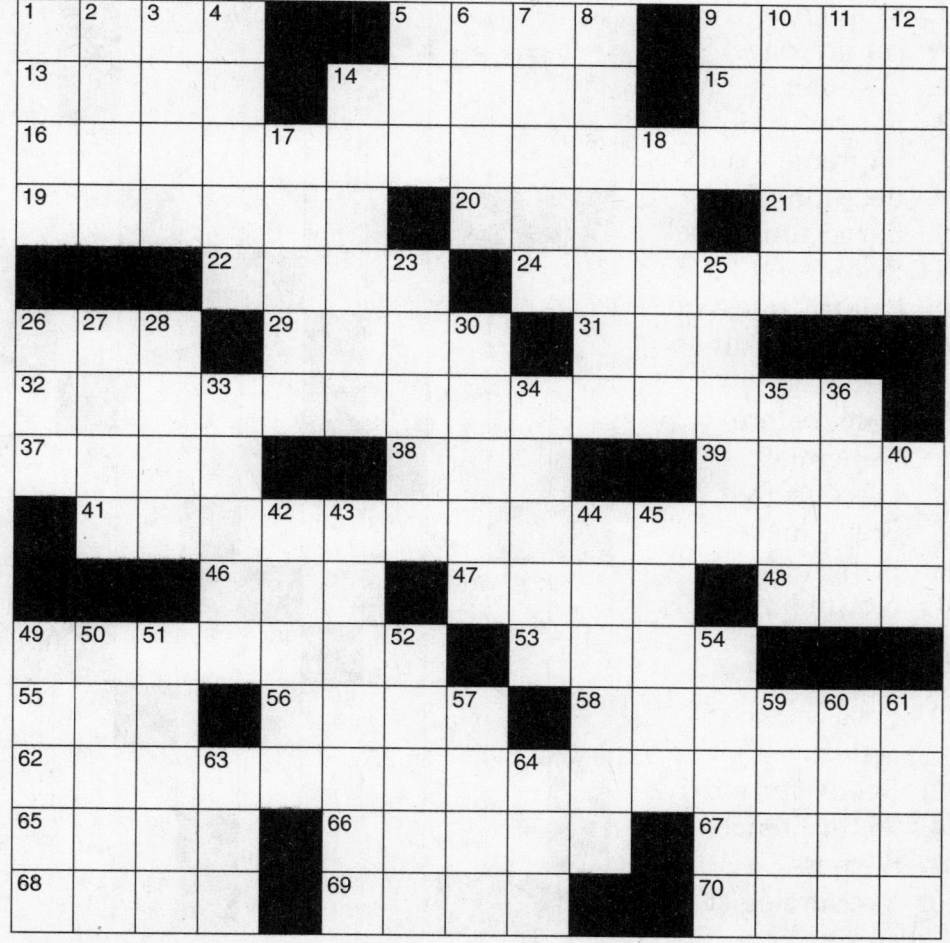

ACROSS

1. Thermometer part
5. Early touring car
8. O.J. or hot choc., e.g.
11. More anxious
13. Basra native
16. Game played with 192 cards
18. "__ company . . ."
19. Demand
21. Bret Harte character
24. Park it
25. Old flames
26. What newbies read on-line
27. Pleasantville, so to speak
29. __-Rivières, Qué.
30. Sheepskin holder
31. Morgan of the comics page
32. __ suiter
33. Start of a 1973 Supreme Court decision
34. Barbecuing block
36. Response to a bailiff's question
39. Preceding times
41. Little __
42. Book before Nehemiah
43. Disconcerted
45. Brava maker
46. Bring up
47. Not unter
48. "__ who?"
49. Fall colors
50. Post-workout activity
52. Ready for a drive
54. 75, in French
59. Surpass
60. Volcanologist's study
61. Lao-__
62. It's at the top of a face
63. Son of Seth

DOWN

1. Clean tables
2. Prefix with lateral
3. Certain Big Apple train, with "the"
4. Early rite
5. Not pobre
6. Cries of horror
7. Eyeball
8. "Roma" symphonic composer
9. "ER" actor LaSalle
10. Southwestern cowboy
12. Like logs
14. Makes idealistic
15. Middle of a famous palindrome
17. Green land
20. Skiing maneuver
21. At a distance
22. Nimbus
23. Concertina, informally
24. Cosmo feature
27. Sins
28. __ gratia
29. Tyke
32. Lemon peel
34. Place where a rose arises
35. Actress Merkel
37. "Shoot!"
38. Crew members
40. Foreman's declaration
42. Learned
43. Stole
44. Battery, e.g.
45. Actress Sherilyn
48. 1984 Kentucky Derby winner
49. Sign on for another tour
51. Clumsy fellows
52. Garr with a "Tootsie" role
53. Prefix with lateral
55. Houstonian's nickname
56. "Delta of Venus" writer
57. Madhouse
58. "Star Trek" off.

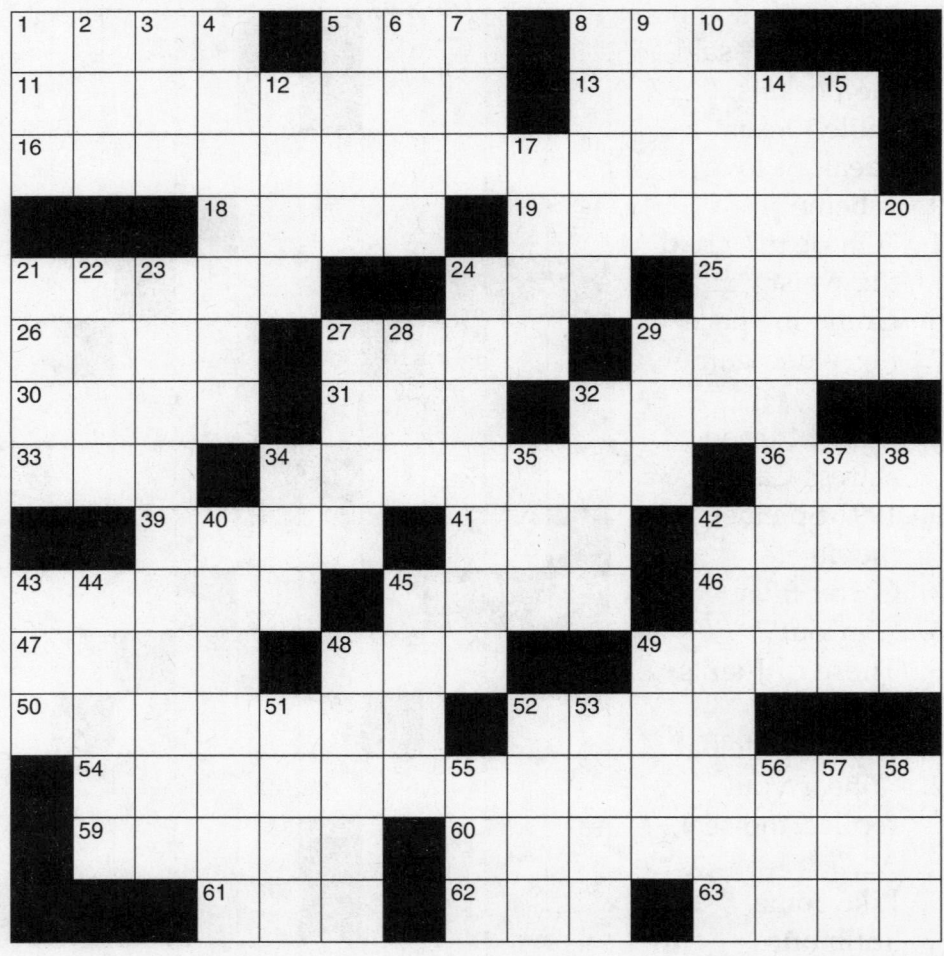

MARK YOUR CALENDAR *by David J. Kahn*

ACROSS

1. "__ first you . . ."
5. Sgt. of 50's TV
11. Cousin of "Phooey!"
14. Emergency CB channel
15. Some former dictators, e.g.
16. Skating champion Midori
17. Some Broadway performances
19. Hoedown participant
20. Braided
21. With indifference
23. Crackerjack
24. Chi paper, with "The"
26. Jeer
27. Actress Oberon
29. Chunk or clunk
32. Slam-dance, 90's-style
33. Put together, in a way
35. __-Altaic languages
37. Nashville inst.
38. Winter feature with a hint to this puzzle's theme
41. Bird of legend
43. Linguist Chomsky
44. Cockney's abode
45. Word on a coin
47. Fac. member
49. Kitchen gizmo
53. When repeated, a vitamin B deficiency
54. Alliance since 1949
56. Compass dir.
57. Football stat
61. Betrayed
63. Prefix with angular
64. Dilettantes, maybe
66. Adaptable truck, for short
67. Encroach on
68. Superiority
69. Surprised comments
70. 1966 Fonda-Robards movie
71. Guatemala natives

DOWN

1. Fashion line
2. Ring bearer?
3. Horn
4. Puccini melody, e.g.
5. 1996 A.L. Rookie of the Year
6. Like rust
7. German article
8. Kind of bag
9. It might wind up on a boat
10. "That __ you!"
11. Yeti-like creatures
12. Puzzled
13. Pre-Easter time
18. Followed, as an impulse
22. Man with a law
25. Post-weekend letdown
28. __-di-dah
30. Onetime Esposito teammate
31. Pedestal part
34. Word with anchor or dead
36. Harvard tradition
38. Hightails it
39. Bluejacket
40. Voice vote
41. 1967 Rolling Stones hit
42. Here, not in heaven
46. Term start?
48. Pretense
50. California locale whose name is an anagram of 52-Down
51. Oomph
52. Biblical locale
55. Heard in court
58. Where Myanmar is
59. "Treasure Island" character
60. It's a sin
62. Main part of a word
65. Hand, slangily

450 WISHFUL THINKING *by Jim Page*

ACROSS

1. How-to stuff
5. Toasted food
9. "Watership Down" author Richard
14. Say quickly
15. The art of weaving
16. Remains in Red Square?
17. Sign of goodness
18. Holder of combs, perfumes, etc.
19. Espresso order
20. With 34-Across, a child's 12/24 lament
23. Gift in Maui
24. One of the Kennedys
25. Pecs' kin
28. Schmooze
30. Worse than poor
34. See 20-Across
37. Chow chow chow
38. Not carrying a heater
39. Barley beard
40. Carving, e.g.
41. "Family Ties" son
42. With 51-Across, Ma Bell's response
44. Brass-yellow minerals
46. "Yeah, __!"
47. Like a hit show
48. It adjoins une côte
49. Big Band __
51. See 42-Across
59. Agglomerate
60. Exploits
61. Auto dealer's deal
63. The Louvre, par exemple
64. Object of gossip
65. Snake, so to speak
66. Locks horns (with)
67. Lifeguard's equipment
68. Whimpered

DOWN

1. It may be cast in a flick
2. __ B'rith
3. Baby whale
4. Embroiderer's purchase
5. Melancholy
6. Computer command
7. Problem in the joints
8. Drop
9. Idiotically wrong
10. Journal opening
11. Dead against
12. Burn protection
13. Snicker-__
21. Daughter of King Lear
22. Singer Redding
25. Music publishing acronym
26. Big name in pinball
27. Scrooge's look
29. Despondency, with "the"
30. Producing groans, maybe
31. Custard pies
32. __ grabs
33. Kind of ticket
35. It runs while you ride
36. Bowl over
40. Agitate
42. Garr of "Mr. Mom"
43. "Oh, what am I to do?"
45. Tiny laughs
50. Lit
51. Canine holders
52. __ to one's ears
53. Traveler's need, maybe
54. "Steep Trails" author
55. About
56. Army wheels
57. Theater area
58. Foe of the Clantons
62. Circus catcher

A LOT TO TAKE IN (DIGEST) by Lyell Rodieck

ACROSS

1. Auntie, dramatically
5. "La Classe de danse" artist
10. Birds in barns
14. Quizmaster Trebek
15. Humble
16. Cookie since 1912
17. Asset for 34-Across?
20. Bee activity
21. Classical lyric poet
22. Creative work
23. Book after Nehemiah: Abbr.
24. Sites of crosses
27. Meadow sounds
28. __ Na Na
31. No longer on the plate
32. Doughnut shapes
33. Extent
34. Circus act
37. Place for a revival
38. Kind of desk
39. Flowerless plants
40. Before, in poetry
41. Rules out
42. Not yet sunk
43. Common hello or goodbye
44. Habeas corpus, for one
45. Spicy cuisine
48. Takes advance orders for
52. Liability for 34-Across?
54. The Urals are west of it
55. Dinner bird
56. Witty Bombeck
57. Put salt on, maybe
58. Bridge positions
59. Time of decision

DOWN

1. Handy computers
2. "There oughta be __!"
3. Southwest sight
4. Glad-handing type
5. Father of Xerxes
6. Dark shades
7. Thieves' group
8. Numbskull
9. Leaves the dock
10. Zing
11. Saran, e.g.
12. Preyer
13. London or New York district
18. Be about to happen
19. Feedbag feed
23. Jumping the gun
24. Romantic adventure
25. More cold and wet
26. Agreeing (with)
27. Marina sights
28. Veep Agnew
29. __-Barbera (big name in cartoons)
30. Feeling of apprehension
32. Coil
33. Took the heat badly
35. Search like wolves
36. Aloof
41. Island near Java
42. Rugged ridges
43. Actor Tom of "The Dukes of Hazzard"
44. Extract by force
45. Symbol of non-communication
46. Trick
47. Oscar winner Jannings
48. Light: Prefix
49. Byron or Tennyson
50. Tibetan monk
51. Corset part
53. __ fault (overly so)

ACROSS

1. Nabisco cracker
5. Respond to seeing red?
9. Central highway
14. Brainstorm
15. Not taped
16. Former
17. Summon Warsaw citizens?
19. Hint of color
20. Opposite of masc.
21. F.B.I. workers
23. The I's have them
24. Mileage testing grp.
25. Undercover operation
27. Small change for a Brit
32. Unimagined
35. Broadcast studio sign
36. Any hit by Elvis
38. Hubbub
39. Artificial locks
40. Summon the elected?
42. Hit on the knuckles
43. Sorbonne summer
44. Bottle capacity
45. Common nest locale
47. Fine point
49. Under pressure
51. __ Nile
53. Opponent of D.D.E.
54. Songstress Vikki
56. Dressed, so to speak
59. Trendy
62. Talk a blue streak
64. Summon actress Sharon?
66. __ football (indoor sport)
67. Cartoonist Peter
68. "A Clockwork Orange" hooligan
69. Cattail's locale
70. Made a bubble, in a way
71. Crème de la crème

DOWN

1. Jazz phrase
2. Goofing off
3. Broncos or Chargers
4. Veer suddenly
5. Campaign ad feature
6. Scrabble piece
7. Broiling locale
8. Pains in the neck
9. To the point
10. The East
11. Summon Michael Jordan and John Stockton?
12. Take-out words
13. War god
18. Office fastener
22. Gravy spot
24. Prefix with center
26. Glaciers
27. Like illegally parked cars, sometimes
28. Get together
29. Summon a cable magnate?
30. Derby prospect
31. French fashion magazines
33. "Waste not, want not," e.g.
34. Ran
37. Malicious gossip
41. Was bedbound
46. Snaky letter
48. Chefs' wear
50. Was almost out of inventory
52. Get-well site
54. Study late
55. Ambiance
57. Baseball's Yastrzemski
58. German article
59. Links target
60. Washington bills
61. Student's book
63. "No dice"
65. Bill

SHOCKING HUMOR *by Kelly Clark*

ACROSS

1. Penniless
6. Frank of the Mothers of Invention
11. Pharmaceuticals overseer, for short
14. Whose 1961 record Mark McGwire beat
15. Hägar the Horrible's dog
16. __ Lingus
17. Part 1 of a song parody
19. __ tai
20. Funny old guy
21. Bog
22. Hilarious jokes
25. Book after Job
27. "Put a lid __!"
28. Song parody, part 2
31. Cuban coins
33. "I don't believe it!"
34. Song parody, part 3
40. Tiny bit
41. Tartish plums
43. Song parody, part 4
48. Spy's secret
49. Kvetch
50. Stalemate
52. Pleasant tune
53. Clean the hands before dinner
55. A Gardner
56. End of the song parody
61. Singer Shannon
62. Jack of "The Great Dictator"
63. It's positively electric
64. Time in history
65. Stimulates
66. Attach a patch

DOWN

1. Maker of the 5-Series
2. "Yay!"
3. Dig it
4. Jamaica's capital
5. "Terminal Bliss" actress Chandler
6. A Gabor
7. Upfront amount
8. Equal
9. Start with school
10. Pac.'s counterpart
11. Zoological classification
12. "Stars above!"
13. Bold, impatient type, astrologically
18. Ginseng, e.g.
21. West of Hollywood
22. Republican
23. Once more
24. Enthusiastic reply in Mexico
25. Gasp
26. Snooty types
29. Attire at fraternity blasts
30. "Be still!"
32. Burlesque bits
35. After-bath cover
36. Resident: Suffix
37. 1931 convictee
38. Talks amorously
39. Shoes introduced by the United States Rubber Co.
42. Match in poker
43. Golf club
44. "How luxurious!"
45. Screwball
46. Snake sounds
47. Jewish youth org.
49. Forest clearing
51. Big cats
53. Boat follower
54. Arguing
56. Pull along
57. "That'll show 'em!"
58. It's one thing after another
59. Stir
60. Hankering

454 CROSSTALK *by Brendan Emmett Quigley*

ACROSS

1. Airline founded in 1927
6. Garden smoother
10. Bygone Mideast leader
14. D-Day beach
15. "Make it quick!"
16. Showed up
17. "Look who just showed up!"
20. Uncle of rice fame
21. Court game
22. Cluckhead
25. Marooned motorist's need
27. Scouting job
28. __ Gras
30. Perpendicular to the keel
34. "__ With a View"
35. Where cold cuts are cut
36. "This __ fair!"
40. Popular basketball shoe
43. Midleg point
44. Rudely abrupt
45. Escape detection of
46. Expire
47. Eagle's home
48. Pitcher Hideo Nomo's birthplace
52. Popular oil additive
54. "Spy vs. Spy" magazine
55. Intern in the news
59. Spooky sighting
61. Rutgers, e.g.
66. Raison d'__
67. Numbskull
68. Blast from the past
69. Drifts off
70. Leave be
71. Thugs

DOWN

1. Not neg.
2. Sound booster
3. Highland negative
4. Captain of the Pequod
5. Provide (for), in a schedule
6. "A Yank in the __" (1941 war film)
7. Regarding
8. Actress Madeline
9. Fencer's blade
10. Public row
11. Ruinous damage
12. Protein building block
13. Her face launched a thousand ships
18. Lennon's lady
19. Quad building
22. Impact sound
23. Baseball's Hank
24. Lying facedown
26. Crumples into a tiny ball
29. Peacenik
31. A round at the tavern, say
32. Delights
33. Do poorly
36. Castaway's spot
37. __ und Drang
38. Gymnast Comaneci
39. In a corner
41. Company with a dog in its logo
42. Quaint children's game
46. Shady route
48. Sportscaster Merlin
49. Brawl
50. O. Henry, in the literary world
51. Toys with tails
53. Wed. preceder
56. Brewski
57. Shoelace problem
58. Cry of pain
60. 1993 peace accord city
62. November honoree
63. Joining words
64. Food container
65. "Right"

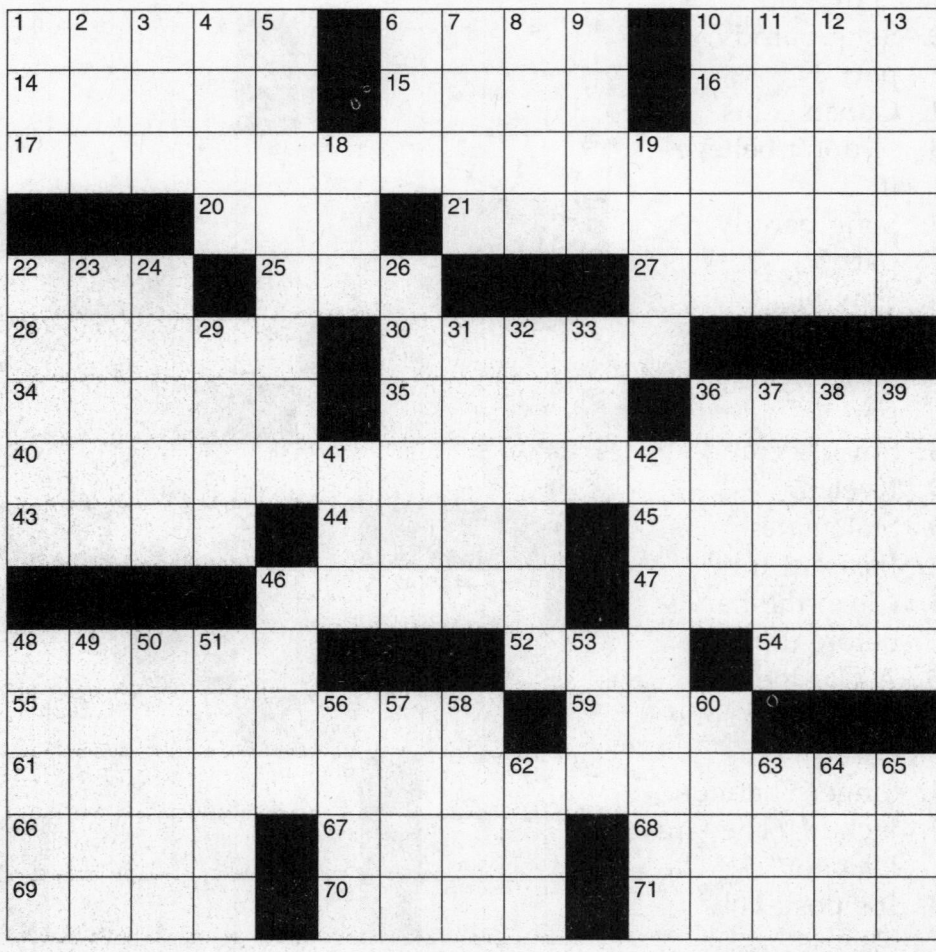

ACROSS

1. Con game
5. Given an R or PG
10. 60's do
14. Standard
15. Elicit
16. It may be entered in a court
17. Request for artist Georgia's forbearance?
20. __ Tin Tin
21. Enticed
22. Washing jobs
23. They're apt to get into hot water
25. Sweetie
26. 1952 and '56 campaign name
27. Grand
32. Like __ out of hell
35. Drives off
36. Of the congregation
37. Mexico City portrait painter?
41. Behave
42. Western "necktie"
43. Revival meeting cry
44. Deficiency
46. Pale
48. OPEC export
49. Filled in
53. "Beat it!"
56. Plait
58. Eggs
59. "Georges paints as he pleases"?
62. Exploit
63. Appropriate
64. Marquis de __
65. Recipe amts.
66. Schnozzes
67. Ogled

DOWN

1. [Hmmph!]
2. Newswoman Roberts
3. Scene of the action
4. Lady de la maison: Abbr.
5. Sanctuary
6. Swears
7. Heavy reading
8. __ out a living (scraped by)
9. Org. involved in raids
10. Blacksmiths' wear
11. Kind of market
12. Study
13. Slow-growing trees
18. Antiaircraft fire
19. It may be worn under a sweater
24. Bridle parts
25. Catcall
27. Them there
28. Sharpen
29. Astringent
30. Specify
31. Actress Cannon
32. Epiphanies
33. "Art of the Fugue" composer
34. Choir part
35. Air apparent?
38. Punctual
39. Farm delivery
40. Author Grey
45. Lies in the summer sun
46. Places for watches
47. Adjutant
49. Shower
50. Incursion
51. Skirt
52. Saw
53. Room meas.
54. They're waited for at a theater
55. Glean
56. Vivacity
57. Tatters
60. Ashes holder
61. "__ as directed"

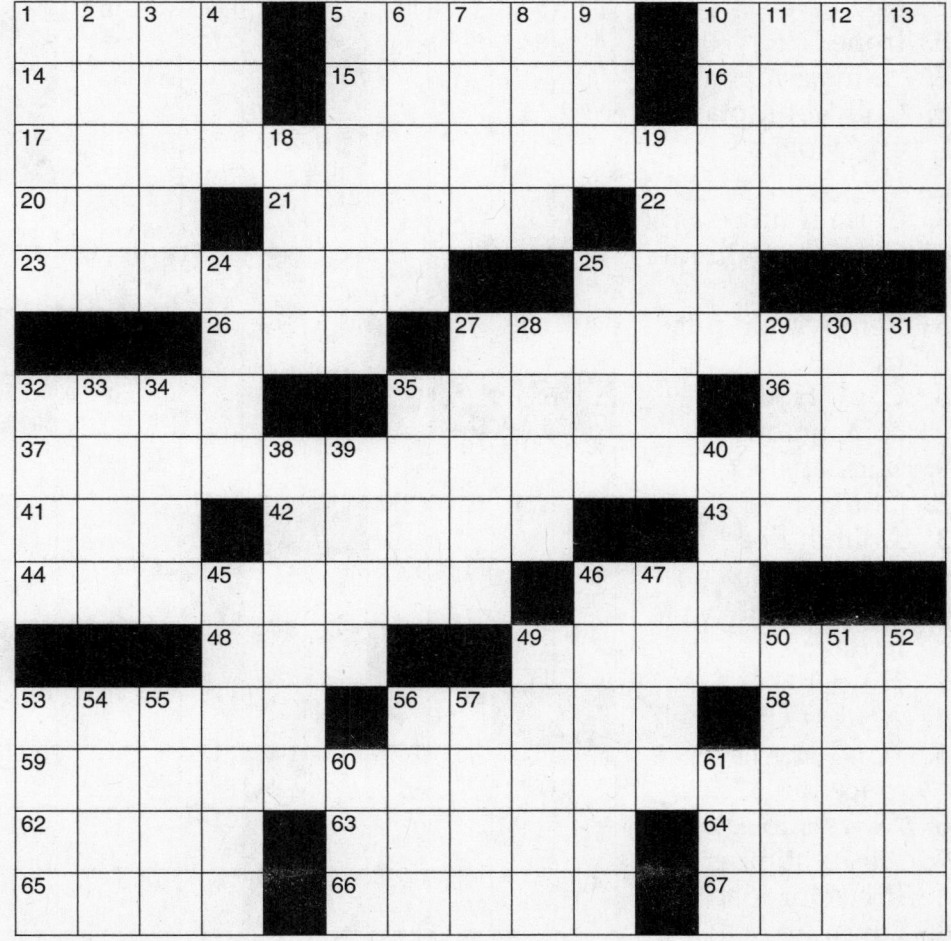

456 AT EASE by Janet R. Bender

ACROSS

1. Does a standard dog trick
5. Flock members
9. Actor Cary of "Twister"
14. To be, in Toulon
15. Ernie's "Sesame Street" pal
16. __-lance (pit viper)
17. Kind of instrument
18. The "B" of N.B.
19. Nourishes
20. Country club employees
23. Ink for une plume
24. Sulky state
25. Lao-__
28. Originally named
29. Coral formation
33. Long John Silver, e.g.
35. Ironed
37. __-majesté
38. Col. Klink player on "Hogan's Heroes"
43. Certain util.
44. Channel swimmer Gertrude
45. Remove the pits from
48. Capt. Hook's companion
49. Martians, e.g.
52. Glimpse
53. Animal doc
55. Assail
57. Peppermint liqueur
62. Hinder
64. Actress Campbell
65. "God shed His grace on __"
66. News subject
67. Large number
68. Projector load
69. Gives up
70. They're seven positions after this puzzle's theme
71. Scots Gaelic

DOWN

1. "Murphy Brown" star
2. Timeless, to a poet
3. Where Zeus was worshiped
4. Passover meal
5. Recedes
6. Time span
7. Sea eagle
8. Brew
9. Decadent
10. Playboy's gaze
11. Hulk Hogan, for one
12. Hall-of-Famer Roush
13. His or her, in France
21. Audacity
22. Energy
26. Late ruler Mobotu __ Seko
27. River through Bavaria
30. Poetic contraction
31. Three-time speed skating gold medalist Karin
32. Circus impresario Irvin and others
34. Mirth
35. Suffix with exist
36. Consider
38. Joins in holy matrimony
39. Gen. Robt. __
40. Completely excised, in surgery
41. G.I. chow in Desert Storm
42. Military academy freshman
46. Turns inside out
47. Rep. foe
49. Book after Nehemiah
50. Giggles
51. TV's "Remington __"
54. High-strung
56. __ nous
58. Actress Russo
59. Place for a farmer?
60. Daredevil Knievel
61. British stables
62. Jan. preceder
63. Night before

FACE THE MUSIC *by Randy Sowell*

ACROSS
1. Wind __ (pilot's problem)
6. Comic actor Jacques
10. Ali __
14. How to play a dirge
15. Composer's work
16. Mimic
17. Woolf's "__ of One's Own"
18. Peacekeeping force in Bosnia
19. Not strict
20. Infallible fact
23. "There but for the grace of God __"
24. Copacabana site
25. Westerns
27. Small tropical lizards
31. Arrest record
33. Jai __
34. Eisenhower's boyhood home
36. Biblical sin city
38. Klutz
39. Woods on the fairway
43. Paramaribo is its capital
46. Achy
47. Halite
50. "Paper Roses" singer Marie
52. Strands, as by a winter storm
53. Just ducky
54. Speed: Abbr.
55. Rural route
62. Pub stock
64. Calf's meat
65. Fret
66. Grandparents' stories, e.g.
67. English essayist
68. Prince Valiant's wife
69. Name on which ancient oaths were taken
70. Brother, aunt, etc.: Abbr.
71. Southernmost part of Arabia

DOWN
1. Smelting residue
2. Long lunch?
3. Son of Seth
4. On
5. The Joker's portrayer on TV
6. Kemo Sabe's sidekick
7. On __ with
8. Ballerina's skirt
9. U-235 or C-14, e.g.
10. __-relief
11. Orbital high point
12. Prior to
13. One who makes a scene?
21. Actress Bonet
22. Lacks, in brief
26. Belief in one God
27. Neon, e.g.
28. "Shine a Little Love" rock grp.
29. Ungentlemanly sort
30. Newsstands
31. Laughing
32. Code word for A
35. Seethe
37. Orchestra output
40. Sticky stuff
41. Sea eagle
42. Badly chapped
44. Trampled
45. "The Hound of the Baskervilles" locale
47. Competes equally with
48. Yellow and black cat
49. Salad stalk
51. Bridge between buildings
53. Library volume
56. Congo river
57. Catch but good
58. Part
59. City near Provo
60. Museo holdings
61. Actress Cannon
63. Gender

458 PEAS PORRIDGE *by Robert Zimmerman*

ACROSS

1. It's catching
5. Tenor-soprano combos, e.g.
10. "Look out . . ."
14. Downs of "20/20"
15. Sleeper's breathing problem
16. Figures in tables
17. B-1 insignia
18. 1964 Beatles hit
20. Pressed for cash
22. Black-ink item
23. Northwest European
24. Rembrandt works
26. Royal home
29. Mosquito fleet craft
32. Fancy tie
33. Appraiser
34. Dine
36. Injury's aftermath
37. Paint base
38. El __, Tex.
39. "2001" computer
40. Partner of onions
41. Ex-Gov. Cuomo
42. Adam Dalgliesh's creator
44. One very funny joke
45. __ empty stomach
46. Microscopic
47. Mrs. Gorbachev
50. Bus passenger's request
54. Rating for the risqué
57. Yarn
58. Speechless
59. Target
60. Highland dialect
61. Simon __
62. Divisions of municipal govt.
63. Repast

DOWN

1. Sic
2. Reddish-brown
3. Food thickener
4. How acid-base properties affect the body
5. Spotted horse
6. Discomfit
7. Author Bagnold
8. Address book no.
9. __ Paulo
10. "Battleship Potemkin" locale
11. Makes bales on the farm
12. Western Indian
13. High, in the Alps
19. Heroism
21. Bombard
24. Sleek swimmer
25. Wild goat
26. Payment option
27. Songwriters' org.
28. Heat to just short of boiling
29. Crowns
30. Bygone dictators
31. "Wake Up Little __" (1957 hit)
33. Poe visitor
35. D
37. Andes capital
38. Auditorium fixture
40. Hawaiian isle
41. "Death in Venice" author Thomas
43. Kids
44. 3Com Park team
46. Pick up the tab for
47. Tach readings
48. Spanish water
49. __-bitty
50. Day worker, maybe
51. Bus token, e.g.
52. Hostess Maxwell
53. Lively dance
55. "Far out!"
56. Dead heat

DROP A BOMB? by *Stephanie Spadaccini*

459

ACROSS

1. Parachute —
5. "Animal House" party wear
9. Ham it up
14. In midvoyage, maybe
15. "— restless as a willow . . ." (1945 movie lyric)
16. Morocco's capital
17. Have on
18. Fissure
19. Ready for anything
20. Sage advice, part 1
23. Got fresh with
26. Pennsylvania city
27. "—, two, three, four . . ."
28. Wide shoe specification
30. One making picks and pans
35. The Little Mermaid
37. Bills and coins
40. Aborted mission words
41. Sage advice, part 2
44. Part of Q.E.D.
45. Not masc. or fem.
46. Uncomplaining servant
47. Sandwich meat
49. — Tomé (island on the Equator)
51. Exist
52. Thingy
55. Abba's home country
57. Sage advice, part 3
62. Lasso
63. Thrilled
64. Jodie Foster's alma mater
68. Inquired
69. Author Wiesel

70. Say the paternoster
71. Pasta sauce with basil
72. Lairs
73. Test proctor's declaration

DOWN

1. Leno's got a big one
2. Exploit
3. — culpa
4. It was liberated in August 1944
5. Rant
6. Skip over
7. Faux pas
8. Moving
9. Pencil topper
10. Soda fountain choice
11. Follow the rules
12. Starch source
13. "—, Brute?"
21. Seems
22. Nouveau —
23. Ray-Bans, e.g.
24. The dawn
25. Kind of cord
29. Behold, in old Rome
31. —-European
32. "Tsk, tsk"
33. Tune out
34. Actor Joseph of "Citizen Kane"
36. Songstress James
38. Prefix with pressure

39. Where movies are made
42. Togetherness
43. Go under for the third time
48. Gilbert and Sullivan emperor
50. Digressions
53. Bordered
54. A thousand, in France
56. Pharaoh's land
57. Police sting
58. Get up
59. Beasts of burden
60. Editor's direction
61. Stuck on oneself
65. Mr. Onassis
66. Leave in a hurry
67. CBS symbol

460 SOCIAL DARWINISM by *Harvey Estes and Nancy Salomon*

ACROSS

1. Went airborne briefly
6. Sitcom set in Korea
10. Weary workers' exclamation
14. Eskimo home
15. Division word
16. "__ Rock" (Simon & Garfunkel hit)
17. Musician at a dance?
19. Egyptian cobras
20. Vitamin bottle info
21. Delaney of "N.Y.P.D. Blue"
22. Address part
24. Shade of blond
25. "No" vote from a horse?
28. Funky musical genre, for short
29. Rock singer __ Bon Jovi
30. Julie in "Doctor Zhivago"
32. Needlefish
33. Jack who ate no fat
36. "What's your sign?," for example?
38. The hunted
39. Parson's home
40. Peruvian native
41. Booze for a 50's bash?
43. Fraternity man
44. Time of anticipation
45. Opening amount
46. Shoe part that may pinch
47. Gads about
49. Hells Canyon state
51. Modus operandi
54. Treat badly
56. "Praise be to __!"
57. __ brisk pace
58. Spring feature
59. Critique of an all-night teen dance?
63. Beheaded Boleyn
64. "Terrible" czar
65. MacLeod of "The Love Boat"
66. Relay segments
67. Superman's alter ego
68. Secluded valleys

DOWN

1. The Scales
2. "Holy smokes!"
3. Leader of Islam
4. Washington wheeler-dealer
5. Bun
6. Dolphins' home
7. Whichever
8. Sault __ Marie
9. __ d'oeuvre
10. Miss America's prize
11. Internal combustion device
12. Obstacle
13. Basketball strategy
18. Lender's claim
23. Cafeteria carrier
26. Peeked (at)
27. Unduly severe
29. Blue birds
31. 66, e.g.: Abbr.
33. Sun-shaped
34. Smoked Italian cheese
35. Undoing an act
36. LuPone or LaBelle
37. Italian cabbage?
39. Back-to-work time: Abbr.
42. Singing Mama
43. Friendly, reliable sort
46. Norse bolt maker
48. Symbols of stubbornness
50. Publicity person
51. Forgo
52. Enjoyed home cooking
53. Shows signs of boredom
55. Estrada of "CHiPs"
60. Blvd.
61. Delivery vehicle
62. Kilmer of "At First Sight"

THINKING IN 2-D by Fred Piscop

ACROSS
1. Golf peril
5. South African author Alan
10. Impoverished
14. Latvia's capital
15. TV's Morgenstern
16. Witty Bombeck
17. Bartender's supply, squashed flat?
19. Jack-o'-lantern feature
20. Plunder
21. Working with a dragnet
23. Carpe __
25. Actress Taylor of "The Nanny"
26. Apportioned, with "out"
29. Car safety device
33. Take in
34. Total, as an effort
35. G.I. address
38. Some scams, squashed flat?
41. Nile slitherer
42. Gladiatorial sites
43. Bona fide
44. Trattoria gadget
45. __ Domingo
46. Zeno, notably
49. Actor Montand
51. Game with sticks
55. Brings a smile to
59. No longer mint
60. Meteorologist's study, squashed flat?
62. Catchall abbr.
63. Pacific nation since 1968
64. The life of Riley
65. January song ender
66. Muddleheaded
67. Common flag feature

DOWN
1. Remove the fat from
2. Costa __
3. Ripening factor
4. Rose Bowl site
5. Victorian type
6. "So, it's YOU!"
7. Suit material, perhaps
8. River to the Baltic
9. Discovery grp.
10. Stereotypical pirate feature
11. Utah's Hatch
12. "Mother __" (old standard)
13. Outfielder's asset
18. Pound sterling, informally
22. Vindictive anger
24. Gong hitter
26. Intro to physics?
27. Shuckers' units
28. Junket
30. Actress Graff
31. "Hail Mary" counter
32. Tampa Bay players, in headlines
34. Taj Mahal home
35. "Right on!"
36. Bog stuff
37. Capital on a fjord
39. Pusher's pursuer
40. Crossword solvers' smudges
44. Elasticized garment
45. Top Four matchup
46. Turns on an axis
47. Delicious
48. Neptune's realm
50. Empty spaces
52. Yemen's capital
53. P.D.Q., on "ER"
54. Six-foot avians
56. "Vamoose!"
57. Socialite Maxwell
58. Nostradamus, for one
61. Assayer's specimen

(462) HAVE WHAT IT TAKES *by Nathaniel Weiss*

1. Ayatollahs' predecessors
6. Gunslinger's command
10. "Oh, my!"
14. Hooded snake
15. Othello's false friend
16. "I'm — you!"
17. Start of a quip
20. Summer shirt, informally
21. Mallards' homes
22. Metric volume
23. Place for a 45
24. Clinch, as a deal
25. Part 2 of the quip
32. Son of Venus
33. Stiff denial
34. Old polit. cause
35. Dosage unit
36. Caribbean music
39. Ovine utterance
40. A major, maybe
41. Hydrocarbon suffix
42. Paris recreation area
44. Lucy's partner
45. Part 3 of the quip
50. Entanglement
51. Encumbrances
52. One who grins and bears it
55. Greek S
56. Biol., e.g.
59. End of the quip
62. Novelist Waugh
63. Tallow source
64. Words before sight and mind
65. Entanglement
66. Stumbles
67. Query before "Here goes!"

DOWN

1. "Out!"
2. Balderdash
3. Strong of body and mind
4. Charlemagne's realm: Abbr.
5. Early Greek lyric poet
6. 1934 quintuplet
7. Forcefully stuff, as a throat
8. Turkish generals
9. Took the trophy
10. Chin beard
11. — and for all
12. Move
13. Place for a run
18. Warner Bros. creation

19. Resort island off Naples
23. Word in a price
24. Whit
25. "The Terminator" woman
26. Yemeni's neighbor
27. E-mail need
28. Play — with (damage)
29. Belgian composer Guillaume
30. Newspapers, with "the"
31. "Don't mince words!"
36. Oration
37. Henry Kissinger biographer Marvin

38. Canine cry
43. Thickness measurer
44. Radio staff, for short
46. On/off —
47. Tourist attractions
48. Prefix with spherical
49. Captivate
52. Defraud
53. It may be spun
54. Half of binary code
55. Disparagement
56. — good example
57. Oaf
58. Conjectural
60. Ethnic suffix
61. "So — me!"

INACCESSIBLE *by Randy Sowell*

ACROSS

1. Armed forces females
5. Like a whip?
10. Play parts
14. Fiery gem
15. Synagogue scroll
16. Combustible pile
17. __ Sabe
18. Actress Verdugo
19. Israeli statesman
20. Gizmos for couch potatoes
23. Ace, e.g.
24. "You Are My Destiny" singer, 1958
25. Classic car
26. The "A" in NATO: Abbr.
27. Poem of praise
30. Feline hybrid
32. Constitutional Amendment that abolished slavery
34. Just barely places
38. 1949 Bing Crosby hit
42. Puget Sound city
43. Quotation notation
45. "Grand" piece of furniture
48. Dancer Charisse
50. "The __ Divorcee"
51. Mag. staffers
52. Infamous Rudolf
56. Hardly award-winning writing
58. Franklin and Eleanor Roosevelt, e.g.
62. Together, musically
63. Jetés, e.g.
64. Family problem
66. Stew bean
67. "L.A. Law" lawyer
68. Mother of twins, in myth
69. Watch part
70. Bury
71. Once, once

DOWN

1. Stir-fry pan
2. Preprandial potable
3. Evergreen with roselike flowers
4. Kind of replay
5. Undo a delete
6. Lawn pest
7. Betel palm
8. Didn't stop
9. Do an Oscar winner's job
10. Mimic
11. Six Million Dollar Man, e.g.
12. Town in County Kerry
13. Electric eye, e.g.
21. Oklahoma Indian
22. Shire who had a "Rocky" career
23. Bellum's opposite
28. Moist in the morning
29. Dutch cheese
31. Cuzco-centered empire
33. It smooths things over
35. Cheat
36. DeMille-type film
37. Do in, as a dragon
39. Warm welcome
40. Casey Jones, e.g.
41. Tiny bubbles
44. Old-time humorist Bill
45. 45-Across features
46. "Yippee!"
47. Take for granted
49. Sot's problem
53. Zhou __
54. Back of a boat
55. Meager
57. Ransack and rob
59. "Go, __!"
60. 60's role for Ron Howard
61. Person with a PC
65. Lat. case

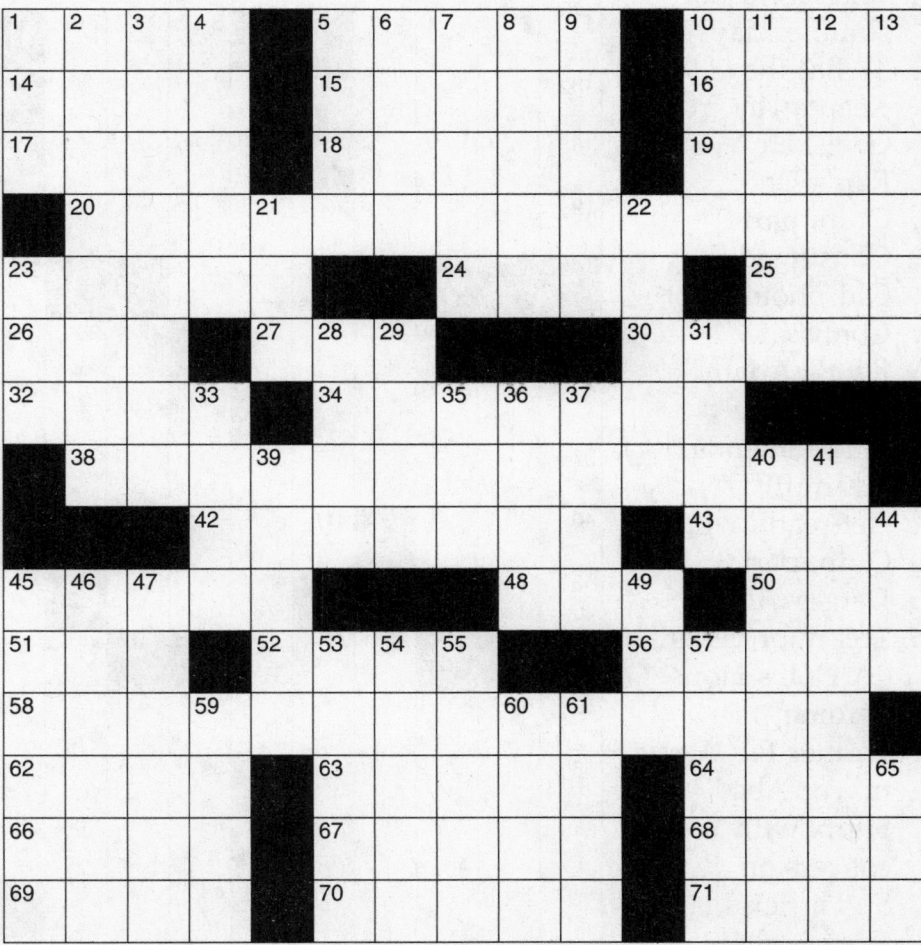

464 WATCH WHERE YOU'RE DRIVING *by Stephanie Spadaccini*

ACROSS

1. Shih Tzus, e.g.
5. One-time Chinese chairman
8. Hoopster Gilmore
13. A Great Lake
14. Zeus's wife
15. Stop
16. Dudley Do-Right's love
17. Apiece
18. Avignon's river
19. Quip about links lovers, part 1
22. Baseball bosses: Abbr.
23. Magazine income producers
24. Beads worn by a nun
27. Wish for a hot summer day
29. "What the __!"
33. Keep away from
34. Gaels, etc.
36. Rap's Dr. __
37. Quip, part 2
40. Consumed
41. Old photo color
42. Confiscate
43. Eliot's Adam __
45. Lobsterlike
46. Made amends (for)
47. "__ nuff!"
49. Get-ready work
50. Quip, part 3
58. Dancer Ailey
59. Treaty preceders
60. "A Doll's House" heroine
61. Former Big Apple mayor Abe
62. Suffix with concession
63. St. Patrick's land
64. Goes it alone
65. Cagy
66. Wallop

DOWN

1. Successor to 5-Across
2. Chocolate-and-cream cookie
3. Part of a fish
4. Successful through one's own efforts
5. Beef, pork, etc.
6. St. Louis landmark
7. Hawaiian island
8. Bitter
9. Go over again
10. Town NNE of Santa Fe
11. "__ She Lovely?"
12. Understands
14. Husband to Catherine, Anne, Jane, Anne, Catherine and Catherine
20. Marsh birds
21. Big bag carrier
24. Therapeutic center, for short
25. Like some leaves
26. Used a piggy bank
27. Malodorous
28. __ Romeo (Italian auto)
30. Newsman Newman
31. Fad
32. Atwitter, with "up"
34. Superhero accessory
35. Many a bridesmaid
38. Long-necked bird
39. Unlocked again
44. Alaska native
46. Get up
48. Dancer Gregory
49. Actor Luke
50. Bell __
51. Butter substitute
52. Race track shape
53. "__ the night before . . ."
54. Honor, as a conquering hero
55. In days of __
56. Skater Heiden
57. Went under

TOUGH PUZZLE *by Fred Piscop*

ACROSS

1. False witnesses
6. Vocalizes like the Beastie Boys
10. Parks in 1955 news
14. Venezuela's __ Falls
15. Clairvoyant's start
16. Has a tab
17. Suffix with sea or moon
18. Grocery vehicle
19. College course division
20. Production in a given period
22. Trait determinant
23. Pirouette point
24. MacNeil's longtime partner
26. Sombrero accompanier
30. Transparent
32. "__ 'Clock Jump"
33. Classic soft drink
35. Italian tourist center
39. Third-stringer
41. Sharpshooter's gift
42. Beat by a whisker
43. Use weasel words
44. Meat loaf serving
46. "Holy moly!"
47. Papa Doc ruled it
49. Stats for a porous defense
51. Battle site of 1916
54. Gulped down
55. Mideast bigwig
56. Pro-slavery Northerners, before the Civil War
63. Mission cancellation
64. Folklore fiend
65. Speechify
66. Lone Star State sch.
67. Chemicals giant
68. Hertz __-Car
69. Slippery critters
70. Sit a spell
71. Alma __

DOWN

1. In the cellar
2. Rainfall measurement
3. Lab gel
4. Bank takeback
5. Mr. Moto, e.g.
6. Nouveau __
7. "Hurry, please!"
8. Pizarro conquest
9. Avoid a trial
10. Hero of 1898
11. Dog tag datum
12. Left Bank river
13. Autumn bloomer
21. Hoodlum
25. Move carefully (into)
26. Swanky
27. Years ago
28. Uncool sort
29. Cold comfort?
30. Burger or dog topper
31. Vegetable soup bean
34. All-star game side, often
36. Waffle brand
37. Warm, so to speak
38. States further
40. Belle's man
45. One of Alcott's "Little Women"
48. Like some pools or paint
50. __ Judaism
51. Stage or stadium, say
52. Ham it up
53. Star in Orion
54. Insurance seller
57. Look lustfully
58. "QB VII" author
59. Field of study
60. Defeatist's word
61. Politically incorrect suffix
62. Mark with a branding iron

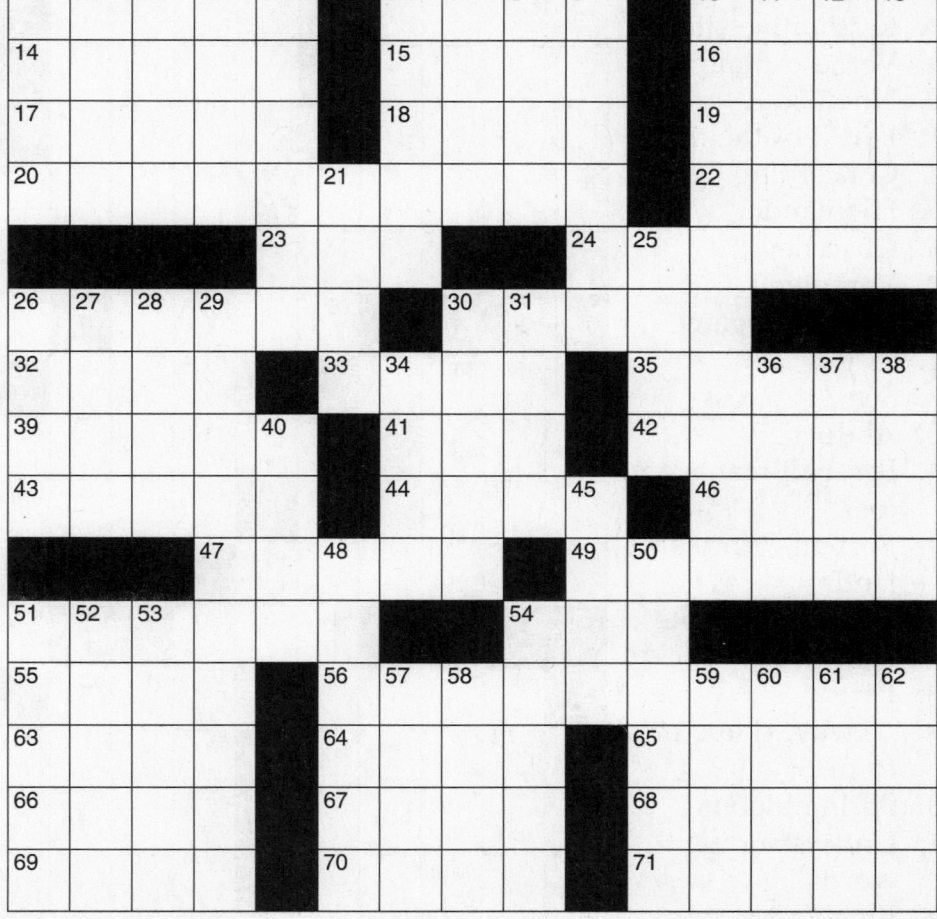

466 A MATTER OF TIME by Elizabeth C. Gorski

ACROSS
1. Apparel
5. Bowls over
9. 1945 Allied conference site
14. It makes things gel
15. Chowderhead
16. Messages that can arrive at any time
17. Start of a quote
19. Move laterally
20. Control __
21. With 53-Across, author of the quote
23. Breadwinner
25. Impeachment trier: Abbr.
26. Small amounts, as of cream
29. One who's "out"
34. Restorative sites
38. Verne captain
40. Not a soul
41. Part 2 of the quote
44. Concerning
45. Highlander
46. Obscene
47. Verboten
49. Gambling game
51. __ judicata
53. See 21-Across
58. Abduct
63. Baseball manager Joe
64. Port-au-Prince's land
65. End of the quote
67. Hand out
68. Part
69. __ way, shape or form
70. Spring bloom
71. Understanding words
72. Breakfast staple

DOWN
1. Faux pas
2. Public square, in ancient Greece
3. Less common
4. 80's–90's singer Adams
5. Critic __ Louise Huxtable
6. Tequila bottle additive
7. Noted socialite Maxwell
8. Mixes up
9. Noncommittal answer
10. Gulf V.I.P.
11. Put on board, as cargo
12. Pinball problem
13. Bass, for one
18. Squeaked (out)
22. Prefix with political or logical
24. South African money
27. "All __ are off"
28. Artist's wear
30. G. I. Joe, basically
31. Fashion
32. Once again
33. Internet addict, perhaps
34. Q-Tip, for one
35. Sunscreen additive
36. Shortly
37. Bowl over
39. Wind quintet member
42. Designer fragrance
43. Sicilian spewer
48. Ph.D., for example
50. Composer Luening
52. Puppeteer Lewis
54. "Gosh, will you look at that!"
55. Space shuttle part
56. Quite a swinger
57. Items sent to record companies
58. Real estate agent's goal
59. Hawaiian port
60. Huge amounts
61. Years in Havana
62. Not working
64. Accident
66. Born

HOOP DREAMS *by Fred Piscop*

ACROSS

1. Back tooth
6. Clash of clans
10. Coal-rich German region
14. Pueblo home
15. Bullets
16. Disassemble
17. Traveler's purchase, maybe
20. Art Deco notable
21. Not 'neath
22. Draws with acid
23. Hamelin critter
25. What's more
26. Playwright Burrows
29. Workshop machine
35. Soap brand since 1899
36. Projector items
37. Raines of filmdom
38. Slightest evidence
40. Camp sight
41. Einstein
42. Eyebrow shape
43. Skylit courts
45. "__ been had!"
46. Disappearing communication device
49. Nancy Drew's beau
50. Inlets
51. Major defense corp.
53. Spanking spot
56. Prospector's find
58. Way out there
62. NASA scientist's concern
65. Capture electronically
66. Obey

67. Where Goodyear's headquarters are
68. Puppeteer Tony
69. Part of A.D.
70. French river to the English Channel

DOWN

1. Stallion's mate
2. Polecat's defense
3. Oaf
4. One of the Yokums
5. Cincy player
6. Hack's customer
7. Kuwaiti bigwig
8. Diamond authority
9. "Go on!"
10. Giver of relief
11. Egyptian cross
12. "Zip-__-Doo-Dah"
13. Goes to waste
18. Comic Fields
19. "__ wrap!"
24. Vineyard measure
25. The __-Prussian War (1866 conflict)
26. Wedding site
27. Pack animal
28. Right on
30. Summaries
31. Linen or denim
32. Assassinated
33. Still in the game
34. Tapered off
39. Explorer's activity
41. 30's boxing champ Max
44. Silicon Valley giant
47. Run amok
48. Popular motorcycle
52. Nutcase
53. Order (around)
54. Killer whale
55. Skier's transport
56. Baker's need
57. Overhaul
59. Al dente
60. Molecule part
61. Baseball's Sandberg
63. Novelist Deighton
64. Western treaty grp.

(468) SLICED FRUITS AND VEGETABLES by Sam Bellotto Jr.

ACROSS

1. Add-ons
5. Firefighter Red
10. Sheik __ Abdel Rahman
14. Outdoor party
15. Mimi's thanks
16. Meteorological effect
17. Pump kin?
20. American charge
21. Zoo creatures
22. Fix, as a voiceover
23. No-goodnik
26. Yank's foe
28. Mediums for announcements, in brief
29. "Gandhi," for one
33. Bar order
36. 12 points
38. Award bestowed by Queen Eliz.
39. Mush room?
42. Rocky crag
43. Surf sound
44. Large's opposite
45. Letters at Camp Lejeune
47. Some forensic evidence
48. Priest of I Samuel
49. Having handles
52. Not tarry to marry
56. Accelerate
59. Colts may be found here
61. Car rot?
64. Wedlock, so to speak
65. TV exec Arledge
66. Umbrian tourist town
67. Sensible
68. Tie up
69. "... __ open fire"

DOWN

1. Composer knighted in 1904
2. Pulitzer-winning author Alison
3. Scot with a lot
4. Kind of acid
5. Marc Antony's love
6. Star in Cygnus
7. "You __ here"
8. Suffix with electron
9. Marksman's aid
10. Woofer measure
11. Injure
12. "It was __ mistake!"
13. Rogers and others
18. Office gizmo
19. Math. course
24. Political power structure
25. "Pore Jud Is __ ..." ("Oklahoma!" song)
27. Bullfighting, e.g.
30. __ Sci
31. "Yeah, right!"
32. Turn over
33. Queue after Q
34. "Iliad" and "Odyssey," e.g.
35. Spread
37. Undying
40. Children's caretaker
41. Kind of heel
46. O. Henry award winner for "Shut a Final Door"
50. Kernel
51. Brings home
53. Part of "the works"
54. Cuddly carnival prize
55. Ex-Laker Baylor
56. Fashionable store since 1902
57. Florida catch
58. 007's alma mater
60. Is penitent
62. Golden, in France
63. "That means __!"

ACROSS

1. Sulu portrayer, in "Star Trek"
6. Prego competitor
10. Fakery
14. Out of whack
15. Where Qum is
16. Prefix with -gon
17. October and November?
19. Co-fighter
20. Ogee shape
21. Good time
22. A whole lot
24. Hoped-for review
25. Warning at St. Andrews
26. Bedouin's domain
29. Memorable
33. Potters' supplies
34. It leaves its mark on the beach
35. Ancient marketplaces
36. Kind of clef
37. Didn't just shrug the shoulders
38. Football Hall-of-Famer Tarkenton
39. Sea-diving area
40. Topple from power
41. Minotaur's land
42. Necessarily
44. Like this puzzle
45. Play the siren
46. Not legally binding
47. Yellowstone sight
50. Lo-cal
51. Brenda who sang "I'm Sorry"

54. Cassini of fashion
55. When origami flourished?
58. Foolhardy
59. All, to start with
60. Co-op contract
61. Speed unit
62. Diatribe
63. Red Sea nation

DOWN

1. Unexciting
2. "Famous" name
3. It's sometimes stolen
4. Extreme suffix
5. Lines on a weather map
6. M-1, for one
7. Uzbekistan's __ Sea
8. Cowboy's date
9. Set free
10. Flintstone tone?
11. Scratch pad?
12. Bar on a car
13. Giant great
18. Broad bean
23. Scrap for Spot
24. Bradbury as an aviator?
25. __ mignon
26. Line of cliffs
27. French walk
28. Misanthrope
29. Buggy power
30. Composer Ned
31. All worked up
32. Punished, schoolmaster-style
34. Pesto, e.g.
37. Restricted air lane
41. For the most part
43. In the open
44. 1939 movie canine
46. Call on
47. Have an effect
48. Rock-and-roll pioneer Freed
49. Colombian money
50. City between Boston and Salem
51. Potting soil
52. Different
53. First place
56. G.P.'s grp.
57. Invoice amount

470 OUT AND OUT *by Fred Piscop*

ACROSS

1. "Lydia" poet
5. Beethoven dedicatee
10. Dugout, for one
14. "Jake's Thing" author
15. "O come, __ . . ."
16. Prefix with skeleton
17. Fairy who loved Peter
19. "Show Girl" tune
20. At home, but available
21. Popped in on
23. __ Dame
24. Individually
26. Noted name in civil rights
31. Modern ink source
34. It's served in spots
35. Not o'er
36. Galoot
37. One of the Brady Bunch
38. Deposit
40. Galilee, e.g.
41. Horse of the Year, 1960–64
43. __ Percé
44. Abbr. for F. Lee Bailey
45. Risk-taker's declaration
49. Like some tennis courts
50. Footnote abbr.
55. Goes postal
58. What "I love" in a 1915 Irving Berlin song
59. Stratford's stream
60. Hint to this puzzle's theme
63. Like some plating
64. Photographer Adams
65. 60's talk show host Joe
66. Beat by a nose
67. Broken-down
68. Pink-slipped

DOWN

1. "__ a Hot Tin Roof"
2. Acid type
3. Color slightly
4. Schindler of "Schindler's List"
5. Suffolk, for one, in Shakespeare
6. Legal deg.
7. __ Royale, N.S.
8. Popular Nicole Hollander comic
9. More slippery
10. Trust in
11. "Don't bet __!"
12. Wood trimmer
13. Sticky-tongued critter
18. Kind of sch.
22. Hound's trail
24. Mideast port
25. Links letters
27. LAX guesstimate
28. The life of Riley
29. A.A.A. suggestions
30. Hoops nickname
31. Literary pseudonym
32. European car
33. "Gimme a C!" etc.
37. Long __
38. Use a keyhole, perhaps
39. Dangerous gun
42. Knowledge
43. Certain G.I.
46. Gymwear name
47. Zero
48. Hit the bottle
51. "__ Passes" (Browning poem)
52. Flower part
53. Lacking substance
54. Fiddled
55. Loaf
56. "Tristia" poet
57. Dance's partner
58. Compatriot
61. Bring into play
62. Convertible, after conversion

ACROSS

1. Not shut tight
5. Royal crown
10. O.K. in any outlet
14. Like Silver's rider
15. Up to
16. "Oops!"
17. Greek salad ingredient
18. Dolly, for one
19. Tear
20. RAMSEYS
23. Schoenberg opera "Moses und __"
24. "Boola Boola" singer
25. POWELLS
31. Org. in old spy stories
34. Athol Fugard's "A Lesson From __"
35. Mouse manipulator
36. Company, proverbially
37. Verb, for example
38. Planck's "thanks"
40. Lots of bucks
41. King's domain
42. Cousin's mother
43. "The House of Dies __" (Virginia Hamilton Edgar-winning mystery)
44. Attack a sub?
45. STILLERS
48. Cataract site
50. Like Patagonia
51. ROGERS
57. Culbertson coup
58. Showed again
59. Wrinkle remover
61. Wear out the carpet in the waiting room
62. Gatling gun feature
63. Rosetta's river
64. "Now hear this!": Abbr.
65. Rail riders
66. Traditional Hanukkah gift

DOWN

1. Landon of politics
2. One of the Coen brothers
3. It's just for openers
4. Arouse
5. Popular retirement destination
6. Not on the shore
7. Heaps and heaps
8. Zest
9. Tess's seducer in "Tess of the D'Urbervilles"
10. Hearing-related
11. Ben Hur, e.g.
12. Deduct from
13. Fighter with Fidel
21. Roth offerings
22. Groucho's expression
25. Twist or stomp
26. Actress Massey
27. Work against
28. Undemocratic government
29. "Don't __!"
30. Born, in Bordeaux
32. Talk a blue streak?
33. Contrite
38. Expected to arrive
39. First name in advice
40. Using a dragnet
42. Out for the night
43. Bottled spirit?: Var.
46. 1998 Olympics site
47. They may be on the house
49. Mocha's country
51. Off-pitch
52. Ogee, e.g.
53. Agrippina's son
54. Colorless
55. U.S. port, or its locale
56. Throw, as dice
57. Health haven
60. Place to surf

472 PLAY UNFAIR by Glenn E. Sykes

ACROSS

1. Open-mouthed
6. Jacket part
10. Den
14. Allied
15. + or −
16. Riding the waves
17. Coin of Stockholm
18. __ impasse
19. Hunting target
20. Part 1 of a quip by the writer named in the circled letters
23. Born
24. No longer secret
25. 1950's White House name
27. "Jeopardy!" host
30. Place to view a Goya
31. Is responsible for
35. Midmorning
36. Part 2 of the quip
41. "Alice" waitress
42. First in a line of cars
43. Sprites
46. Bordering
50. Actress Dianne
51. Balm ingredient
54. "__ the ramparts . . ."
55. End of the quip
59. All there
60. In olden times
61. River through Switzerland
62. Adenauer nickname, with "Der"
63. Film director Peter

64. Put into the ground
65. Grab, slangily
66. Former spouses
67. Gadabouts

DOWN

1. Obliquely
2. Steel beam
3. Actress Renée
4. Former Transportation Secretary Federico
5. Dutch cheese
6. "Star Trek" setting
7. __ Dame
8. Acteur Delon
9. Shut (up)
10. Daytona 500 organization
11. Body shop figure
12. Shores
13. Cry before "You're it!"
21. Crookedly
22. Mischief-maker
26. Centuries and centuries
28. Troop grp.
29. Poetic contraction
32. Library sound
33. Italy's bottom
34. Ending with pay
36. Generally
37. Approach, as the next item of business

38. Fish-eating eagles
39. Enzyme suffix
40. Bother
41. Small number
44. Respect
45. Actor Erwin
47. This evenin'
48. High schooler
49. They may be marching
51. Not the main building
52. One of the Arnazes
53. Humdingers
56. T. __ Price of finance
57. Math course
58. "Oops!"
59. Wane

ACROSS

1. Fast runners
6. "There!"
10. Cut of marble
14. Rep
15. Paradise
16. Paradise's opposite
17. "I can't use my Q . . ." (1959)
20. __ king
21. Puts two and two together
22. Chilled
23. Plea of a player drawing KILLJO- (1952, 1964 and 1990)
25. "There!"
27. Jerk
28. Kills, slangily
32. Money guru Greenspan
35. Of the ear
36. Divinity sch. subj.
37. Theme of this puzzle
41. "I __ Camera" (1955 film)
42. Bluecoats, with "the"
43. This, to Tomás
44. Ingredients in some pancakes
46. "Bards of Passion and of Mirth," e.g.
48. Laura's daytime lover
49. "Double letter score" refrain (1925)
53. Big name in computer printers
56. Londoner
57. Okey-dokes
58. Where to place DRAMATI-(1914)
62. Domain
63. Civic group
64. Frenzy
65. Takes home, in a way
66. Cut the fat
67. Walk in

DOWN

1. Sets upon
2. Not hidebound
3. Kidney-related
4. Letter accompanier: Abbr.
5. Does a slow burn
6. Bear that kids bear
7. Hornets' nests
8. Site of iniquity
9. Picnic crasher
10. Flubs a golf shot
11. Dolly __ of "Hello, Dolly!"
12. Actor Guinness
13. Off-color
18. Midmonth date
19. Hype
24. Singer k.d.
25. Pitch suddenly
26. Gen. Bradley
28. Gang woes
29. Basketballs, but not footballs
30. Had a sensation
31. Dog botherer
32. P.D.Q.
33. Car with a bar
34. Gray's subj.
35. Match
38. Without a sour note
39. Hide-and-seek hideout
40. Miller, for one
45. Ho's his
46. Just for the thrill __
47. Stay in the cooler
49. Something to leave money in?
50. Razz
51. "Generation of Vipers" author Philip
52. Star's statuette
53. Israel's Abba
54. Combustible heap
55. Leave be
56. Lie on the beach
59. Foundation
60. Priest of I Samuel
61. Idol worshiper

474 PET-AGREES by Nancy Salomon and Harvey Estes

ACROSS
1. Mayberry toper
5. C sharp
10. Sound astonished
14. Job for a body shop
15. Baghdad native
16. "Takin' __ the Streets" (Doobie Brothers hit)
17. Newswoman Klensch
18. Kind of calendar
19. Enthusiasm
20. Beginning of a prayer
23. Author Bennett
24. Popeye's Olive
25. Schlemiel
26. Walrus hunter
28. Yankee legend Rizzuto
31. Pub. workers
32. Collar stain
33. Butts of jokes
36. Middle of the prayer
41. Suffer sans air conditioning
42. __ Honor
43. Sch. for ministers
46. Fateful day
47. Davis of Hollywood
48. Hunger (for)
50. __ minérale
52. Agony
53. End of the prayer
58. Clunker
59. Language of 380 million
60. Sports figure
62. After-lunch sandwich

63. Just kidding around
64. Clears
65. Easter preparation
66. Quits
67. Not just a trip across town

DOWN
1. Words of praise
2. Fib
3. Mouthing off
4. Night light
5. Totally uncool
6. Bell or whistle
7. Pool demarcation
8. Marine shade
9. Q followers?
10. Thingamajig
11. Loose
12. Slew a vampire, perhaps
13. Raft steerers
21. Part of an E-mail address
22. 1990's sitcom
23. Injure
27. Bad reviews
28. Ship refueling places
29. Water (down)
30. Composer Stravinsky
33. Scurried
34. Prefix with photo
35. Eye sore
37. Knicks center who was the 1986 Rookie of the Year
38. Deep trouble

39. Mechanize
40. It has a bark but no bite
43. $, #, %, or &
44. Pooh's grumpy pal
45. Maniacs
47. Clear tables
49. Martian explorer, e.g.
50. Come out in the long run
51. Actor Claude
54. "What's __?"
55. Clue
56. Dope
57. Ain't correct?
61. Condescending cluck

CHEESE IT *by Mark Elliot Skolsky*

ACROSS
1. Make fat
5. Teaser
10. Survivalist's stockpile
14. Needle case
15. "They Died With Their Boots On," e.g.
16. Bad news for a bookie
17. It may be hit with a hammer
18. Cheesy part of the neck?
20. Kind of nerve
22. Ballpark figure
23. Tennis call
24. Cheesy 60's TV show?
28. Frito-Lay's parent
31. Longtime Delaware Senator
32. Put away
33. Not be a polite winner
35. Eerie sightings
39. Cheesy 1977 comedy?
44. Coupling
45. Element found in Geiger counters
46. Word with snake or quake
47. Writer on music David __
51. View
53. Cheesy TV private eye?
57. "Wheel of Fortune" purchase
58. Ballpark figure
59. Lowest deck
63. Cheesy gabber?
67. "Hawaii Five-O" locale
68. Item designed to be blown up?
69. Jungle vine
70. Tito's family name
71. Bones, zoologically
72. Like happy diners
73. Exxon, once

DOWN
1. Kind of blocks
2. On
3. Shrimp
4. Fingers
5. "Ulalume" poet
6. Dosage unit at a reactor
7. Northern Japanese city
8. Initiate
9. "Twelfth Night" lover
10. Dadaism founder
11. Common bedroom furniture material
12. Track athlete
13. Dramatist Clifford
19. Secy.
21. City north of Sacramento
25. Hosiery shade
26. Kind of ring or swing
27. Racketeer
28. Ruefulness
29. Feature of an empty house
30. Furtive look
34. Pallid
36. Denizens of the 46-Across
37. It comes in black and white
38. Part of a deck chair
40. Will of "The Waltons"
41. Complaint
42. "Space cadet"
43. Año starter
48. Not an iron
49. Peers
50. Beaverlike fur
52. Photographer's light
53. "Thriller" singer, in tabloids
54. "It's __ Kiss" (1964 hit)
55. Track events
56. Convocation of witches
60. Cousin of Sven
61. Cries of surprise
62. Corleone's creator
64. Narcs' employer: Abbr.
65. Half and half
66. Crossed through

(476) SPRINGTIME IN HOLLYWOOD *by Rich Norris*

ACROSS

1. Relative of a gator
5. Many miles off
9. Sign of healing
13. City southeast of Honolulu
14. "Damn Yankees" girl
15. Strong will?
16. "A New Leaf" actress/director, 1971
18. Hackneyed
19. Athletes need good ones
20. Bowls
21. Victory
22. Slippery ones
23. "Deep Purple" singer, 1963
28. In on, with "to"
29. Overly brainy sort
30. Nourished
33. Grub
34. Take another shot
36. Cry that stops traffic
37. Ending sequence
38. Kind of therapy
39. Strong-willed athletic type, supposedly
40. Best Actor of 1932 and 1946
43. Haunted house sounds
46. French pooh-bah
47. Snakes
48. Iditarod runners
53. Signed
54. "Brewster's Millions" actress, 1945
55. Devoutness
56. Similar
57. Change the decor
58. Architect Saarinen
59. Geometric fig.
60. Be sure of

DOWN

1. "If I Could Turn Back Time" singer
2. Anger
3. Norwegian king
4. Stamp purchase
5. "Dynasty" conniver
6. Kindle
7. Woeful word
8. Beam
9. Destroys, as documents
10. Queeg's command
11. Site of many promises
12. Sanctify
15. Beach
17. Freshly
20. New York's — Fisher Hall
22. At any time
23. Zenith
24. Beseech
25. Big name in hotels
26. R.N. responsibilities
27. Oft-used computer key
30. Carnival
31. Corp. kingpin
32. Any course
34. Stinks
35. Means justifiers
36. "La la" preceder
38. Midaslike
39. Mennonites
40. 55 minutes past the hour
41. Unexpectedly appropriate, maybe
42. Sound
43. Steal
44. Skater Sonja
45. Autumn sight in suburbia
48. — it out (fight)
49. Songbird
50. Tied
51. No Einstein
52. Boat with an open hold
54. Disconcert and then some

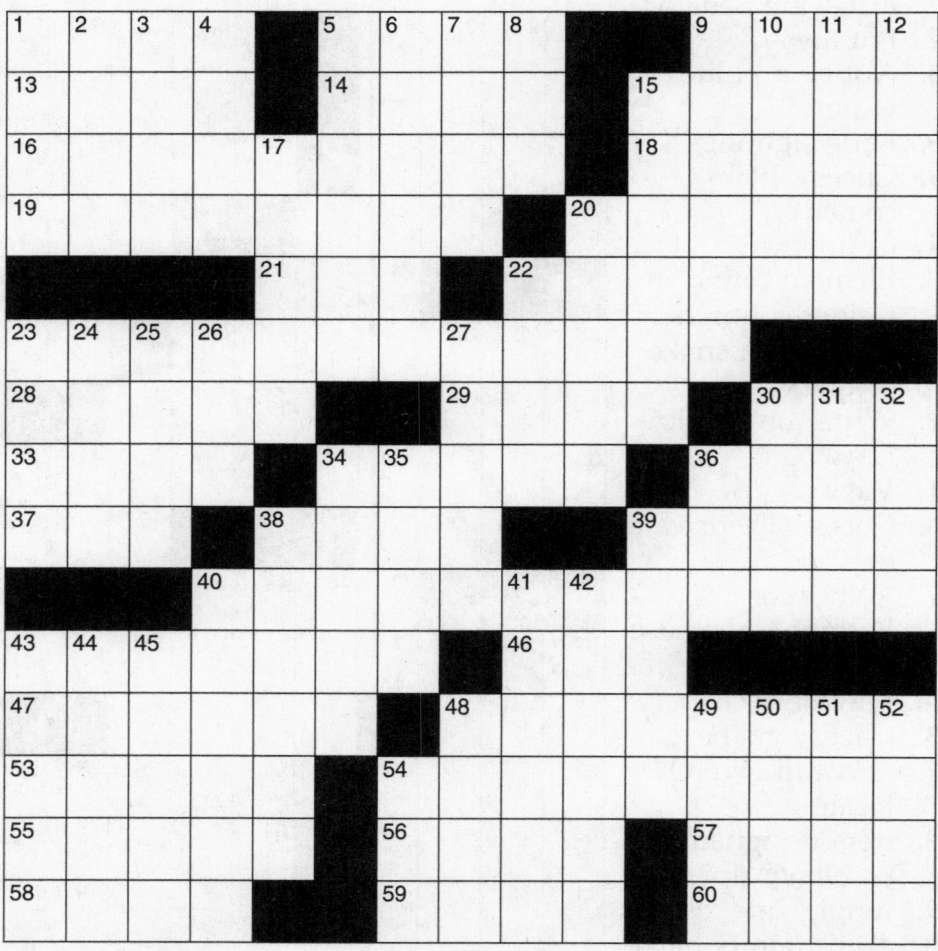

ROCKY ROAD? *by Wesley R. Johnson*

ACROSS

1. Center of an old-fashioned roast
5. Old Jewish scholars
10. Kid
14. Fully fit
15. Coin being replaced by the euro
16. Got down
17. What boxer #1 did
20. Got up
21. More wily
22. Political grp. since 1854
23. Umbrella part
25. Launch of 1986
27. What boxer #2 was
36. Slice of history
37. "__ so right!"
38. "Li'l" guy
39. Othello's betrayer
41. Dishonest sort
43. Actor Morales
44. Bloodhound's guide
46. "A Garden of Earthly Delights" author
48. Pipe joint
49. What boxer #2 then had to do
52. Late Cabinet Secretary Brown
53. White House souvenir
54. Draft org.
57. Schiller's "__ Joy"
61. Swindler's name, possibly
65. What the boxers and fans now do
68. "What a shame!"
69. Certain fur
70. Say __ (deny)
71. "__ No Angels" (Bogart flick)
72. Studio stock
73. "Go ahead!"

DOWN

1. Scroogeisms
2. Life preserver?
3. Kind of flute
4. Like some Christians
5. Union in a 1955 merger
6. Ringling __
7. Wail
8. Hostile to
9. Machination
10. Boxer's move
11. Designer Cassini
12. Forage holder
13. Start of a Web site address
18. Uplift
19. Writer Jong
24. Ringside responses
26. Boxer's wear
27. Franklin, religiously
28. Spinachlike plant
29. It's made at fights
30. Like some sentences
31. Trick's alternative
32. Moor
33. Remove stitches from
34. Football Hall-of-Famer Greasy __
35. Bird's sound
40. __ about (near)
42. Hoard
45. __ a kind (pair)
47. Recipe direction
50. Protected from the elements
51. Back from flying
54. "Pygmalion" dramatist
55. Only
56. Practice in the ring
58. Art Deco name
59. London's __ Gallery
60. Hurler Hershiser
62. Classic Langston Hughes poem
63. Play opener
64. Whisky amount
66. Opp. of WNW
67. E.M.T. destinations

478 LOOK BOTH WAYS *by Myles Callum*

ACROSS
1. Castoff from an ice shelf
5. Kind of pad
10. N.B.A. M.V.P., 1984–86
14. United Steelworkers leader I. W. __
15. McGwire blast
16. Fad item of 1961
17. Basketball's Archibald injured the Dalai Lama, palindromically
20. Ingratiated
21. Where many changes take place
22. Sci. course
23. Exceedingly
24. Soprano Maria
27. Wham!
28. Subsides
32. Disgrace
33. Pelvic
35. Coach Parseghian
36. Assail rioters dressed in gray, palindromically
39. Sphere
40. Business types
41. Small drum
42. Discounted by
44. Darn site
45. "Well, __!" ("Ain't you hot stuff!")
46. Control spot
48. Shiny on top?
49. Flattened at the poles
52. Petty cash in London
56. "What a shame your footwear is missing," palindromically
58. Vampire's hideout

59. Measurer
60. Track event
61. Mind
62. Finished
63. "For heaven's __!"

DOWN
1. Deadly poison
2. Israel's Abba
3. No longer working: Abbr.
4. Happy chorus?
5. English counties
6. Certain carving
7. "Diary of __ Housewife"
8. Caught up with
9. Bargain hunter's delight
10. "So long"
11. Jot
12. Clancy hero Jack
13. Spanish woman
18. Popular vacation locale
19. Axle, e.g.
23. Annuls
24. Computer language
25. Love to death
26. They branch out
27. Word with hot or home
29. Dear deer
30. The Brady kids, e.g.
31. Tel Aviv native
33. Expression
34. Tree with white flowers
37. Lincoln's supposed fiancée Ann
38. Write-offs, perhaps
43. Threadbare
45. "The Eagle has __"
47. Sched. letters
48. Ecru
49. Palindromic comics dog
50. Palindromic ninny
51. Togo's capital
52. Dropping sound
53. Asta's mistress
54. One who's home on the range?
55. Palindromic suffix
57. Bond's Fleming

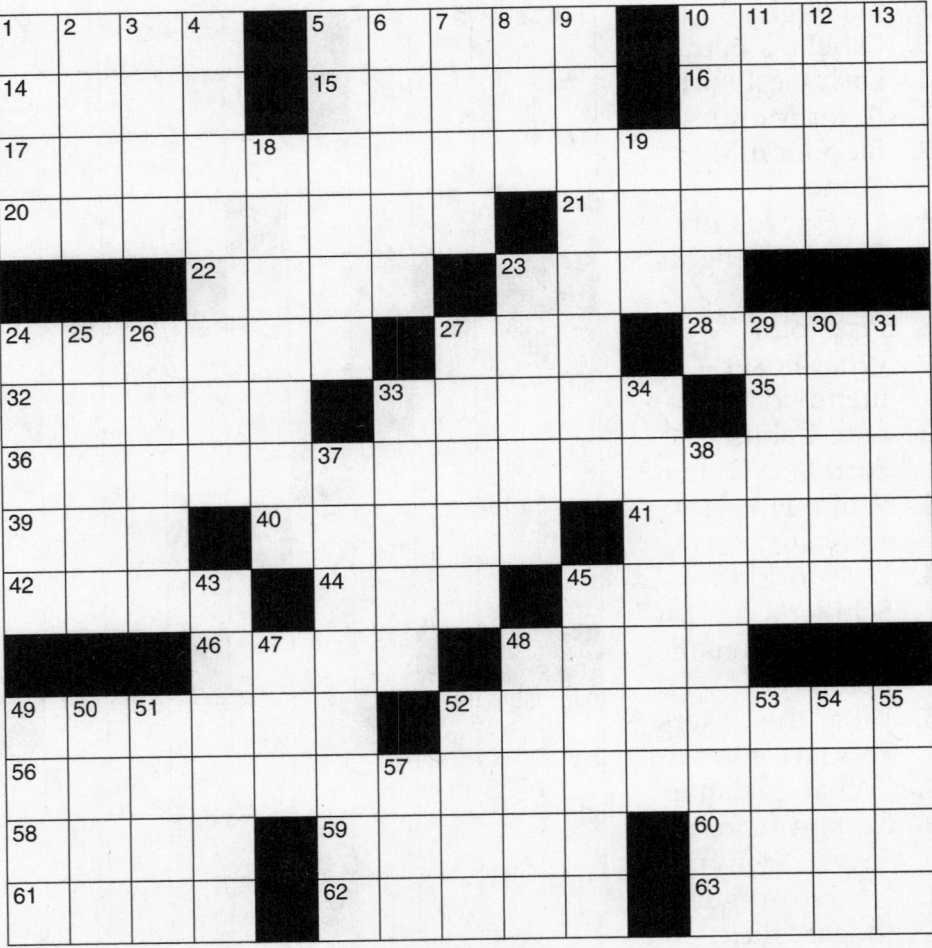

UNREAL ESTATE *by Nancy Salomon*

ACROSS

1. London Fog, e.g.
5. Multigenerational story
9. Betray, in a way
14. Up to the task
15. Zippo
16. Play hard to get
17. Sage lands?
19. Torments
20. Barfly's roost, perhaps
21. ". . . blackbirds, baked in __"
23. Professional suffix
24. Do a post-laundry job
27. Poet __ St. Vincent Millay
29. Joe's lands?
34. __ de mots (pun)
35. Feds
36. Looked with desire
38. Makes a scene?
40. Largest Cornhusker city
42. Have on
43. Hotel Bible
45. Peewee people
47. One of the "Little Women"
48. Dieters' lands?
51. Last name in cruelty
52. Took note of
53. Pal, rapper-style
56. Spot in the Senate
58. Arab emirate
62. Sly character
64. Bad lands?
67. Slicker in the winter
68. Superior's inferior
69. Gold medalist Lipinski
70. Insinuate
71. Dummy
72. Command to a boxer

DOWN

1. Crow calls
2. Parting words
3. Plus
4. Make mad
5. Env. stuffer
6. Hole number
7. Inspiration
8. Comics ghost
9. Money coming in
10. Ancient greeting
11. It has a prominent horn
12. Words from Wordsworth
13. Catbird seat?
18. On high
22. Star worship
25. Stand buy
26. Consider
28. Once again
29. Mr. Rhodes of Rhodes scholarships
30. Better
31. Biters
32. Hate the thought of
33. Tailor's joints
34. Bender
37. Like some humor
39. Uses a Singer
41. Crossed fingers symbolize it
44. Somewhat
46. Like rye, usually
49. Kidded around
50. Full-price payers
53. Sailor's stir
54. Gallop
55. Forget about
57. Dangerous charger
59. Go sailing
60. Gillette product
61. Brit's interjection
63. Emmy winner Arthur
65. Free
66. __ Speedwagon

480 DOESN'T RING A BELL *by Patrick Jordan*

ACROSS
1. Unforeseen difficulty
5. Dwelling
10. Gauguin or Cézanne
14. Soybean dish
15. Like lymphatic tissue
16. "Giant" author Ferber
17. Get
18. Start of a joke
20. Response to 18-Across
22. Big name in computers
23. Bell and Barker
24. Less slovenly
25. Smooth in motion
28. Move down the computer screen
31. Right on the map
32. Deli sausage
33. Short punch
36. With 49- and 55-Across, response to 20-Across
39. Miscalculate
40. Made invalid
41. Wife in "Finnegans Wake"
42. Serving dish
43. Gives off
44. Hot as a pistol, e.g.
47. "Big Blue"
48. Makes a cardigan, say
49. See 36-Across
55. See 36-Across
57. Seasick sailor's support
58. Yorkshire river
59. Gill of country music
60. Light brown
61. Sediment
62. Protected by levees
63. Honeybunch

DOWN
1. Lose sleep over something
2. Ark architect
3. Retro hairdo
4. Barrel maker?
5. Egyptian crosses
6. Matter of contention
7. Unpleasant aura
8. Small freshwater fish
9. __ Grove Village, Ill.
10. Letter getter, maybe
11. Assume
12. Last word in a wrestling match?
13. Abdul-Jabbar, 1975–89
19. Kato of Simpson trial fame
21. Bit
24. One for whom all roads lead to roam
25. Honor with a party
26. Actor Bert
27. Conniver
28. Miss Hawkins of Dogpatch
29. Half of a famous outlaw duo
30. Japanese noodle dish
32. Insomniac's annoyance
33. Folk singer Mitchell
34. 12-Down partner
35. Tops
37. Tear off with force
38. Talked, talked, talked
42. Collection plate amounts
43. Outward flow
44. Cheer with beer
45. Bellybutton type
46. British bishop's headdress
47. Angry
49. Sixth-century date
50. Sound at Old MacDonald's
51. At some prior point
52. Filigree
53. Milan moola
54. Many a campaign tactic
56. Hanes competitor

AA BATTERY *by Rich Norris*

ACROSS

1. Slender-bodied insect
5. Rogue
10. Kind of sax
14. Johnson of "Laugh-In"
15. Tyrolean refrain
16. Equal
17. Loses to a late-night host?
20. W.W. II Gen. __ Arnold
21. "September __" (Neil Diamond hit)
22. Fuse
23. Prefix with cycle
24. Emissions control grp.
25. It may be wild
28. One of the Fondas
30. Tout's hangout, briefly
33. Agile
34. Initiates
38. Menlo Park monogram
39. Fills in for an actor?
42. Shade maker
43. Exposed as false
44. Ali __
46. Old geog. initials
47. Bar at the bar
51. "Mr. Tambourine Man" group, with "the"
53. Cutting tool
55. Capek play
56. Put in or take out, maybe
58. "Peter Pan" pirate
59. "Make __ double"
60. What the foreign car driver does after a trip?
64. Look longingly at
65. Japanese commercial district
66. Together, in music
67. Incite
68. Have the helm
69. Sew up

DOWN

1. Mom's pre-meal instruction
2. Mysterious
3. "Enough!"
4. A pop
5. On-line V.I.P.
6. Deadly snake
7. Yemen's Gulf of __
8. Funnyman Brooks
9. Clear the roads, in a way
10. Lunchbox items
11. Approach carefully, as a subject
12. Social
13. N.H.L. Hall-of-Famer since 1979
18. May birthstone
19. United
26. Grouch
27. Pupil's locale
29. Plumbing connection
30. Transpire
31. Compared to
32. Bill
35. Puts to work
36. Catches
37. Blessed events?
39. Be in the game
40. Kind of insurance policy
41. Law degs.
42. Go back
45. Confused
48. Vacuum tube with three elements
49. Beat to the finish line
50. Hoped for the best
52. Lisa Simpson, to Bart
53. Wow
54. Exclude
57. Some ID's
58. On one's rocker?
60. Dress (up)
61. I, to Claudius
62. Take a load off
63. Hat with a pompon

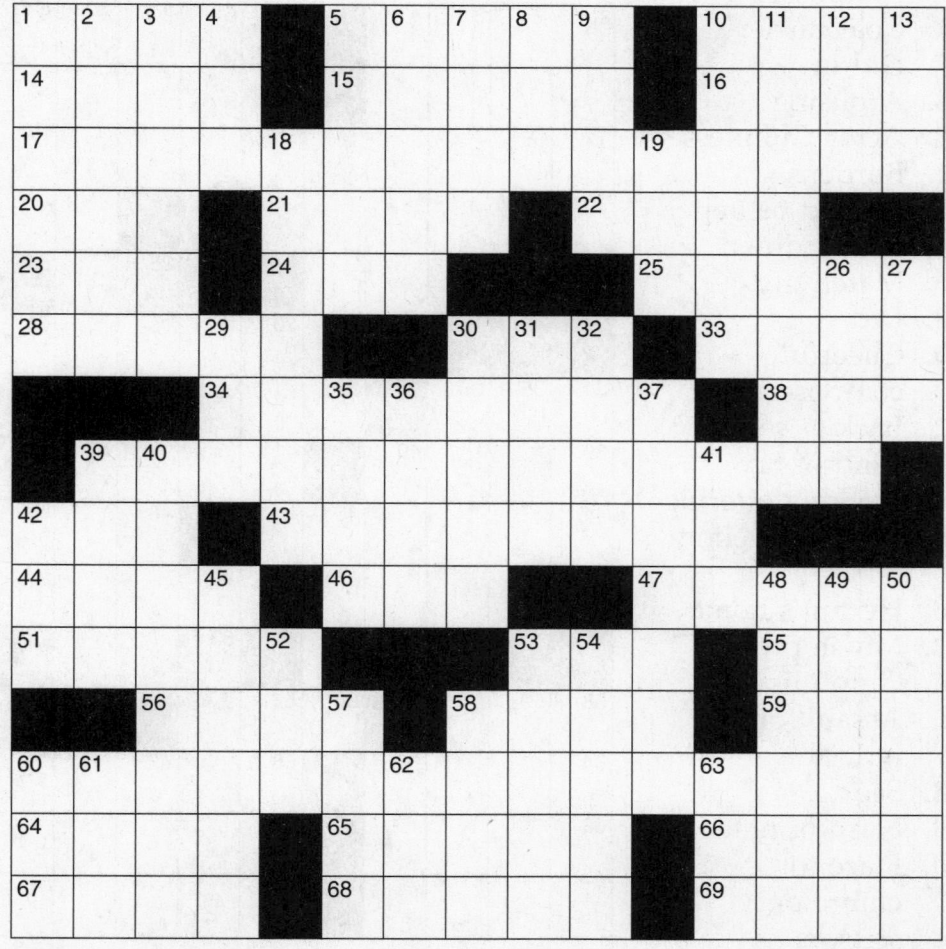

482 WRITING TEAM PUNS by Alan Arbesfeld

ACROSS

1. List ender
5. Most populous member of the British Commonwealth
10. Sneakers brand
14. Part of the Hindu trinity
15. Booze
16. Door sign
17. Leisurely lyricist?
19. Playground cry
20. Teacher
21. Place for a nap
23. Mischief-maker
24. Intravenous injection
25. Mouths
27. Center
29. Side view of a composer?
34. Coal carrier
37. Did in
38. Arousing
39. Actor Guinness
41. Burdens
43. "Could be better"
44. Knock down
46. March org.
48. Led
49. Cheerful composer?
52. Back at sea
53. Kind of tax
54. La Scala offering
58. Before toweling off
60. Hermit's home
62. Movie promo
64. Graph line
66. Assault on a lyricist?
68. See
69. Nash of note
70. Place for embroidery scissors

71. Polo need
72. Sympathy
73. Bruce or Laura

DOWN

1. Massachusetts quartet
2. Type squiggle
3. To have, in Le Havre
4. Permitted
5. Words said with a nod
6. More restricted
7. Dull brown
8. Polar buildup
9. Prefix with nautical
10. __ Gardens, N.Y.
11. Show participant

12. Carpe __ (seize the day)
13. Measure
18. Wheels for big wheels
22. Norse hammer thrower
26. Perks
28. Saucers, maybe
30. Church leader
31. Remainder, in Rouen
32. Actress Kudrow
33. Greenspan concern: Abbr.
34. Muslim journey
35. Spread out on the dining table
36. Reason for some hisses

40. Young rhino
42. One with drive
45. Story
47. Serb foe
50. Dark time, maybe
51. Treated maliciously
55. Tickle pink
56. Come again
57. Actor Alan
58. Stinger
59. Northern major-leaguer
61. "Look out . . ."
63. Go on and on
65. Hardly a neat house
67. Vitamin info, in brief

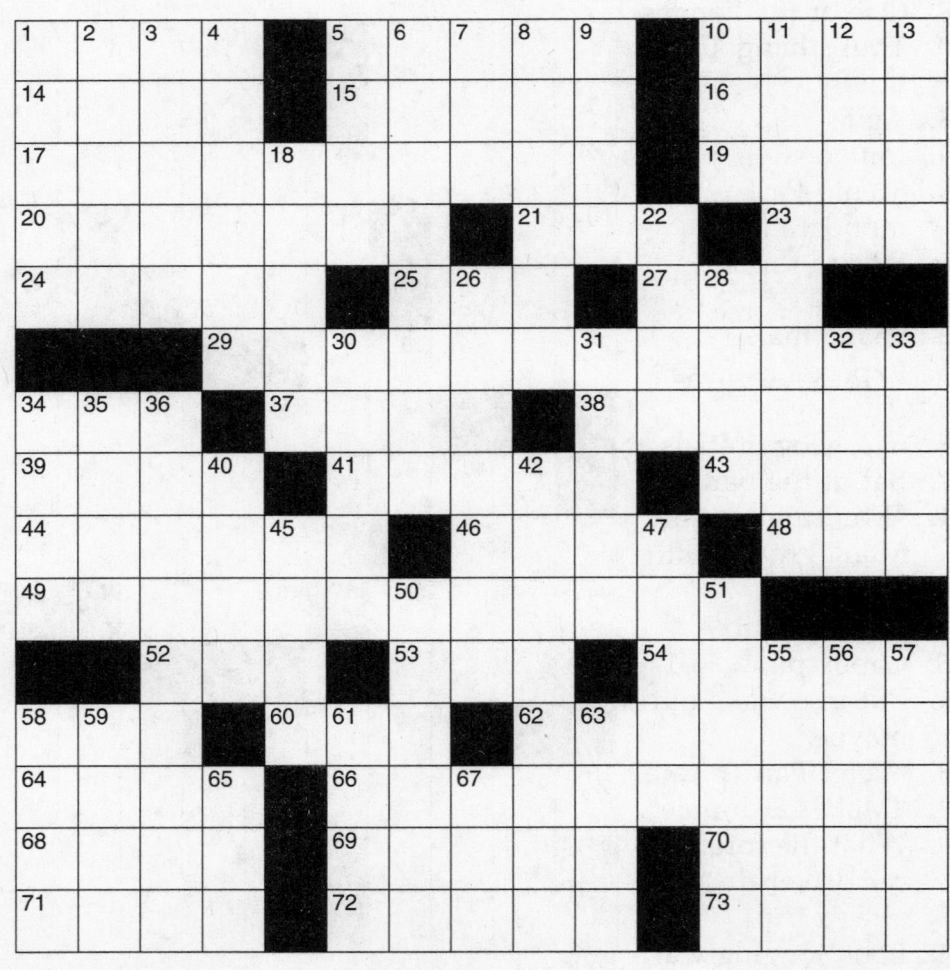

CASH BOXES *by Mary E. Brindamour*

ACROSS

1. "Jumpin' Jack Flash, it's __" (1968 lyric)
5. Give a hand
8. Wood-cutting tool
12. About
13. Like many Halloween masks
14. Quickly
15. Precipitate
16. Site of annual floods
17. Prodded
18. Errol Flynn kind of role
20. "Buenos __"
21. Gulf ship
22. Actress Tyler
23. Go without input
26. Rustic carriages
30. Bobby of hockey
31. Dimethyl sulfate and others
34. Precisely
35. Fictional daddy
37. "Well, I'll __ monkey's uncle!"
38. Competitor of New York Life
39. Dutch cheese
40. Touchdown area?
42. Part of H.R.H.
43. Covetous one
45. X-shaped warning sign next to railroad tracks
47. __ King Cole
48. Diamond side
50. Sundry: Abbr.
52. Columbus's home
56. Overact
57. All __
58. Captain with the "overbearing dignity of some mighty woe"
59. Wingdings
60. __ chic
61. City on the Brazos
62. Olden despot
63. Fizzle sound
64. "Unto us __ is given"

DOWN

1. Haughtiness
2. Nibble
3. Diva's piece
4. Electric eye, e.g.
5. Lively
6. More sick, in dialect
7. Fabric worker
8. Low Army rank
9. Not a short story
10. Makes a hole-in-one
11. Tie the knot
13. Loosens, as a belt
14. Television minus the vision
19. Busy places
22. Weight abbr.
23. Planted
24. Ball club deal
25. Tapestry
26. Interlining stiffener
27. Author Philip and others
28. Queen Margrethe's subjects
29. 58-Across's first mate
32. Ski lift
33. Always, to a poet
36. Fuller name?
38. "Green __"
40. Asian holiday
41. Get into
44. Revs
46. Where Carleton University is
48. Phobias
49. Actor Lew
50. Parisian ladies: Abbr.
51. Little bit
52. Amount of rain
53. Cries while brainstorming
54. Sandwich with a crunch
55. Black
56. Newt

484 SWEENEY RAVE *by Harvey Estes and Nancy Salomon*

ACROSS

1. Actress Gaynor
6. "__ la vista, baby!"
11. Serpent's sound
14. Flareup of crime?
15. Dizzying pictures
16. Goon
17. Watch a shaky Japanese money market?
19. Passing assistance?
20. Lean and lovely
21. With 33-Down, 1978 Nobel Prize recipient
23. Cold war foe
26. Contemptuous looks
27. Unblocks
28. Librarygoer
30. __ d'oeuvre
31. Fictional hero first filmed in 1920
32. N.Y. winter hrs.
35. Not straight
36. What each of today's four long answers is vis-à-vis New Year's Eve
38. The Seine is full of it
39. Pitches
40. Words for actors
41. Briefs, briefly
42. Band on a limb
44. Run in the raw
46. Dessert not for the diet-conscious
48. Popular magazine since 1926
49. Off drugs
50. Jean of "Bombshell"
52. Get one past
53. This little poem or that?
58. Kitten's cry
59. Lighthouse sites
60. Fall away
61. Prefix with Columbian
62. Forfeits fur
63. Actress Danning of "Hercules"

DOWN

1. Women with shavers
2. It makes one hot
3. Mao __-tung
4. Asian grasses popular on lawns
5. "Well!"
6. Bays
7. Pit-__ (heart sound)
8. Reliever's triumph
9. Three for Sophia
10. Haphazardly
11. Call off the debt?
12. Headhunter's equipment
13. J. C. Penney rival
18. Takes home
22. Wedding notice word
23. Pronunciation symbol
24. Prayer opening
25. Sheep with all its marbles?
26. She played Darlene on "Roseanne"
28. Writer's reference
29. Does the wrong thing
31. Author Grey
33. See 20-Across
34. Wild boar features
36. Astronomical data providers
37. Bank-washer in Cairo
41. Suds source
43. Cereal box info
44. Shopaholic's delight
45. Pirates' stashes
46. Rogue
47. Cause of a nasty gut feeling?
48. Basketball tactic
50. Hoopla
51. Starstruck
54. Down-home turndown
55. Rip off
56. Star Wars letters
57. Electrifying swimmer

CHILD'S PLAY by William I. Johnston

ACROSS

1. Creators of booms
5. Like some classical architecture
10. Free
13. Kind of pricing
14. Levi's "Christ Stopped at __"
15. Midvoyage
16. Lowest card in pinochle
17. He follows Jay
18. Marionette maker Tony
19. Some outdoor festivals
21. Case in Latin
23. Loaded Londoners
24. Turns in
25. Bring to light
28. Elvis's middle name
29. Obstacle
32. Duffer's dream
35. Lock
36. It may be missed
37. Assayer's measure
39. Fooled
40. Hoisting apparatus
42. Conceal, as cards
44. Outbursts
45. Asylum seeker
48. Fall follower
49. Frittata
50. Novelist's frustration
54. Ne plus ultra
55. Judge, e.g.
57. Country singer Mason
58. __ ex machina
59. Bother terribly

60. Bumped off
61. Tight end, at times
62. Doesn't work
63. It may be cracked

DOWN

1. Beach application
2. Trim
3. "Pride's Crossing" playwright Howe
4. Breastbones
5. Amount of sound
6. They're found among the reeds
7. Silver and Brown
8. Dockworkers' org.
9. Masonry unit
10. Carrier name until 1997
11. Chutzpah
12. Artery problems
15. Actor John of "The Addams Family"
20. Valley of the Kings sites
22. From __ Z
24. Wasn't merely mad
25. Job preceder: Abbr.
26. Remarkably, in commercialese
27. Shaded
30. First of Caesar's claims
31. Sister or mother
32. Places of protection
33. Yachter's bane

34. Times for vacances
37. Done for
38. Kind of year
40. Sans-serif typeface
41. Vacation souvenirs
42. Whines
43. Tree rings indication
45. Dragnet operation
46. Host
47. Leg bone
48. Doctor
50. Clever ones
51. Anticrime acronym
52. Where runners are found
53. It may get a runaround
56. "Norma __"

486 LOCATION IS EVERYTHING *by Rand H. Burns*

ACROSS

1. Turned on the waterworks
5. Former East German secret police
10. Hot tub inlets
14. In charge of
15. Range feature
16. Half of dieciseis
17. CBS reporter Braver
18. You must remember this
19. Tartan representation
20. Snake in the grass, literally
23. Take potshots (at)
24. Wren's wing
25. Let down, say
26. Scooted
28. "The Mystery of __ Vep" (Charles Ludlam play)
30. Arm muscle
33. Villains, at times
37. Awarder of badges: Abbr.
38. Swaddles
40. Stay flat
41. Mariachi topper
43. Cossack chief
45. Parks on a bus
46. Where the Saône and Rhône meet
47. __ High Dam
50. Big Board's Can. equivalent
52. Midsection
56. Flash in the pan, literally
59. Needle dropper
60. Underway
61. Road __
62. Work units
63. "The Unbearable Bassington" writer

64. Attention-getter at sea
65. Untouchables chief
66. More devious
67. Symbol of inactivity

DOWN

1. Diet site
2. Lake Geneva spa
3. Kind of dish
4. Gallivant
5. Sojourn
6. Out of plumb
7. Menotti title role
8. Pasta ingredient
9. Unyielding
10. Waggish
11. Showiness
12. Anglo-Saxon aristocrat
13. Whale finder
21. Alternative to mushrooms
22. Where John Rolfe married Pocahontas
27. Anglo-Saxon laborers
29. Indemnify
30. Small shot
31. Prefix with diametric
32. Picture taker, in combinations
33. Sign of a big crowd
34. Hackberry's kin

35. Estuary
36. Hill person: Abbr.
39. Hardly kindly
42. Not in one's cups?
44. 8-Down, to Sal Mineo
46. Poe poem
47. Quaker?
48. Cathedral topper
49. Waiting area, with "the"
51. Unsentimental
53. Sun Valley locale
54. Bell-shaped flowers
55. Low poker pair
57. Schools of whales
58. ". . . like __ not!"

ACROSS

1. Cause of gray hair
5. Olympic success
10. They may be collared
14. Flier's feat
15. Professor Hill
16. Stub __
17. Distribute a 1964 Sidney Lumet film
20. Bell site
21. Quarrel
22. Suds
23. "High Noon" sheriff Will __
24. Seedy second-floor apartment
29. 1997 Masters winner
31. Frozen dew
32. Go __
33. 1990's singer Tori
34. Substantive
36. Nile menace
37. E.R. employees
38. Bluebelle, e.g., in old TV ads
39. Phony phone caller
40. Protest leader
44. Awaken
45. 401(k) cousins
46. Blue
49. Racing vehicles
53. Hipsters' ballpark lunch
56. Confusion
57. Carnation holder
58. Issue
59. Keatsian works
60. Trades jabs
61. N.B.A. personnel

DOWN

1. Dangerous nestful
2. Charge
3. Choice word
4. Crown material, in the Wisdom of Solomon
5. Beaten badly
6. Intestinal prefix
7. Subtraction amt.
8. __ standstill
9. Used a payment plan
10. Bunch
11. Division politique
12. Sukiyaki ingredient
13. Slip (in)
18. Leads the bidding
19. Like some calendars
23. Masseur's target
24. It's ruled
25. "__ Fool Believes" (1979 #1 hit)
26. Jeweler's unit
27. Familiar with
28. Amount of corn
29. Occasions when the arms are raised
30. Hawks' former arena
34. Broadway fare
35. __'acte
36. Person with a cause
38. Bit of high jinks
39. Do together
41. Carpet fibers
42. Closer
43. Needs a bib
46. Second time around?
47. Way to go
48. Slip (in)
50. "Coriolanus" setting
51. Work-weary exclamation
52. J. F. K. jets
54. Water source
55. Loser's place?

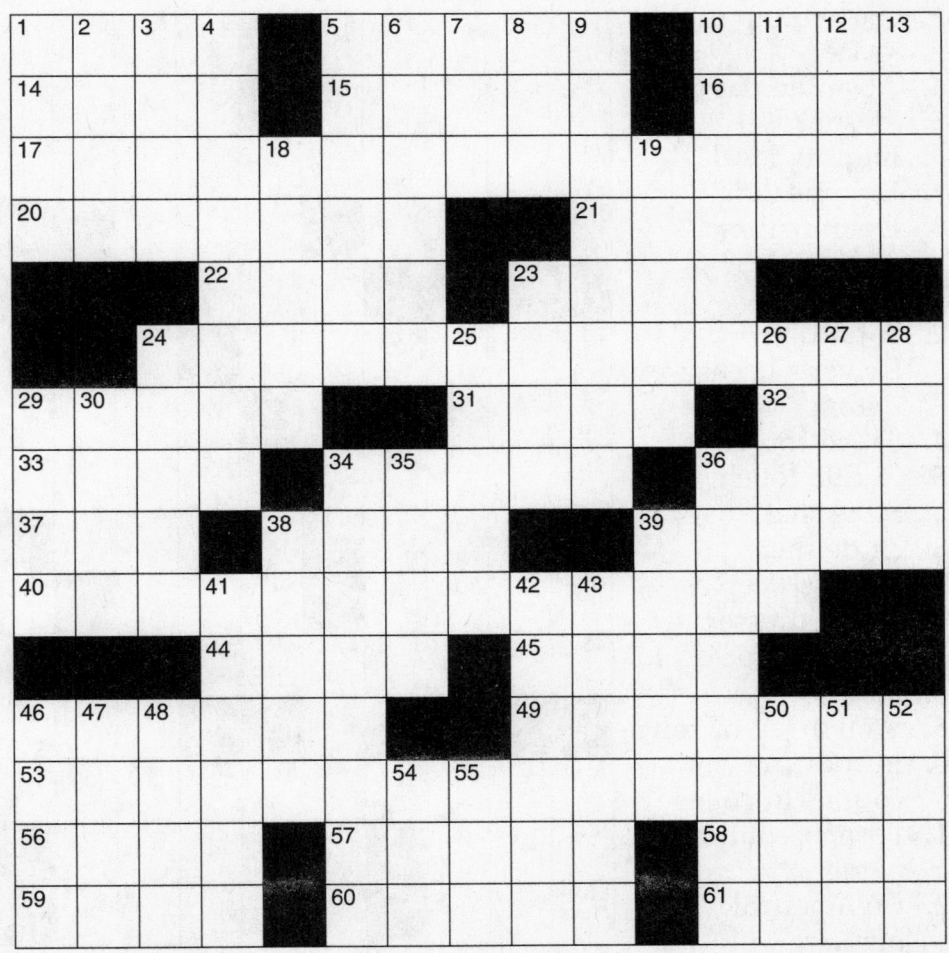

488 HOLD EVERYTHING *by Henry Hook*

ACROSS

1. Overwhelm
6. Prince in "The Arabian Nights' Entertainments"
11. Word of indecision
14. Mischief-maker
15. String quartet member
16. Popular cable channel
17. Start trouble
20. Probation
21. Best-selling
22. Over: Prefix
23. Actor Wheaton
24. Challenging potato chip quantity
28. Go on a gamboling spree
32. A welcome sight?
33. 1961 chimp in space
34. Absinthe flavor
35. #1 spot
36. Iniquity locales
37. Unappealing
40. Examination format
41. On
42. A bit daft
43. Driver's license datum
44. Sauce source
45. Gentle touch
46. Straw hat
48. __ de mer
49. Actress Peeples
50. Smart dresser
51. Comic strip "__ & Janis"
55. Wall array of song
60. Introductory course, in college
61. Former country name
62. Commercial bovine
63. Fever reading, maybe
64. Buck of note
65. Letters from overseas

DOWN

1. Lady Macbeth's problem
2. Piece of absorbent material
3. Lets go
4. Moneymaking venture
5. Royal insomnia cause
6. Profit
7. Suggestion
8. Low
9. Little one
10. Coolidge's Veep
11. One who's left hanging
12. Texas __
13. "Undeniably"
18. It might go into a pot
19. Chose
23. Valuable insect-eater
24. Clog
25. Western Athletic Conference sch.
26. Some musical groups
27. Montaigne output
28. Comprehensive book lists
29. Hooded jacket
30. Aid for the anemic
31. 1899 Eduardo di Capua melody
32. A real man?
35. V.I.P. on the Titanic's casualty list
38. Smooth
39. Autumnal stone
45. Syndicate bigwig
47. Ball material
48. He took two tablets
50. Forest growth
51. Competent
52. Balance
53. Movie princess
54. Bonanza finds
55. Emergency call
56. Popular Saab model
57. Choice marble
58. Trumped-up story
59. Red topper

ROOM FOR FAILURE *by Rich Norris*

ACROSS

1. Harmful
4. Insufficient, as an excuse
7. Kind of gun
12. Reveals, à la Shakespeare
14. Potential C.I.A. problem
15. Unequaled
16. Amble
17. In __ (clueless)
18. Woman of letters?
19. Deli counter order
22. Campus groups
23. Reproducible in great detail
27. In demand
28. Like most stadiums
30. Dumb cluck
31. Literary monogram
32. First name in jazz
33. Brave
34. It creates a big splash
37. Obscure
40. Eastern ties
41. Jerk
44. Enthralled
45. Send away
47. Capt.'s prediction
48. Perdue product
50. Retracted reluctantly
52. It was first tested in 1952
54. "The Wolf in Sheep's Clothing" writer
57. Rising locale?
58. Adah's spouse
59. Totaled
60. Hungers
61. Mil. education grp.
62. Betray
63. Scrap
64. "Mighty __ a Rose"

DOWN

1. Soup served with sour cream
2. Hunks, so to speak
3. Drift
4. Marketing technique
5. Slugger Moises
6. Extent
7. Kept
8. Emphasized
9. Former Dodger Cey
10. Richards of Texas
11. Formal vote
13. Brief moments?
14. Sickened
20. Honor
21. Youngster
24. Youngster
25. Fingers
26. Playing hard to get
29. Jersey fabric
33. Israelites' pre-Exodus home
34. Moguls
35. "Mississippi Burning" part
36. Is attentive
37. Obstacle
38. Inflatable item
39. 1988 Meg Ryan film
41. Kind of can
42. Leaf apertures
43. Carpenter's aid
45. Night spot?
46. Gulch
49. Editor's concerns
51. Breaker, maybe
53. Surpassing in rank
54. Line made with a compass
55. Keen perception
56. __-Cat

490 SPENT by Cathy Millhauser

ACROSS

1. Engrossed
5. Pooch originally from Wales
10. "J'accuse" penner
14. Limerick land
15. To __ (perfectly)
16. Nephew of Abel
17. Handle many deer carelessly?
20. Agnes and Cecil B.
21. Go ballistic
22. Blockheads
23. Garfield's owner
24. Criticize singer Johnny?
31. With 43-Across, use bubble gum?
35. Teems
36. Cookie in stacking contests
37. Physics Nobelist Isidor
38. One Knight
39. Hand (out)
40. Constant
41. Attack
43. See 31-Across
44. Prepare a Time Inc. magazine?
47. Foot, in zoology
48. Appointed
52. "__ fideles . . ."
56. Nacre sources
59. Transfer hay?
61. Prefix with knock or lock
62. Be superior
63. Cooer
64. Clarinet part
65. Future fern
66. Dolly and others

DOWN

1. Fred's portrayer on "Sanford"
2. Broadcast
3. Spot broadcast, often
4. Halfhearted
5. Telephones
6. Missouri Indian relative
7. Tracks in mud
8. Miracle-__ (plant food brand)
9. Affluxes
10. Olympian ruler
11. In the past
12. Mischievous Norse god
13. Entourage part: Abbr.
18. In an unbalanced way
19. Beethoven's birthplace
23. Noted athletic retiree of 1999
25. Pole images
26. Caused by
27. Musical wrap-up
28. In line
29. Ward of TV's "Sisters"
30. Readied some beds
31. Songwriter Jacques
32. Stromboli output
33. Mind
34. Lush, perhaps
41. Works as a longshoreman
42. Having some merit
45. Words before speed or snuff
46. Korea Bay feeder
49. Parisian daily, with "Le"
50. Set up financially
51. Search (into)
52. Yon
53. Completed
54. Art Deco designer
55. Winter fender-bender cause
56. With a bow, to Stern
57. Boxer Max
58. Gets the picture
60. Food pkg. abbr.

ACROSS

1. Belle of the old West
6. Jackpot
10. Michigan college
14. Some are super
15. One-named designer
16. Pushes off
17. Betray?
19. Irish novelist O'Brien
20. They have black eyes
21. Study
23. Read (for)
26. Peer Gynt's mother
29. Amazed looks?
33. Places where it's sunny
35. Quick
36. Persisted
37. Ax to grind
38. Spanish folk song
39. One in the minority
42. Some social outings?
44. Three times: Prefix
45. Places for knickknacks
47. "Little Orphan Annie" henchman
50. How not to run a business
55. __ Kong
56. Fakes, in basketball?
59. Artist Nolde
60. Some needlework
61. Cloth fold
62. Technique
63. Timeline divisions
64. Mongolian tents

DOWN

1. 1960's civil rights org.
2. Foe for El Cordobés
3. Swear
4. Barely speak
5. Turn forward or back, say
6. Cyrus the Great, e.g.
7. Metal precioso
8. Nail-biting events: Abbr.
9. Land famous for its lyric poets
10. Secretive figure?
11. Big deposit
12. Item often left at apartment doors
13. "By yesterday!"
18. Bring by the truckload
22. Utility woe
24. Hosp. readout
25. __ Arc, Ark.
26. "Be-Bop-__" (Gene Vincent hit)
27. Overseas legislature
28. Old coin?
30. "Roots" role
31. Patriarch
32. Brand
33. Neighbor of Sudan
34. Country parties
37. Ledger column
39. U.N.'s Hammarskjöld
40. Suffix with Gotham
41. Woolen covers
43. Spot
46. Maudlin
47. 1954 sci-fi film
48. Our genus
49. "Idylls of the King" lady
51. Humdinger
52. "The Leaves of Life keep falling one by one" poet
53. Restaurant bar?
54. They're not baby boomers
57. Former pol. entity
58. Major record label

492 STRIKEOUTS *by Jim Page*

ACROSS

1. Chest display
6. __ and Span
10. Taken
13. Out
14. "__ Rebel" (1962 #1 hit)
15. Glittery material
16. Mysterious "Ivanhoe" character, with "the"
18. Actress Merkel and others
19. German article
20. Years on end
21. Dissolved substance
23. Eventual period
25. Polo period
26. Suffix with hip or quip
27. Striped antelopes
30. Self: Prefix
31. Ninny
33. Choice reading?
34. Stats for Sosa: Abbr.
35. Jar
37. Lunched
38. "Friends" role
40. "Rescue 911" action
41. Division word
43. Goddess: Lat.
44. "It must be him, __ shall die"
45. Knock down
47. Call at camp
51. Work on cud, say
53. "Satanic Verses" author
55. "P.T.L. Club" couple, once
56. Faction
57. Easy chair site

58. Seat of Jackson County, Tex.
59. Figureheads?
62. Angry, with "off"
63. Arkie neighbor
64. Third-largest city in Puerto Rico
65. Number after due
66. North Sea feeder
67. Factions

DOWN

1. Cabaret singer Mercer et al.
2. Cass __ of the Mamas and the Papas
3. Sen. Feinstein
4. Epitome of simplicity
5. Hooch
6. Climb (up)
7. Good baseball throws
8. Somewhat: Suffix
9. Hospital image
10. Jewish festivals
11. Dilettantes
12. Strands
15. Corker
17. Everyday names
22. "Yeah, right"
24. 1965 Pulitzer novelist Shirley Ann __
28. "Are not!" comeback
29. Jeans brand
32. Baseball Hall-of-Famer Duke

35. Butter knife
36. Athlete's problem
37. Cash dispenser, for short
39. Curse
40. Heavyweight champ of 1892–97
42. Paper pusher?
43. Difference between 19 and 21
46. One on a long walk
48. Calculator figure
49. Drill through
50. Common pentad
52. Commander
54. Advances
56. French silk
60. Endorses
61. Luau serving

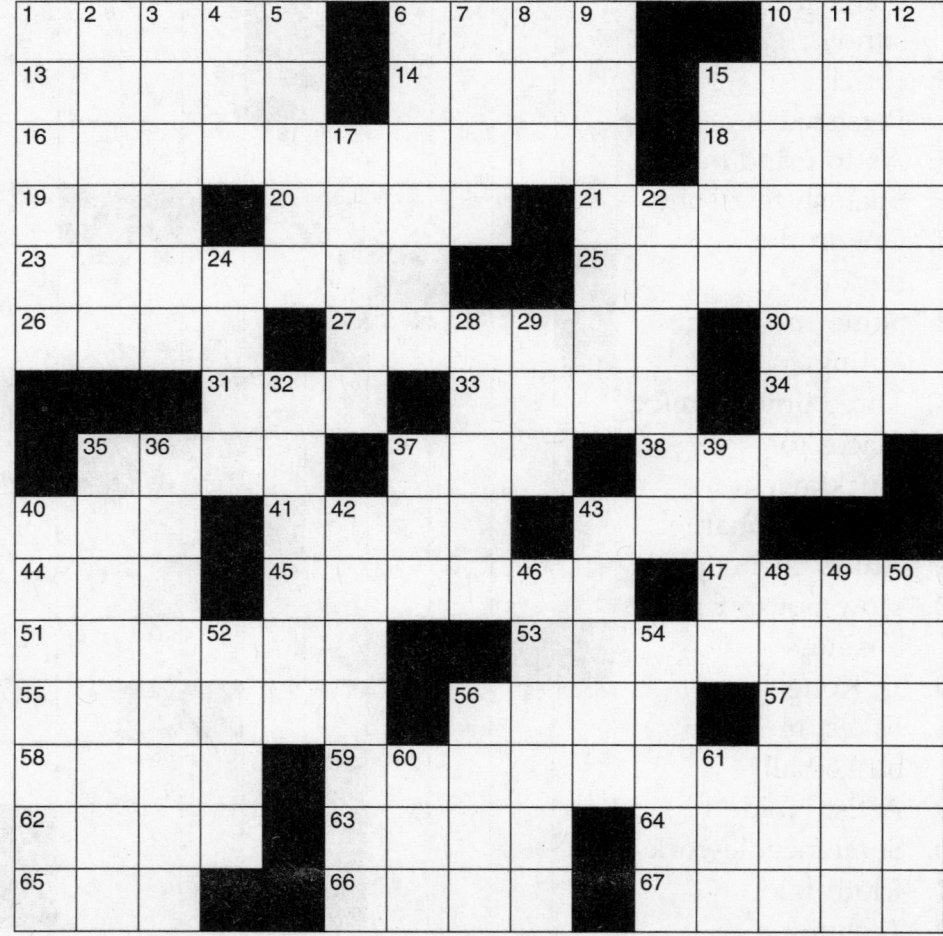

BUSY BODIES? *by Cathy Millhauser*

ACROSS

1. Work on a pumpkin, perhaps
6. Secular
10. Bogus
14. Xenophile's friend
15. It may get a licking after dinner
16. "Voilà!"
17. Agency that manages kiosks?
19. Don Juan's mother
20. Refraction phenomenon
21. Put away
22. "__ on $45 a Day"
24. Sellers of miniatures?
27. Short stop?
30. Sack
31. Gaff or boom
32. Marx with a horn
34. "Shine a Little Love" rock grp.
35. Designer's need
39. Overnight mail services?
43. "How to Murder Your Wife" star Virna
44. Kind of juice
45. Fictional Italian town
46. Hockey great __ Broten
48. Recovery place
50. Sushi may be sold in this
51. Maker of car components?
56. Release from an eye
57. Part of MOMA
58. Hit the helipad
62. Stead
63. Hairdressing operation?
66. __-major (staff office)
67. 1930's–40's pianist Templeton
68. Actress Gia __
69. Insolence
70. Make a bundle
71. Wired

DOWN

1. Change, perhaps
2. __ Loma, Calif.
3. 100 dinars
4. Toxic stuff
5. Stoppage
6. Made a high ball?
7. Prospero's servant
8. Suffix with 1-Down
9. Discover
10. Like Chinese pepper steak
11. Capital on the Red River
12. Skilled
13. Some pencil puzzles
18. "The Sweetest Taboo" singer, 1985
23. Hagen of Broadway
25. It's in the winds
26. Capital on the 60th parallel
27. Illustrator Silverstein
28. Hack
29. Surrealist Jean and others
33. Hard copy pages
34. Popular 90's essayist
36. Sturdy cart
37. Feminine suffix
38. ". . . and shall bring forth __": Matthew
40. Squarely
41. Tension-producing performance
42. Actor James
47. Placido's "that"
48. Spiff (up)
49. Shows of approval
51. Whines
52. "West Side Story" girl
53. Flightless birds
54. Normand of the silents
55. Old TV's "__ Derringer"
59. Spring
60. Vacation spot
61. Rimsky-Korsakov's "The Tale of __ Saltan"
64. Motor suffix, commercially
65. -like

494 SINGLE SPACE *by Manny Nosowsky*

ACROSS

1. Coffee get-together
7. V.I.P.'s
13. Low-fat meat
14. Stumped
16. Relaxing
17. Affectedly dainty
18. Photo __
19. It's strapped around the head
21. Predatory fish
22. Hotsy-__
24. Tchaikovsky's Symphony No. 5 __ minor
25. Outpouring
27. Communist-hunting grp. of the 50's
28. Setup
30. Stirs
31. First call, perhaps
33. Zingers
35. Suffix with acetyl
36. $$$ for old age
37. Gambling game
41. Some
45. W.W. II org.
46. Not give __
48. Top parts of suits
49. __ in the right direction
51. Business magazine
52. Opera singer Simon __
53. Mathematician's ordinal
54. Tell accidentally
57. Overseas article
58. Most dreary
60. Risky way to run
62. Arranged in order
63. Some West Indians
64. Borrower's quest
65. Mug

DOWN

1. Unwelcome sign?
2. Cigarette ad claim
3. Back on board
4. It's pulled at a carnival
5. This, for example
6. Stroke of excellence
7. Most people look out for it
8. Samoan capital
9. Mamie's hairdo
10. Stock page heading: Abbr.
11. Fighting force
12. Forum participant
13. Servings for the sick
15. Way out
20. Modern means of identification
23. It "is nothing but perception," wrote Plato
26. Tropical toppers
28. "Ta-ta!"
29. "The Sacred Wood" writer
32. Old Eng. title
34. Letters on seconds
37. Sounds in archery
38. Spendthrift
39. Diner sign
40. Pitcher's triumph
41. Wee hour
42. Like an amazing return on an investment
43. Type in again
44. Features of The New York Review of Books
47. Switch positions
50. Make a case
52. They're guarded in competition
55. Italian art patron
56. Christian inscription
59. Negative side
61. Criminal patterns, for short

ACROSS

1. Wisconsin dairy product
8. Clad
15. Like Niccolò Paganini
16. Basement fixture
17. Vagabond, in 37-Across
18. Big banana exporter
19. Fed. money overseer
20. Don Juan
21. Pale __
22. District in Japan
26. Not just a hike
27. Nipper
28. Physicist Sakharov
30. Overseas ties
32. Lingerie item
33. Fawns
37. National song, theme of today's puzzle
40. Solid alcohol
41. Third qtr. time
42. Vale
43. Shoelace tips
45. Great Basin Natl. Park locale
46. Influence
49. Electricity pioneer Volta
53. Duty
54. Grand slam foursome
55. Buzzing about
56. Forming an exact proper divisor, in math
58. Sheep, in 37-Across
62. Not ersatz
63. University in Garden City, N.Y.
64. Border decorations
65. Apple variety

DOWN

1. Like a system of scientific meas.
2. Chop
3. 1930's Spanish queen
4. "A __ Flanders" (1959 tear-jerker)
5. Director Jonathan
6. Easy __
7. Stimpy's TV pal
8. Trepid, dialectally
9. Food carrier, in 37-Across
10. Align
11. Actress Balin
12. "M*A*S*H" role
13. St. Cyr, for one
14. Movie "10"
20. Fugitives
22. Tractor blades
23. Morocco's capital
24. Ancient Roman magistrate
25. Mountain pool
26. Pusillanimous
29. Chow down
31. It may be rounded up in a roundup
32. Backwater, in 37-Across
34. Mix
35. Clock watcher
36. Blast
38. Last king of Albania
39. Rumple, with "up"
44. In groups
46. Put on
47. Like corduroy
48. Firing
50. Gulf war ally
51. Slogan writers
52. Highborn
54. Totally botch
57. On the __ vive
58. Head bone
59. Pkg. deliverer
60. When repeated, a dance
61. One of TV's "Bosom Buddies"

ACROSS

1. Natl. Adopt-a-Dog Month
4. Concert gear
8. Knickerbockers
13. Malted drink that's not a malted
14. Experiences losses
16. Budget alternative
17. U.S. 36 crosses it
18. Accessory
19. Defraud
20. Obliged
22. With 54-Across, hit from 36-Across
24. Hosted
25. "__ far, far better thing . . ."
26. North Sea feeder
27. Got off the ground
29. Popular candy
32. Tether
34. Heiress, maybe
36. Broadway premiere of 1946
41. Active
42. "Must-__" (NBC slogan)
43. 1939 Bogart title role
44. Actor Hawke
46. Mosque V.I.P.
50. Comical introduction
52. In the rococo style
54. See 22-Across
57. Weyerhaeuser Co. employee
58. Specks
59. On __ (carousing)
61. "Platoon" setting
62. Canticle
63. Mantelpiece

64. I.O.C. member
65. Remains
66. Baseball's Ordoñez et al.
67. Blokes

DOWN

1. 36-Across surname
2. What adjusters adjust
3. Playing card combo
4. Designer Simpson
5. Assortment
6. Prized
7. Apt description of 1-Down
8. Treaties
9. Football's __ Bowl
10. Axis figure
11. Capone's adversaries
12. Dance partner
15. Popular legend of Dutch origin
21. See 35-Down
23. Yang's opposite
28. London-to-Dover dir.
29. Solitaire puzzle piece
30. Old French coin
31. Meditative thought
33. Hosp. scan
34. Fanatic
35. With 21-Down, composer of 36-Across
36. Combine

37. Hide-hair link
38. Rule out
39. Its anagram is a synonym of itself
40. Winemaking science
44. Ocean flier
45. Word with bore or wave
47. Selleck TV role
48. Not troubled
49. 36-Across star
50. Brouhaha
51. Bridge positions
53. Some school methods
54. 1979 disco classic
55. Circus cries
56. Kings Peak locale
60. Jonson work

SPOIL FOR A LADY *by Kelly Clark*

ACROSS
1. Cutoffs, maybe, before they were cutoffs
6. Sound of breaking up?
10. Masterpieces
14. Sylvia Plath book
15. Religious image
16. Baker's need
17. Oft-quoted Yogi
18. Old Spanish kingdom
19. Coin no longer being minted
20. What happens when Kansas City wins a World Series?
23. Sea's partner
25. Draw
26. Boston team, in brief
27. Why is the milk production survey so screwy?
32. Kind of wrench
33. Like a Burns acquaintance
34. Sharp
35. Detroit's county
37. Item in which to do a plié
41. Resistance units
42. Not just a franchisee
43. Why is the drought-plagued swim club bankrupt?
47. Film maker Frank
49. Playboy head, to friends
50. Lake Okeechobee's state: Abbr.
51. What's the anagrammatic reason for these odd questions?
56. Kind of gin
57. Food for Fido

58. Songs "di sentimento"
61. High scores
62. 1963 Liz Taylor role
63. Busybody
64. New England's locale
65. Fish locale
66. "Broca's Brain" author

DOWN
1. Elbows do it
2. Before
3. BB gun, e.g.
4. Peter Lorre's role in "The Story of Mankind"
5. Mercury astronaut Deke

6. Noted Talmudic sage
7. Ones that may be high?
8. Tough
9. __ Domini
10. Green party?
11. In a bad way
12. Excellence
13. Says quickly
21. Be in a bad way
22. Kind of wit or test
23. Saturate
24. Curly cabbage
28. Compose
29. Authority
30. Press for payment
31. Ginger __
35. "__ me?"
36. Band aid?
37. Air letters?

38. Making whole
39. Make known
40. Bear with us at night
41. Voiced
42. Times when you're not at your peak
43. Pinafores
44. Thirstiest
45. "Hey, check that out!"
46. Guitarist Paul
47. Class
48. Cop __
52. It's the truth
53. Spanish pot
54. Available
55. Vicinity
59. __ standstill
60. Mateo or Miguel, e.g.

498 TWO DEGREES OF 35-ACROSS *by David J. Kahn*

ACROSS

1. Orchestra alternative
5. Comment around the deck?
10. Terrible __
14. Last words?
15. Opposite of sur
16. Four-letter word
17. Architect Saarinen
18. Company whose logo has a red "o"
19. Cogitate
20. Noted director who acted in 30-Across with 35-Across
23. Bud of baseball
24. Before, once
25. Isle of Man residents
28. Brought up
30. See 20-Across
32. Calif. neighbor
33. Midpoint: Abbr.
34. On a roll
35. See 20-Across and 54-Across
40. Big __
41. Link
42. Classified inits.
43. See 54-Across
46. Singer Mel and namesakes
49. Napoléon led one
50. "Forget it!"
52. __ Park, N.J.
54. Noted director who acted in 43-Across with 35-Across
57. Drunk's tipoff
59. Plant and animal life
60. Andrews of "The Mod Squad"
61. Money writer Marshall __
62. "A house __ a home"
63. __ Bator
64. The rich man in "Rich Man, Poor Man"
65. Some guard dogs, for short
66. Get better

DOWN

1. Loamy deposit
2. Good dog
3. Slimming device
4. Some English students
5. "__ Room" (Beach Boys hit)
6. Spent
7. Shady alcove
8. Kind of heel
9. Push, maybe
10. Tabby's mate
11. Wisconsin city
12. Exciting times in the N.I.T.
13. __-wolf
21. Plume source
22. Earlier
26. Brave one
27. Harden
29. 1980 Tony winner
31. Gluck's "__ ed Euridice"
33. 29-Down role
35. Precious
36. Not permeated (with)
37. Silly
38. 1938 Physics Nobelist
39. Campaign asset
40. Support provider
44. Nigh
45. Terre's opposite
46. A lonely place, so they say
47. Store, as fodder
48. Ad dressing?
51. Let __
53. Successively
55. Power stats
56. Tanks
57. Certain camera, for short
58. Baseball's Brock

ACROSS
1. They go into drives
6. Waste
11. Rapscallion
14. Outdo
15. Station
16. Postal creed word
17. Embarrassed person's nickname?
19. John __
20. Made some lace
21. Elusive
23. Monogram ltr.
25. High points
26. Well-fed baby in a multiple birth?
31. "Shell and Head" sculptor Hans
32. "Love __ Around" (1968 Troggs hit)
33. Action after a default
37. Reprimand
39. Air show formation
40. Vetoed
41. French door part
42. Related on the mother's side
44. Skater Midori
45. One who dropped a pill on the floor?
49. Cigar
52. Word with work or Web
53. Procrastinator's refrain
56. "Peer Gynt" composer et al.
60. Actress Hagen
61. Shakespearean sunburn victim?
63. "Like, I get it"
64. Heart chambers
65. Cleo or Frankie

66. __ City (Saratoga Springs nickname)
67. Adjusts
68. Scoffing look

DOWN
1. Old-style auxiliary verb
2. Ancient terrace farmer
3. Pants part
4. "Third Rock From the Sun" co-star
5. Magnificent
6. "Silent Spring" topic
7. Judges
8. Notorious '95 hurricane
9. Like bees and ants
10. Treeless plain
11. Kind of card
12. Melba, for one
13. Emulates raptors
18. Revamps, in a way
22. Kind of dish
24. Tour
26. Woodworking tool
27. Cetacean killer
28. Atop
29. Actress Graff
30. Kilt features
34. Get away
35. Tennis's Sampras
36. Radon lacks it
38. "Unhand me!"

40. Muted tones
43. Chicken cut
46. Lifesaver, at times
47. Dress down
48. Marcus's retail partner
49. Lath perpendiculars
50. Tally
51. Brando's birthplace
54. Pod vegetable
55. Milldam
57. Composer Siegmeister
58. Item in a pool
59. Song ending
62. German article

500 AYE-AYE! *by David J. Kahn*

ACROSS

1. Aid's partner
5. Things to be edited: Abbr.
8. __ buco
12. One who won't budge
13. Stir up, in a way
15. King who married Jezebel
16. 1961 Elvis film
18. Reformer Jacob
19. Fortune
20. Lose sleep (over)
22. Notre Dame is on one
23. It's 50–50
25. Makes ineffective
27. Arm bones
28. Grp.
30. Mortarboard tossers
31. Make up (for)
33. 1993 expansion team member
34. Dance specialty
37. Spanish queen
39. Denouement
40. Captivate
43. "Brazil" hit-maker, 1943
46. Caught in __
47. Hill person: Abbr.
48. Bottled spirits
52. Wrongly desire
54. Job for a rancher
56. Year in the papacy of St. Leo IX
57. Part of a series
59. Day-__
60. Others, in Latin
62. Theme of this puzzle
64. Check
65. Piano exercise
66. "Tell __ the judge"
67. Salinger story subject
68. Ushered
69. Dermatologist's concern

DOWN

1. "Journey Into Fear" mystery novelist, 1940
2. Popular watch
3. Removed chemically
4. Pipe joint
5. Complaint
6. Sport in which competitors don't want breaks
7. Collar
8. Sweep
9. Large, meaty mushroom
10. Came to port
11. Haunted
13. Pundit
14. Like some shoes
17. Equestrian's attire
21. Kellogg brand
24. Actress Peeples
26. __ lamp
29. Keep treating a black eye, maybe
32. Onetime Bruin star
33. Tease
34. Pippen, to Jordan, once
35. Greater __
36. Bombay-based religion
38. Sister's calling
41. Gullet
42. Mayberry boy
44. Correspond
45. Guitarist Nugent
47. Islamic worshiper
49. Bedwear: Var.
50. Coastal features
51. Member of a headhunting people in the Philippines
53. Salesman's preparation
55. Upper hand
58. Tire feature
61. Suburban finale
63. Game opener

1

```
ATE   SEALUP   HOSS
TUN ENTIRE   EVOE
UNDERCOVER   CEDE
BASTION    SATRAP
   HARES  ISIS
SEDATE  THATCHER
ABONE  TRINI  ALA
ROWE  ROOTS  ADIT
ANN  CORPS  SMOTE
HYACINTH  STOWED
   NORD  ESTAR
ADDUCE   CANASTA
MOOR  LOWERCLASS
ONUS  EVINCE  MAE
SATE  TORAHS  ERA
```

2

```
WEST   DADS   WADS
ANTI  ILIAD  ASIA
TERP  VINCE  KISS
CRESSIDA  FRENCH
    HOWOLDAREYOU
   VIE  DIMPLED
PACEM  ARENA  EXE
ODOR  STUNG  PAIN
RAM  CLANS  DIRTY
EMBROIL   ERA
  IMPLENTYNINE
REDCAP  CONSOLER
ERIK  EMOTE  LOWE
MICE  DELTA  AVEC
INKY  LEON  SERT
```

3

```
  AAF  MAIZE  ROCK
ECRU  IDLER  EBAN
SMILESMILESMILE
TELLALIE   TITLE
   BRET  MART
GERALD  MATA  ABC
ALEC  SABOT  MIR
TICKLETHEPALATE
OTT  ADEAL  AITS
REO  VEIN  BONNET
   MINN  BARD
ARRAS  FOREMAST
LAUGHCLOWNLAUGH
LIEN  AERIE  RETE
ALDA  POKEY  KRS
```

4

```
ABLE  DRAY  OPAH
SOUL  POISE  COLA
TOMBROWNSSCHOOL
APPEARED  ARLES
   GEL  SOME
SHAPED  INVESTS
PAGE  AMOUR  RAG
ORANGEMARMALADE
TEM  ADAGE  EDAM
  MARLENE  FLEETS
  ALLS  KEA
ADAME  ENTRANCE
BYEBYEBLACKBIRD
ENOL  BELCH  ULAN
DENE  BEAK  TEWA
```

5

```
ASIA  CLEO  CURB
HORN  HAITI  ANIL
ALASKANMALAMUTE
BON  INAPT  BESET
   CLOD  EER
ALEUTIANISLANDS
COLT   ANNE  AUT
ROBE  EMCEE  PUCE
ESO  EDAR  ORAL
SEWARDPENINSULA
   MAY  OBOE
ASSET  ASTER  IMA
WILLOWPTARMIGAN
ALAI  ASORT  CODE
YOGA  DEWY  CREW
```

6

```
OMAR  SALAD  AMEN
CEDE  PIECE  SAVE
HEASKEDWHATSNEW
STROLLED  DRIEST
   RELS  CHIS
PASTIS  THEATERS
ALIEN  BREAD  ROC
WILD  MOIST  RAGA
EBA  HOOKS  PETER
DISPERSE  SAVORY
   ANAT  TARE
BIMINI  HOMERUNS
INANANTIQUESHOP
DOIT  ENDUE  ALVA
ENDS  STEEL  LEAN
```

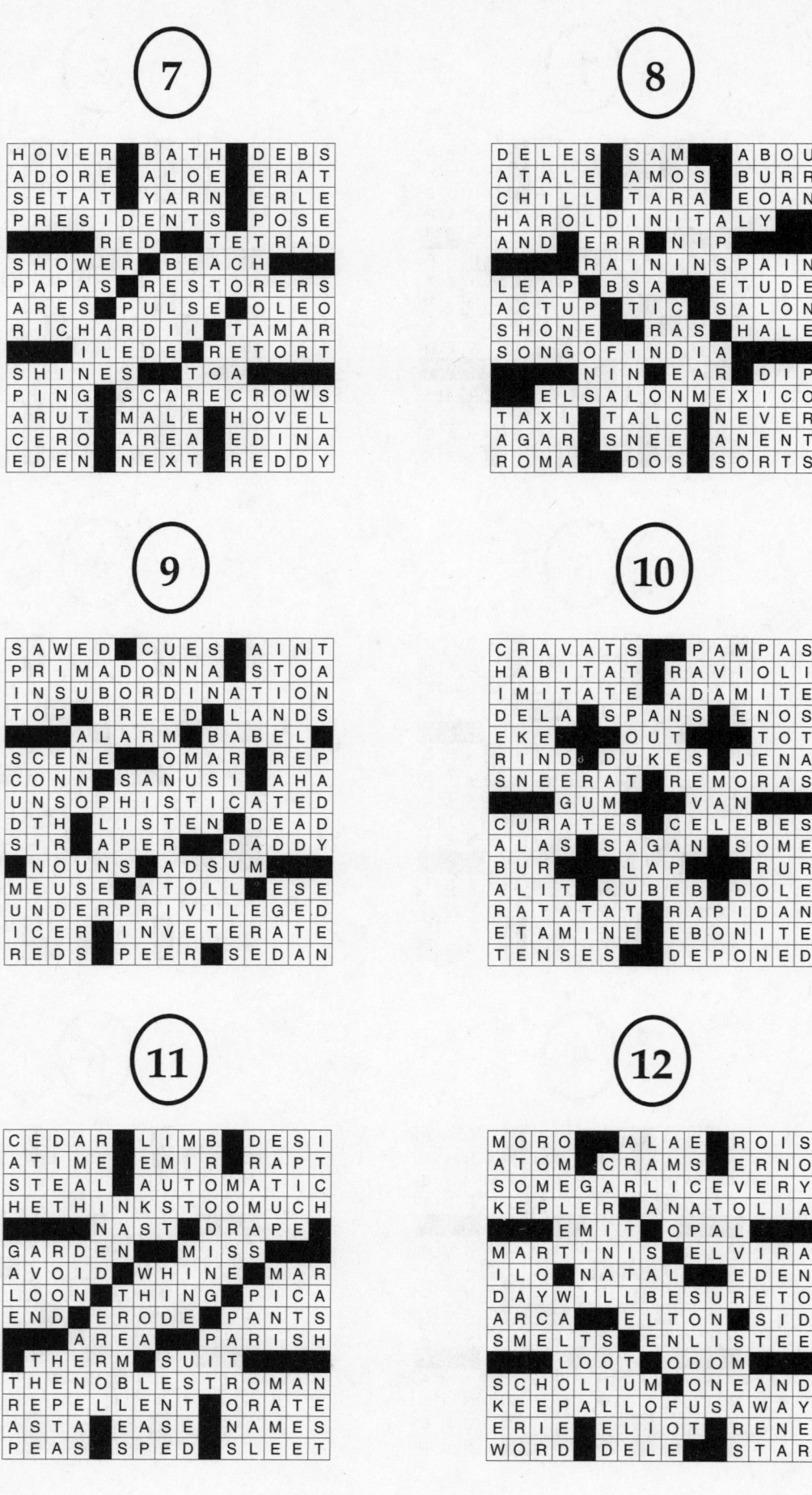

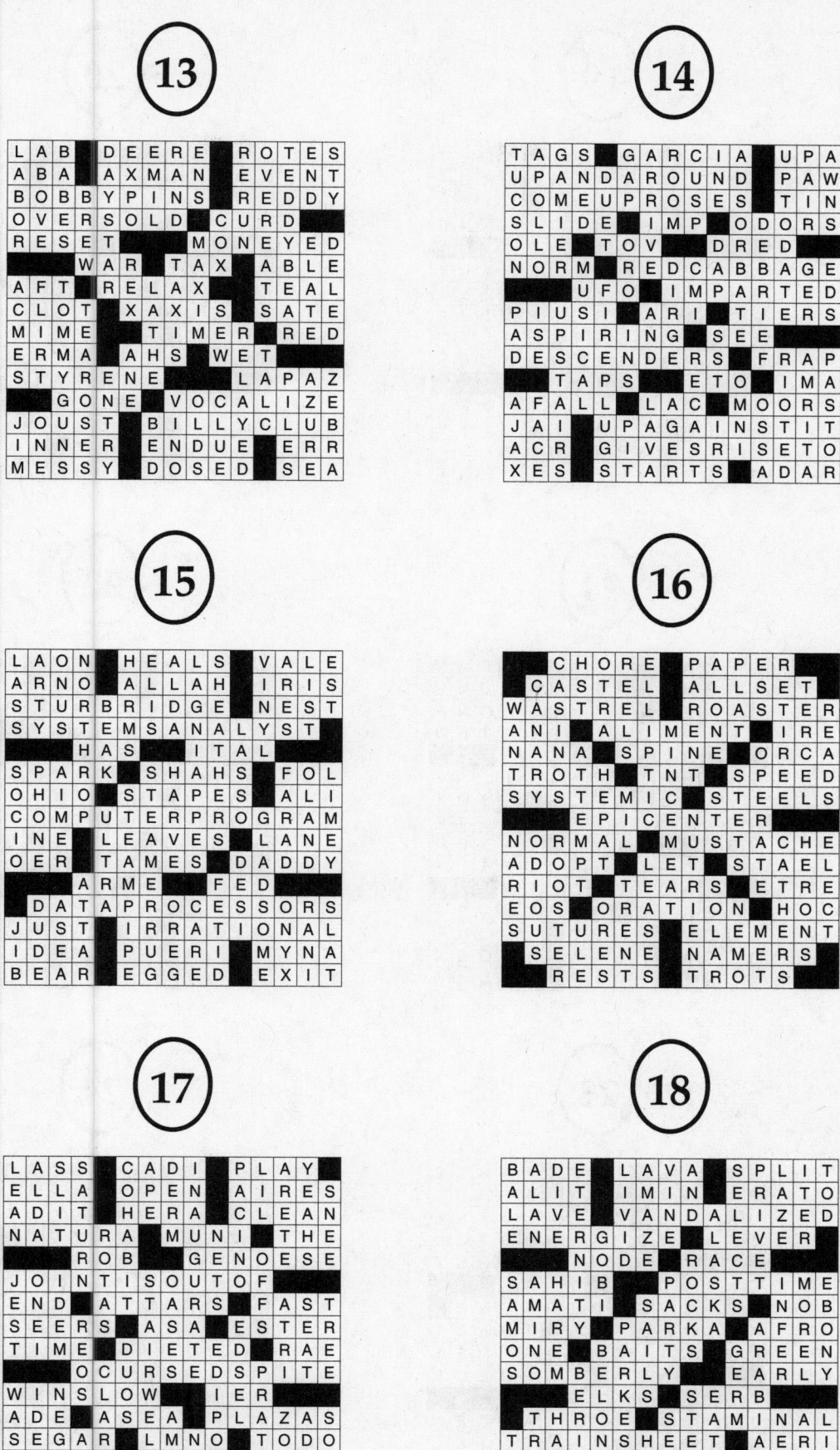

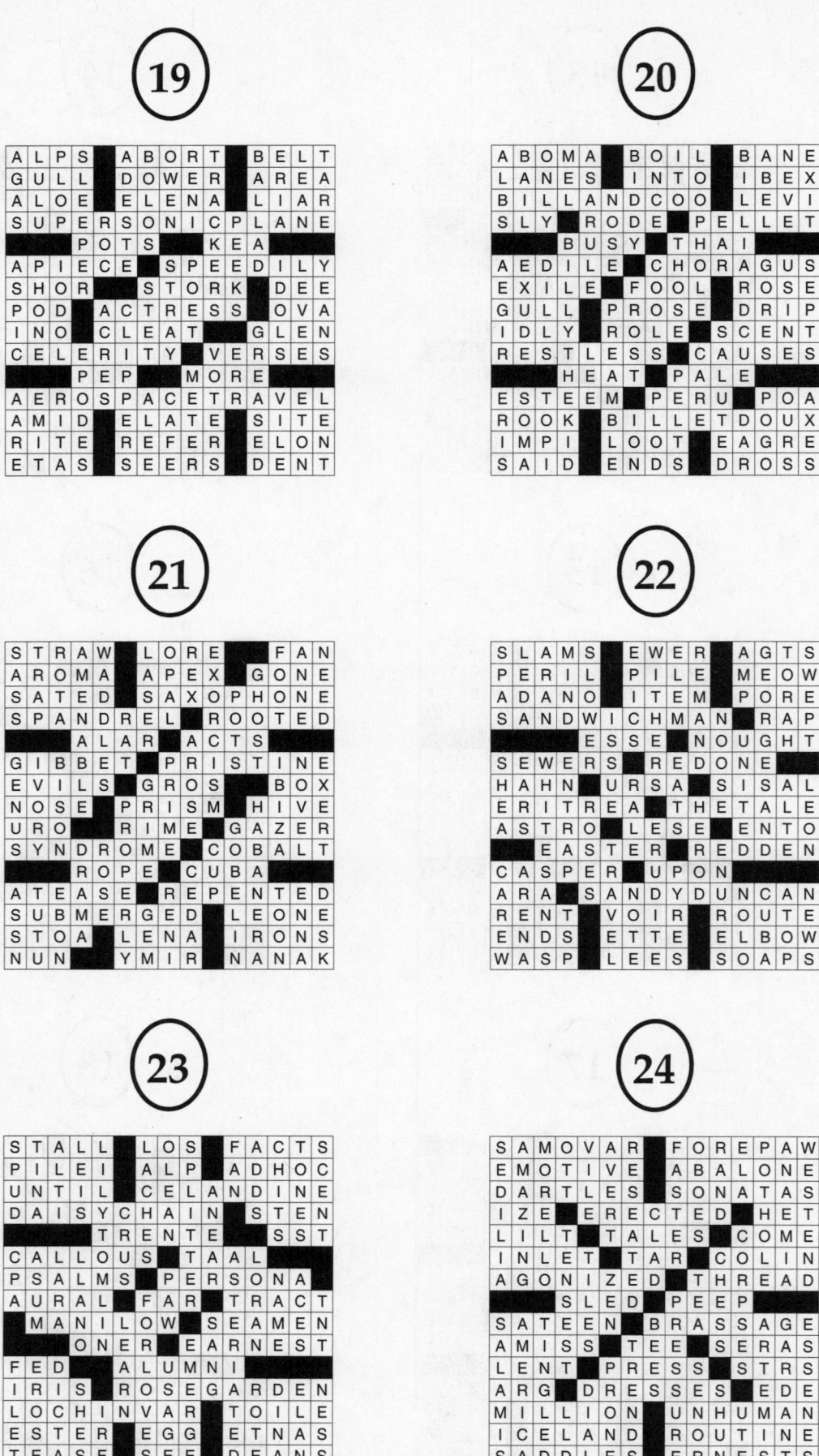

19

```
A L P S   A B O R T   B E L T
G U L L   D O W E R   A R E A
A L O E   E L E N A   L I A R
S U P E R S O N I C P L A N E
    P O T S   K E A
A P I E C E   S P E E D I L Y
S H O R   S T O R K   D E E
P O D   A C T R E S S   O V A
I N O   C L E A T   G L E N
C E L E R I T Y   V E R S E S
    P E P   M O R E
A E R O S P A C E T R A V E L
A M I D   E L A T E   S I T E
R I T E   R E F E R   E L O N
E T A S   S E E R S   D E N T
```

20

```
A B O M A   B O I L   B A N E
L A N E S   I N T O   I B E X
B I L L A N D C O O   L E V I
S L Y   R O D E   P E L L E T
    B U S Y   T H A I
A E D I L E   C H O R A G U S
E X I L E   F O O L   R O S E
G U L L   P R O S E   D R I P
I D L Y   R O L E   S C E N T
R E S T L E S S   C A U S E S
    H E A T   P A L E
E S T E E M   P E R U   P O A
R O O K   B I L L E T D O U X
I M P I   L O O T   E A G R E
S A I D   E N D S   D R O S S
```

21

```
S T R A W   L O R E   F A N
A R O M A   A P E X   G O N E
S A T E D   S A X O P H O N E
S P A N D R E L   R O O T E D
    A L A R   A C T S
G I B B E T   P R I S T I N E
E V I L S   G R O S   B O X
N O S E   P R I S M   H I V E
U R O   R I M E   G A Z E R
S Y N D R O M E   C O B A L T
    R O P E   C U B A
A T E A S E   R E P E N T E D
S U B M E R G E D   L E O N E
S T O A   L E N A   I R O N S
N U N   Y M I R   N A N A K
```

22

```
S L A M S   E W E R   A G T S
P E R I L   P I L E   M E O W
A D A N O   I T E M   P O R E
S A N D W I C H M A N   R A P
    E S S E   N O U G H T
S E W E R S   R E D O N E
H A H N   U R S A   S I S A L
E R I T R E A   T H E T A L E
A S T R O   L E S E   E N T O
  E A S T E R   R E D D E N
C A S P E R   U P O N
A R A   S A N D Y D U N C A N
R E N T   V O I R   R O U T E
E N D S   E T T E   E L B O W
W A S P   L E E S   S O A P S
```

23

```
S T A L L   L O S   F A C T S
P I L E I   A L P   A D H O C
U N T I L   C E L A N D I N E
D A I S Y C H A I N   S T E N
    T R E N T E   S S T
C A L L O U S   T A A L
P S A L M S   P E R S O N A
A U R A L   F A R   T R A C T
  M A N I L O W   S E A M E N
  O N E R   E A R N E S T
F E D   A L U M N I
I R I S   R O S E G A R D E N
L O C H I N V A R   T O I L E
E S T E R   E G G   E T N A S
T E A S E   S E E   D E A N S
```

24

```
S A M O V A R   F O R E P A W
E M O T I V E   A B A L O N E
D A R T L E S   S O N A T A S
I Z E   E R E C T E D   H E T
L I L T   T A L E S   C O M E
I N L E T   T A R   C O L I N
A G O N I Z E D   T H R E A D
    S L E D   P E E P
S A T E E N   B R A S S A G E
A M I S S   T E E   S E R A S
L E N T   P R E S S   S T R S
A R G   D R E S S E S   E D E
M I L L I O N   U N H U M A N
I C E L A N D   R O U T I N E
S A D D L E S   E R N E S T S
```

25

```
F O G S   G O T     F A R G O
A L O E   A P U S   A G O R A
W E A N   R I T A   R E M I T
N O S T E R N U N T O N E D
    I D E E   D R E D
D E C E I T   E D E   A J A R
I C A N T   S Q U A B   E R A
N O S T O N E U N T U R N E D
A L T   R O Q U E   L E N T A
H E S S   S U S   P L A Y E R
    E R I E   S E E D
  N O T E R N U N S T O N E D
A O R T A   C L O T   P A V E
D R Y E R   E N O L   T R E S
Z A X E S   A P E   S A N K
```

26

```
P O P U P   S P A T   F R A Y
E R A S E   E R L E   R O S E
R A C E R   N O T A   E N N A
A L T R U I S T I C   E D E R
    K N E E   U S H E R S
B O B B E D   C A P P A
O R L E   R A T S   A N A M E
S A U N T E R   H U R D L E R
S N E E R   O P E N   E L A N
    F E W E R   T O D A T E
B E T I S E   O S I S
A V E C   B I G H E A R T E D
R O T E   B O R A   G U I D O
O K E N   E T A L   E N T E R
N E S T   D A M E   S T O N Y
```

27

```
S O R O R A L   P A L A V E R
A V E R A G E   E L E V A T E
M E N A C E S   S T E E R E D
P R A T E   C A T E R   I R E
L A M E   T A P E R   M A N Y
E T E   L A Y E R   V I T A E
R E S T O R E S   M O T E L S
    R A T S   C I T E
R O S I N S   T O L E R A T E
A R I E S   S I R E D   M A N
M I N D   O P E N S   D A R C
E G G   S W E D E   S O T T O
S A L T I N E   R E T R E A D
E M E N D E D   E R A S U R E
S I S T E R S   D E S I R E S
```

28

```
A S S T   B L I P S   B R O W
S L A W   E A T I T   R O T A
P I G E O N H O L E   O L O R
S P E E D E R   O R I O L E S
    T E T   S T E A D
S A T E S   R E S   S E P A L
P U R R   V I A   P I R A T E
I D O   T O P P L E S   T O W
E I L E E N   I A N   A O N E
S O L A R   E E G   A G N E S
    G R A N S   F L A
M A L L A R D   S E A N C E S
A L O E   T U R T L E D O V E
S L I T   U R I E L   E P E E
H E N S   R E A M S   R Y N D
```

29

```
P E R U   A D D E R   S L O T
I V A N   S E R R A   T O G A
L E N D   S C E N D   A D E N
E R I E E E R I E A E R I E S
    R A T E   R B I
S O F A R   S T S   O S A G E
P R I G   A C E T A L   S I L
A L E E E L E E E L I E E L I
C O N   V A N N E D   N A D A
E N D U E   T Y P   A T L A S
    N N W   W H I R
A T E E T E I T E O T E U T E
R A S A   A C I E R   A R O W
N U T S   V E N D S   T I M E
O T O E   E R A S E   Y S E R
```

30

```
  S T E A M   W A S P S
S T O R M E R   T I P T O E S
H I R S U T E   O C T U P L E
A R T   R E M A R K S   U L E
F R O G   S A G O S   S L E D
T U N E S   I O U   D E A R Y
  P I N K I N G S H E A R S
    U A R   I L S
  W H I T E E L E P H A N T
S H O N E   L O N   I L I A D
W I S E   R E M A P   T O T O
E S T   L O V A B L E   B T U
E P I T O M E   L O R R I E S
P E L I C A N   E P I C U R E
  R E S I N     S E A M S
```

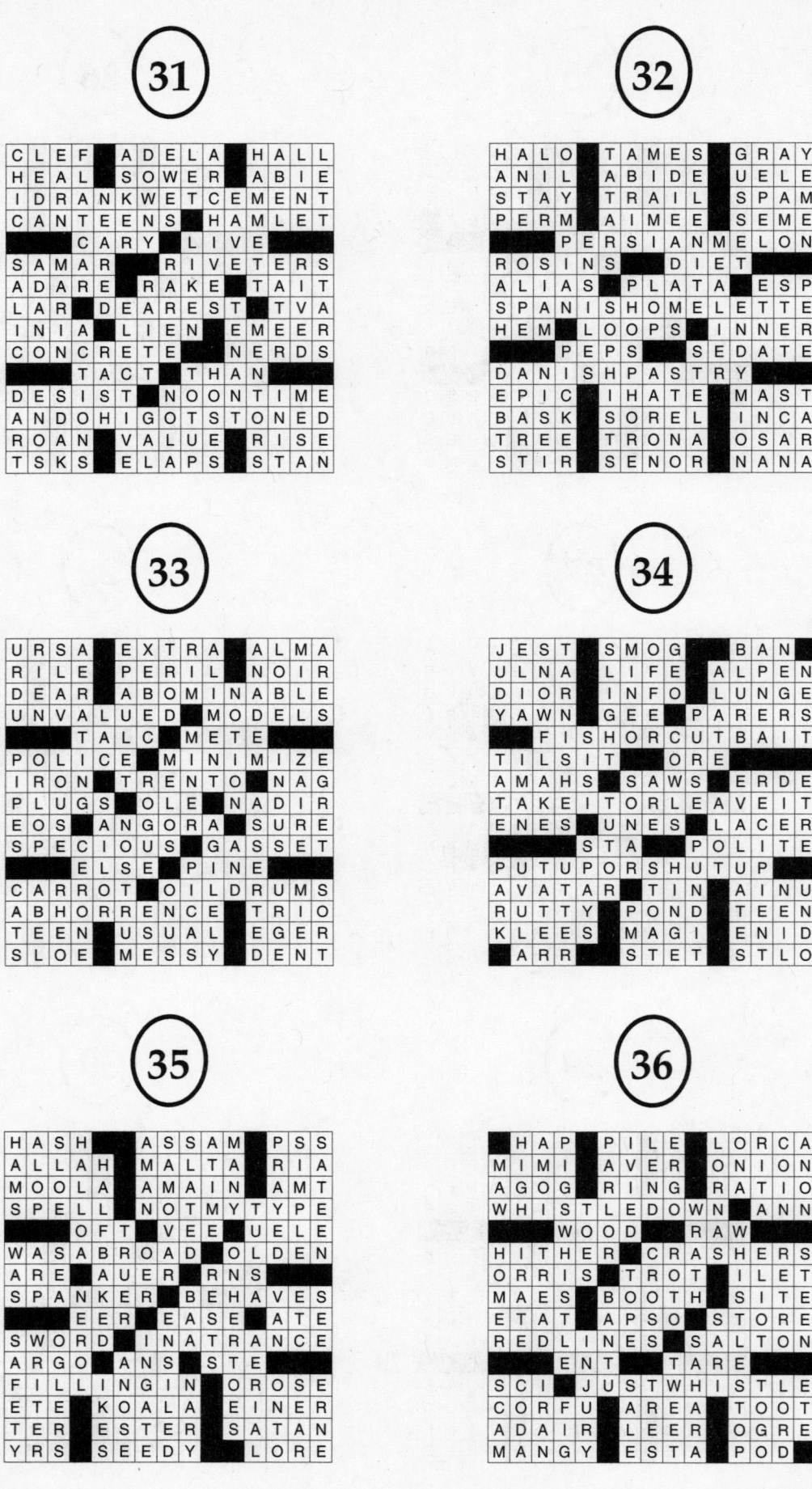

31

CLEF · ADELA · HALL
HEAL · SOWER · ABIE
IDRANKWETCEMENT
CANTEENS · HAMLET
· CARY · LIVE ·
SAMAR · RIVETERS
ADARE · RAKE · TAIT
LAR · DEAREST · TVA
INIA · LIEN · EMEER
CONCRETE · NERDS
· TACT · THAN ·
DESIST · NOONTIME
ANDOHIGOTSTONED
ROAN · VALUE · RISE
TSKS · ELAPS · STAN

32

HALO · TAMES · GRAY
ANIL · ABIDE · UELE
STAY · TRAIL · SPAM
PERM · AIMEE · SEME
· PERSIANMELON
ROSINS · DIET ·
ALIAS · PLATA · ESP
SPANISHOMELETTE
HEM · LOOPS · INNER
· PEPS · SEDATE
DANISHPASTRY
EPIC · IHATE · MAST
BASK · SOREL · INCA
TREE · TRONA · OSAR
STIR · SENOR · NANA

33

URSA · EXTRA · ALMA
RILE · PERIL · NOIR
DEAR · ABOMINABLE
UNVALUED · MODELS
· TALC · METE ·
POLICE · MINIMIZE
IRON · TRENTO · NAG
PLUGS · OLE · NADIR
EOS · ANGORA · SURE
SPECIOUS · GASSET
· ELSE · PINE ·
CARROT · OILDRUMS
ABHORRENCE · TRIO
TEEN · USUAL · EGER
SLOE · MESSY · DENT

34

JEST · SMOG · BAN
ULNA · LIFE · ALPEN
DIOR · INFO · LUNGE
YAWN · GEE · PARERS
· FISHORCUTBAIT
TILSIT · ORE ·
AMAHS · SAWS · ERDE
TAKEITORLEAVEIT
ENES · UNES · LACER
· STA · POLITE
PUTUPORSHUTUP
AVATAR · TIN · AINU
RUTTY · POND · TEEN
KLEES · MAGI · ENID
· ARR · STET · STLO

35

HASH · ASSAM · PSS
ALLAH · MALTA · RIA
MOOLA · AMAIN · AMT
SPELL · NOTMYTYPE
· OFT · VEE · UELE
WASABROAD · OLDEN
ARE · AUER · RNS ·
SPANKER · BEHAVES
· EER · EASE · ATE
SWORD · INATRANCE
ARGO · ANS · STE
FILLINGIN · OROSE
ETE · KOALA · EINER
TER · ESTER · SATAN
YRS · SEEDY · LORE

36

· HAP · PILE · LORCA
MIMI · AVER · ONION
AGOG · RING · RATIO
WHISTLEDOWN · ANN
· WOOD · RAW ·
HITHER · CRASHERS
ORRIS · TROT · ILET
MAES · BOOTH · SITE
ETAT · APSO · STORE
REDLINES · SALTON
· ENT · TARE ·
SCI · JUSTWHISTLE
CORFU · AREA · TOOT
ADAIR · LEER · OGRE
MANGY · ESTA · POD

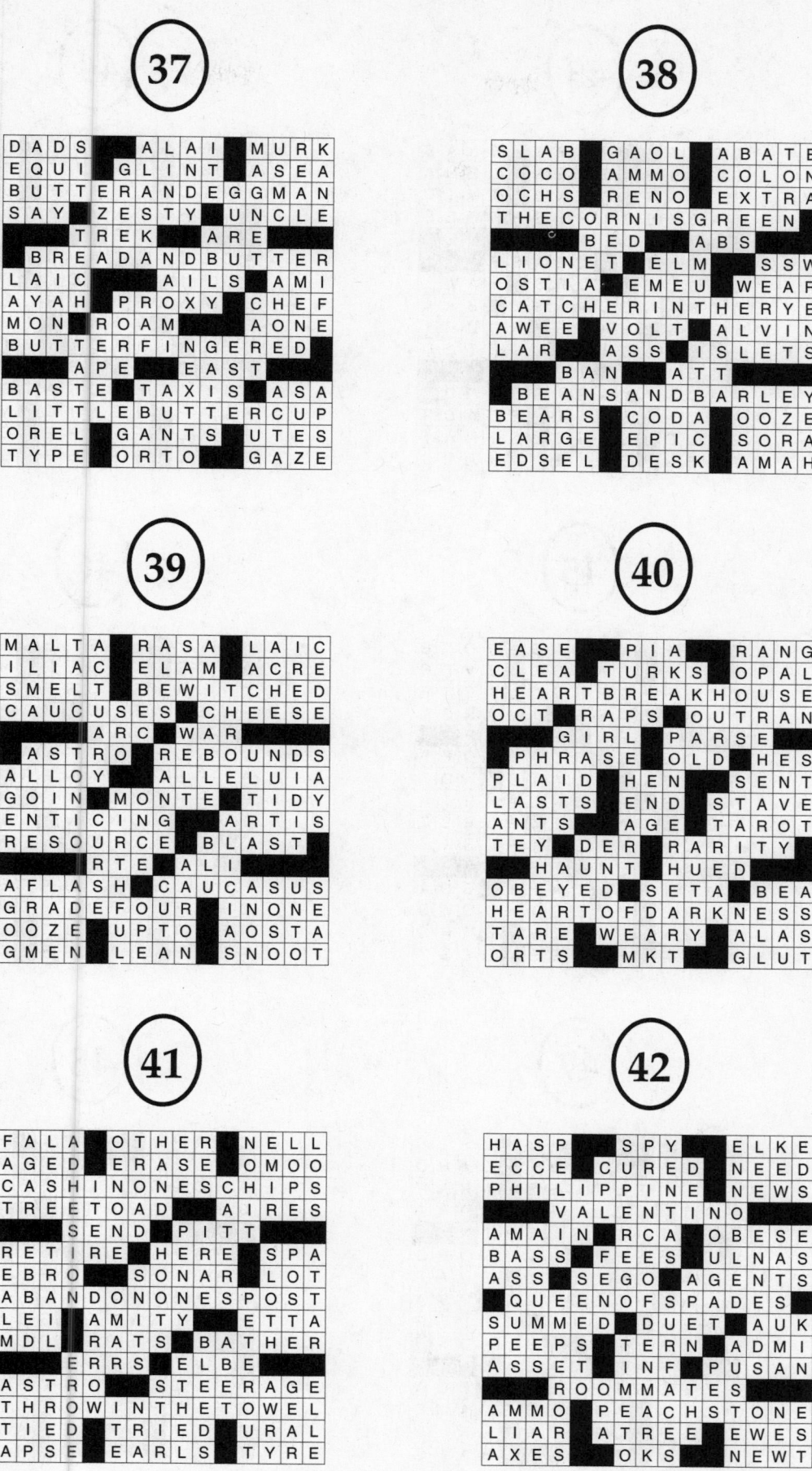

37

```
DADS . ALAI . MURK
EQUI . GLINT . ASEA
BUTTERANDEGGMAN
SAY . ZESTY . UNCLE
. TREK . ARE .
. BREADANDBUTTER
LAIC . AILS . AMI
AYAH . PROXY . CHEF
MON . ROAM . AONE
BUTTERFINGERED
. APE . EAST .
BASTE . TAXIS . ASA
LITTLEBUTTERCUP
OREL . GANTS . UTES
TYPE . ORTO . GAZE
```

38

```
SLAB . GAOL . ABATE
COCO . AMMO . COLON
OCHS . RENO . EXTRA
THECORNISGREEN
. BED . ABS .
LIONET . ELM . SSW
OSTIA . EMEU . WEAR
CATCHERINTHERYE
AWEE . VOLT . ALVIN
LAR . ASS . ISLETS
. BAN . ATT .
BEANSANDBARLEY
BEARS . CODA . OOZE
LARGE . EPIC . SORA
EDSEL . DESK . AMAH
```

39

```
MALTA . RASA . LAIC
ILIAC . ELAM . ACRE
SMELT . BEWITCHED
CAUCUSES . CHEESE
. ARC . WAR .
. ASTRO . REBOUNDS
ALLOY . ALLELUIA
GOIN . MONTE . TIDY
ENTICING . ARTIS
RESOURCE . BLAST
. RTE . ALI .
AFLASH . CAUCASUS
GRADEFOUR . INONE
OOZE . UPTO . AOSTA
GMEN . LEAN . SNOOT
```

40

```
EASE . PIA . RANG
CLEA . TURKS . OPAL
HEARTBREAKHOUSE
OCT . RAPS . OUTRAN
. GIRL . PARSE .
. PHRASE . OLD . HES
PLAID . HEN . SENT
LASTS . END . STAVE
ANTS . AGE . TAROT
TEY . DER . RARITY
. HAUNT . HUED .
OBEYED . SETA . BEA
HEARTOFDARKNESS
TARE . WEARY . ALAS
ORTS . MKT . GLUT
```

41

```
FALA . OTHER . NELL
AGED . ERASE . OMOO
CASHINONESCHIPS
TREETOAD . AIRES
. SEND . PITT .
RETIRE . HERE . SPA
EBRO . SONAR . LOT
ABANDONONESPOST
LEI . AMITY . ETTA
MDL . RATS . BATHER
. ERRS . ELBE .
ASTRO . STEERAGE
THROWINTHETOWEL
TIED . TRIED . URAL
APSE . EARLS . TYRE
```

42

```
HASP . SPY . ELKE
ECCE . CURED . NEED
PHILIPPINE . NEWS
. VALENTINO .
AMAIN . RCA . OBESE
BASS . FEES . ULNAS
ASS . SEGO . AGENTS
QUEENOFSPADES
SUMMED . DUET . AUK
PEEPS . TERN . ADMI
ASSET . INF . PUSAN
. ROOMMATES .
AMMO . PEACHSTONE
LIAR . ATREE . EWES
AXES . OKS . NEWT
```

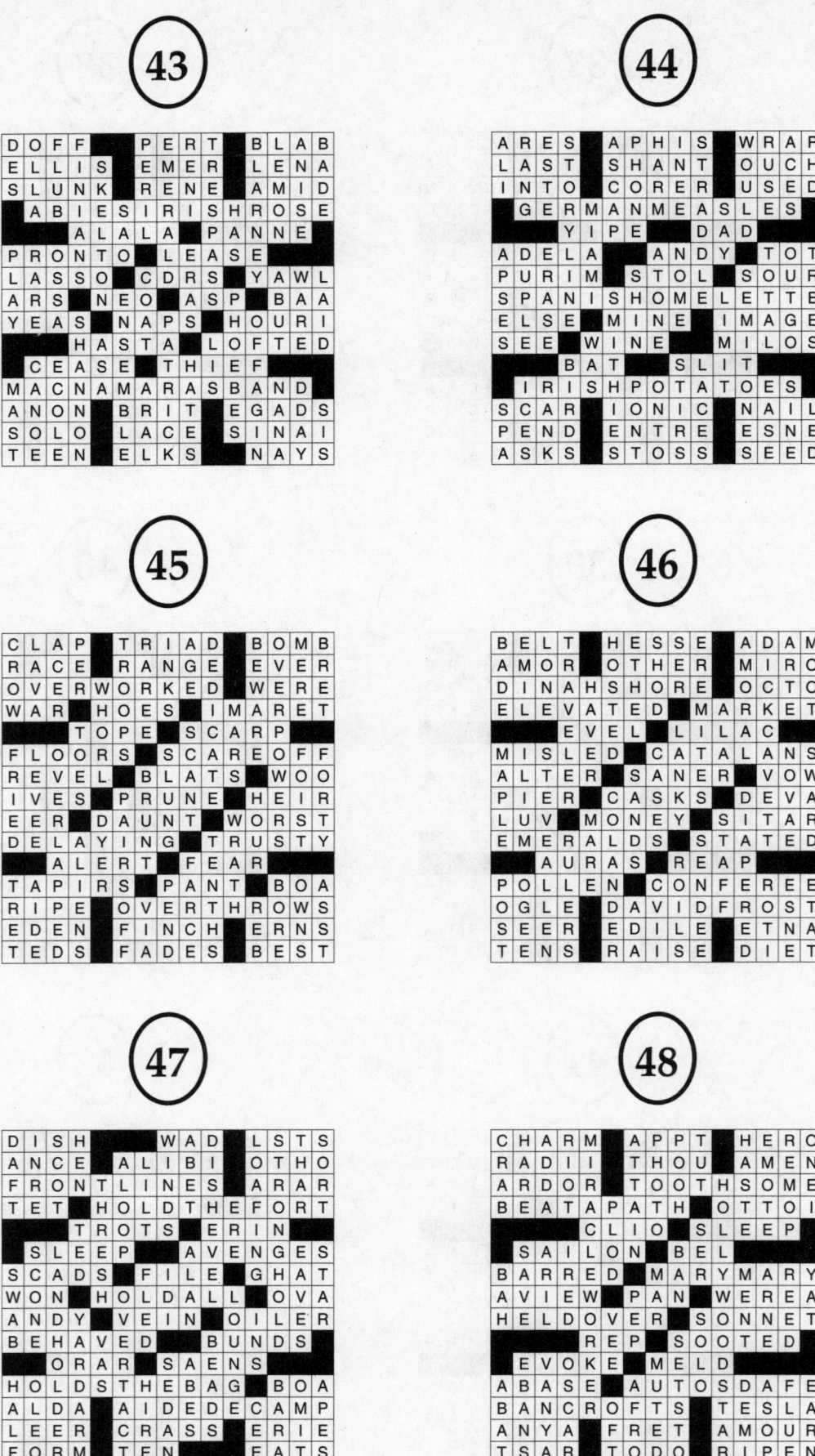

43

DOFF · PERT · BLAB
ELLIS · EMER · LENA
SLUNK · RENE · AMID
· ABIESIRISHROSE
· ALALA · PANNE ·
PRONTO · LEASE ·
LASSO · CDRS · YAWL
ARS · NEO · ASP · BAA
YEAS · NAPS · HOURI
· HASTA · LOFTED
· CEASE · THIEF ·
MACNAMARASBAND
ANON · BRIT · EGADS
SOLO · LACE · SINAI
TEEN · ELKS · NAYS

44

ARES · APHIS · WRAP
LAST · SHANT · OUCH
INTO · CORER · USED
· GERMANMEASLES ·
· YIPE · DAD ·
ADELA · ANDY · TOT
PURIM · STOL · SOUR
SPANISHOMELETTE
ELSE · MINE · IMAGE
SEE · WINE · MILOS
· BAT · SLIT ·
· IRISHPOTATOES ·
SCAR · IONIC · NAIL
PEND · ENTRE · ESNE
ASKS · STOSS · SEED

45

CLAP · TRIAD · BOMB
RACE · RANGE · EVER
OVERWORKED · WERE
WAR · HOES · IMARET
· TOPE · SCARP ·
FLOORS · SCAREOFF
REVEL · BLATS · WOO
IVES · PRUNE · HEIR
EER · DAUNT · WORST
DELAYING · TRUSTY
· ALERT · FEAR ·
TAPIRS · PANT · BOA
RIPE · OVERTHROWS
EDEN · FINCH · ERNS
TEDS · FADES · BEST

46

BELT · HESSE · ADAM
AMOR · OTHER · MIRO
DINAHSHORE · OCTO
ELEVATED · MARKET
· EVEL · LILAC ·
MISLED · CATALANS
ALTER · SANER · VOW
PIER · CASKS · DEVA
LUV · MONEY · SITAR
EMERALDS · STATED
· AURAS · REAP ·
POLLEN · CONFEREE
OGLE · DAVIDFROST
SEER · EDILE · ETNA
TENS · RAISE · DIET

47

DISH · WAD · LSTS
ANCE · ALIBI · OTHO
FRONTLINES · ARAR
TET · HOLDTHEFORT
· TROTS · ERIN ·
· SLEEP · AVENGES
SCADS · FILE · GHAT
WON · HOLDALL · OVA
ANDY · VEIN · OILER
BEHAVED · BUNDS ·
· ORAR · SAENS ·
HOLDSTHEBAG · BOA
ALDA · AIDEDECAMP
LEER · CRASS · ERIE
FORM · TEN · EATS

48

CHARM · APPT · HERO
RADII · THOU · AMEN
ARDOR · TOOTHSOME
BEATAPATH · OTTOI
· CLIO · SLEEP ·
SAILON · BEL ·
BARRED · MARYMARY
AVIEW · PAN · WEREA
HELDOVER · SONNET
· REP · SOOTED ·
EVOKE · MELD ·
ABASE · AUTOSDAFE
BANCROFTS · TESLA
ANYA · FRET · AMOUR
TSAR · TODO · RIPEN

49

```
C L E F . S H O D . B A F F S
R O A R . M E R E . O L L I E
A R C A . U R A L . B L I N D
B E H I N D O N E S B A C K
. . . L O G E . T H I N .
H A T . H E S S I A N . C P A
A L I B I . L O P . C L A N
S C R A T C H O N E S B A C K
P O E T . H O P . U S U A L
S A D . W I R E T A P . S S E
. . S A P S . I R E S .
. B A C K S E A T D R I V E R
C A N O E . M I L E . D A L E
A D O R N . A D E N . E S S E
P E N N S . N E S S . S E E K
```

50

```
B E S T . B A S E . R A S P
A L T O . E D E N . H A G U E
L I A R . H O R S E O P E R A
L O G . S O R A . P R I D E
S T E E P L E C H A S E .
. H A R D . A C E R A T E
A W A R E . C A R T A . N O R
M A N N A . H I P . R O T O R
I N D . D A I L Y . O M I T S
D E S S E R T . D U N S .
. P A R S I M O N I O U S
S L I G O . N A R D . C P A
W H I R L W I N D S . T I E R
H O R A E . M E R E . R A N G
O P A L . P R E Y . A L D O
```

51

```
D E L I B E R A T E . I R M A
U N I L A T E R A L . L O I N
D O M I N A N T L Y . L O F T
E L B A . D Y E S T U F F S
. D A W . S I A M .
S R A . B A A L . A S I A N S
P E R F E C T I O N . N E A P
A V E R T . L E G . A E G I R
T U N A . D I G R E S S I V E
S E A N C E . E E L Y . S E E
. K A P H . M E A .
S H I F T L E S S . T H E E
H O B O . A L L I G A T O R S
O V E R . N E A T A S A P I N
T E X T . E N T E R P R I S E
```

52

```
G R I M . F L A G . C A S T
L A T E . L I M E S . A B L E
U S E D . A R E N A . R O O T
T H R E E M E N I N A T U B
. A R I . S E A T O .
B A S . A N T . S A T U R N
A R P S . G E O . I C H O R
S L O W B O A T T O C H I N A
K O R E A . T A R . E N O L
. S E E S T O . I N C . E S E
. T I E R S . A R S .
T H E C A I N E M U T I N Y
M I E N . S E I N E . A S E A
I R A E . E N D I N . R I A L
G E L D . T E N T . E T T U
```

53

```
S O P O R . H E W N . A B A B
C R E D O . E L I E . M O M A
O N C E I N A B L U E M O O N
T A C O . E L E C T R O N I C
. A N T S . O E S .
C U D . U T A H . R E N A M E
O B I . R O L E S . A L O P
B O L T F R O M T H E B L U E
B A L I . T A L E S . E R E
S T O O G E . L O A N . G A S
. E L F . V E N I .
A B B R E V I A T E . E A S E
B L U E R I B B O N P A N E L
L U N D . R E U P . O R C A S
Y E D O . A R T E . I S E R E
```

54

```
H O S T . R A M O S . A I N T
A N T E . A W A K E . B N A I
S T A N . F E R A L . E T I C
P A I N S . S P E T . E L K
S P R I N G C H I C K E N .
. S I L O . T O R T E S
S A C . P A L E R . G I S T
C O O K E D O N E S G O O S E
A N N O . R E N E E . N E W
T E S L A S . I N T O .
. T A L K I N G T U R K E Y
B A A . L A N E . P E N C E
A N N S . T A P E R . G A L L
L O C I . E N A T E . O V A L
K A Y S . R E L A Y . N E T S
```

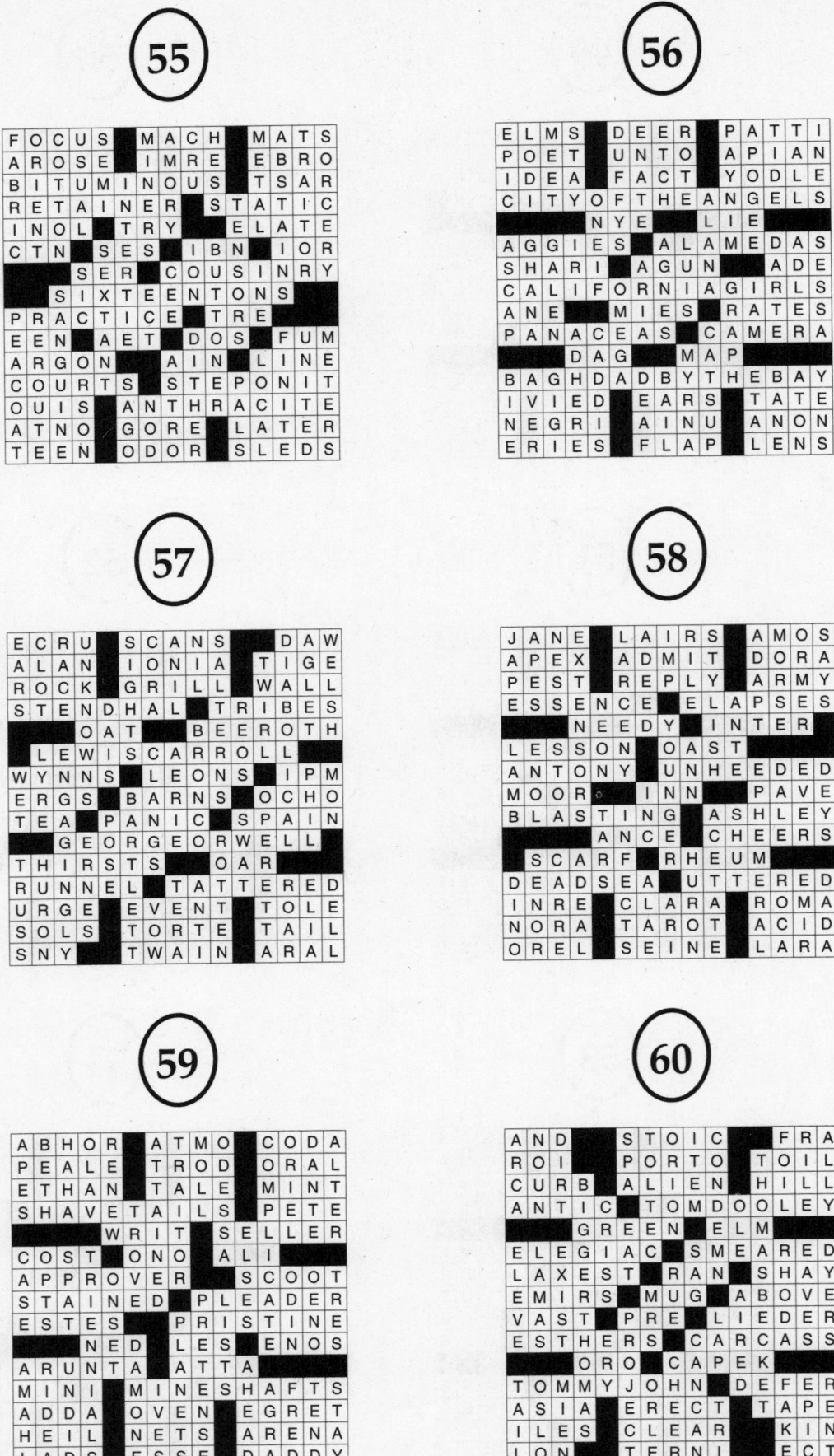

55

```
FOCUS   MACH   MATS
AROSE   IMRE   EBRO
BITUMINOUS   TSAR
RETAINER   STATIC
INOL   TRY   ELATE
CTN  SES  IBN  IOR
   SER   COUSINRY
   SIXTEENTONS
PRACTICE   TRE
EEN  AET  DOS  FUM
ARGON   AIN   LINE
COURTS   STEPONIT
OUIS   ANTHRACITE
ATNO   GORE   LATER
TEEN   ODOR   SLEDS
```

56

```
ELMS   DEER   PATTI
POET   UNTO   APIAN
IDEA   FACT   YODLE
CITYOFTHEANGELS
   NYE   LIE
AGGIES   ALAMEDAS
SHARI   AGUN   ADE
CALIFORNIAGIRLS
ANE   MIES   RATES
PANACEAS   CAMERA
   DAG   MAP
BAGHDADBYTHEBAY
IVIED   EARS   TATE
NEGRI   AINU   ANON
ERIES   FLAP   LENS
```

57

```
ECRU   SCANS   DAW
ALAN   IONIA   TIGE
ROCK   GRILL   WALL
STENDHAL   TRIBES
   OAT   BEEROTH
   LEWISCARROLL
WYNNS   LEONS   IPM
ERGS   BARNS   OCHO
TEA   PANIC   SPAIN
   GEORGEORWELL
THIRSTS   OAR
RUNNEL   TATTERED
URGE   EVENT   TOLE
SOLS   TORTE   TAIL
SNY   TWAIN   ARAL
```

58

```
JANE   LAIRS   AMOS
APEX   ADMIT   DORA
PEST   REPLY   ARMY
ESSENCE   ELAPSES
   NEEDY   INTER
LESSON   OAST
ANTONY   UNHEEDED
MOOR   INN   PAVE
BLASTING   ASHLEY
   ANCE   CHEERS
   SCARF   RHEUM
DEADSEA   UTTERED
INRE   CLARA   ROMA
NORA   TAROT   ACID
OREL   SEINE   LARA
```

59

```
ABHOR   ATMO   CODA
PEALE   TROD   ORAL
ETHAN   TALE   MINT
SHAVETAILS   PETE
   WRIT   SELLER
COST   ONO   ALI
APPROVER   SCOOT
STAINED   PLEADER
ESTES   PRISTINE
   NED   LES   ENOS
ARUNTA   ATTA
MINI   MINESHAFTS
ADDA   OVEN   EGRET
HEIL   NETS   ARENA
LADS   ESSE   DADDY
```

60

```
AND   STOIC   FRA
ROI   PORTO   TOIL
CURB   ALIEN   HILL
ANTIC   TOMDOOLEY
   GREEN   ELM
ELEGIAC   SMEARED
LAXEST   RAN   SHAY
EMIRS   MUG   ABOVE
VAST   PRE   LIEDER
ESTHERS   CARCASS
   ORO   CAPEK
TOMMYJOHN   DEFER
ASIA   ERECT   TAPE
ILES   CLEAR   KIN
LON   TERNI   ECT
```

61

```
AMOS  SCROD  REDO
SIDE  PAINE  EBAN
PRINCESSES  DOME
SENTENCE  KEENER
     INDO  ALLEYS
AGENTS  SPASM
LOBE  SWAMI  DEW
PUBLISHORPERISH
STS  START  ERNE
   HEAVE  RACKET
  BOURNE  SAGE
SENSED  CARESSES
WAIT  PROFESSORS
ITOL  AIDES  EMIT
MANE  TOAST  DENS
```

62

```
HARM  TAPER  CHAR
ALIA  EMILE  RUNE
WOLVERINES  ORNE
STEELER  MOTORED
   RAT  IRANI
ARBITERS  BISCAY
MULCH  EASEL  AMA
ANAK  DATED  SNOW
TIC  PILOT  STERN
INKERS  NASTASES
  BREST  EER
POINTER  APATITE
ABRI  COMMODORES
RODE  TODAY  FANS
TESS  SPINS  FETE
```

63

```
SEAL  SELL  SCALP
ARGO  ATEE  CURIA
BRAV  HONE  APTLY
ROMEOANDJULIET
ERASER  RED
  ESAU  LASSIES
HADAT  TAIL  RCA
ACUTE  INN  AHORN
IRE  GLAD  VENUS
GERMANE  ASIA
   ARA  HARPER
SAINTVALENTINE
ROLLO  AMOR  ELAN
ANGEL  REAR  NOTE
HEARD  ANDY  STEW
```

64

```
ESTES  GALES  CPA
CHIDE  ICARE  LEG
CAPITOLHILL  ENA
EMOTIVE  REFRACT
  FINITO  INEE
ASTO  PIEALA
JOHNNY  POSSESSD
ALE  ASTONES  ANA
ROISTERS  STEWED
  COARSE  SHEA
ACES  DONATI
REBOISE  NATASHA
ADE  FOGGYBOTTOM
GAR  IDIOM  MELBA
ERG  TASTY  ODEON
```

65

```
AGAPE  ADAM  RAMS
MORAL  DEJA  ANAT
OSTIA  ONAN  ZANE
SHARPSBURG  OMEN
   SEED  LAREDO
ALINED  EVENS
LONE  EASE  DELE
FOREARM  ELIDING
  TEDS  EIRE  GENU
  LEARN  ARENAS
APPEAL  DANE
LEAF  POINTBLANK
ALLI  ARAD  AERIE
RELS  CANE  TITLE
MESH  ALAS  ESSEN
```

66

```
WEST  ERGOT  DDT
EACH  NORTH  TREY
TSAR  ABATE  YEAR
STREAMED  ADMIRE
   ETO  ESTOP
ASS  ORB  ERRATA
LOCAL  LEVI  NONE
INALLDIRECTIONS
TALL  ITER  ACTIN
  LATISH  EMS  SEE
   HATES  ATE
METEOR  UNRESTED
AVER  EDNAS  TIME
RILE  SOUTH  ERIN
ELL  SEPOY  RELY
```

67

```
DANCED  LOWEST
CEDILLA EVINCES
ORATION VETERAN
HIM PIGMENT OSA
EVIL NEARS BOER
RETIA RTE BUGLE
EDENIC STARLESS
EDER SHEL
BURDENED SAPPER
ALOUD SOB MERGE
LUMP ATOLE NEOS
ALA ANOMALY CIE
TANAGER REALIST
ATOMISE ENLISTS
EVENTS SAUTES
```

68

```
REPUTED CHORALE
EMANATE RECITAL
MINORCA ACADEMY
ORA SHRINKS LES
VAC ERI ILI
ETHIC SEA STELA
REENACT LATERAN
ENA REM
DESPOTS PREPARE
ABATE PAR LOCAL
PBS EXE OVA
PTS RENEWAL LET
LIONETS ANODYNE
EDOMITE STPETER
DENUDER HEELERS
```

69

```
LOOP SPLAT LAMP
ALCO PROBE ALAR
HITSTHEBULLSEYE
ROO RESET ASSAY
MART IDI
THEEYEOFANEEDLE
REAMS IRON EIR
ALTO ADORN TUNA
WIN TOUR SECTS
LOOKONEINTHEEYE
ITE ERIN
EARTH ALLIN IST
CLOSEONESEYESTO
ROTC TENOR VIEW
UTAH BRANS ESPY
```

70

```
EMUS CESTA LAMB
DALE UNTIL ILIA
ISLANDCONTINENT
THO ADAPT NEEDS
FILM ASA
EUCALYPTUSTREES
ANILS USER ANT
VITA BARNS ISNO
ETE CORK ODEUM
SYDNEYAUSTRALIA
ODD HAMS
SCUBA GLARE CHA
AURORAAUSTRALIS
GRAD VISTA FIJI
ALLY ETHAN ROOS
```

71

```
ALONE ALSO CHEW
DEALT SITS HOLA
MAKEHASTESLOWLY
ICI SERA AREAS
THEWASTELAND
RON NESTER
SPAIN LOAN URI
WASTENOTWANTNOT
ART ANTE ERASE
TRICKY SRO
HASTYPUDDING
CLOUT ROLE NIL
HASTEMAKESWASTE
OGLE IDEA STERN
WOOD GELT PATON
```

72

```
ARAM SCALA PARK
TOME PANEL OBOE
OWED OCTAL SLAG
MANISTHEHUNTER
CITE DAD
INTONE ELEVATED
SAO GRACE ETHER
LING SORER EURE
EVILS NUKES MIA
DECEIVES JABBED
AVE COMB
WOMANISHISGAME
TAXI IOWAN USER
ADEN ANISE NEAR
RING LAMED SANS
```

73

```
IRAS  MIRV  EASE
BETH HANOI XRAY
NATO OTTOS HOSE
 MURDEROFCROWS
   TOR   OAR
CADETS LENGTHEN
ASANA WILT  ERA
KINDLEOFKITTENS
EDT  VOTE RELIT
DEEDLESS HUSSEY
   RON   ACT
 SLEUTHOFBEARS
OTIS FAROE BOLT
PASS UNDER LAIR
TRAY LAOS  EMMA
```

74

```
ROLL  WAFS  PALE
ONEI SALON OKAY
BATTINGPRACTICE
ENTITIES PRANKS
    GETS ABIT
SPEARS CRETONNE
CLAN  SERAI  EEL
AUSTRALIANCRAWL
MME EMILY  ALEE
PELICANS PANELS
   CALK HUMS
ACHING AIRBOATS
MOUNTAINCLIMBER
APIG MONKS  EBRO
NETS SUES  DAMS
```

75

```
PAIL  HOPI  BAMA
ACRE ORAD FADES
CHINAWARE LAIRS
TESSIE BABA  EYE
  HEM POLEVAULT
BOSS CAISSON
ACT  ALL HUTCH
THEMARE HORIZON
SWEET SUN   ERA
TREEPIE  SCAB
BRAZILNUT  BAH
LAR ASIR TINMAN
ANNUL GREATDANE
COILS MEND  ETNA
KNEE  ADDS  DEER
```

76

```
PSIS  ABLE  SALTS
ATME FOAM UBOAT
PUPPYLOVE NEVER
UFO PAPERED  ILS
AFFIRM  YEARN
   TEETH REAGAN
ALAS ROTI  SCIO
IDOL MARIE PURR
LEVI APSE  NIPS
KNEADS  ARSON
 SNEAK  CIGARS
POE RIALTOS  MAT
ALARM FORTYLOVE
ALTAI INIT  TREE
RASES REPS  REND
```

77

```
CAPE  COMIC  SMIT
OVER OVULE AIRE
PERRYMASON TSAR
EST EELS TERSER
   BARS HIRAM
PAPERS SAMSPADE
ETHAN BERET  ROD
LOIN PORTS APSE
ELL SLOGS ALLEN
ELONGATE PLIERS
 VETCH  ROOT
PRAISE SETH  ALE
HONG MIKEHAMMER
OUCH ARISE OMNI
TEES TAPER BOON
```

78

```
SODA  BALES  RACE
ELAN OGIVE ADIT
TIRE NADER RIDE
 ONCEUPONATIME
    DOSE  ITER
SCION  HASTY
PANT SPIRAL DAP
ONCEINALIFETIME
TEA RATTLE EVIL
 RAGES  GRADE
 DIET  OMAR
 ONCEANDFORALL
CREE SEATS POOH
BIRD PALES INGE
SATE SPINY NEON
```

79

```
TABS  REAR    SPAN
ACAT  ERSE  SHONE
RITE  VASE  CANTO
ADHERES  FRANCES
  SPARES  INKED
SPHERE  TENSE
THERE  SEAS  DARK
EBB  ROTATED  GAI
TSAR  MEMS  ADAMS
  ACARE  SLUMPS
 ALLAH  RECANE
STELLAR  THINMAN
TRAIL  OCHO  INGE
AIDES  OLEO  NORA
BASS  FULL  GNAT
```

80

```
SCRAPS    RELATE
ALABAMA  KARELIA
VAPORED  RINGERS
ERI  TADPOLE  WAT
REDS  RUINS  BIDE
STATE  CEE  FIFER
 SNEEZE  RHODES
   ARE    OLD
 TORIES  ADDICT
MARIE  HUR  SNORT
ERIN  SEPIA  GROW
SAN  SEASONS  STE
SNOOPER  SEAGATE
ETCHERS  ENGAGED
ROOSTS    TOPERS
```

81

```
SHILL  GMAN  JAPE
AUDIO  EASE  AVIV
WESTWARDHA  LINE
   SLIDE  PONDER
LUV  AMAH  HAL
ARIOT  AMMO  ISS
CANDIDEYAM  ASIA
ELEANOR  RIESSEN
RIGS  PROVIDENCE
SCA  LESE  GAELS
  RAY  DALI  RET
IMPOSE  INANE
SOUR  SJPERELMAN
INST  SPUN  SLADE
NASA  ASST  SANDY
```

82

```
ETRE  STOAT  CARD
ROOT  LANCE  ALOE
NONEBUTTHEBRAVE
STARLET  ENEMIES
   NODE    ADE
STOIC  RANGELAND
THATS  LEES  VOA
EERY  REFER  MART
ESE  DESI  PASSE
REDRESSES  ASTER
   ATE  TEST
IRONERS  ATTIRED
DESERVESTHEFAIR
ETTE  ENSUE  FIRE
SEES  STEEL  SLEW
```

83

```
GADS  SCALE  LAMB
ALII  PARIS  OMAR
OLAN  ARRAS  NONE
LONGGREEN  EGRET
STEER  STARCH
   RIAS  SOROSIS
COW  TMEN  AURORA
ORAL  PRIAM  NOEL
BECOME  PLEB  TSE
SOONERS  IDES
  GREASE  LEAVE
PHASE  LONGLIVED
EACH  MALAR  NERI
ALTO  AMATI  ERST
TEST  WIRED  STES
```

84

```
SLOT  GREG  START
CEPA  RICE  HONEY
OVERSIGHT  OWNER
RENOWN  OTIC  UFO
NESTING  YOKEL
  STERE  SALAMI
DAS  CRASH  BATON
ENOCH  STA  SNERD
ENURE  SETTO  DAY
RAREST  SEERS
  DEGAS  RABATOS
APO  ENOS  SENORA
SOUSA  UNDERDOGS
TIGER  NEAT  ELAS
ASHES  DEMS  DENY
```

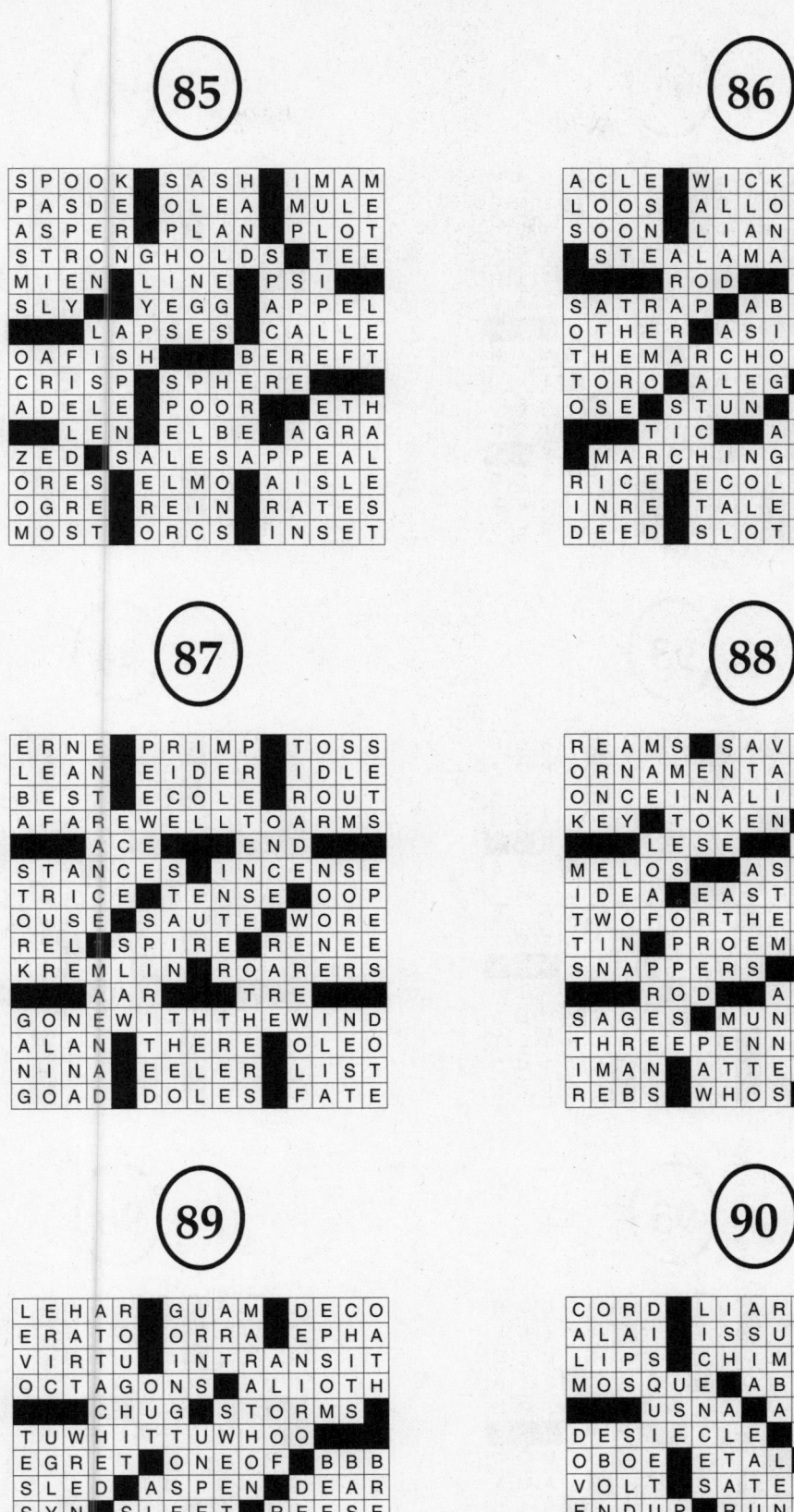

85

S	P	O	O	K		S	A	S	H		I	M	A	M
P	A	S	D	E		O	L	E	A		M	U	L	E
A	S	P	E	R		P	L	A	N		P	L	O	T
S	T	R	O	N	G	H	O	L	D	S		T	E	E
M	I	E	N		L	I	N	E		P	S	I		
S	L	Y		Y	E	G	G		A	P	P	E	L	
	L	A	P	S	E	S		C	A	L	L	E		
O	A	F	I	S	H		B	E	R	E	F	T		
C	R	I	S	P		S	P	H	E	R	E			
A	D	E	L	E		P	O	O	R		E	T	H	
	L	E	N		E	L	B	E		A	G	R	A	
Z	E	D		S	A	L	E	S	A	P	P	E	A	L
O	R	E	S		E	L	M	O		A	I	S	L	E
O	G	R	E		R	E	I	N		R	A	T	E	S
M	O	S	T		O	R	C	S		I	N	S	E	T

86

A	C	L	E		W	I	C	K	S		P	E	L	E
L	O	O	S		A	L	L	O	T		I	B	I	S
S	O	O	N		L	I	A	N	A		T	R	O	T
	S	T	E	A	L	A	M	A	R	C	H	O	N	
			R	O	D			T	R	Y				
S	A	T	R	A	P		A	B	O	Y		G	A	R
O	T	H	E	R		A	S	I	F		G	A	L	E
T	H	E	M	A	R	C	H	O	F	D	I	M	E	S
T	O	R	O		A	L	E	G		I	R	A	N	I
O	S	E		S	T	U	N		F	A	L	L	E	N
			T	I	C		A	I	N					
	M	A	R	C	H	I	N	G	B	A	N	D	S	
R	I	C	E		E	C	O	L	E		I	D	O	L
I	N	R	E		T	A	L	E	R		C	A	R	E
D	E	E	D		S	L	O	T	S		E	Y	E	S

87

E	R	N	E		P	R	I	M	P		T	O	S	S
L	E	A	N		E	I	D	E	R		I	D	L	E
B	E	S	T		E	C	O	L	E		R	O	U	T
A	F	A	R	E	W	E	L	L	T	O	A	R	M	S
			A	C	E			E	N	D				
S	T	A	N	C	E	S		I	N	C	E	N	S	E
T	R	I	C	E		T	E	N	S	E		O	O	P
O	U	S	E		S	A	U	T	E		W	O	R	E
R	E	L		S	P	I	R	E		R	E	N	E	E
K	R	E	M	L	I	N		R	O	A	R	E	R	S
			A	A	R		T	R	E					
G	O	N	E	W	I	T	H	T	H	E	W	I	N	D
A	L	A	N		T	H	E	R	E		O	L	E	O
N	I	N	A		E	E	L	E	R		L	I	S	T
G	O	A	D		D	O	L	E	S		F	A	T	E

88

R	E	A	M	S		S	A	V	E		B	A	R	K
O	R	N	A	M	E	N	T	A	L		A	L	O	E
O	N	C	E	I	N	A	L	I	F	E	T	I	M	E
K	E	Y		T	O	K	E	N		S	T	E	E	L
			L	E	S	E		S	S	E				
M	E	L	O	S			A	S	T	E	R	I	S	M
I	D	E	A		E	A	S	T	O	N		S	H	E
T	W	O	F	O	R	T	H	E	S	E	E	S	A	W
T	I	N		P	R	O	E	M	S		P	U	R	L
S	N	A	P	P	E	R	S		F	E	E	D	S	
			R	O	D		A	B	L	E				
S	A	G	E	S		M	U	N	R	O		B	A	T
T	H	R	E	E	P	E	N	N	Y	O	P	E	R	A
I	M	A	N		A	T	T	E	N	D	A	N	T	S
R	E	B	S		W	H	O	S		S	L	E	E	K

89

L	E	H	A	R		G	U	A	M		D	E	C	O
E	R	A	T	O		O	R	R	A		E	P	H	A
V	I	R	T	U		I	N	T	R	A	N	S	I	T
O	C	T	A	G	O	N	S		A	L	I	O	T	H
			C	H	U	G		S	T	O	R	M	S	
T	U	W	H	I	T	T	U	W	H	O	O			
E	G	R	E	T		O	N	E	O	F		B	B	B
S	L	E	D		A	S	P	E	N		D	E	A	R
S	Y	N		S	L	E	E	T		R	E	E	S	E
			H	A	S	E	N	P	F	E	F	F	E	R
	S	E	A	G	O	D		O	R	A	L			
M	A	I	L	E	R		S	T	O	W	A	W	A	Y
A	U	S	T	R	A	L	I	A		A	T	O	N	E
A	T	E	E		N	O	C	T		K	E	N	Y	A
S	E	N	D		S	O	S	O		E	S	T	A	R

90

C	O	R	D		L	I	A	R	S		A	G	E	D
A	L	A	I		I	S	S	U	E		W	A	V	E
L	I	P	S		C	H	I	M	P	A	N	Z	E	E
M	O	S	Q	U	E		A	B	A	D		E	R	R
			U	S	N	A		A	L	I	F			
D	E	S	I	E	C	L	E		S	O	R	A	S	
O	B	O	E		E	T	A	L		S	A	L	A	D
V	O	L	T		S	A	T	E	S		G	L	U	E
E	N	D	U	P		R	U	N	E		M	O	T	E
	Y	O	D	E	L		P	I	C	K	E	T	E	D
			E	W	E	R		N	O	O	N			
S	P	Y		I	D	O	L		N	O	T	B	A	D
L	O	O	K	T	O	W	A	R	D		A	E	R	O
O	G	L	E		F	E	R	A	L		R	A	I	L
P	O	K	Y		F	L	A	W	Y		Y	U	L	E

91

```
TODATE  MATA  RAM
DAUBER  ALAS  ENE
STRAND  NIGHTMEN
  ATTACHE  AROMA
PATES  HUN  SATIN
ARID  MANSE  DEAD
LEO  BUST  VIE
MANHOLE  MANSMAN
  EWE  NODS  ILO
HEAR  STORE  UNES
ASTAR  AMA  SLICE
STOLE  MALLETS
LANDSMAN  EDITED
ETE  TSLI  NAMELY
TED  BEES  SNARLS
```

92

```
HODS  LATHE  CLAD
ABEL  ALIAS  HALO
NOLI  WELTS  AVER
KEEPOFFTHEGRASS
  PLUS  NOG
REPEAL  RECREANT
UTURN  LEVEE  MAI
MANY  PACES  PITT
OPT  POLAR  BASAL
RESTSTOP  HASSLE
  RIA  MOST
PEDESTRIANSONLY
UPON  OUNCE  ROAM
SEED  ESTES  ANTE
HERS  SHORT  LEER
```

93

```
AVAST  SPED  AWLS
TERSE  CUBA  SHOP
BROWNDERBY  PICA
ADM  SANE  BRITON
TEATIME  BRACE
  ILE  TEEN  CES
AMBLE  BRAGGART
CALL  CRANK  APSE
CLASSIER  ASSET
TIC  ANTS  GNP
  KERNS  FREEAIR
DAHLIA  TRAM  USA
UNAL  BLUEBONNET
ANTI  AINU  NITRO
LOSS  REED  EBSEN
```

94

```
HALS  LITHE  PALI
ABUT  ACHEN  OLAN
GALA  PEERS  STIR
  SUMMERSOLSTICE
  PAL  UNARM
ANDERSON  VIALS
SAUDI  LATE  NULL
IMP  AGELESS  MIA
SEEP  ROSE  AMEND
DRAMA  ONABINGE
  LONER  SOS
THEMIDNIGHTSUN
HOPI  EASEL  INON
ALES  STELE  OTTO
NYET  TESTY  NOES
```

95

```
ONUS  BARI  COLOR
RENT  RYAN  OPINE
BOWEDANDSCRAPED
  INON  ITAS  PTA
  CLOUDFORMATION
GAL  BIL  PGA
ANI  TEARS  ELBOW
LONG  STEAK  KAMA
AEGIR  SOLAR  RID
  LAI  ATE  ONE
HOWDYDOODYTIME
AFR  LEOV  DALE
GAUDEAMUSIGITUR
AGNES  PLOD  KENO
REGIS  HENS  ERIE
```

96

```
COST  LEAD  BABA
OATH  MANSE  IRAN
RHEE  ETNAS  AINT
PUTONAHAPPYFACE
  BINE  OER
  CRASS  ESTRANGE
ARULE  ETUI  EUR
SENDINTHECLOWNS
OTO  UTES  EVENT
PENTAMER  AVERY
  ORB  ACER
STRIKEUPTHEBAND
HAIL  REESE  ERIE
AXLE  ELLES  ANKA
WILD  DELA  REEF
```

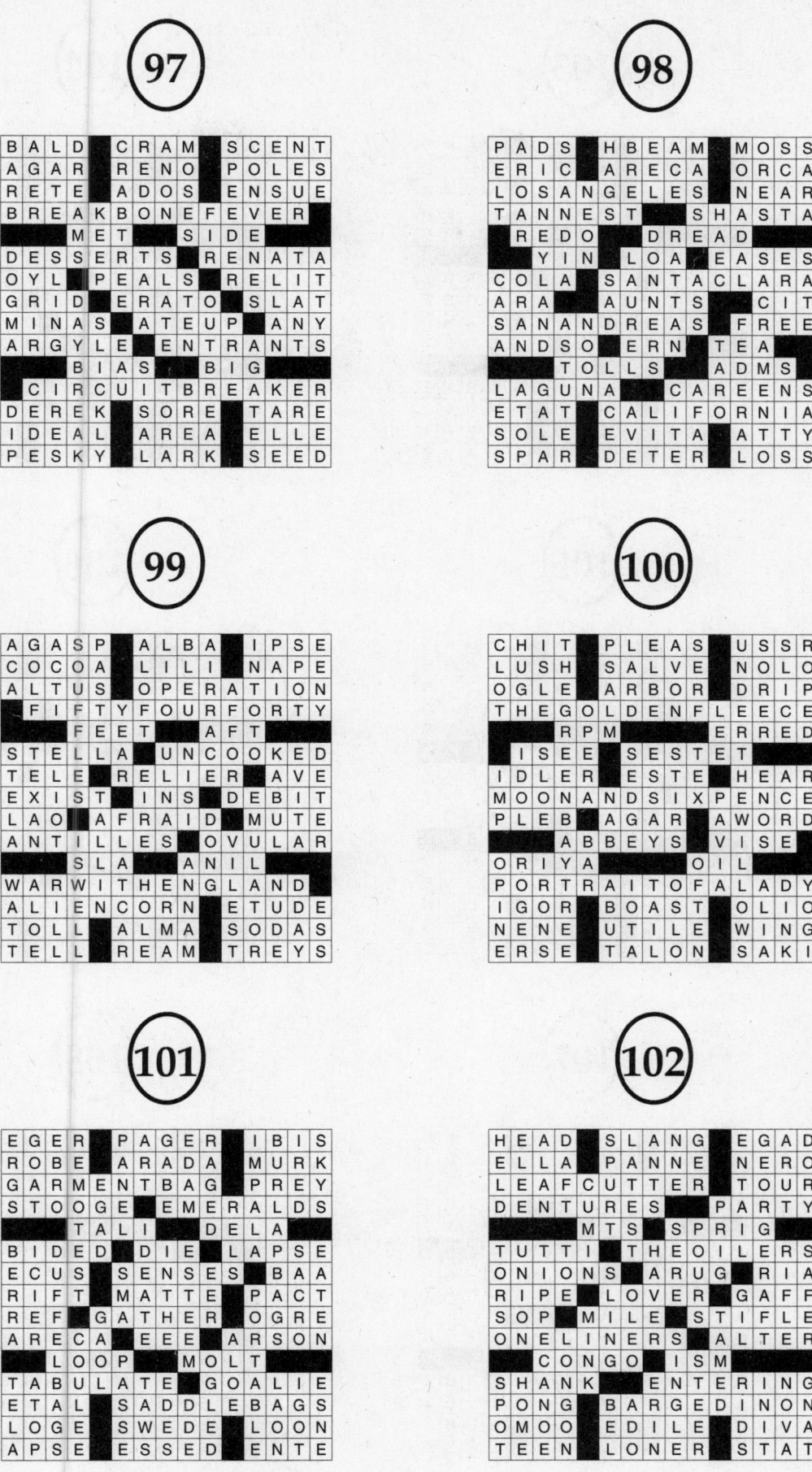

97

BALD · CRAM · SCENT
AGAR · RENO · POLES
RETE · ADOS · ENSUE
BREAKBONEFEVER
MET · SIDE
DESSERTS · RENATA
OYL · PEALS · RELIT
GRID · ERATO · SLAT
MINAS · ATEUP · ANY
ARGYLE · ENTRANTS
BIAS · BIG
CIRCUITBREAKER
DEREK · SORE · TARE
IDEAL · AREA · ELLE
PESKY · LARK · SEED

98

PADS · HBEAM · MOSS
ERIC · ARECA · ORCA
LOSANGELES · NEAR
TANNEST · SHASTA
REDO · DREAD
YIN · LOA · EASES
COLA · SANTACLARA
ARA · AUNTS · CIT
SANANDREAS · FREE
ANDSO · ERN · TEA
TOLLS · ADMS
LAGUNA · CAREENS
ETAT · CALIFORNIA
SOLE · EVITA · ATTY
SPAR · DETER · LOSS

99

AGASP · ALBA · IPSE
COCOA · LILI · NAPE
ALTUS · OPERATION
FIFTYFOURFORTY
FEET · AFT
STELLA · UNCOOKED
TELE · RELIER · AVE
EXIST · INS · DEBIT
LAO · AFRAID · MUTE
ANTILLES · OVULAR
SLA · ANIL
WARWITHENGLAND
ALIENCORN · ETUDE
TOLL · ALMA · SODAS
TELL · REAM · TREYS

100

CHIT · PLEAS · USSR
LUSH · SALVE · NOLO
OGLE · ARBOR · DRIP
THEGOLDENFLEECE
RPM · ERRED
ISEE · SESTET
IDLER · ESTE · HEAR
MOONANDSIXPENCE
PLEB · AGAR · AWORD
ABBEYS · VISE
ORIYA · OIL
PORTRAITOFALADY
IGOR · BOAST · OLIO
NENE · UTILE · WING
ERSE · TALON · SAKI

101

EGER · PAGER · IBIS
ROBE · ARADA · MURK
GARMENTBAG · PREY
STOOGE · EMERALDS
TALI · DELA
BIDED · DIE · LAPSE
ECUS · SENSES · BAA
RIFT · MATTE · PACT
REF · GATHER · OGRE
ARECA · EEE · ARSON
LOOP · MOLT
TABULATE · GOALIE
ETAL · SADDLEBAGS
LOGE · SWEDE · LOON
APSE · ESSED · ENTE

102

HEAD · SLANG · EGAD
ELLA · PANNE · NERO
LEAFCUTTER · TOUR
DENTURES · PARTY
MTS · SPRIG
TUTTI · THEOILERS
ONIONS · ARUG · RIA
RIPE · LOVER · GAFF
SOP · MILE · STIFLE
ONELINERS · ALTER
CONGO · ISM
SHANK · ENTERING
PONG · BARGEDINON
OMOO · EDILE · DIVA
TEEN · LONER · STAT

103

```
S T O L E   S P A S   C A R D
H U R O N   W I N E   O D O R
A R E N A   O R A L   N E V A
D E L I B E R A T E   F L E W
      L E N T   C L E A R S
H O P P E R   E N T E R
O L E O   I P S O   N E A R S
P E R U S E R   S T A N D E E
I N E R T   O G E E   C A N E
    P A S S E   P E E R E D
M A N A G E   N E I N
A M O R   R O U N D T A B L E
T O O L   I R I D   A R R A S
E L S E   A N N O   I N E P T
D E E R   L E E R   L E A S E
```

104

```
L A K E   S T E R S   E T R E
A R I L   T R A I T   X R A Y
D E N I G R A T O R   P A V E
D A D   L E I   I R O N E D
    J O A N R I V E R S
  P R I S M   E R E C T I O N
G L E N S   T S A R S   T H E
L U C K   P O E T S   B I A S
I T O   R A R A E   S P O R T
M O N A U R A L   S T O N E
    D I N A H S H O R E
T I E R E D   A P O   T E D
A D M I   I M P R O P E R L Y
P E N S   N I T E R   R I S E
S A S H   G L A S S   A G E D
```

105

```
S O S O   A G O N   D E G A S
T I P S   P A V E   I M A G E
A L A S   S L E W   F I T I N
F E D   H E A R T O F G O L D
F R E R E       V E R S E S
  W I T S   W H E R E
S H O G U N   O U R   S C A T
E A R   P O T O M A C   L I E
T Y K E   W A D   C L A U D E
  L A M B S   T O M B
I M P E D E     A P H I D
D I A M O N D B A C K   O N E
E S T E R   A R C H   G U N N
S E I N E   D A M E   U S E S
T R O T S   A N E W   M E R E
```

106

```
C Z A R   S C O P E   F E S S
L A S T   A R R A Y   R O L E
I N T E R N A L R E V E N U E
P E A S E   F O A   E S S E N
    D S T   L A T H
C L A R E T   A L D O   E L F
H O L I E R   D A D   A Q U A
I N C O M E T A X R E F U N D
M E A T   A R M   E N R A G E
E R N   E M U S   S T O L E S
    M E S S   I S R
A R E A R   T A M   E G R E T
D O W J O N E S A V E R A G E
I D E O   B E I G E   A V I S
T E R R   A S S E T   B E S T
```

107

```
C U B E   O P E N S   C A F E
O R A L   R A T I O   O L L A
L A W M A K I N G B O D I E S
E L L   A N N A   R E V E T
    A R E S   R E G R E T S
P A R L E Y   P E R I S
A S E A   I A N A   D E S
T H E S U P R E M E C O U R T
E E L   N O I R   A S I A
  R I O T S   R A S T E R
R E T I C L E   S E N T
E T A P E   C O V E   A B E
C H I E F E X E C U T I V E S
T E N N   E X I L E   R E S T
O R T S   R I L E S   E R S E
```

108

```
S R O   A C E S   I R E S
C O N F R O N T   D E N U D E
A L T I T U D E   L E D G E R
L E A N   N O W   E L P A S O
A S P E C T     I R I S
    H E A T   P R E C
H E M I S P H E R I C A L
O V E R S T A T E M E N T
T E M P E S T T O S S E D
  R O S S   S A R K
E N G R     D Y N A S T
B O R A G E   T A A   E S T E
O P E N E R   A N I M A T O R
N E E D E D   M I N O T A U R
  N A S A   E L S A   R T E
```

109

```
ABLE NADER ACME
MOOD IMAGE LOIN
ASIN MURAT INGE
SCRAMBLEDEGGS
SHE OLE SANTAS
    RETORTS RNA
AFOOT UNE LAIC
COFFEEANDDANISH
TOFF VIC AGNES
ETE SENEGAL
DENSER RIS COS
  BUTTEREDTOAST
SOAP ORATE ORCA
ONCE RAVED ZEAL
LAHR STILE EYRE
```

110

```
SAPS MALA SHEAR
ORAL ATIC HARRY
PERU SHEA IRATE
HARRYHOUDINI
  POEM ENS CCS
ACH DREAMS OHIO
THANE LIU LIGN
HAROLDMACMILLAN
EPOS EAT CADRE
NILE CRECHE EST
AND MOM AYNS
  HAROLDPINTER
BRIER SIGH OHNE
AUDIT ELEE RAID
STORY TARN ENDS
```

111

```
TACOS MINA HARM
INURE ORES OGEE
PORED GOES DATA
SALMAGUNDI GRAD
  TOLA SLEDGE
SLICER GETUP
TOTO SEES LORIS
EVINCED STUDENT
MECCA IDEA GATE
  ORDER STEPON
MUSCLE ESTE
ABET MISCELLANY
ROTI ERSE LAGOS
NATO AMEN EVADE
ETON NARD RARER
```

112

```
TOLD COTES PEER
AMOR OSAKA ATRI
TINY NIVEN RUIN
ITERATES DATING
  OVER GALS
BASTES GALLOPER
ARC SCAB ONICE
SLOWFARSLOWGOOD
SETAE APER ULA
INTIMATE ARISEN
  TUNE STUN
FLURRY RAINBOWS
LOSE ONETO OLIO
AGES NINON REEL
PODS EDENS NONO
```

113

```
STAT DOEST SPAT
CAME EARTH TRIO
ILED FRERE AERO
FONDUE ODENSE
INDESCRIBABLE
  RETIRE REATA
LAS DODO BOYSOF
EGAD RENTA SODA
DETERS ERNE NOR
ARICA PRONTO
  RETROSPECTIVE
  LINEAR RHINOS
FACT DIODE OMIT
OVAL INLET SALE
RELY OGEES EYER
```

114

```
BETA DOORS OHIO
EMIT ARTIE CODA
EIGHTYFIVE CULT
PRELATES PAUSES
  ETO LIBRE
OFTEN NINESPOT
ARAI AVENGE ALE
MATCH EVE THREE
ETH ASSIST ATOM
SEEDLETS RORYS
  ROLLS AND
SETTEE BLUEBIRD
OBIT CELEBRATOR
NOME TWINE COLE
GEED SEPAL KNEW
```

115

```
BAMBI ■ STAN ■ ASHE
OCEAN ■ PAGE ■ SHOW
WHENSORROWSCOME■
LET ■ PLY ■ SCORER
■ ■ LEE ■ REBATERS ■
THEYCOMENOT ■ ■
HEART ■ ARTY ■ ESSE
RARE ■ ARIAS ■ LAIR
URNS ■ MINI ■ AORTA
■ ■ SINGLESPIES
AMERICAS ■ RTE ■ ■
MALAGA ■ ■ ADO ■ PAU
BUTINBATTALIONS
IDOL ■ LIKE ■ ALONE
TENS ■ EROS ■ TALES
```

116

```
CONE ■ BADE ■ SODA
EVER ■ BETEL ■ KRAN
DAWNSEARLYLIGHT
ELS ■ ERNIE ■ AISLE
■ ■ ANTI ■ SYN ■ ■
■ NORTHERNLIGHTS
HEWN ■ ■ ICAN ■ EON
AGIO ■ PIVOT ■ NINA
URN ■ SURE ■ ■ ADIP
LIGHTFANTASTIC ■
■ ■ AEF ■ WEAL ■ ■
CAIRN ■ STERN ■ SAD
ONCEOVERLIGHTLY
LOOM ■ AGAVE ■ ELAN
ENNS ■ TOME ■ NOSE
```

117

```
GROG ■ SALIC ■ SLAP
YOUR ■ AMARA ■ TODO
MICE ■ FAVOR ■ OTIS
■ SHAKEHANDSWITH
■ ■ TOTS ■ IRE ■ ■
MISLAY ■ ALGA ■ RAW
IDEAL ■ AREA ■ AIRE
DARKANDHANDSOME
GHEE ■ ORAD ■ OPTED
EOS ■ FRAT ■ ARISES
■ ■ AUS ■ STIR ■ ■
HANDLEWITHCARE
OVAL ■ MITRE ■ TALL
LENI ■ ARSON ■ EMMA
DRAB ■ NEAPS ■ DIOR
```

118

```
HINT ■ ASIS ■ AFREE
ASEA ■ HOWE ■ ROOST
NEWT ■ AJAR ■ TRUTH
DREAM ■ ONER ■ ETES
SELMA ■ UTTERS ■ ■
■ ■ INERT ■ BEATLE
SOB ■ TENON ■ VIRAL
PROFILE ■ AMELITA
ATOLL ■ RATER ■ GEM
TAMALE ■ UTHER ■ ■
■ ■ XANADU ■ NEVER
ACTS ■ STIR ■ DEERE
CRIER ■ ATNO ■ FROG
HALEY ■ LOEW ■ EDDA
SWEDE ■ ERRS ■ RIEN
```

119

```
PACT ■ RFD ■ MATCH
ALAS ■ ELAS ■ IDAHO
NOME ■ LUMP ■ NOTED
GNP ■ PAMPASGRASS
■ EFFACE ■ RULERS ■
■ IOLE ■ STEED ■ ■
TERRE ■ LADS ■ TIN
ALEM ■ STONE ■ PANE
TIS ■ SIRE ■ NOMAD
■ LINUS ■ PEEP ■ ■
■ DOODAD ■ ORATES
LAMPLIGHTER ■ ROT
ETAPE ■ EATS ■ NINO
ETHER ■ STET ■ ENID
ROADS ■ SRO ■ EGAD
```

120

```
AMATI ■ LASS ■ PRAY
DEMOB ■ ALOP ■ RUSE
ANILE ■ CALEDONIA
SUNDRIES ■ COPTER
■ ■ IND ■ AIL ■ ■
■ DAMAS ■ ANATOLIA
PALO ■ ARIL ■ REND
OLIO ■ CRESS ■ DALE
SAMS ■ ORNE ■ EVEN
HIBERNIA ■ EGRET
■ ■ ASS ■ SEA ■ ■
PATENT ■ DECLAIMS
AQUITANIA ■ LICIT
TURN ■ NORM ■ IRENA
HAKE ■ THEY ■ ASSET
```

121

```
. R A F . C L A M P . P I C A
H E L L . R A D I I . H A L E
O T T O . A R E C A . I G O R
O R A T I N G . A N A L O G Y
F O R S A K E . I L L . . .
. . A M Y . P A S T I M E S
C L I M B . J U X T A P O S E
A E S . . P A L E S . A S P
P A L I S A D E S . B E N E T
E N A M E L E D . B O A . .
. . P R E . Q U A R T E T
S T R E E T S . A R T L E S S
T O U R . O U S T S . D A T A
O M N I . T R E A T . O M E R
P E E L . S E A R S . M S S
```

122

```
S T U D F I S H . A L M O S T
C A L I E N T E . D E D U C E
R E S T A R E A . A N I T R A
A N T . R E P R I N T . F O G
P I E R . D U T R A . B L U R
E A R E D . P S I . C R A N E
. . G O T T O . C H A N G E
B R E A S T O F C H I C K E N
O O D L E S . L A I N E . .
A L G E R . P E R . A R B O R
S L E D . R E T I A . S E B A
T E W . H U S T L E R . W I N
E D I T E D . U L T I M A T E
R U S H E D . C O A T T R E E
S P E E D Y . E N T E R E R S
```

123

```
S O W N . T A L L . B L A H
A R I A . E S A U . E Y R E
C O M D E N A N D G R E E N
R I P E S T . S W A N S O N G
A D O L P H . O I L S . L E A
D E L . . E N G . T E E R S
. S E L J U K . . B E T T Y
. O U S E . S W I T .
. S A L L E . . L I N E A R
B E L L E . P L O . D E P
E R A . S T O A . I N T I M E
D E M O T I O N . T O R P O R
N E W Y O R K N E W Y O R K
A D E N . E L E M . O S S E
S A N E . R Y E S . N E E D
```

124

```
H A N G . M E R E . S T A R E
O L E O . A X I S . T A P E R
E V I L . R A C E H O R S E S
S A N D W I C H . A R M E D
. . M E A T . A S I A .
S T R I P . D E T E C T E D
H A U N T . G A G E S . A V E
E S N E . B R U I N . S P O T
E S T . S L A B S . S P I K E
P O S I T I V E . C O R E R
. . M A N Y . S C A R .
. V A P I D . P O R T A B L E
D E V O N S H I R E . D U A L
E R O S E . A S T A . I R K S
W A N E D . M A S K . C R E E
```

125

```
C R I B . D O R E . . E T A
H A M E . A R U B A . E V A N
A M A S . R A D A R . L I N T
. B R O O K L Y N B R I D G E
A L E M A N . . O U S E L S
G E T . F E L T . R E I N E
A D S . . S O A P . D O T S
. . M I S S H A P E N .
. M O O R . T O L L . P V T
. A B R A S . E L A M . R I D
O C T A N E . . Y A H O O S
T H E L I B E R T Y B E L L
O I S E . A L O H A . L A I C
E N T S . T I M E R . E T N A
S E S . S P A D . N E S T
```

126

```
M A I M . S P O T . M I S T S
O R R A . P U R A . A N T O N
B E A N B A L L S . S N A F U
Y E N T A . P O T A T O B U G
. L I E N S . N E G E V . .
. . E Z E R . A R A F A T
S S H . A R I S E . T O B E
C A U L I F L O W E R E A R S
U G L I . L I E G E . L I T
P A L M A S . . R A B E
. . E D G A R . D O R I S
C A R R O T T O P . R A N T S
A L A I N . O N I O N S K I N
R I C C I . M D L I . E L L A
P E E K S . S E L L . D E E P
```

127

```
A T O M I Z E ░ H E A R T E N
C A K E B O X ░ A C Q U I R E
O P A L I N E ░ S T U D E N T
R E P ░ S E C T S ░ A Y R E S
░ ░ R I A ░ D U E L S ░ ░ ░
░ ░ P R E T E E N ░ H A H A
░ S T R A F E D ░ A V E N U E
A R R I V E D ░ S K I R T E R
S T O L E N ░ T U E S D A Y
H A Y S ░ S P O N D E E ░ ░
░ ░ ░ E L E N A ░ D O R ░ ░
S H A V E ░ U D I N E ░ R O W
C A M E R A S ░ E C L O G U E
O V E R A G E ░ S E L V A G E
P E N A T E S ░ T R A I N E D
```

128

```
░ ░ M I S ░ S A C ░ ░ A L B
A S I D E ░ T I R E ░ D Y E
E L I X I R ░ A L A N ░ A L E
O L D E ░ E R N ░ G A G M E N
S W E D E ░ A D E S T E ░ ░
E S N E ░ D I D ░ E T T E S
░ H O L D I N G S ░ S H O E
A H O T ░ P A G E T ░ C E N T
N O W I ░ S N O W P L O W ░
D I S C O ░ C V I ░ E L O N
░ E A S Y A S ░ A D R O P
S H A S T A ░ T E A ░ F L Y A
T A R ░ E T U I ░ N E E D E D
O I L ░ R E N O ░ T R E S S
P R O ░ D A N ░ E A T ░ ░
```

129

```
R A J A S ░ H I T S ░ C A P P
E X U D E ░ A N E C ░ O V E R
A L L O T ░ I D L E ░ N E R O
R E Y ░ F I F E A N D D R U M
░ F U R C A P ░ I O O ░ ░
S T O R E Y ░ E S C A R P S
C A U S E ░ S N E A K ░ A L F
A U R A ░ P E D A L ░ A P I E
T N T ░ T R E E S ░ C R E M E
░ T H E H O R N ░ A I G R E T
░ S A W ░ C U S T O M ░ ░
B A S T I L L E D A Y ░ O W L
O B O E ░ C A D I ░ M A N I A
S U R E ░ A M A N ░ A D E P T
S T E M ░ R A Y E ░ P A Y E E
```

130

```
I O W A N ░ S T I R ░ C A R T
S P I R E ░ T O N E ░ O D E A
L A T R A V I A T A ░ R O L L
E L S E ░ E L D E R ░ E R A L
░ ░ S L I T ░ R E F L E X
R O T T E N ░ P E N A L ░ ░
E R A S E ░ D I S D A I N E D
E L L ░ T I N T S ░ A D E
D E C R E A S E S ░ M E R G E
░ O L P E S ░ B A N K E R
░ O L E F I N ░ D E A F ░
G L O B ░ O G E E S ░ O L A F
A L O U ░ C A P I S T R A N O
D I S C ░ A G E S ░ A C U T E
S E E K ░ S E E M ░ M E D E S
```

131

```
A T O M ░ C A D E T ░ P A A R
C I M A ░ A R E N A ░ R E N O
H E A D P R O J E C T I O N S
S A R D I N I A ░ K I D N E Y
░ ░ E K E D ░ B E N E ░ ░
R O M N E Y ░ S U D S ░ A G A
A V O I R ░ E C R U ░ K N A R
T U R N S O N A S P I N D L E
A L E G ░ U C L A ░ G O R E N
L E S ░ S T E P ░ C U T E S T
░ ░ P A L S ░ A H A H ░ ░
A N G O R A ░ A D E N O I D S
W I L L I S A N D W A L T E R
O N E A ░ T I T L E ░ E T N A
L E E R ░ S T E E D ░ S O Y S
```

132

```
M A C H O ░ P A V E ░ C M S
A B O U T ░ O M E N ░ F A I T
G E N G H I S A N D K U B L A
I L E ░ E V E N T ░ I R O N Y
░ S O R E R ░ E M O T E S
H O T A S ░ A R D O R ░ ░
A L O T ░ S L A I N ░ M E T
N I G H T A T T H E O P E R A
G O A ░ H A L O S ░ A S I T
░ C A R O N ░ M I M E S
A L E R T E ░ P E A L E ░
T O X I C ░ D R I N K ░ R O O
S W A S H B U C K L E R I N G
E L M S ░ A T M E ░ D O Z E R
A Y S ░ G Y P S ░ O B E S E
```

133

```
PORT  RUER  PITH
AVER JINRIKISHA
LEVY UNINFORMED
ORE FIST BASE
SLUICE SHOT
CHARGE VIOLETS
IOTAS FARAD RIB
TOIL CAPER GAGA
ETO SATON FEINT
SNAPPER DALLAS
DIPS DORSET
LION RATE RUB
TERREHAUTE FIRE
UNINTENDED UTES
BASS PIED NEST
```

134

```
TAUPE ABASE SAP
APRIL CAVES ELL
CRACKERJACK ALA
TALK REA TIDBIT
LEA DOMAINS
BIRETTA IRONS
ODA TORTES ACID
ALGAE COS PIUTE
TEAK CAMERA ICE
MELON LENGTHS
ADULATE NEA
DEFAME RAE RAPT
OFF BREADWINNER
POI DINGO TENSE
TEN AEDES STATE
```

135

```
ABED PHASE AVER
SOME LORAN DESI
TRIP ARIAN DIAL
INTERNALREVENUE
NOTES AIR
SADIE ADR OSE
ATLE DEAL GELID
RAINS RNS OXIDE
GRATE ATOP EVEN
OKS ROT ARMED
SUP LETUP
INCOMETAXRETURN
COOL RECTO IRAE
OMNI ALTON OGRE
NEED SAILS NEAR
```

136

```
AMA BID TAPS
HEMAN SATE ALIT
ELAND HEEP TEES
MINDOVERMATTER
FARED ROO
NOTRE NOTTOBE
KOREA TEPEE RLS
IDAS RAVED ROUT
TEL METES PETTY
SLEEPER BATHE
CSA OUTRE
INTOPLOWSHARES
ALOE EIRE ACRES
LEON RELS NEARS
ESNE SNY DDT
```

137

```
AWED ACTS CABBY
BOHR CREE OLLIE
SWEETCORN ROOTS
SUGARANDSPICE
SLUTS WON
HAS LES OAR NNE
ELIA TOMATOES
ALLGODSCHILDREN
POLECATS SIDE
STY TIA LAB ASS
SOS CATER
PUPPYDOGTAILS
BURRO ABOUTFACE
BRAID IRON LIAR
CELTS SANE EDDA
```

138

```
LETS TITO ORGAN
ELIA ASIS NAIVE
ALLFORONE ECLAT
PATENTLY DWELLS
READ SOAR
SCH TRE IVY ELI
THEIRS ONESIDED
AORTA ERG TRINE
TWOSCORE CRATES
ESS KGS HOE HST
SMEE OREL
COLLIE TWOTIMER
OLEIN TRANSMUTE
OLAND AURA ISON
PARKS MEDE TENT
```

139

```
ADDS  GAL   SPAR
DIET ARIAN  TAPE
ESEL RADIO  OWED
 CROSSSECTIONS
    POP   REP
ANDEAN  POUR  SIN
ROOST  CALM  EINE
CROSSWORDPUZZLE
EMMA  INKS  BREED
LAS  ONES  BOASTS
   DUD    MAA
 CROSSQUESTION
TAIL  OUSTS  DUEL
ORAL  ROMEO  ERSE
NESS   DAR   ASTO
```

140

```
SIDE  DEMOS  HAIR
KNOX  UTILE  ARNO
ITNO  ESSEX  MANX
FRECKLE   TOMBOY
 FAERIEQUEENE
   IND  NATURALS
EBOND  DARTS  TOP
AONE  JUSTE  POOR
ROZ  BUNKO  HINNY
PRESENCE   SAL
 TAKEDOWNAPEG
VAGARY   MASSAGE
ALAN  ALBAN  TARE
RAZZ  REINE  EVES
ASEA  DIXIE  ROTE
```

141

```
RAJA  GATO  ASTAR
AMIR  ICAL  SKATE
MAMA  BARD  CITED
 HABERDASHERIES
   GAI  AUNT
TABERNACLED  PAC
IRATE  LTS  GALA
TIBET  TIS  DONOR
USES  ARM  ANDRE
SEL  FLABBERGAST
   MAGI  RAE
 JABORANDITREES
ALARM  EINE  DRIP
PARSE  EVER  ANTE
ESKER  SASS  MESA
```

142

```
SLIM  ACRE   ARCH
LADE  ROUTS  QUAI
ITISNOTTHEBULLS
THESOUTH  CLOAKS
    BSA  PROM
APPLE  MAEWESTS
OMORE  OUST  THAI
NORISITTHEBEARS
ELEM  NOTA  ERNES
RESERVES  MASKS
    RIIS  LOT
ONEACT  MARINADE
TISTHEBUMSTEERS
TETE  DONEE  IRON
OLES   GIRL  LOPE
```

143

```
BRAN  FLECK  FIAT
RIME  RURAL  ALTI
AGAS  ONICE  LIES
COTTAGECHEESE
TROOP    ESTE
   RIANT   ATTAR
ORC  SLOOPS  TYRE
TOLLHOUSECOOKIE
ISEE  ESCROW  ELK
CAFFE   AETNA
   TROD   ELSIE
 CHATEAUBRIAND
BELA  HARPY  EROS
AGON  ERNIE  NANE
DODD  REINS  SHEL
```

144

```
 POIROT  HOLMES
VARNISH ORIENTS
INSTORE TITANIA
SSH  SIB  WEH ORD
OOID  CABAL  ABRA
RUNES  NUT  FILET
STEROL  REVELERS
   MAIGRET
PELLMELL  TAPPET
ADIGE  LAP  SLOSH
NUBS  FURLS  ORSO
ICE  GAS  APE  TEN
CARNERO  SERVING
STAINER  MANIOCS
 ELLERY  ARSENE
```

145

```
JOYCE  ANN  GLYN
UBOAT  BIO  LOOIE
MOUSE  AGT  ADULT
PENT  ACHE  CERES
GETOUT  TESS
AFB  ANSATE  THIS
MALICE  THELOOSE
INONE  STY  UNWED
SCOTTISH  AREONE
HYDR  STEELE  FDR
HIRT  OXIDES
OSAGE  SPIT  SHAD
SEWUP  LES  STOLE
TAKEA  ART  SEWER
MESS  GAS  ESSEN
```

146

```
RANA  BATH  ASH
OMIT  ALIAS  ELLA
MANO  CAPRA  STAR
PHENAKISTOSCOPE
ELL  YENTA
PAL  EAT  SEEPED
ONIT  SEA  LARRA
TETRAHEXAHEDRON
SARAN  ETO  EENS
REVEAL  EST  DEE
ESSES  TAP
BOUSTROPHEDONIC
RAPT  AVEIL  KERR
AHOY  MINER  ERIE
GUN  ITSY  ROSE
```

147

```
DOWER  BOILS
BEGONE  ASCOTS
ALFREDHITCHCOCK
DALES  EMMA  IRON
DIAS  CAPER  ARE
EST  KORAN  BOGIE
DEEPNESS  BOREAL
LODESTONE
SCREWS  IRRIGATE
ALIAS  COIGN  BAR
DIV  MANSE  MEMO
ACIS  ILET  HAYES
THEPARADINECASE
ERASES  CEMENT
AMISH  HOIST
```

148

```
TABS  COD  ORAN
ARAT  DEVIL  CITE
BARE  ELEVE  AGRA
UNDERTENANT  HER
LEERS  TASTES
CALGARY  NEWTS
ALEUT  SOON  ETAL
SOFIA  EVE  SPUME
HUTT  SEAL  ELFIN
HALED  CARAFES
SHARER  BOVID
EEN  OVERWINDING
VADE  ELIAS  ELUL
EVEN  SACRO  RILE
NERD  NED  SALE
```

149

```
MESA  ORALE  ADEN
OARS  DECAL  PACE
TRESEDEHTFOPIHS
END  ANDY  BESOT
NOSES  SETA
STILTS  SHOULDER
CRAG  SATINS  ERA
ROMAN  DAN  EELER
AVE  OLIVET  PUCE
PERORATE  AVIATE
ADDS  SLASH
AMATI  AILS  REE
STNECEVIFYTNEWT
IGOR  GIRTH  OVEN
SENS  GESSO  DORA
```

150

```
OSCARS  AMELIA
CARLOTA  ONALINE
THEBOYSOFSUMMER
IMET  EXPEL  ERA
ODOR  CABAL  WATT
HINT  ISON  SADIE
SCAB  VOW  BEREA
FEIN  QUAM
SPALL  PUN  STEW
RALLY  PLAN  PRAY
ELUL  LEARY  RUSE
TIM  AUDIT  MIST
REBECCADEWINTER
ONEGIRL  RANGERS
STRODE  RESENT
```

151

```
BOSOM  APSO  ARAL
ALIBI  IRON  POCO
RELIC  DELICIOUS
BOO  REESE  HASTE
   LORDS  GARTER
THROWN  UNIFY
RIATA  IRANI  MPH
ARM  VETERAN  100
YES  ERICA  GETUP
   MOSSO  ADDERS
REMOVE  ORRIS
ADORE  SKITS  LOS
DETONATED  HOIST
INES  LORE  ERASE
ISLE  LASS  STRAP
```

152

```
SITE  CANEM  BLIP
ESOX  OLIVA  RANA
ABUT  MIDASTOUCH
MACRAME  SOAKERS
   HELEN  INRE
ETAMINE  VISITED
DINETTE  ECONOMY
NED        UCA
AUGMENT  SPRUCED
SPOONER  TRASHES
   DORE  AIMED
INDICIA  IMPLODE
TOUCHSTONE  EWER
UNAU  SEDER  SNUG
PALM  ADARS  SSTS
```

153

```
ALE  SPAT  ACTOR
DOLL  ARAR  NOONE
DIMESTORE  SLUMP
URANO  VONS  ORES
PENNYPINCHER
   YARN  HEMATIC
BOA  OCS  INANE
ATCLOSEQUARTERS
NORIA  NNE  LET
KEEPHIS  TOGA
   PUMPERNICKEL
SCAM  PALA  MUNRO
POLAR  RECEPTION
OPINE  TMEN  ESSE
TEENS  AIDS  HER
```

154

```
IRS  OSMAN  PEACE
LEW  WHOLE  ALLAY
SEE  LOVEFORLOVE
ADES  RIC  REEFER
   TASTE  SCENTS
WALRUS  SHH
AVIAN  ALAIS  CBC
DAPHNISANDCHLOE
ESS  ANITA  AHEAD
   TAE  SNOOZE
   SHARON  ACTUP
SPIRIT  PGA  RACE
TAKETOHEART  TOM
IRENE  ALICE  ROM
RESTS  GENET  AKA
```

155

```
GRAB  OPERA  GLUM
RUBY  FINES  LIRA
IDOL  FUDDYDUDDY
DEVISE  SERIOUS
   ENTRAP  TEE
ABBEY  RAW  ARENT
BOOS  MAYHEM  VIA
AGA  BABBITT  EEN
SER  OPIATE  ANCY
HYDRO  ACE  ATSEA
   UGH  KNIGHT
FISSION  NEWEST
ONTHELEVEL  AVER
AGEE  EXILE  RENE
MEWS  STILT  TNTS
```

156

```
MOWS  ICHOR  DOGS
AREA  MOUTH  OMOO
GILD  MOTHERWELL
MOLDAU  SETASIDE
ANILINE  ROVE
   NEREUS  RESNIK
ANGRY  SOLID  EVA
VATS  COLIC  SEAL
ETO  NOLAN  MARNE
CONCUR  REGARD
   AIRE  RANGOFF
OVERTURN  GNAWER
WELLSPRING  SETA
LALO  TONAL  SLIT
SUES  SLATE  OLDS
```

157

```
OPAL  TOGAS  SNOW
DELI  ANILE  TIDE
SLAT  MIRED  ALOT
  FREDANDGINGER
    RILES  TEE
ESCAPE   MIASMAS
LOOT  AMOON  ART
FLYINGDOWNTORIO
IVE  ALDEN  UNAU
NERUDAS   DETEST
    NID  CORES
  EDWARDEHORTON
BLUR  AUDIO  RIOT
ASEA  GNARL  ISLE
HELP  SARAS  PEON
```

158

```
BOASTS  PTA  OAST
ATMOST  ERS  DUPE
SHIPPEDOUT  ETRE
SODS  PENMANSHIP
     TIARA  ONE
ITSA  KEEN  VERGE
SHIPPERS  TIAS
RESHIPS  THESHIP
   TINT  DOESTIME
CREDO  AIRY  SPAT
OER  LASER
MASTERSHIP  APRA
ECHO  LEADERSHIP
STIR  ERR  NATIVE
ASPS  STD  DEALER
```

159

```
MOAB  SEWN  ABBA
YALE  THREE  FERN
THEECHOINGGREEN
HUE  OILED  RIFLE
   SINE  SEC
PURPLEMOUNTAIN
ASIA  PLEA  NUB
DUAD  CHIME  JUDO
SAT  COIN  ARGO
  LAVENDERSGREEN
  INK  ICAL
BUILT  SABOT  YAK
ONCEINABLUEMOON
ODES  EMBER  DRNO
PORT  BEET  SKEW
```

160

```
FLAT  REGAL  SPAR
LIRA  ERASE  HARI
AMERIGOVESPUCCI
NEAPTIDE  SANTAS
   HOE  LEST
SEAMAN  PENT  HAJ
ANTIC  MATE  SOLO
VALLADOLIDSPAIN
ETAL  ETON  AURAE
DES  STES  PINERS
  LAOS  HAL
RETURN  GENOVESE
ITALIANAMERICAN
ANIL  TAMIL  TOLD
SALS  EGANS  ANTS
```

161

```
DEMI  PEST  PASHA
ATOM  EVER  ASPEN
DROMEDARY  THERE
SERENADE  SIENNA
   DOLE  SPENSER
CHAISE  SHUN
LOMA  REPERTOIRE
EMIT  LEA  BROW
FOREANDAFT  SATE
  REEK  ARENAS
EMPEROR  AVES
LEAVEN  PHEASANT
MARIS  GUERRILLA
EDICT  ORAN  OARS
RESTS  BEDS  NIBS
```

162

```
PELF  SATIN  REFS
ODOR  CLOSE  ELLA
TARO  OONAS  GUAM
  MENOFFEWWORDS
   TAFT  PEEK
   AIRS  VALET
ECTO  REASON  DUO
THEWEIRDSISTERS
EER  DONETS  IAGO
  NITER  ANNE
  OPEC  PINS
  ARETHEBESTMEN
ARID  EMILE  ICON
SELL  AMEER  THEE
IDLE  RAREE  HOLE
```

163

```
GASP   ALMS   AMPLE
APIA   TOOK   SALAR
FELL   TATI   TRUSS
FROMLEFTTORIGHT
    BASSO   MON
ATLAST   BOA   ASES
TOOLS   SENNA   TRI
TFELOTTHGIRMORF
IFS   SEATO   TAROT
CYST   ARM   RULERS
    ARC   OHARE
ONTHEHORIZONTAL
PARIS   AFRO   KILO
AMATI   SPAR   OLEO
HEMIN   TUMS   VEST
```

164

```
BOMB   BRAGG   IRA
ADAR   REGAL   NORA
HOLYTOLEDO   EMIL
TRINIDAD   WAVELL
    LIX   DENEB
CAJOLE   FORTRESS
AMASS   ALLEE   AAA
NICE   PLIED   PUNT
INK   TREES   BETTY
SOLDIERS   PLAYER
  OREST   LAE
HONEST   SERENADE
ALDA   ILOVEPARIS
EDOM   GALEN   SIDE
  SNY   EXERT   IDOL
```

165

```
ABC   DECO   POSSE
BOAT   IDEM   ONICE
USSR   ASIN   LEGAL
  CHANNELISLANDS
    BAAL   TOR
CAPED   MARIMBAS
ALARIC   EDO   UNA
SANTAYNEZVALLEY
ETE   RES   EDIBLE
DELAWARE   LOSER
    RAN   ASAN
RANCHODELCIELO
IDAHO   ELLE   SOON
CAMEO   BIEN   SIZE
OMERS   SANE   SEW
```

166

```
  TEASET   PARLAY
RANCHER   OLEATES
INTHENICKOFTIME
SAWED   CHESS   MER
EGIS   DYERS   BENE
SEN   PACES   CUTIN
  RETAILS   MOROSE
    AGREEMENT
PULLEY   CELESTA
ERIES   SLATY   INT
TATS   ROOTS   SPAR
ANT   FIFTH   KAPPA
LILYOFTHEVALLEY
STEEPLE   AIRLESS
  ERASER   DESERT
```

167

```
MASC   BORG   SHOAL
ALLO   ARIA   HORSE
LEON   BELL   ENATE
APPT   BALLERINAS
  HERALD   IMI
    ARE   SNIFFLED
STALK   POUT   OILY
HALT   ORALS   LESE
ARLO   CERE   SKUAS
HAYSEEDS   AUS
    TAI   UNKIND
TAPDANCING   NERO
ORLOP   ANTE   GREW
LEAVE   TOIL   EVAN
DANES   EWES   REDS
```

168

```
ROTC   MICA   PREP
OMAR   PETER   ROAR
PERILATENDHOUSE
ENE   INERT   ETTES
    TRIO   ALE
THESECRETWOMAN
RARA   NEAT   GAB
IBAR   DADDY   HOMO
PIT   SOSO   IRED
  TOSEEAFINELADY
  ONS   LULL
START   SLEDS   ADO
THEEAGLESGATHER
EARS   SUEDE   RAJA
RIOT   MERE   EBAN
```

169

```
T A S S   S C O U R S   C A R
S L A T   C O R N E A   A N O
A L L E G O R I C A L   L A B
R E V E R T   O L D   D O P E
I N A N E   O L E   P O R E R
N I G   G E N E A L O G I S T
A C E T O N E   R E L I C T S
      A R T     E Y E
H A R R I E S   P R E S I D E
U N I T A R I N E S S   N E T
S E D A N   M O T   T R U C E
T M A N   S P T   N E U T E R
L O B   C A L I F O R N I A N
E N L   C R E O L E   E L S A
S E E   C A R N A L   S E E L
```

170

```
A H E M   I C O M E   D S M S
R O D E   M O L E S   E T A L
S U G A R M A P L E   S A L A
  R E T A I L E D   O C T E T
    S H E M     F A R E
A R A   S I S   A T I M E
G U L P   N E I G H B O R S
A S W E   P E D R O   E T N A
S T A T E T R E E   S T E N
  S Y R I A   R L S   O S E
  S O N S     A P E S
R I F L E   P I N E T R E E
I N R E   H E A D W A T E R S
D I E U   A R M E E   A L I T
S T E M   S T A R R   S Y N E
```

171

```
    M O S S     S P A S
  F I L T E R   S P A R T A
C O R D I T E   P I C T U R E
O R A   R A P P O R T   M R S
P A C S   E L I T E   S P A T
S Y L P H   Y E T   A L E N E
  S E R I N   D E S S E R T
    E N I D   D O S E
S C A T T E R   S E P A L
S H A D S   S O B   T E N O N
P I T S   S P A R S   R A V E
U R N   O K I N A W A   T E A
D R A G N E T   D I S T O R T
  S P E C I E   S P O O L S
    S T E N     E R N E
```

172

```
D A L E   A N J O U   A N E W
E T U X   N E O N S   R O L E
C O M P A T R I O T   R O S E
I M P O S E O N   I R O N E D
    R H U S   S N O W
I N S T E P   S T O P   T I P
M A T I N   S T E V E D O R E
A V O N   S H A M S   E K E S
G A N G S T E R S   S P E N T
E L Y   T R E K   P H E N E S
    P O E T   L O O N
D I S O W N   P A R A D R O P
O V E N   G O N D O L I E R I
N O T E   T R E E S   N E L L
E R A S   H O U S E   G L E E
```

173

```
A R A B   P A P A   A C U P
P O L A R I S A N D M A R I S
L A S S I E A N D M A S S E Y
  D O E G   B E A S T   I T S
    H A U L     G N A T
A M A   T U G   W A L E S
N O T A S B I G   I R E
N A L D I A N D T E B A L D I
  A D D   S O N I N L A W
C I T E E   L I T   B R O
R A S E     S E E R
O U R   A M E E R   A M B I
B L A I R A N D A S T A I R E
S K E L T O N A N D E L T O N
  S L O E   A N T S   T E N D
```

174

```
T I T O   S C R A M   C L A P
O N Y X   P H A S E   H U G E
A C R E   R O M P S   I N R E
  H E N R Y K I S S I N G E R
    T E E     C E A S E S
D I P P E R   C H A R T
O D O R S   J O E L   O C H S
M E R E   S E P A L   W H E T
E A T S   C A S T   S N A I L
  I N A N E   B I S T R O
L E A D E N   M U G
I N T E R N A T I O N A L E
E T O N   E B O N Y   L I N T
T E N T   R E T I E   I N D O
O R E S   S T E E D   T E S T
```

175

```
TOTO  USTED   FAR
OAHU  SHUTE   PAGE
TRET  HIGHSIERRA
 STREEP   INROAD
 HAIRS    WRIT
ALIGNS  THETHIEF
RANEE  SHIES  NMI
MUM    PEN    TEX
ORA  HARDY  SCENE
FANTASIA  CHORDS
    RITT  CHELM
SOWETO   HAMLET
THEKILLERS  EZRA
OILS  AERIE  CZAR
WOK   TRESS  TOME
```

176

```
ALAS  REBS   SPEED
RENO  OLLA   TABLE
CANYOUSEWMYROBE
ANABASIS   AMENED
   ESTES   RIN
  THAIS  DIETING
TRANS  BLOND   DOR
HERS  MOIRA  METE
EVE  LINDY  MISTY
MISTAKE   FESTE
   IMA  SALAD
SPACED  ANATOLIA
NOIKNOWNOTSEAMS
ARRET  EDDA  RTEI
PESTS  DYES  SETS
```

177

```
CLUBS  WEFT   SGT
CONAN  HAIR  ATUB
CIRCE  ECRU  MANS
 TAKESTHESTAND
REVERE   STANDUP
BRED  PEP  SLATES
ISL  DIDOS  ENOLA
   HEADSTAND
PASOS  YEAST  TLR
ACTUAL  SRI  THOU
STANDAT  AIRING
 UNDERSTANDING
BADE  DARN  LANES
ARID  ENOS  EGEST
AYN   RAYE  RESTS
```

178

```
  DANCE    LEWD
  BOREAS   ONION
DOGGEREL   DOGGED
RIGOR  ODES   WEE
ILOT  ADIOS  CODA
FEN  WRONG  DROLL
TREPANG  PARADES
   ALEE   ALIF
CEDILLA  TEETHES
EMORY  RECUR  AET
LOGS  HECHT  ANTI
LTD  SADR   BEGIN
SEADOG  UNDERDOG
 SYRIA   MAROON
 SUER    USING
```

179

```
TSAR  IRIS   TREES
APSE  NENE   READE
POSTPONED   EERIE
ERASE  TREPANNED
REMITS   TRYST
   NAPE   MORTAR
CANALIZED   NYASA
ACE  TROUT   CHI
STOIC  ANTEDATED
TENSOR    YARD
   OREAD  KOALAS
IMPLOSION   OPERA
MILAN  SWORDTAIL
PLATA  LETO  OSSA
SONES  ELAN  REED
```

180

```
BLOW   EGBA    HID
BABE  STORMTRACK
LIEN  CONATIONAL
 CYCLONE    TOOL
   HOT  WAIST
CREEPS  IST  ECHO
ROUSE  THE  RAYA
AIR  ZEPHYRS  NET
PLUM  RAT  HBONE
ESSE  ISH  BOREAS
  TANTE   ORE
 CHET  WALTERS
THEOLOGIST  ZEUS
HURRICANES  EARL
OBE   ALDA   SLEY
```

181

```
SCARE HAW   . SAG   .
AUGER . OBI . DEBAR
GRAVELPIT  . ITALO
ETRE . AIR . TRUCES
. . IMP . DUSTPANS
AEOLUS . . NATS . .
COULD . SHIRR . RTE
INSET . CAT . AFOUL
DST . UKASE . CLARK
. ARAL . . SKINKS
SANDTRAP . ASP . .
AREOLA . RAN . POLO
SNARE . MUCKRAKER
HIRES . ODE . ANITA
. ESS . PER . STEAL
```

182

```
PLUMP CERO . DADE
EASEL ORAL . EDOM
EVERY . TOTEMPOLE
PESTERED . SILVER
. ORARE . NEEDY
AMEN MIN . CAT . .
RID . SPET . ARENAS
AMELIAS . PRESENT
LINING . PERT . RIO
. MEE . RPI . HASA
FAMED . OPERA . .
AMATIS . PERORATE
CORRECTOR . COLON
ERIE . OISE . CLOUD
TENE . WEED . ODETS
```

183

```
APAR . BANC . PEPIN
MALE . AMAH . ORATE
INAPPLEPIEORDER
RESEAL . SPUR . SAO
. AGRA . IRED . .
APPLEOFONESEYE
CAR . DORR . TROLL
TRIM . MOTHS . NUDE
EMMAS . HATE . VEE
. APPLEPOLISHERS
. SORE . OPTO . .
SEA . VEER . EASIER
APPLEBROWNBETTY
SHEEN . ENID . RUNE
HARTS . DANS . SPAS
```

184

```
JADE . ANEST . MEOW
AXEL . PADUA . ANGE
PINK . ASSEMBLERS
ELI . ACHE . ATREE
. GODHELPSTHOSE
STRIDE . OAHU . .
TRADE . SHUN . SLAB
OAT . RETIRES . IDA
WYES . VETS . HEMIN
. PLIE . SERENE
WHOHELPOTHERS .
ROVES . LOON . TOE
OVERSHADOW . FOXX
TETE . ADELE . ONEI
ERAS . GONER . BENT
```

185

```
PIMA . PARSE . SNAP
IDES . EDITH . TOPE
LEEK . ROCAS . EVIL
LAKEHURON . FEAST
. DIKE . DEALS . .
AIM . VERBIFY . COD
STERES . ANTELOPE
TAXI . TUG . STEN
OLIBANUM . MATINS
ROC . LATERAL . ASE
. ALAMO . ORAL . .
AGNES . RIOGRANDE
DAWN . PASTE . BAIL
ETAT . OGLER . OPAL
NERO . PEARY . RAZE
```

186

```
APIE . RECAP . SWAB
SODA . EMAIL . PANE
PEER . APPRECIATE
STAB . TOEDANCER
. EASY . GRE . .
AGENDA . TREE . FHA
MENDACIOUS . ERAS
ALDER . SIS . DYERS
TIER . SILHOUETTE
ODD . APSE . CLOSET
. AIR . PALP . .
HEADLINER . ELLA
IMPOSTURES . NEON
LEER . ELITE . ETON
LURE . SLEET . RATE
```

187

```
FACT  HART  TROPE
CHER  OLEO  HOMES
CARE  LAIN  ETAPE
 BOARDINGSCHOOL
    TOO   ASH
TEA  OVEN  SANEST
ATLE ELIS  RAREE
SHIVERMETIMBERS
KNEEL SCAD  SCAT
SONNET ERLE  TIA
    GEE   ETC
BABEINTHEWOODS
ODORS HARI  VEER
LEANT EVIL  ELLA
ESTES REED  RIFF
```

188

```
BOOR  LADES  NAPE
ANNA  ALIST  OPUS
NETS  PLATA  TENT
CROCODILETEARS
   AMO   RUS
ALLIGATORPEARS
DUO  TSAR  EYELET
ARID  RUR  LAME
CARESS SACO  MUM
ELEPHANTFOLIOS
   ALA   NEG
KANGAROOCOURTS
HIRE ARIDE  ATOP
ALMA MOTOR  NERO
STAR SWART  ASST
```

189

```
CLASS SRTA  BOMB
AETNA PIER  ARAL
SHOAL OPEN  CARE
HIPPODROME  KNEE
    METS  SAGGED
CANCEL TOSCA
OHOH  IMET  EMBER
PELISSE HORMONE
OMANI STEW  ORDO
   CLEAR INNESS
FISHOR ARNE
ALTI  ARMAGEDDON
COOL  SEMI  DROVE
ENOL  EVES  LATEX
DADA  DELE  EBERT
```

190

```
 NOMS  FLAP  TSE
LOPAT  LASH  HITE
CHICAGOWHITESOX
TIN  DAWN  LARINE
STEPINS  ALSO
   RUG  GRISSOMS
BROOM ROLE  ERAT
EAR SPAREST  AMA
SMEW  IRES  RELAY
SPLATTER  SIR
   LUCE  STARTED
HEALTH STAN  EVE
STLOUISCARDINAL
TRAP NEAR  OVENS
 ENS GENE  SETS
```

191

```
BEST  SAFES  ASEA
AREA  ALATE  CARL
RILL  LORNA  CLAD
BELIEVE  APPEASE
    STE  LADDER
ASAMARCHHARE
CANAL LEONE  NIB
MIEN  TONNE  RATA
EDT  PRUNE  KEPIS
  ASADAYINJUNE
CONRAD  NEO
ICEDTEA  SLEIGHT
NAPE  IGETA  COIR
CLAN  NISEI  ERSE
HALT  SNERD  DESK
```

192

```
SNAPS  SPOUT  ESQ
TONIC  LARGO  SOU
ANDTOMORROW  PIE
BEY  FATS   ALLS
OFTHINGSPAST
PERUSES  OATEN
EROS  AGRA  ABE
WAITINGFORGODOT
SSS  FOAL   BELA
  TONAL  ARRESTS
THETIMESTHEY
HERO  ITON  AIM
EXO  PERSISTENCE
FEU  ALTAR  AGNES
TDS  LISLE  LOESS
```

193

```
BAMA   APRES   KETA
ELAM   SHARP   EGAN
ELLE   CORGI   ROTO
FILTRATE   KANSAN
    HOPI   FETE
  PAYS   CARNELIAN
SENSED   LOAN   DIE
ERST   ESTER   SOMA
ADE   OTTO   DEALER
TURQUOISE   APSE
    USNR   RASP
DAKOTA   NORTHERS
EMIT   TRADE   IDEA
LONE   EATEN   RING
EKED   SEEST   ETTE
```

194

```
 OLAV   GAME   PATE
ARECA   ASIN   ILES
CANIS   SENT   COPS
CLODHOPPER   KNEE
     TUES   EILEEN
 LAPIN   IRENE
MAGI   CASE   EPODE
ELAPSED   STEUBEN
WORST   ASTO   SING
    QUART   WASTE
 ALBUMS   OVEN
MILE   SPOILSPORT
UVEA   ERGO   WIDER
SINK   NOEL   ELITE
EDDS   TASS   RENE
```

195

```
PREP   PLAID   SPAD
RIDE   LAINE   LAME
OVERPASSES   ESAU
FASTENS   REPASTS
   ANE   TRAVE
ENKINDLE   TIESON
TEENY   INNER   TRY
AVES   UNDER   FIDE
PIP   SNEER   ARMET
ELEVES   DOSSIERS
   RICES   HOT
CAPSTAN   BANTERS
HILO   TIMEKEEPER
ADAR   EDILE   RENO
DAYS   DEBAR   SETS
```

196

```
ATPAR   WAGE   CLEW
BRICE   IMAN   AIRY
OILED   NOSH   SAME
MEL   CATSPAJAMAS
BROCADE   SNUB
  WIPER   CLAWED
MATT   SIRREE   ETA
OKAYS   ZOE   POTTY
NIL   AGENTS   MBAS
ANKARA   REGAL
 RAZE   INANAME
FEATHERBEDS   NAM
LADE   TRAV   BAKIE
USER   TELE   ALENE
EENY   EDER   GATER
```

197

```
TOM   FRET   EROSE
OPAL   ROMA   LIMIT
FELICECAPODANNO
FRAMED   NIX   LIEN
YARNS   ACRES
   SEMI   NEARED
ALOE   RIPS   RHONE
MUMMERSANDBANDS
ONAIR   STAY   BASK
SENLIS   ICES
   KAPOK   ESTES
IANS   GIN   LATENT
SWEARANDRESOLVE
IRENE   TAUS   PLOW
TYRES   AYRE   SYS
```

198

```
PATH   SALAD   SCAR
AREA   ELOGE   ARIA
SCARLETTANAGERS
TAMPER   TIRED
ODEON   CREME   EAT
RED   COO   ONCE
  SHAMUS   PACED
 SCARLETLETTER
GAOLS   TIARAS
OGLE   NNE   PAP
BAL   CARET   AROSE
  APARA   ADAPTS
ASTUDYINSCARLET
REEL   ASCOT   EARL
CEDE   NEONS   ERSE
```

199

H	E	L	D		A	P	A	R	T		I	S	M	S
E	R	I	E		C	R	I	E	R		N	O	A	H
M	I	M	I		T	E	R	S	E		H	A	R	E
S	C	A	R	V	E	S		T	A	P	E	R	E	D
		D	I	S	T	O	R	T	E	R				
S	N	A	R	L		O	B	I		R	I	A	T	A
M	O	T	E	L	S		S	C	A	T	T	E	R	S
U	F	O		A	H	A		T	W	I		G	I	S
T	A	N	A	G	E	R	S		E	N	C	I	N	A
S	T	E	V	E		T	A	R		E	A	S	E	D
		A	R	M	E	N	I	A	N	S				
A	D	V	I	S	O	R		O	C	T	A	V	O	S
R	I	A	L		P	I	E	T	A		B	E	D	E
C	A	N	E		E	A	V	E	S		A	G	E	E
S	L	E	D		S	L	A	D	E		S	A	R	D

200

K	O	P	S		S	A	H	I	B		O	G	R	E
E	L	L	A		O	P	E	R	A		C	R	A	W
P	L	A	Y	B	Y	P	L	A	Y		H	A	Z	E
T	A	Y		T	A	E	L		H	O	R	N	E	R
			I	O	U		A	C	E		B	E	D	
C	O	N	S		P	L	A	Y	P	O	S	S	U	M
O	L	G	A		O	S	T	E	A	L		T	I	E
M	E	T	R	O	S			T	I	T	A	N	S	
B	A	H		S	I	S	A	L	S		A	N	T	S
O	N	E	A	C	T	P	L	A	Y		D	D	A	Y
			F	R	A		A	L	P		A	S	P	
S	K	I	I	N	G		U	S	E	R		L	E	T
T	O	E	S		U	N	D	E	R	P	L	A	Y	S
E	L	L	E		L	E	E	R	S		E	Y	R	A
P	A	D	S		P	A	S	S	E		I	S	E	R

201

G	O	T		O	V	A	L	S		R	A	T	S	O
A	N	A		A	I	M	E	E		O	T	H	E	R
L	E	I		H	O	P	O	M	Y	T	H	U	M	B
L	A	W	F	U	L		N	I	E	C	E			
I	T	A	L		C	A	S	S		N	A	V	E	
C	A	N	A	S	T	A			H	A	C	E	K	
		S	T	A	R	D	A	T	E		L	Y	E	
	S	K	I	P	T	O	M	Y	L	O	U			
A	L	E		R	E	A	S	O	N	E	R			
P	E	R	M	S			R	E	N	D	E	R	S	
T	O	F	U		M	A	M	E		E	L	A	N	
	P	I	E	T	A		H	O	R	A	C	E		
J	U	M	P	S	T	A	R	T	E	D		I	K	E
A	G	R	E	E		L	I	K	E	D		N	E	Z
W	H	I	T	E		L	O	O	P	S		E	R	E

202

L	A	D	D		R	I	V	E	R		C	H	E	R
A	W	A	Y		E	M	I	L	E		L	I	V	E
M	A	N	E	E	V	E	N	T	S		A	R	I	A
A	R	E		L	I	T		O	I	L	W	E	L	L
S	E	S	A	M	E		A	N	N	I	E			
			I	O	W	A	N		S	E	D	A	T	E
W	E	A	R		E	X	E	S		S	M	I	R	K
A	L	D	A		D	E	M	O	S		O	D	I	E
F	L	A	P	S		S	O	F	T		N	A	P	S
T	E	M	P	U	S		N	A	I	V	E			
		A	M	P	L	E		N	I	T	W	I	T	
S	C	O	R	P	I	O		A	K	A		O	R	E
L	O	V	E		C	R	E	W	E	L	H	O	A	X
O	M	E	N		E	N	T	E	R		B	E	T	A
B	E	R	T		S	E	E	D	S		O	D	E	S

203

A	S	H	E	S		A	U	R	A		E	R	M	A
S	P	A	R	E		E	R	I	C		N	O	O	N
P	O	I	N	T	O	F	N	O	R	E	T	U	R	N
S	T	R	E	A	M			O	S	A	G	E	S	
			E	A	R	S		S	P	I	E	S		
L	A	M	B		R	E	C	I	T	A	L			
A	S	I	A		L	E	N	I	N		L	I	T	
W	E	S	T	P	O	I	N	T	C	A	D	E	T	S
S	A	T		A	R	E	T	E		I	N	C	A	
			T	R	I	D	E	N	T		B	O	H	R
	S	L	A	V	E		D	D	A	Y				
S	T	A	L	I	N			R	I	F	L	E	S	
C	O	M	E	S	T	O	T	H	E	P	O	I	N	T
O	R	A	N		A	B	I	E		E	R	A	T	O
W	E	S	T		L	I	E	N		S	T	R	O	P

204

R	E	D	P	E	P	P	E	R		A	P	H	I	D
I	R	R	A	D	I	A	T	E		G	R	E	C	O
C	H	A	R	G	E	D	A	F	F	A	I	R	E	S
H	A	W	S	E	R			L	I	M	I	T		
E	R	L	E		S	I	M	O	N		T	O	W	
R	D	S		S	E	E	S	A	W		L	A	N	A
		B	A	R	T	O	K		S	O	G	G	Y	
	B	E	L	L	E	S	L	E	T	T	R	E	S	
T	R	Y	I	T		H	A	W	A	I	I			
S	E	E	P		H	O	T	A	I	R		C	P	O
P	A	P		L	A	T	E	R		G	A	R	R	
	T	I	T	U	S			D	A	R	R	I	N	
C	H	E	R	C	H	E	Z	L	A	F	E	M	M	E
D	E	C	O	R		G	O	O	N	A	T	E	A	R
C	R	E	T	E		G	E	N	E	R	A	L	L	Y

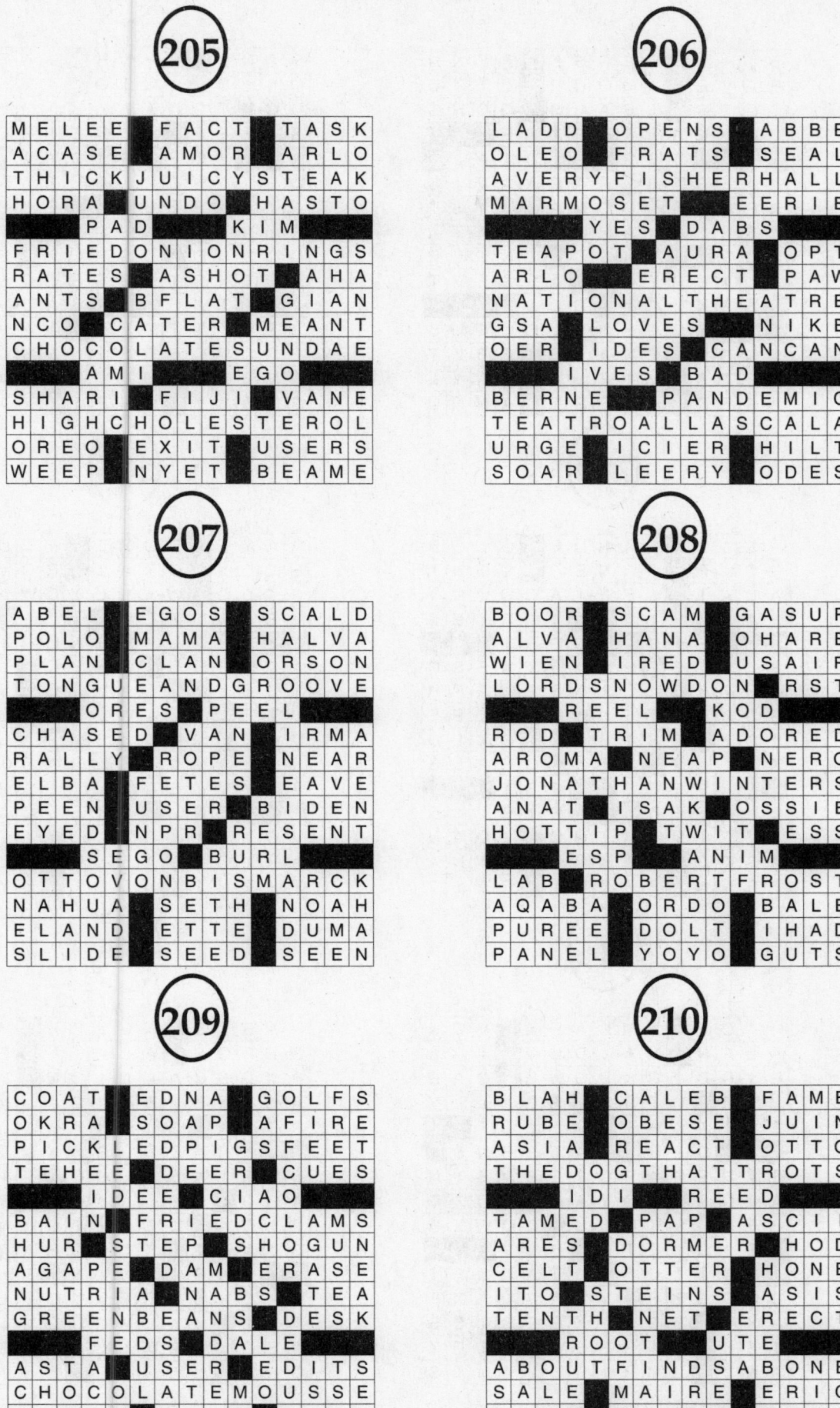

205 206 207 208 209 210

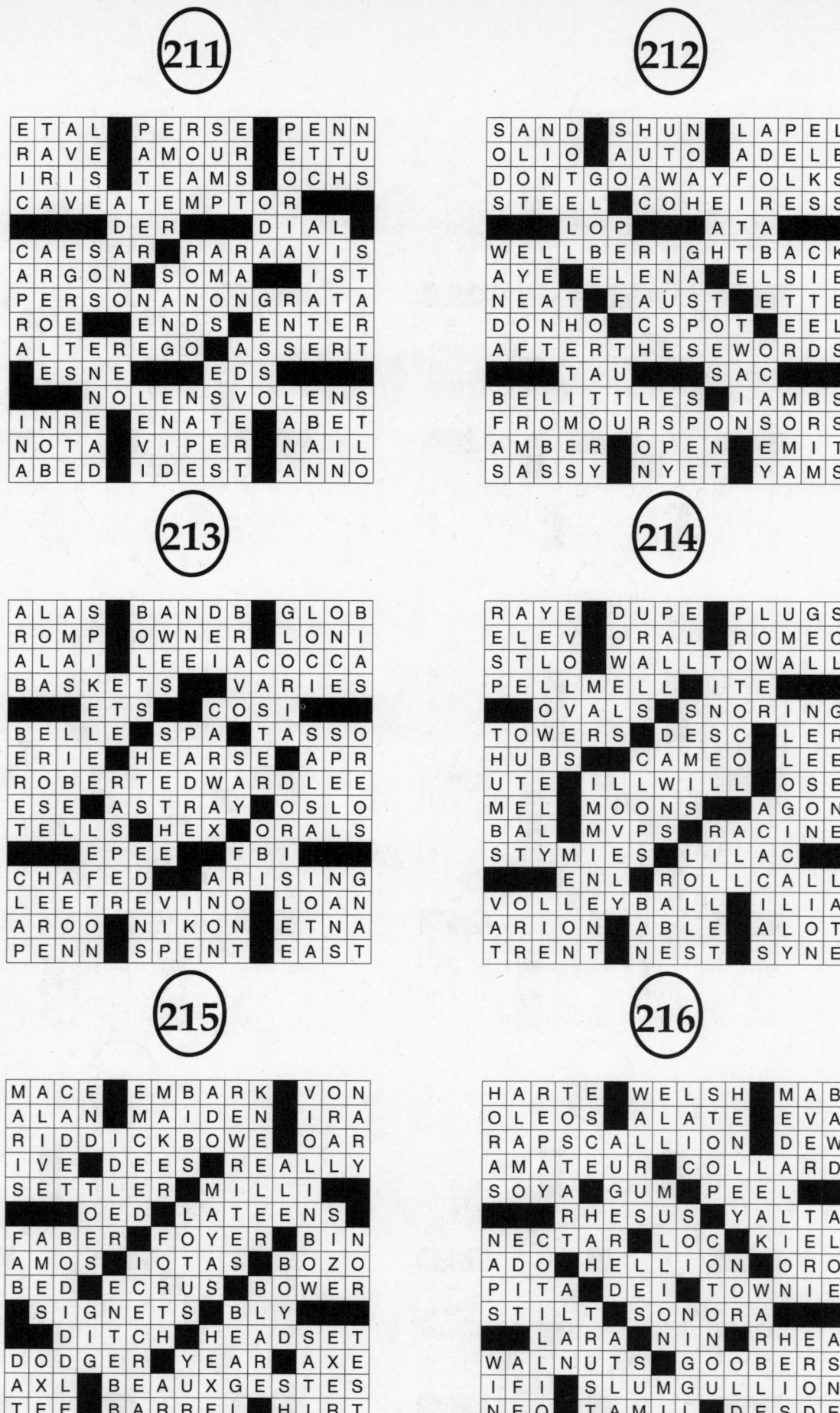

211

```
ETAL PERSE PENN
RAVE AMOUR ETTU
IRIS TEAMS OCHS
CAVEATEMPTOR
   DER  DIAL
CAESAR RARAAVIS
ARGON SOMA IST
PERSONANONGRATA
ROE ENDS ENTER
ALTEREGO ASSERT
 ESNE  EDS
 NOLENSVOLENS
INRE ENATE ABET
NOTA VIPER NAIL
ABED IDEST ANNO
```

212

```
SAND SHUN LAPEL
OLIO AUTO ADELE
DONTGOAWAYFOLKS
STEEL COHEIRESS
   LOP  ATA
WELLBERIGHTBACK
AYE ELENA ELSIE
NEAT FAUST ETTE
DONHO CSPOT EEL
AFTERTHESEWORDS
   TAU  SAC
BELITTLES IAMBS
FROMOURSPONSORS
AMBER OPEN EMIT
SASSY NYET YAMS
```

213

```
ALAS BANDB GLOB
ROMP OWNER LONI
ALAI LEEIACOCCA
BASKETS VARIES
  ETS COSI
BELLE SPA TASSO
ERIE HEARSE APR
ROBERTEDWARDLEE
ESE ASTRAY OSLO
TELLS HEX ORALS
 EPEE  FBI
CHAFED ARISING
LEETREVINO LOAN
AROO NIKON ETNA
PENN SPENT EAST
```

214

```
RAYE DUPE PLUGS
ELEV ORAL ROMEO
STLO WALLTOWALL
PELLMELL ITE
 OVALS SNORING
TOWERS DESC LER
HUBS CAMEO LEE
UTE ILLWILL OSE
MEL MOONS AGON
BAL MVPS RACINE
STYMIES LILAC
 ENL ROLLCALL
VOLLEYBALL ILIA
ARION ABLE ALOT
TRENT NEST SYNE
```

215

```
MACE EMBARK VON
ALAN MAIDEN IRA
RIDDICKBOWE OAR
IVE DEES REALLY
SETTLER MILLI
 OED LATEENS
FABER FOYER BIN
AMOS IOTAS BOZO
BED ECRUS BOWER
 SIGNETS BLY
 DITCH HEADSET
DODGER YEAR AXE
AXL BEAUXGESTES
TEE BARREL HIRT
ANY EMPIRE ANTS
```

216

```
HARTE WELSH MAB
OLEOS ALATE EVA
RAPSCALLION DEW
AMATEUR COLLARD
SOYA GUM PEEL
 RHESUS YALTA
NECTAR LOC KIEL
ADO HELLION ORO
PITA DEI TOWNIE
STILT SONORA
 LARA NIN RHEA
WALNUTS GOOBERS
IFI SLUMGULLION
NEO TAMIL DESDE
OWN SWORE ESTER
```

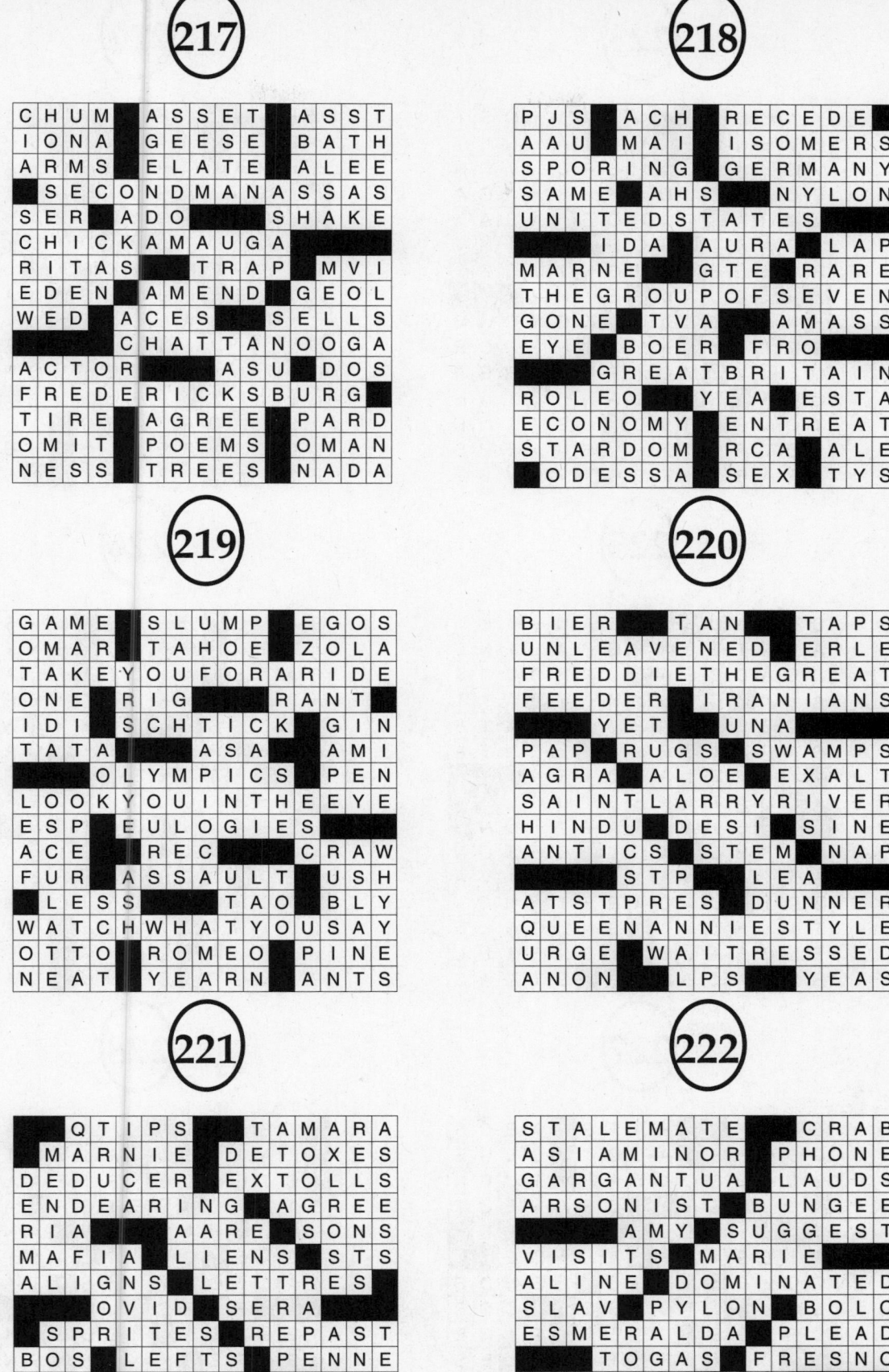

217

C	H	U	M		A	S	S	E	T		A	S	S	T
I	O	N	A		G	E	E	S	E		B	A	T	H
A	R	M	S		E	L	A	T	E		A	L	E	E
	S	E	C	O	N	D	M	A	N	A	S	S	A	S
S	E	R		A	D	O			S	H	A	K	E	
C	H	I	C	K	A	M	A	U	G	A				
R	I	T	A	S		T	R	A	P		M	V	I	
E	D	E	N		A	M	E	N	D		G	E	O	L
W	E	D		A	C	E	S			S	E	L	L	S
		C	H	A	T	T	A	N	O	O	G	A		
A	C	T	O	R			A	S	U		D	O	S	
F	R	E	D	E	R	I	C	K	S	B	U	R	G	
T	I	R	E		A	G	R	E	E		P	A	R	D
O	M	I	T		P	O	E	M	S		O	M	A	N
N	E	S	S		T	R	E	E	S		N	A	D	A

218

P	J	S		A	C	H		R	E	C	E	D	E	
A	A	U		M	A	I		I	S	O	M	E	R	S
S	P	O	R	I	N	G		G	E	R	M	A	N	Y
S	A	M	E		A	H	S		N	Y	L	O	N	
U	N	I	T	E	D	S	T	A	T	E	S			
		I	D	A		A	U	R	A		L	A	P	
M	A	R	N	E		G	T	E		R	A	R	E	
T	H	E	G	R	O	U	P	O	F	S	E	V	E	N
G	O	N	E		T	V	A		A	M	A	S	S	
E	Y	E		B	O	E	R		F	R	O			
	G	R	E	A	T	B	R	I	T	A	I	N		
R	O	L	E	O		Y	E	A		E	S	T	A	
E	C	O	N	O	M	Y		E	N	T	R	E	A	T
S	T	A	R	D	O	M		R	C	A		A	L	E
	O	D	E	S	S	A		S	E	X		T	Y	S

219

G	A	M	E		S	L	U	M	P		E	G	O	S
O	M	A	R		T	A	H	O	E		Z	O	L	A
T	A	K	E	Y	O	U	F	O	R	A	R	I	D	E
O	N	E		R	I	G			R	A	N	T		
I	D	I		S	C	H	T	I	C	K		G	I	N
T	A	T	A			A	S	A			A	M	I	
			O	L	Y	M	P	I	C	S		P	E	N
L	O	O	K	Y	O	U	I	N	T	H	E	E	Y	E
E	S	P		E	U	L	O	G	I	E	S			
A	C	E			R	E	C			C	R	A	W	
F	U	R		A	S	S	A	U	L	T		U	S	H
	L	E	S	S			T	A	O		B	L	Y	
W	A	T	C	H	W	H	A	T	Y	O	U	S	A	Y
O	T	T	O		R	O	M	E	O		P	I	N	E
N	E	A	T		Y	E	A	R	N		A	N	T	S

220

B	I	E	R		T	A	N		T	A	P	S		
U	N	L	E	A	V	E	N	E	D		E	R	L	E
F	R	E	D	D	I	E	T	H	E	G	R	E	A	T
F	E	E	D	E	R		I	R	A	N	I	A	N	S
			Y	E	T			U	N	A				
P	A	P		R	U	G	S		S	W	A	M	P	S
A	G	R	A		A	L	O	E		E	X	A	L	T
S	A	I	N	T	L	A	R	R	Y	R	I	V	E	R
H	I	N	D	U		D	E	S	I		S	I	N	E
A	N	T	I	C	S		S	T	E	M		N	A	P
			S	T	P			L	E	A				
A	T	S	T	P	R	E	S		D	U	N	N	E	R
Q	U	E	E	N	A	N	N	I	E	S	T	Y	L	E
U	R	G	E		W	A	I	T	R	E	S	S	E	D
A	N	O	N		L	P	S			Y	E	A	S	

221

	Q	T	I	P	S		T	A	M	A	R	A	
	M	A	R	N	I	E		D	E	T	O	X	E	S
D	E	D	U	C	E	R		E	X	T	O	L	L	S
E	N	D	E	A	R	I	N	G		A	G	R	E	E
R	I	A			A	A	R	E		S	O	N	S	
M	A	F	I	A		L	I	E	N	S		S	T	S
A	L	I	G	N	S		L	E	T	T	R	E	S	
		O	V	I	D		S	E	R	A				
	S	P	R	I	T	E	S		R	E	P	A	S	T
B	O	S		L	E	F	T	S		P	E	N	N	E
A	M	A	S		D	R	I	P			O	E	R	
S	A	N	T	A		A	R	E	A	C	O	D	E	S
A	L	D	O	R	A	Y		A	N	A	L	Y	Z	E
L	I	Q	U	I	D	S		R	E	L	I	N	E	
T	A	S	T	E	D		S	W	I	N	E			

222

S	T	A	L	E	M	A	T	E		C	R	A	B	
A	S	I	A	M	I	N	O	R		P	H	O	N	E
G	A	R	G	A	N	T	U	A		L	A	U	D	S
A	R	S	O	N	I	S	T		B	U	N	G	E	E
			A	M	Y		S	U	G	G	E	S	T	
V	I	S	I	T	S		M	A	R	I	E			
A	L	I	N	E		D	O	M	I	N	A	T	E	D
S	L	A	V		P	Y	L	O	N		B	O	L	O
E	S	M	E	R	A	L	D	A		P	L	E	A	D
		T	O	G	A	S		F	R	E	S	N	O	
C	A	V	E	M	E	N		H	U	E				
O	M	O	R	E	S		D	I	S	P	O	S	E	D
M	A	C	A	O		P	I	N	E	A	P	P	L	E
T	H	A	T	S		U	N	D	E	R	T	A	K	E
E	L	L	E			P	O	S	S	E	S	S	E	D

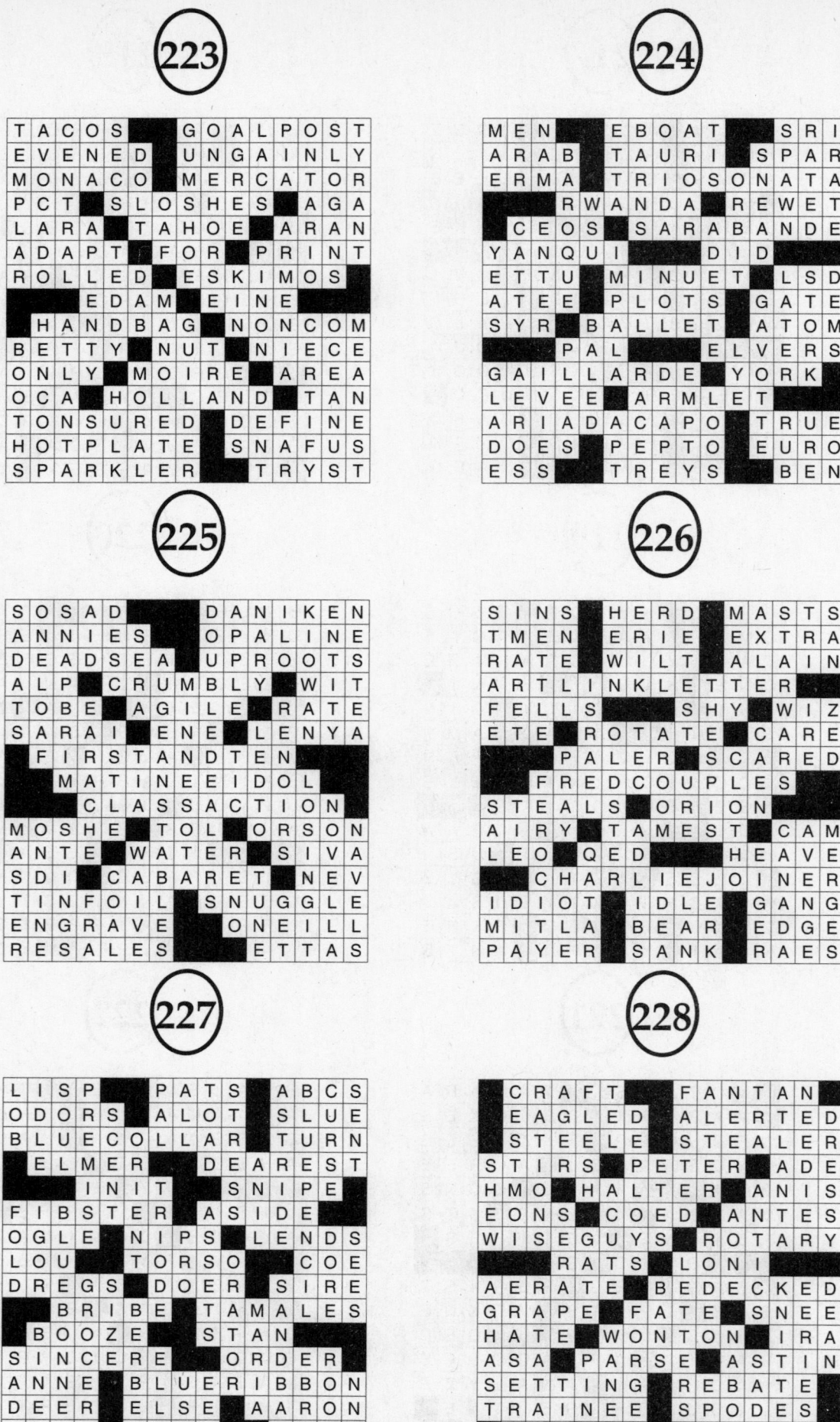

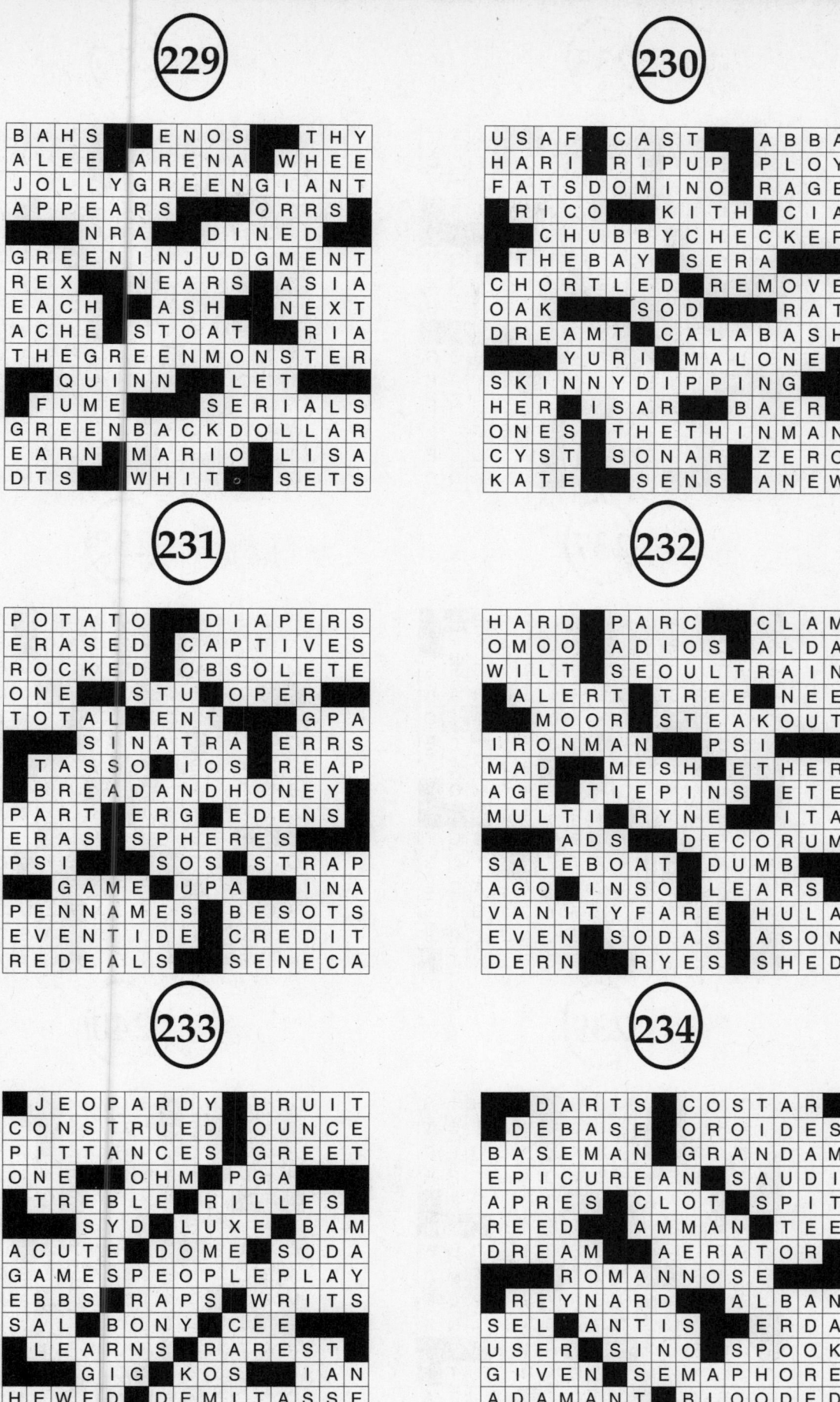

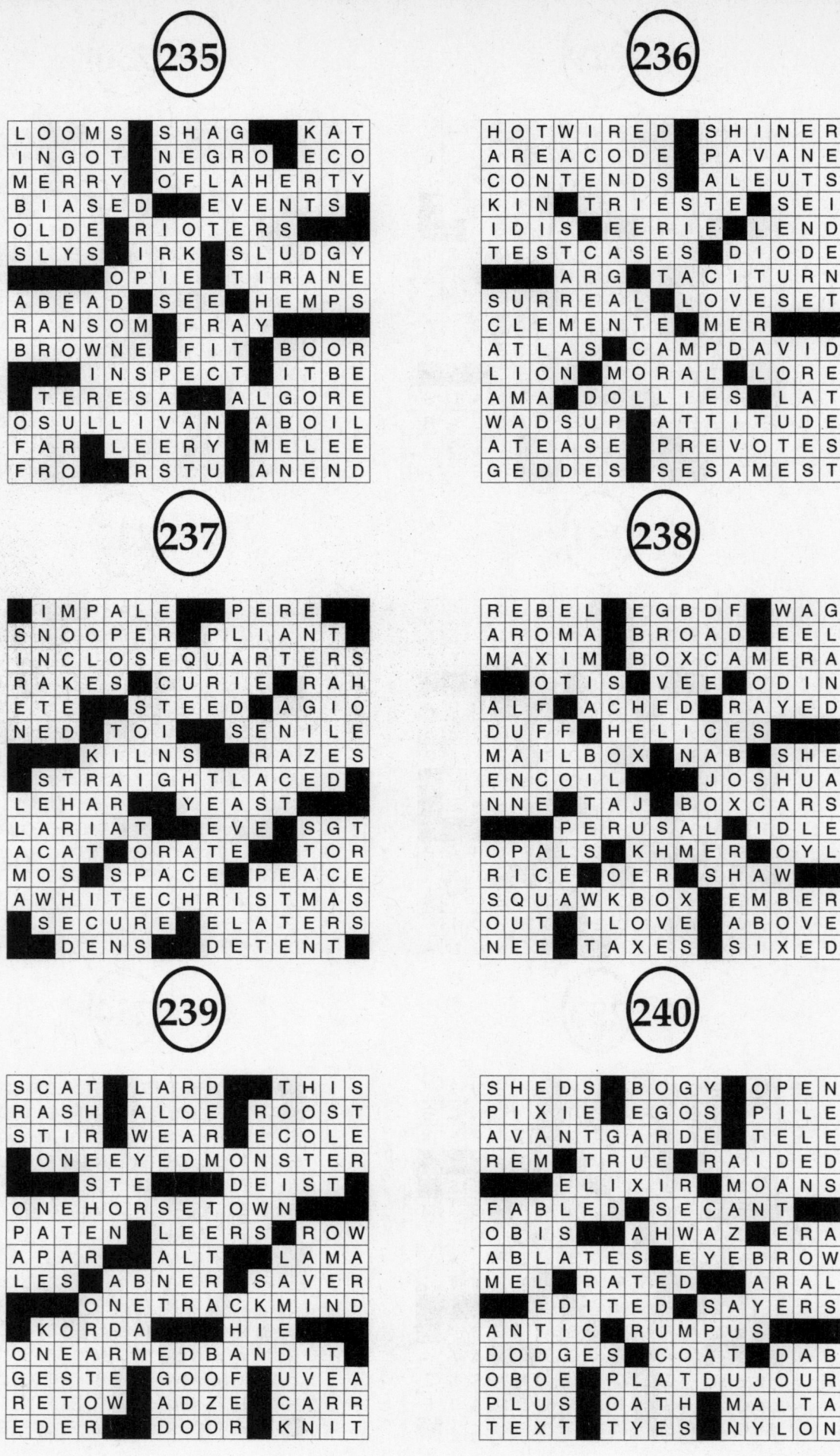

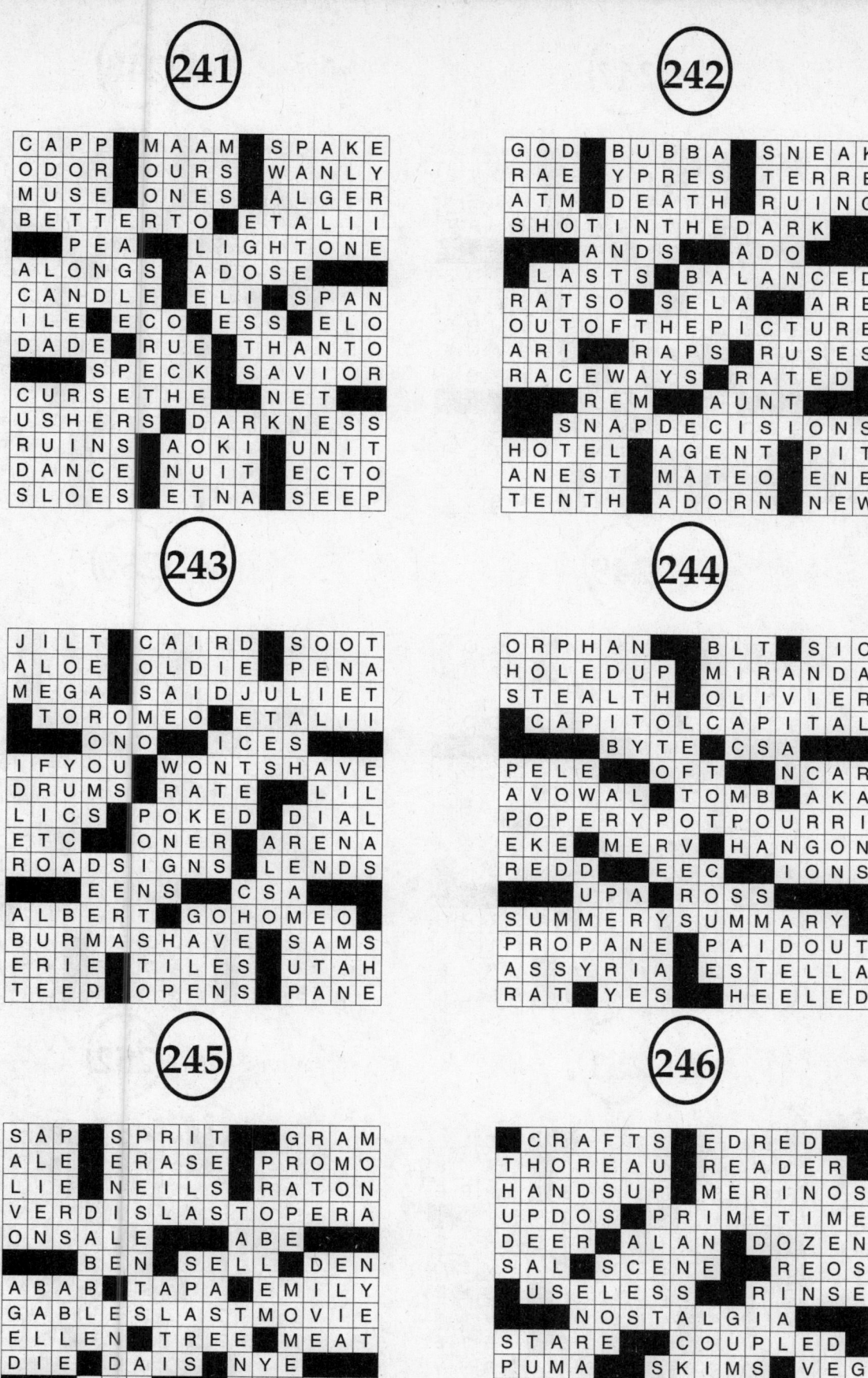

241 242 243 244 245 246

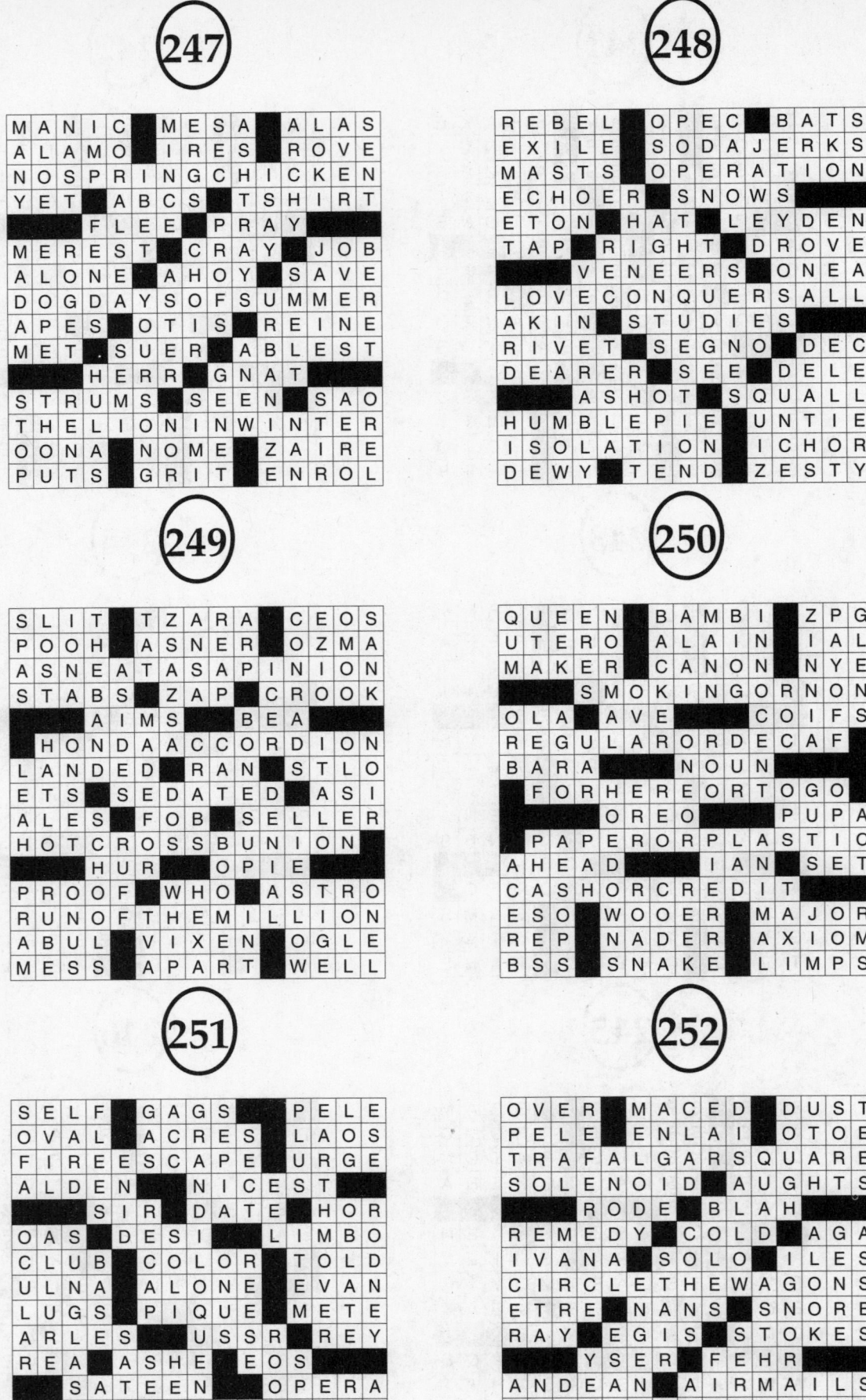

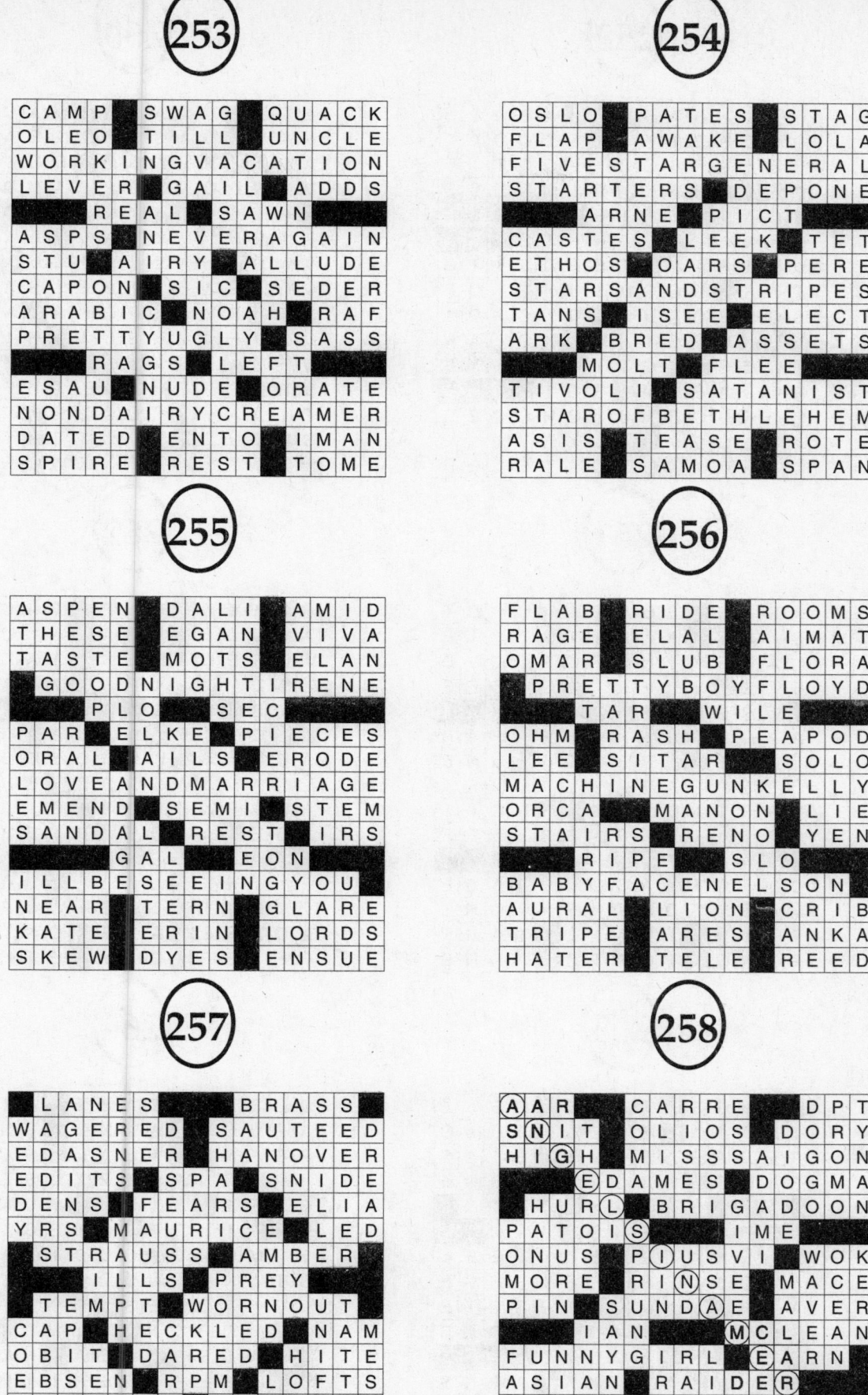

253

C	A	M	P		S	W	A	G		Q	U	A	C	K
O	L	E	O		T	I	L	L		U	N	C	L	E
W	O	R	K	I	N	G	V	A	C	A	T	I	O	N
L	E	V	E	R		G	A	I	L		A	D	D	S
			R	E	A	L		S	A	W	N			
A	S	P	S		N	E	V	E	R	A	G	A	I	N
S	T	U		A	I	R	Y		A	L	L	U	D	E
C	A	P	O	N		S	I	C		S	E	D	E	R
A	R	A	B	I	C		N	O	A	H		R	A	F
P	R	E	T	T	Y	U	G	L	Y		S	A	S	S
			R	A	G	S		L	E	F	T			
E	S	A	U		N	U	D	E		O	R	A	T	E
N	O	N	D	A	I	R	Y	C	R	E	A	M	E	R
D	A	T	E	D		E	N	T	O		I	M	A	N
S	P	I	R	E		R	E	S	T		T	O	M	E

254

O	S	L	O		P	A	T	E	S		S	T	A	G
F	L	A	P		A	W	A	K	E		L	O	L	A
F	I	V	E	S	T	A	R	G	E	N	E	R	A	L
S	T	A	R	T	E	R	S		D	E	P	O	N	E
			A	R	N	E		P	I	C	T			
C	A	S	T	E	S		L	E	E	K		T	E	T
E	T	H	O	S		O	A	R	S		P	E	R	E
S	T	A	R	S	A	N	D	S	T	R	I	P	E	S
T	A	N	S		I	S	E	E		E	L	E	C	T
A	R	K		B	R	E	D		A	S	S	E	T	S
			M	O	L	T		F	L	E	E			
T	I	V	O	L	I		S	A	T	A	N	I	S	T
S	T	A	R	O	F	B	E	T	H	L	E	H	E	M
A	S	I	S		T	E	A	S	E		R	O	T	E
R	A	L	E		S	A	M	O	A		S	P	A	N

255

A	S	P	E	N		D	A	L	I		A	M	I	D
T	H	E	S	E		E	G	A	N		V	I	V	A
T	A	S	T	E		M	O	T	S		E	L	A	N
	G	O	O	D	N	I	G	H	T	I	R	E	N	E
			P	L	O		S	E	C					
P	A	R		E	L	K	E		P	I	E	C	E	S
O	R	A	L		A	I	L	S		E	R	O	D	E
L	O	V	E	A	N	D	M	A	R	R	I	A	G	E
E	M	E	N	D		S	E	M	I		S	T	E	M
S	A	N	D	A	L		R	E	S	T		I	R	S
			G	A	L		E	O	N					
I	L	L	B	E	S	E	E	I	N	G	Y	O	U	
N	E	A	R		T	E	R	N		G	L	A	R	E
K	A	T	E		E	R	I	N		L	O	R	D	S
S	K	E	W		D	Y	E	S		E	N	S	U	E

256

F	L	A	B		R	I	D	E		R	O	O	M	S
R	A	G	E		E	L	A	L		A	I	M	A	T
O	M	A	R		S	L	U	B		F	L	O	R	A
	P	R	E	T	T	Y	B	O	Y	F	L	O	Y	D
			T	A	R		W	I	L	E				
O	H	M		R	A	S	H		P	E	A	P	O	D
L	E	E		S	I	T	A	R		S	O	L	O	
M	A	C	H	I	N	E	G	U	N	K	E	L	L	Y
O	R	C	A		M	A	N	O	N		L	I	E	
S	T	A	I	R	S		R	E	N	O		Y	E	N
			R	I	P	E		S	L	O				
B	A	B	Y	F	A	C	E	N	E	L	S	O	N	
A	U	R	A	L		L	I	O	N		C	R	I	B
T	R	I	P	E		A	R	E	S		A	N	K	A
H	A	T	E	R		T	E	L	E		R	E	E	D

257

	L	A	N	E	S			B	R	A	S	S		
W	A	G	E	R	E	D		S	A	U	T	E	E	D
E	D	A	S	N	E	R		H	A	N	O	V	E	R
E	D	I	T	S		S	P	A		S	N	I	D	E
D	E	N	S		F	E	A	R	S		E	L	I	A
Y	R	S		M	A	U	R	I	C	E		L	E	D
		S	T	R	A	U	S	S		A	M	B	E	R
			I	L	L	S		P	R	E	Y			
	T	E	M	P	T		W	O	R	N	O	U	T	
C	A	P		H	E	C	K	L	E	D		N	A	M
O	B	I	T		D	A	R	E	D		H	I	T	E
E	B	S	E	N		R	P	M		L	O	F	T	S
D	I	O	X	I	D	E		I	V	O	R	I	E	S
S	E	D	A	T	E	D		C	O	N	N	E	R	Y
		S	E	N	S	E			N	E	E	D	S	

258

Ⓐ	A	R		C	A	R	R	E		D	P	T
S	Ⓝ	I	T		O	L	I	O	S		D	O	R	Y
H	I	Ⓖ	H		M	I	S	S	S	A	I	G	O	N
		Ⓔ	D	A	M	E	S		D	O	G	M	A
	H	U	R	Ⓛ		B	R	I	G	A	D	O	O	N
P	A	T	O	I	Ⓢ			I	M	E			
O	N	U	S		Ⓟ	I	U	S	V	I		W	O	K
M	O	R	E		R	I	Ⓝ	S	E		M	A	C	E
P	I	N		S	U	N	D	Ⓐ	E		A	V	E	R
			I	A	N			Ⓜ	C	L	E	A	N
F	U	N	N	Y	G	I	R	L		Ⓔ	A	R	N
A	S	I	A	N		R	A	I	D	E	Ⓡ		
S	H	E	L	O	V	E	S	M	E		K	Ⓘ	S	S
T	E	L	L		A	N	T	O	N		Y	A	Ⓒ	K
S	R	S		L	E	A	S	T		M	I	Ⓐ	

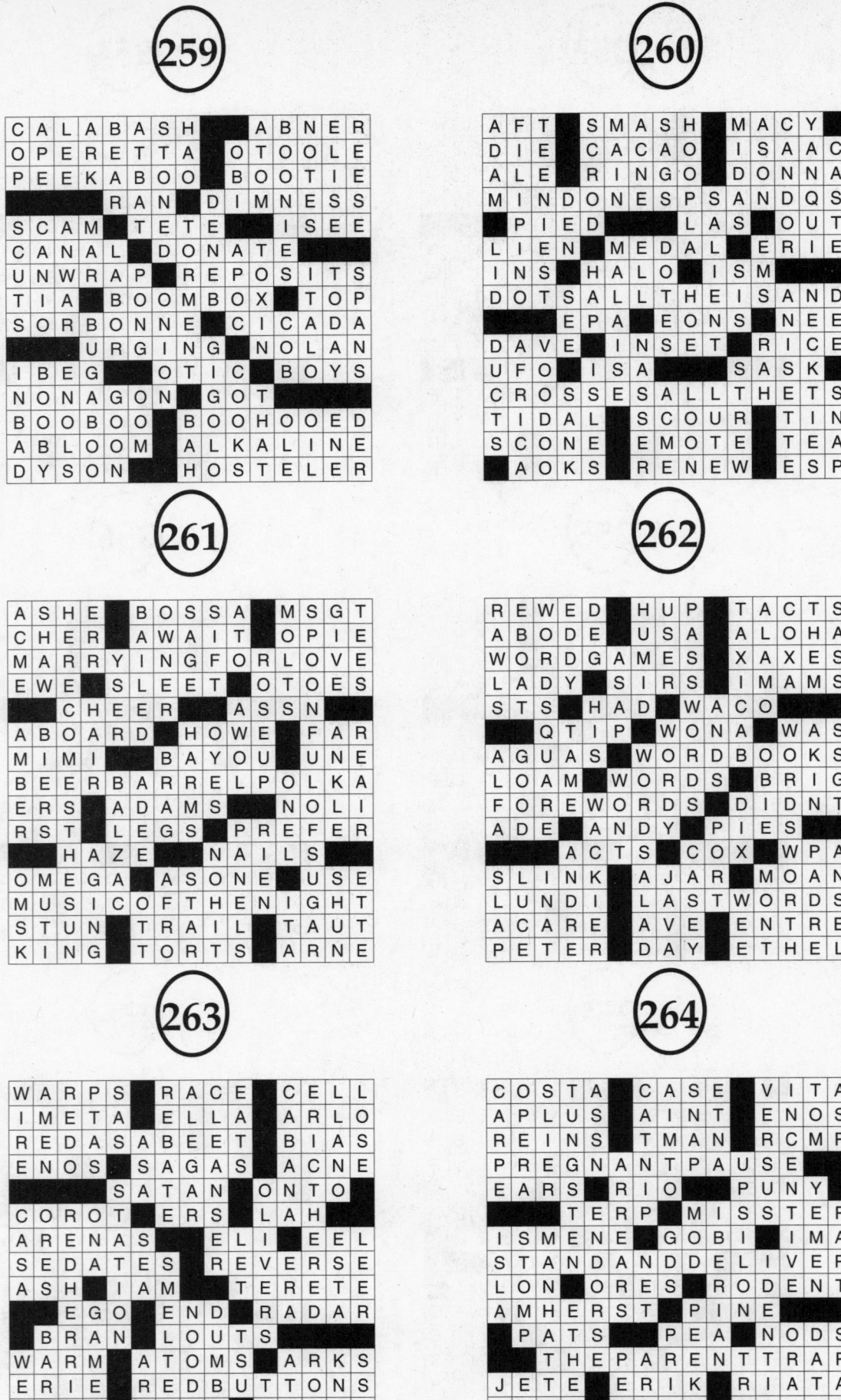

259

```
CALABASH   ABNER
OPERETTA  OTOOLE
PEEKABOO  BOOTIE
     RAN DIMNESS
SCAM TETE    ISEE
CANAL  DONATE
UNWRAP  REPOSITS
TIA BOOMBOX  TOP
SORBONNE  CICADA
    URGING  NOLAN
IBEG   OTIC  BOYS
NONAGON   GOT
BOOBOO   BOOHOOED
ABLOOM   ALKALINE
DYSON    HOSTELER
```

260

```
AFT  SMASH  MACY
DIE  CACAO  ISAAC
ALE  RINGO  DONNA
MINDONESPSANDQS
 PIED   LAS   OUT
LIEN  MEDAL  ERIE
INS   HALO   ISM
DOTSALLTHEISAND
   EPA   EONS  NEE
DAVE  INSET  RICE
UFO   ISA    SASK
CROSSESALLTHETS
TIDAL  SCOUR  TIN
SCONE  EMOTE  TEA
 AOKS  RENEW  ESP
```

261

```
ASHE  BOSSA   MSGT
CHER  AWAIT   OPIE
MARRYINGFORLOVE
EWE  SLEET  OTOES
  CHEER    ASSN
ABOARD  HOWE   FAR
MIMI   BAYOU  UNE
BEERBARRELPOLKA
ERS  ADAMS   NOLI
RST  LEGS  PREFER
  HAZE    NAILS
OMEGA  ASONE   USE
MUSICOFTHENIGHT
STUN  TRAIL  TAUT
KING  TORTS  ARNE
```

262

```
REWED  HUP   TACTS
ABODE  USA   ALOHA
WORDGAMES  XAXES
LADY   SIRS  IMAMS
STS  HAD  WACO
  QTIP  WONA   WAS
AGUAS  WORDBOOKS
LOAM  WORDS  BRIG
FOREWORDS  DIDNT
ADE  ANDY  PIES
  ACTS  COX   WPA
SLINK  AJAR  MOAN
LUNDI  LASTWORDS
ACARE  AVE   ENTRE
PETER  DAY   ETHEL
```

263

```
WARPS  RACE  CELL
IMETA  ELLA  ARLO
REDASABEET  BIAS
ENOS  SAGAS  ACNE
    SATAN  ONTO
COROT  ERS  LAH
ARENAS  ELI  EEL
SEDATES  REVERSE
ASH  IAM   TERETE
  EGO  END  RADAR
  BRAN  LOUTS
WARM  ATOMS  ARKS
ERIE  REDBUTTONS
RENT  ERLE  AMBIT
EDGE  AYER  POETS
```

264

```
COSTA  CASE  VITA
APLUS  AINT  ENOS
REINS  TMAN  RCMP
PREGNANTPAUSE
EARS  RIO   PUNY
  TERP  MISSTEP
ISMENE  GOBI  IMA
STANDANDDELIVER
LON  ORES  RODENT
AMHERST  PINE
 PATS  PEA  NODS
  THEPARENTTRAP
JETE  ERIK  RIATA
OVAL  GAZE  AFTER
YENS  SLED  MYERS
```

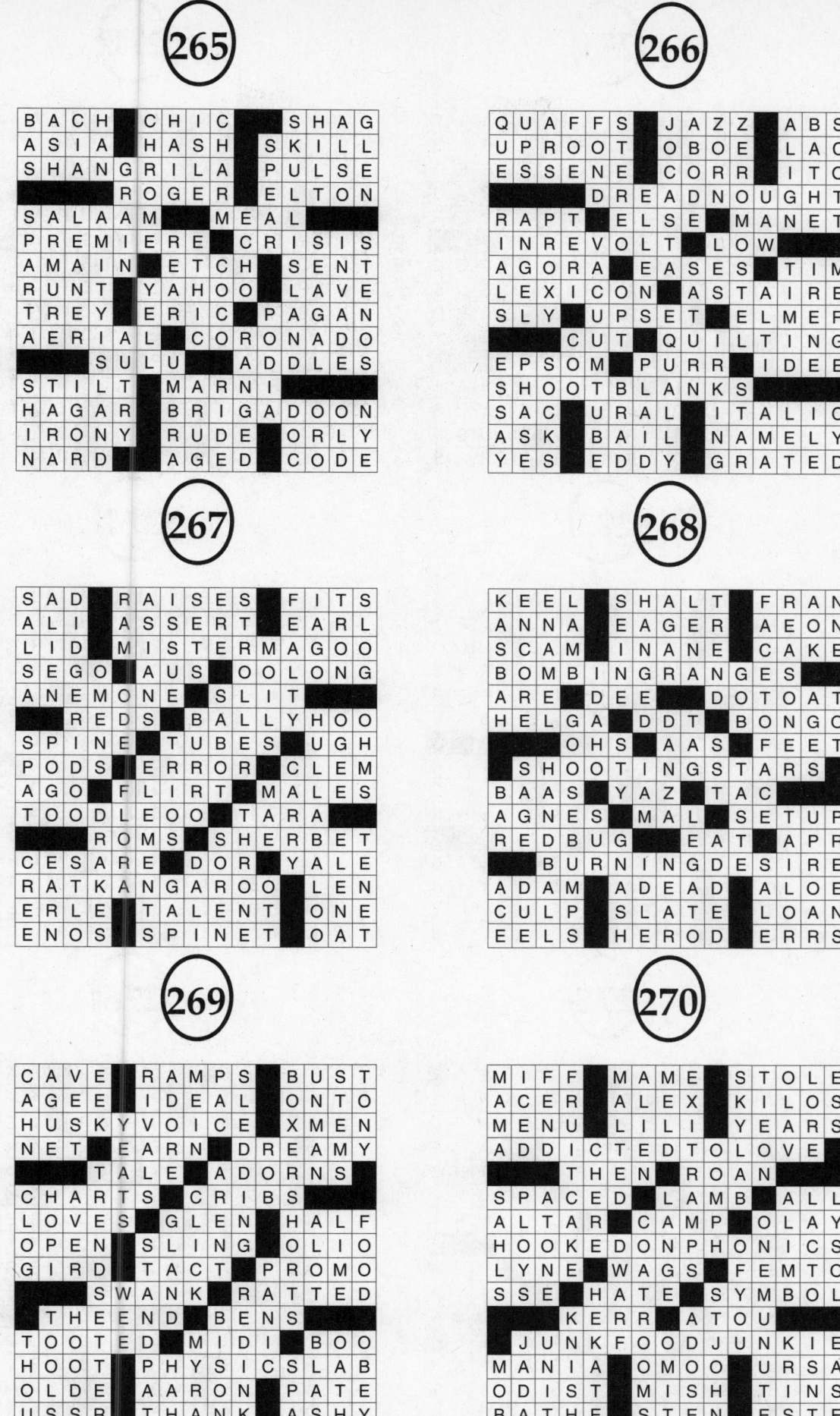

265 266 267 268 269 270

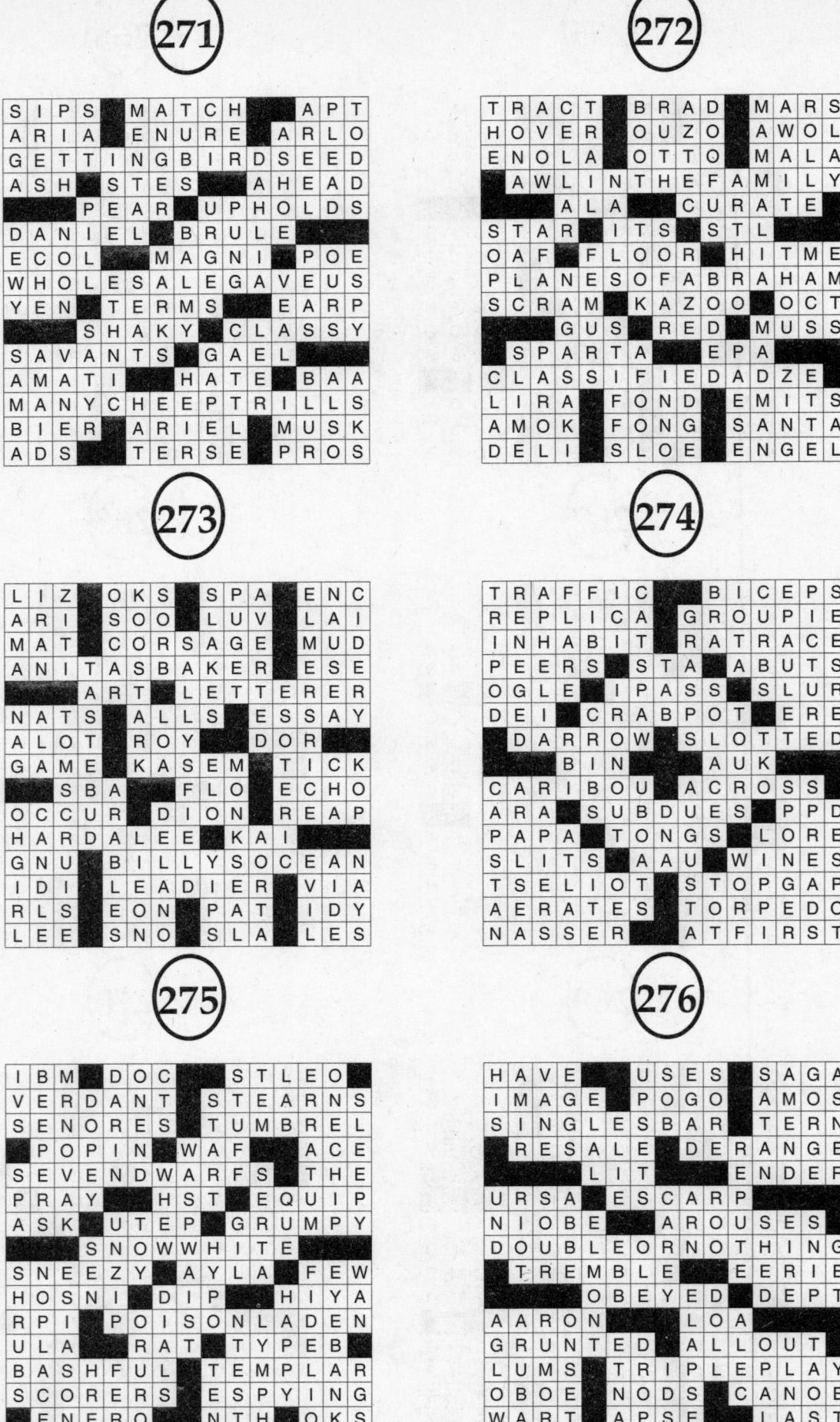

271

```
S I P S . M A T C H . . A P T
A R I A . E N U R E . A R L O
G E T T I N G B I R D S E E D
A S H . S T E S . A H E A D .
. . P E A R . U P H O L D S .
D A N I E L . B R U L E . . .
E C O L . . M A G N I . P O E
W H O L E S A L E G A V E U S
Y E N . T E R M S . . E A R P
. . S H A K Y . C L A S S Y .
S A V A N T S . G A E L . . .
A M A T I . H A T E . B A A .
M A N Y C H E E P T R I L L S
B I E R . A R I E L . M U S K
A D S . . T E R S E . P R O S
```

272

```
T R A C T . B R A D . M A R S
H O V E R . O U Z O . A W O L
E N O L A . O T T O . M A L A
. A W L I N T H E F A M I L Y
. A L A . . C U R A T E . . .
S T A R . I T S . S T L . . .
O A F . F L O O R . H I T M E
P L A N E S O F A B R A H A M
S C R A M . K A Z O O . O C T
. G U S . R E D . M U S S .
. S P A R T A . E P A . . .
C L A S S I F I E D A D Z E
L I R A . F O N D . E M I T S
A M O K . F O N G . S A N T A
D E L I . S L O E . E N G E L
```

273

```
L I Z . O K S . S P A . E N C
A R I . S O O . L U V . L A I
M A T . C O R S A G E . M U D
A N I T A S B A K E R . E S E
. A R T . L E T T E R E R . .
N A T S . A L L S . E S S A Y
A L O T . R O Y . D O R . . .
G A M E . K A S E M . T I C K
. S B A . F L O . E C H O . .
O C C U R . D I O N . R E A P
H A R D A L E E . K A I . . .
G N U . B I L L Y S O C E A N
I D I . L E A D I E R . V I A
R L S . E O N . P A T . I D Y
L E E . S N O . S L A . L E S
```

274

```
T R A F F I C . B I C E P S
R E P L I C A . G R O U P I E
I N H A B I T . R A T R A C E
P E E R S . S T A . A B U T S
O G L E . I P A S S . S L U R
D E I . C R A B P O T . E R E
. D A R R O W . S L O T T E D
. B I N . A U K . . .
C A R I B O U . A C R O S S
A R A . S U B D U E S . P P D
P A P A . T O N G S . L O R E
S L I T S . A A U . W I N E S
T S E L I O T . S T O P G A P
A E R A T E S . T O R P E D O
N A S S E R . A T F I R S T
```

275

```
I B M . D O C . S T L E O
V E R D A N T . S T E A R N S
S E N O R E S . T U M B R E L
. P O P I N . W A F . A C E
S E V E N D W A R F S . T H E
P R A Y . H S T . E Q U I P
A S K . U T E P . G R U M P Y
. . S N O W W H I T E . . .
S N E E Z Y . A Y L A . F E W
H O S N I . D I P . H I Y A
R P I . P O I S O N L A D E N
U L A . R A T . T Y P E B
B A S H F U L . T E M P L A R
S C O R E R S . E S P Y I N G
. E N E R O . N T H . O K S
```

276

```
H A V E . U S E S . S A G A
I M A G E . P O G O . A M O S
S I N G L E S B A R . T E R N
. R E S A L E . D E R A N G E
. L I T . . E N D E R
U R S A . E S C A R P
N I O B E . A R O U S E S
D O U B L E O R N O T H I N G
. T R E M B L E . E E R I E
. O B E Y E D . D E P T
A A R O N . L O A
G R U N T E D . A L L O U T
L U M S . T R I P L E P L A Y
O B O E . N O D S . C A N O E
W A R T . A P S E . L A S T
```

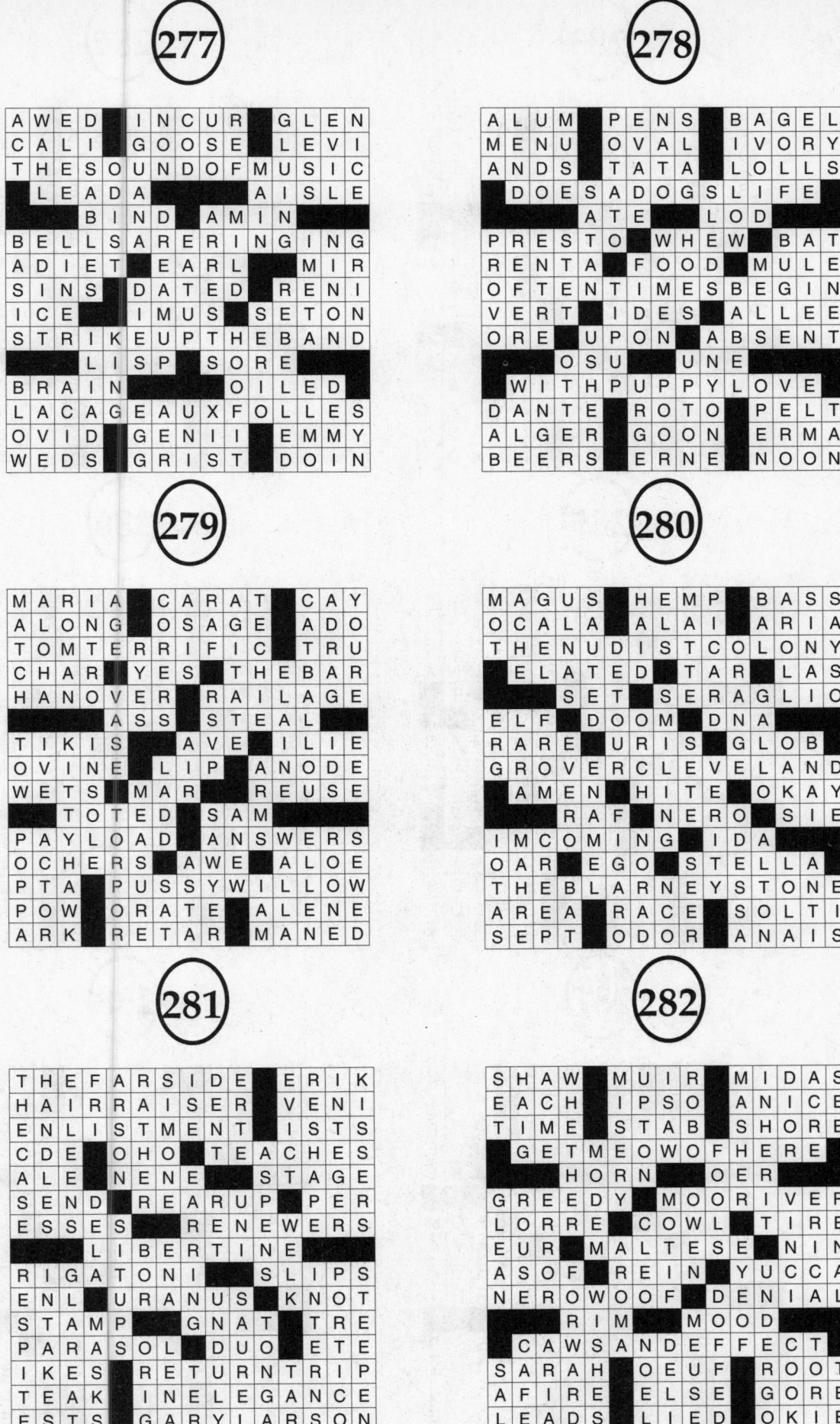

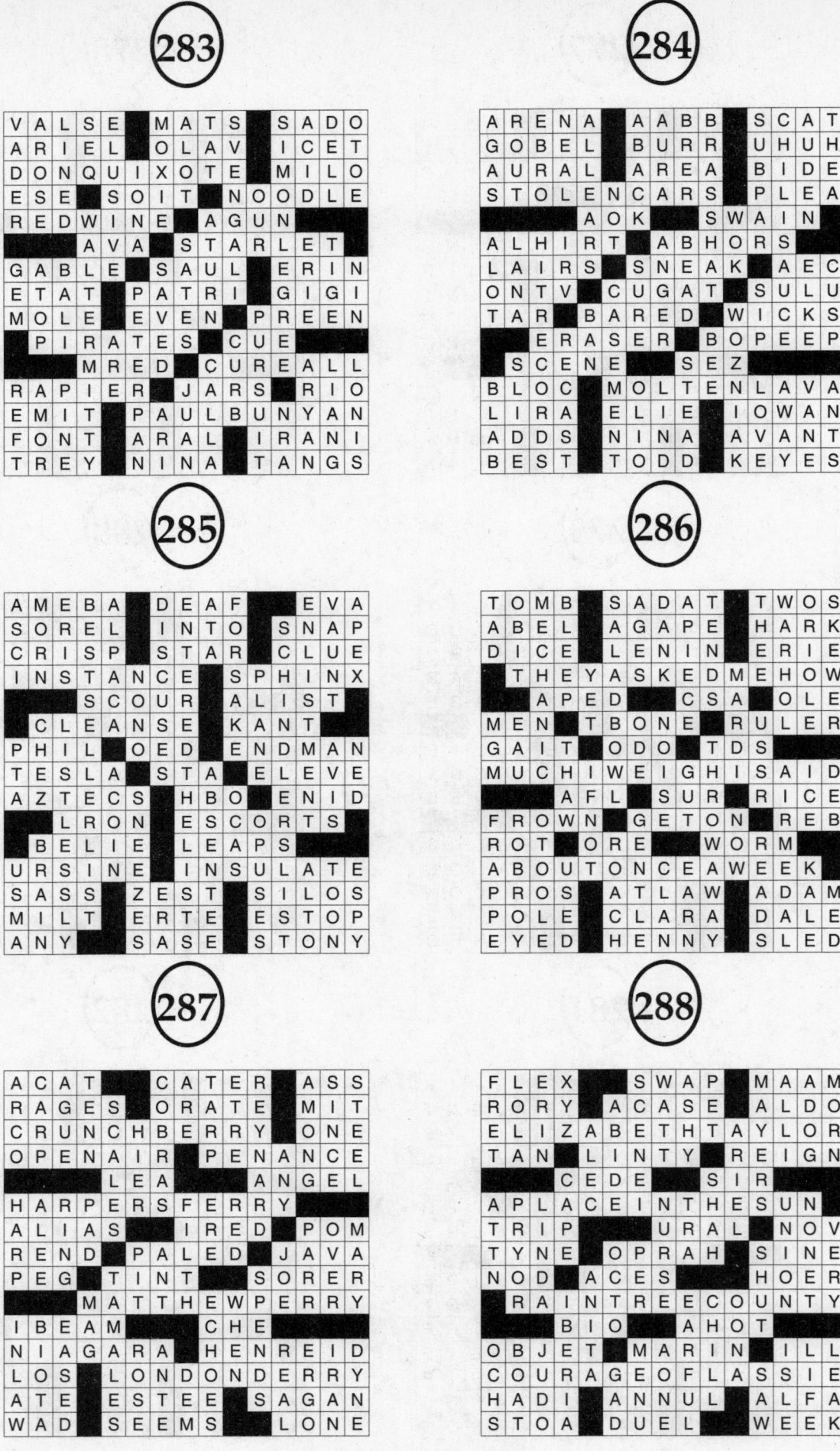

283

V	A	L	S	E		M	A	T	S		S	A	D	O
A	R	I	E	L		O	L	A	V		I	C	E	T
D	O	N	Q	U	I	X	O	T	E		M	I	L	O
E	S	E		S	O	I	T		N	O	O	D	L	E
R	E	D	W	I	N	E		A	G	U	N			
		A	V	A		S	T	A	R	L	E	T		
G	A	B	L	E		S	A	U	L		E	R	I	N
E	T	A	T		P	A	T	R	I		G	I	G	I
M	O	L	E		E	V	E	N		P	R	E	E	N
	P	I	R	A	T	E	S		C	U	E			
			M	R	E	D		C	U	R	E	A	L	L
R	A	P	I	E	R		J	A	R	S		R	I	O
E	M	I	T		P	A	U	L	B	U	N	Y	A	N
F	O	N	T		A	R	A	L		I	R	A	N	I
T	R	E	Y		N	I	N	A		T	A	N	G	S

284

A	R	E	N	A		A	A	B	B		S	C	A	T
G	O	B	E	L		B	U	R	R		U	H	U	H
A	U	R	A	L		A	R	E	A		B	I	D	E
S	T	O	L	E	N	C	A	R	S		P	L	E	A
			A	O	K		S	W	A	I	N			
A	L	H	I	R	T		A	B	H	O	R	S		
L	A	I	R	S		S	N	E	A	K		A	E	C
O	N	T	V		C	U	G	A	T		S	U	L	U
T	A	R		B	A	R	E	D		W	I	C	K	S
		E	R	A	S	E	R		B	O	P	E	E	P
S	C	E	N	E			S	E	Z					
B	L	O	C		M	O	L	T	E	N	L	A	V	A
L	I	R	A		E	L	I	E		I	O	W	A	N
A	D	D	S		N	I	N	A		A	V	A	N	T
B	E	S	T		T	O	D	D		K	E	Y	E	S

285

A	M	E	B	A		D	E	A	F		E	V	A	
S	O	R	E	L		I	N	T	O		S	N	A	P
C	R	I	S	P		S	T	A	R		C	L	U	E
I	N	S	T	A	N	C	E		S	P	H	I	N	X
			S	C	O	U	R		A	L	I	S	T	
	C	L	E	A	N	S	E		K	A	N	T		
P	H	I	L		O	E	D		E	N	D	M	A	N
T	E	S	L	A		S	T	A		E	L	E	V	E
A	Z	T	E	C	S		H	B	O		E	N	I	D
	L	R	O	N		E	S	C	O	R	T	S		
	B	E	L	I	E		L	E	A	P	S			
U	R	S	I	N	E		I	N	S	U	L	A	T	E
S	A	S	S		Z	E	S	T		S	I	L	O	S
M	I	L	T		E	R	T	E		E	S	T	O	P
A	N	Y			S	A	S	E		S	T	O	N	Y

286

T	O	M	B		S	A	D	A	T		T	W	O	S
A	B	E	L		A	G	A	P	E		H	A	R	K
D	I	C	E		L	E	N	I	N		E	R	I	E
	T	H	E	Y	A	S	K	E	D	M	E	H	O	W
		A	P	E	D		C	S	A		O	L	E	
M	E	N		T	B	O	N	E		R	U	L	E	R
G	A	I	T		O	D	O		T	D	S			
M	U	C	H	I	W	E	I	G	H	I	S	A	I	D
		A	F	L		S	U	R		R	I	C	E	
F	R	O	W	N		G	E	T	O	N		R	E	B
R	O	T		O	R	E		W	O	R	M			
A	B	O	U	T	O	N	C	E	A	W	E	E	K	
P	R	O	S		A	T	L	A	W		A	D	A	M
P	O	L	E		C	L	A	R	A		D	A	L	E
E	Y	E	D		H	E	N	N	Y		S	L	E	D

287

A	C	A	T		C	A	T	E	R		A	S	S	
R	A	G	E	S		O	R	A	T	E		M	I	T
C	R	U	N	C	H	B	E	R	R	Y		O	N	E
O	P	E	N	A	I	R		P	E	N	A	N	C	E
			L	E	A			A	N	G	E	L		
H	A	R	P	E	R	S	F	E	R	R	Y			
A	L	I	A	S		I	R	E	D		P	O	M	
R	E	N	D		P	A	L	E	D		J	A	V	A
P	E	G		T	I	N	T		S	O	R	E	R	
		M	A	T	T	H	E	W	P	E	R	R	Y	
I	B	E	A	M			C	H	E					
N	I	A	G	A	R	A		H	E	N	R	E	I	D
L	O	S		L	O	N	D	O	N	D	E	R	R	Y
A	T	E		E	S	T	E	E		S	A	G	A	N
W	A	D		S	E	E	M	S		L	O	N	E	

288

F	L	E	X		S	W	A	P		M	A	A	M	
R	O	R	Y		A	C	A	S	E		A	L	D	O
E	L	I	Z	A	B	E	T	H	T	A	Y	L	O	R
T	A	N		L	I	N	T	Y		R	E	I	G	N
			C	E	D	E			S	I	R			
A	P	L	A	C	E	I	N	T	H	E	S	U	N	
T	R	I	P		U	R	A	L			N	O	V	
T	Y	N	E		O	P	R	A	H		S	I	N	E
N	O	D		A	C	E	S		H	O	E	R		
	R	A	I	N	T	R	E	E	C	O	U	N	T	Y
			B	I	O			A	H	O	T			
O	B	J	E	T		M	A	R	I	N		I	L	L
C	O	U	R	A	G	E	O	F	L	A	S	S	I	E
H	A	D	I		A	N	N	U	L		A	L	F	A
S	T	O	A		D	U	E	L			W	E	E	K

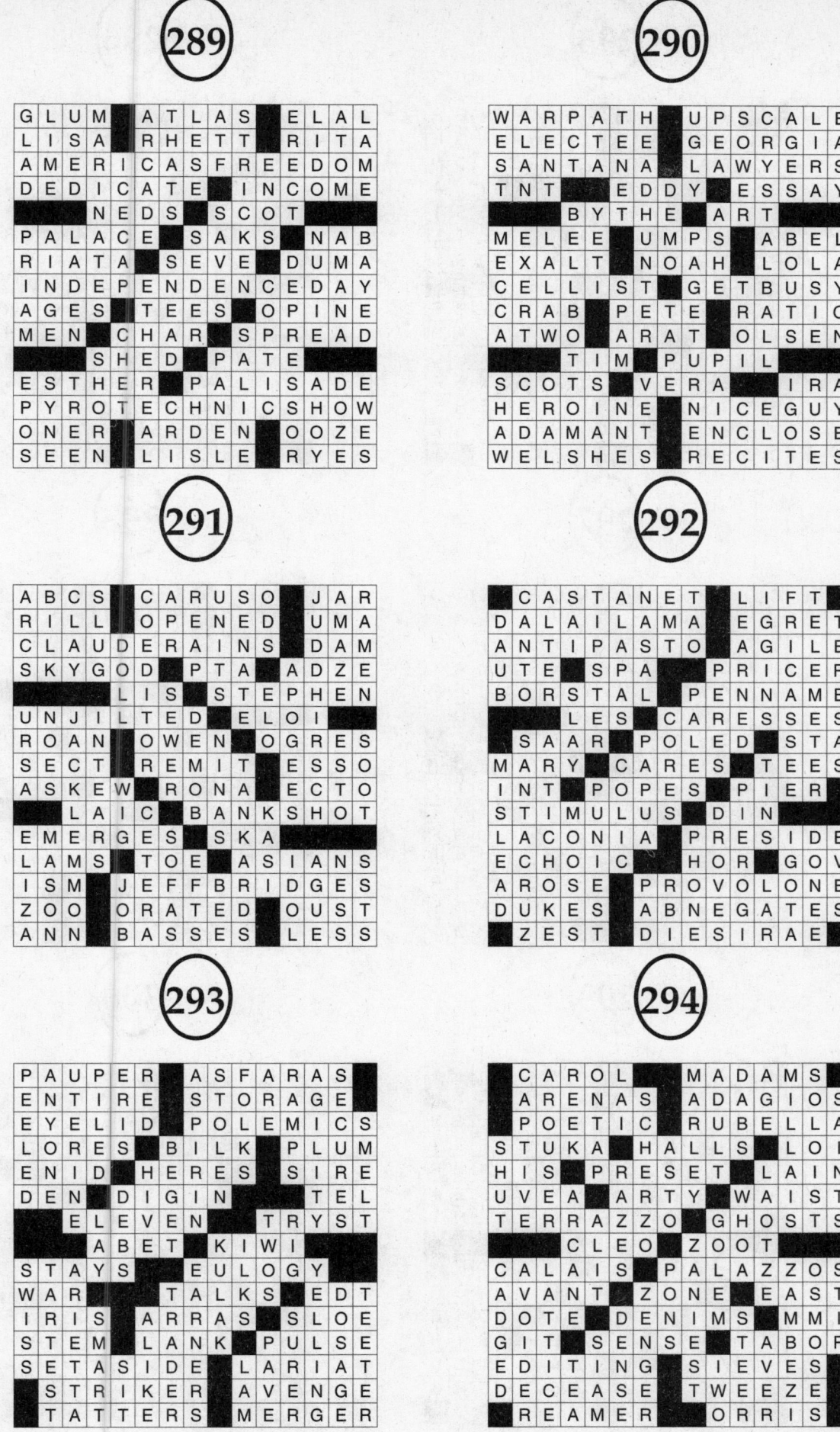

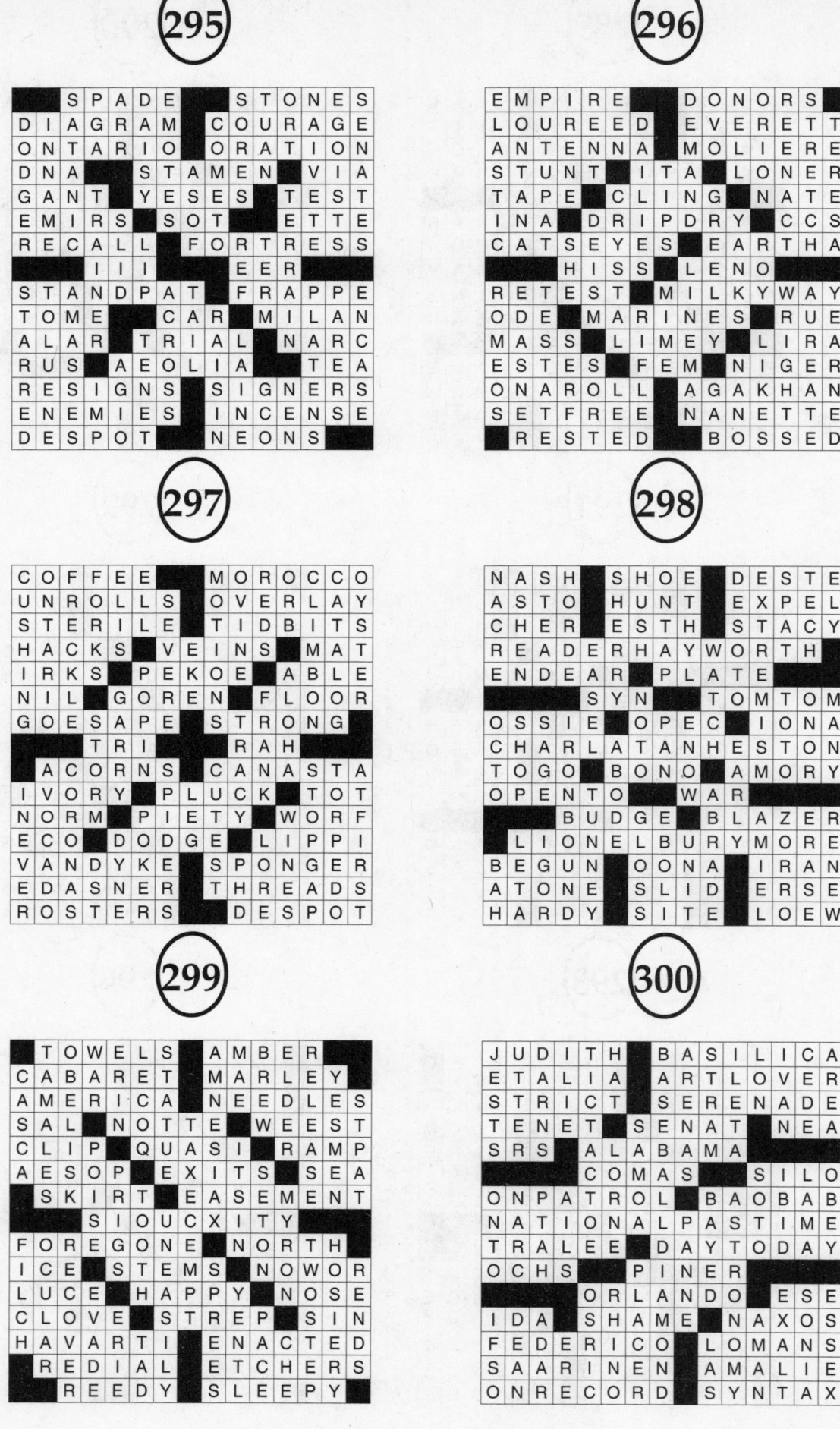

301

B	A	L	D		C	O	E	D			P	E	N	N
A	L	I	E		O	R	L	E		L	E	V	E	E
R	O	B	S		L	A	I	T		I	N	E	R	T
B	U	R	E	A	U		H	A	R	V	A	R	D	
	D	A	R	T	M	O	U	T	H					
		T	A	B	U			O	R	N	E	R	Y	
D	E	M		I	T	L	L		I	O	N	I	A	
I	V	Y	L	E	A	G	U	E	S	C	H	O	O	L
V	I	R	A	L		O	V	A	L			S	S	E
A	L	A	S	K	A		R	I	B	S				
				P	R	I	N	C	E	T	O	N		
	C	O	R	N	E	L	L		K	E	E	P	U	P
S	A	M	O	A		E	L	L	E		P	E	K	E
B	R	O	W	N		S	U	E	R		P	R	E	P
A	D	O	S		S	S	T	S		E	A	S	E	

302

E	A	R	T	H		A	N	T	I			C	A	R
A	R	O	O	M		L	E	A	N		A	R	E	A
S	T	A	R	S	E	A	R	C	H		L	A	R	D
T	E	N	T		S	M	O	K	E		A	S	I	A
			G	P	O			R	A	S	H	E	R	
E	L	A	T	E		S	T	A	I	N				
S	A	B	E	N	A		O	U	T	D	O	E	S	
T	H	E	S	U	N	A	L	S	O	R	I	S	E	S
	R	E	T	I	T	L	E		R	E	S	T	E	D
				N	I	F	T	Y		W	E	E	P	S
A	R	I	S	E	N		E	D	S					
M	I	R	E		O	P	I	N	E		B	R	A	S
P	L	E	A		M	O	O	N	S	T	R	U	C	K
L	E	N	T		I	S	L	E		B	E	L	I	E
E	Y	E		C	H	A	D		S	W	E	D	E	

303

T	H	A	D		B	A	T	S		S	O	C	K	O
A	A	R	E		O	L	I	N		A	S	H	E	N
I	L	K	S		R	I	C	O		Y	E	A	R	S
L	O	S	E	O	N	E	S	W	A	Y		I	R	E
			T	E	N		G	I	E		R	S	T	
I	N	T	O	T	O		M	O	R	S	E	L		
H	O	R	N	E		T	A	O	S		B	I	N	D
A	D	A	I	R		O	H	S		A	S	F	O	R
D	E	V	O		L	U	R	E		B	E	T	T	E
	E	N	T	I	C	E		S	E	N	S	E	D	
G	A	R		O	O	H		A	W	L				
O	P	S		U	N	D	E	V	E	L	O	P	E	D
T	R	I	P	P		O	B	O	E		S	P	R	Y
T	I	N	G	E		W	R	I	T		S	P	E	E
A	L	G	A	E		N	O	D	S		A	S	I	S

304

A	S	T	A		T	E	R	N		O	P	A	R	T
M	E	A	L		K	N	E	E		V	I	R	E	O
P	A	P	A	D	O	C	D	U	V	A	L	I	E	R
S	T	E	R	E		H	O	R	A		S	A	F	E
			M	Y	R	A		A	L	A	N			
S	O	B	S		U	N	C	L	E	R	E	M	U	S
A	T	E		M	E	T	H		T	I	R	A	N	A
M	A	G	D	A		S	I	P		E	S	S	A	Y
O	R	I	E	N	T		N	A	G	S		O	P	S
A	U	N	T	I	E	M	A	M	E		U	N	T	O
			H	A	L	O		P	L	A	T			
A	G	A	R		I	D	E	E		R	A	N	T	O
D	R	J	O	Y	C	E	B	R	O	T	H	E	R	S
D	I	A	N	A		M	R	E	D		A	N	I	L
S	T	R	E	P		S	O	R	E		N	E	M	O

305

C	O	R	M		I	N	C	A		S	C	R	A	P
O	L	I	O		M	E	L	D		A	H	O	M	E
M	E	N	U		P	A	I	L		S	I	M	O	N
M	I	S	S	M	A	R	M	E	L	S	T	E	I	N
A	C	E	T	I	C		B	R	A	E				
			A	T	T	U		T	R	E	B	L	E	
E	V	I	C	T		N	A	P	E		T	R	O	Y
W	I	S	H	Y	O	U	W	E	R	E	H	E	R	E
E	L	I	E		L	M	N	O		L	O	W	E	R
S	E	N	S	E	D		N	O	E	L				
				L	I	S	P		S	N	O	R	E	S
W	H	E	N	W	E	M	E	E	T	A	G	A	I	N
R	O	M	E	O		E	T	T	E		I	N	D	O
A	M	I	N	O		W	A	R	N		S	T	E	R
P	O	L	E	D		S	L	E	D		T	O	R	T

306

P	L	U	G		T	H	I	N	S		S	T	A	Y
O	O	N	A		A	E	S	O	P		P	O	R	E
T	U	T	U		S	I	E	V	E		I	R	I	S
	D	O	N	T	T	R	E	A	D	O	N	M	E	
			T	O	E	S			F	E	E	L		
M	A	D	L	Y		H	U	L	A	S				
O	G	R	E		P	R	O	P	E	L		P	T	A
M	E	E	T	M	E	I	N	S	T	L	O	U	I	S
S	E	W		A	L	L	E	Y	S		P	R	E	Y
			F	U	E	L	S				T	E	R	R	E
	T	H	O	R				S	O	O	N			
	B	E	M	Y	V	A	L	E	N	T	I	N	E	
C	O	M	E		A	B	O	V	E		N	E	W	T
O	N	A	N		T	E	N	E	T		G	R	E	W
W	E	N	T		S	T	E	N	O		S	O	S	O

307

```
DOLT  HAFTS  GLIB
ONEA  ALLAH  REMO
CANTERBURY   OOPS
     AXLE    DUNES
TEA  TEES   JUSTLY
ARTERY  PROPER
TETRA  PROLE  OPT
ACHE  HEIST  STAR
RTE  CORNY   TASSO
    GEHRIG  TALKTO
SPARES  SOON  YAP
ALLOW    MAYA
BALD  TAKESAWALK
OTOE  ANENT  OHIO
TOPS  PANSY  LAPP
```

308

```
ASP   CATTY  FLEA
STEP  APHID  OARS
SEAL  TEAMS  UCLA
EELY  ERNO  CREEP
TREMOR  KRAIT
    OPELS  DAHLIA
DEMURRAGES  TERN
AMITY  RID  AHEAD
RICH  ADVENTURES
TRACER  INAIR
   ONEIN  PESTER
SHALE  OGLE  DIVE
LIMO  ENDOR  AMOS
ALAN  LIANE  YOKE
TONY  LAYER  NEW
```

309

```
PECS  LOAD   BRAID
LION  ANTI   LAUDE
UNSETTLES   UNDER
METAROYALINDIAN
     KEY  MONDO
GALENA   DEEMING
AWARD  NIGER  NOR
PANS  MOVED  PETE
EKE  FIVES  MARTY
DESPISE   PASTES
    ADELE   LOT
BRAVEREDMARINER
MODAL  TWOTIMERS
OMANI  TINE  ELEV
CAMEO  ENOS  SLIP
```

310

```
WONG  ANZAC  ACTS
APAR  MOIRA  LORI
RETIRINGLY   GRIG
ERASE   SOUREDON
  ALTERS   GOBI
   LLAMA  ABRADE
DUDE  CUSS  BALED
IRA  PERKILY  LAG
VISTA  FETA  DYNE
ASHARP   WALDO
   INKA  RAILAT
HANGARED   SPLAT
URGE  SCRATCHILY
CELL  OHARA  ICON
KAYO  NOWIN  NENE
```

311

```
IMAN  ABBEY  ASTA
NOGO  WRITE  ZAHN
GROW  NONEWTAXES
ATNOTIME   ILENE
   NONO   DATE
SEADOG   NOTHANKS
ARRET  CANOE  ARY
BARR  FOGUP  ICON
ITO  TREAT  ETHNO
NOWAYOUT   LASTED
   USER   BARN
OTERO   EATNOFAT
NONONSENSE   URSA
EMIR  ADOSE  SAIL
SADA  NOWIN  ESTE
```

312

```
SAMBA  ACNE  SWAG
ARIEL  SHUN  OHIO
VANNAWHITE   NILE
ELIS  HENS  DATES
     RENE   METED
NEWTON   SEESAW
ETHEL  BEAST  ADA
STILLER   CAROTID
TAT  TRASH  UPEND
   ELOISE  SCARES
   SHAPE   ABET
SLOPS  AWOL  SLIT
PIUS  PEARLWHITE
ELSE  ERLE  ROLEX
DYED  GOLD  YEAST
```

313

```
ALAMO   NAPS   SCAN
LAVIN   ARIA   TARO
SWELL   SALT   INDO
ONCEINABLUEMOON
      NIL    ROPERS
WINDEX   BADLY
ARES    ALAI    SEA
LITTLEGREYCELLS
ESS   AMEN    ROSS
    SCAMS   STREET
STATEN   FAR
WAVESAWHITEFLAG
OBOE   TOAD   ALIBI
ROIL   ERIE   TOMES
NODE   SELL   YEAST
```

314

```
APSIS   NAZI   SLAW
GRANT   OMAN   PINA
TENCOMMANDMENTS
SPEAKEASY   ALDEN
      ENDS   ATLAST
ABOARD    ORTS
SOON   EERIE   SST
HUNDREDYEARSWAR
ETA   ORIEL   AUTO
    SCAT   ZOOMED
CAMPOS   STUN
OLEIC   SCHLEMIEL
CASTOFTHOUSANDS
ACHE   RAMS   EIGHT
SKYS   OBOE   CLASS
```

315

```
AWED   MAO   OSIP
LOVELY   ASP   DEMI
BROCAS   THEBEARS
SNEAKER   ERITREA
    PERIL   AGTS
BOSOM   GIG   SATIE
ACADIA   NOAH   OLD
RAU   CHICAGO   WIN
ELL   HALO   EUREKA
RABBI   KLM   LURES
    EEGS   NEEDS
VULGATE   DRESSER
ILLINOIS   GRIEVE
ANON   ORA   OSAGES
LAWS   LEX   NAST
```

316

```
AJAR   COST   PREGO
LUXE   ABIE   RICED
ANIMALENCLOSURE
NOS   DISK   EGESTS
    LOBE   AGER
ASSURE   CLANSMAN
DANCERSALLY   AWE
ALEE   ETA   AGAS
NEV   PITCHERCURT
AMARANTH   MANSES
    ERNO   SADE
LASSIE   ANNA   SUE
INTENSEYEARNING
STUNG   FLAT   EZIO
PINTS   TAKE   WETS
```

317

```
SIZE   SLEW   SEMIS
ERIK   TONO   PLEAT
CAPEVERDE   RIDGE
      ONES   IXION
  ACTION   CONIC
SNAILS   CHAGRIN
AGREE   LAIRS   NOR
GODS   WELDS   METE
SRI   EAGLE   COHAN
  AGENDAS   TABARD
    ANGEL   CRUSTY
HENRI   WOOS
URBAN   NEWJERSEY
STAGE   AREA   APSE
KEYES   TERN   MASS
```

318

```
HARTE   PUCK   PALE
ADIEU   OSLO   ONYX
ILONG   LEOS   SYNE
GIJOE   OLYMPIANS
  BARNONE   ORT
    SEMIS   SORROW
TSK   ONUS   VOILA
HYANNIS   STINGER
UNTIE   DERN   GOP
SCENIC   EPICS
    ELA   CAPECOD
SETTLEFOR   TIMID
OGEE   SARA   OPERA
FARE   ARUT   WINGY
ADIN   ROME   NOSES
```

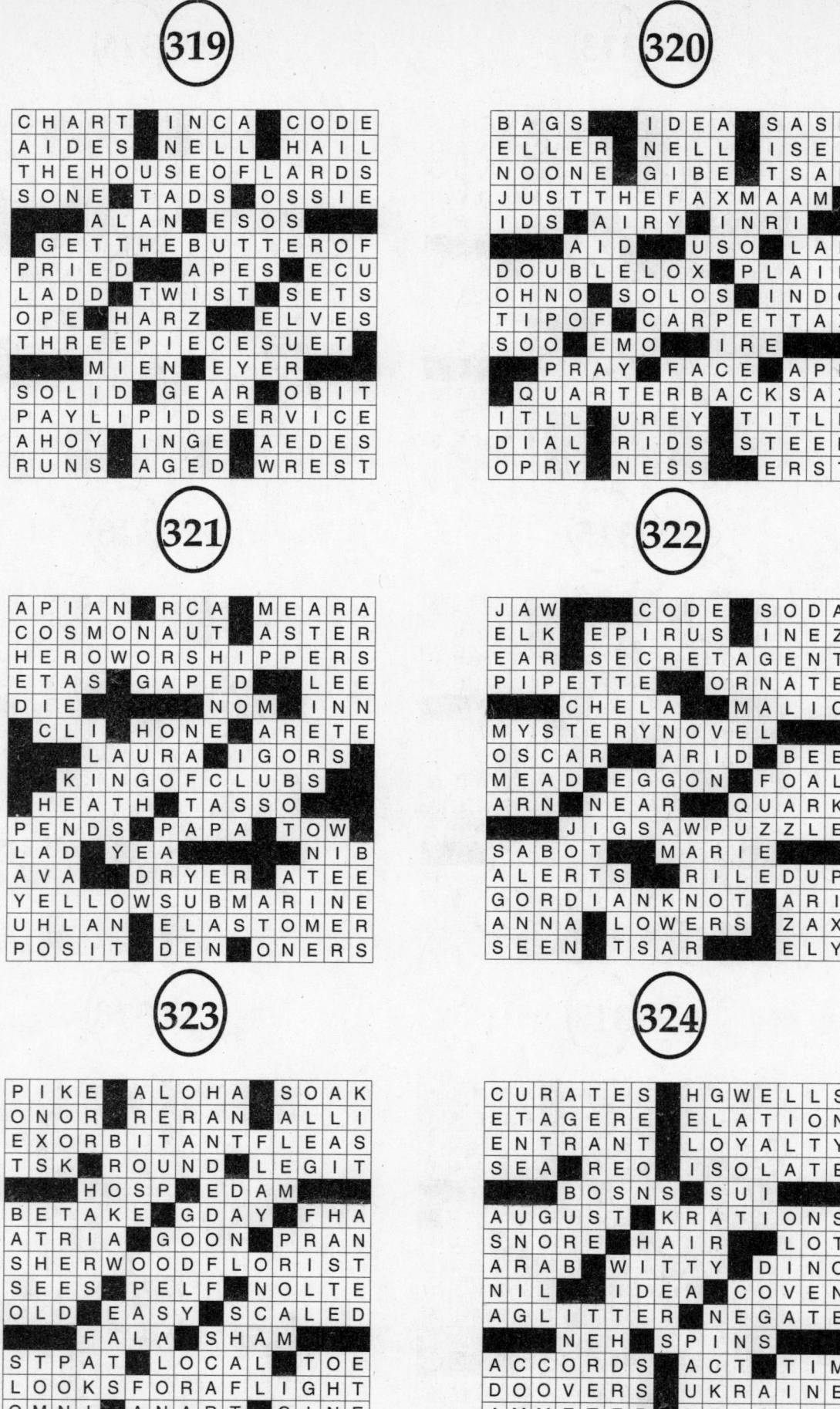

319

```
C H A R T ■ I N C A ■ C O D E
A I D E S ■ N E L L ■ H A I L
T H E H O U S E O F L A R D S
S O N E ■ T A D S ■ O S S I E
■ ■ A L A N ■ E S O S ■ ■
■ G E T T H E B U T T E R O F ■
P R I E D ■ A P E S ■ E C U
L A D D ■ T W I S T ■ S E T S
O P E ■ H A R Z ■ E L V E S
T H R E E P I E C E S U E T
■ ■ M I E N ■ E Y E R ■ ■
S O L I D ■ G E A R ■ O B I T
P A Y L I P I D S E R V I C E
A H O Y ■ I N G E ■ A E D E S
R U N S ■ A G E D ■ W R E S T
```

320

```
B A G S ■ I D E A ■ S A S H
E L L E R ■ N E L L ■ I S E E
N O O N E ■ G I B E ■ T S A R
J U S T T H E F A X M A A M ■
I D S ■ A I R Y ■ I N R I
■ ■ A I D ■ U S O ■ L A K
D O U B L E L O X ■ P L A I N
O H N O ■ S O L O S ■ I N D O
T I P O F ■ C A R P E T T A X
S O O ■ E M O ■ I R E ■ ■
■ P R A Y ■ F A C E ■ A P E
Q U A R T E R B A C K S A X
I T L L ■ U R E Y ■ T I T L E
D I A L ■ R I D S ■ S T E E R
O P R Y ■ N E S S ■ E R S T
```

321

```
A P I A N ■ R C A ■ M E A R A
C O S M O N A U T ■ A S T E R
H E R O W O R S H I P P E R S
E T A S ■ G A P E D ■ L E E
D I E ■ ■ N O M ■ I N N
■ C L I ■ H O N E ■ A R E T E
■ ■ L A U R A ■ I G O R S
■ K I N G O F C L U B S ■
■ H E A T H ■ T A S S O ■
P E N D S ■ P A P A ■ T O W
L A D ■ Y E A ■ ■ N I B
A V A ■ D R Y E R ■ A T E E
Y E L L O W S U B M A R I N E
U H L A N ■ E L A S T O M E R
P O S I T ■ D E N ■ O N E R S
```

322

```
J A W ■ C O D E ■ S O D A
E L K ■ E P I R U S ■ I N E Z
E A R ■ S E C R E T A G E N T
P I P E T T E ■ O R N A T E
■ ■ C H E L A ■ M A L I C
M Y S T E R Y N O V E L ■
O S C A R ■ A R I D ■ B E E
M E A D ■ E G G O N ■ F O A L
A R N ■ N E A R ■ Q U A R K
■ J I G S A W P U Z Z L E
S A B O T ■ M A R I E ■ ■
A L E R T S ■ R I L E D U P
G O R D I A N K N O T ■ A R I
A N N A ■ L O W E R S ■ Z A X
S E E N ■ T S A R ■ E L Y
```

323

```
P I K E ■ A L O H A ■ S O A K
O N O R ■ R E R A N ■ A L L I
E X O R B I T A N T F L E A S
T S K ■ R O U N D ■ L E G I T
■ H O S P ■ E D A M ■ ■
B E T A K E ■ G D A Y ■ F H A
A T R I A ■ G O O N ■ P R A N
S H E R W O O D F L O R I S T
S E E S ■ P E L F ■ N O L T E
O L D ■ E A S Y ■ S C A L E D
■ F A L A ■ S H A M ■
S T P A T ■ L O C A L ■ T O E
L O O K S F O R A F L I G H T
O M N I ■ A N A R T ■ C I N E
P E E R ■ O G L E S ■ U F O S
```

324

```
C U R A T E S ■ H G W E L L S
E T A G E R E ■ E L A T I O N
E N T R A N T ■ L O Y A L T Y
S E A ■ R E O ■ I S O L A T E
■ ■ B O S N S ■ S U I ■
A U G U S T ■ K R A T I O N S
S N O R E ■ H A I R ■ L O T
A R A B ■ W I T T Y ■ D I N O
N I L ■ I D E A ■ C O V E N
A G L I T T E R ■ N E G A T E
■ N E H ■ S P I N S ■
A C C O R D S ■ A C T ■ T I M
D O O V E R S ■ U K R A I N E
A M M E T E R ■ L E A S E R S
H E B R E W S ■ A L L U R E S
```

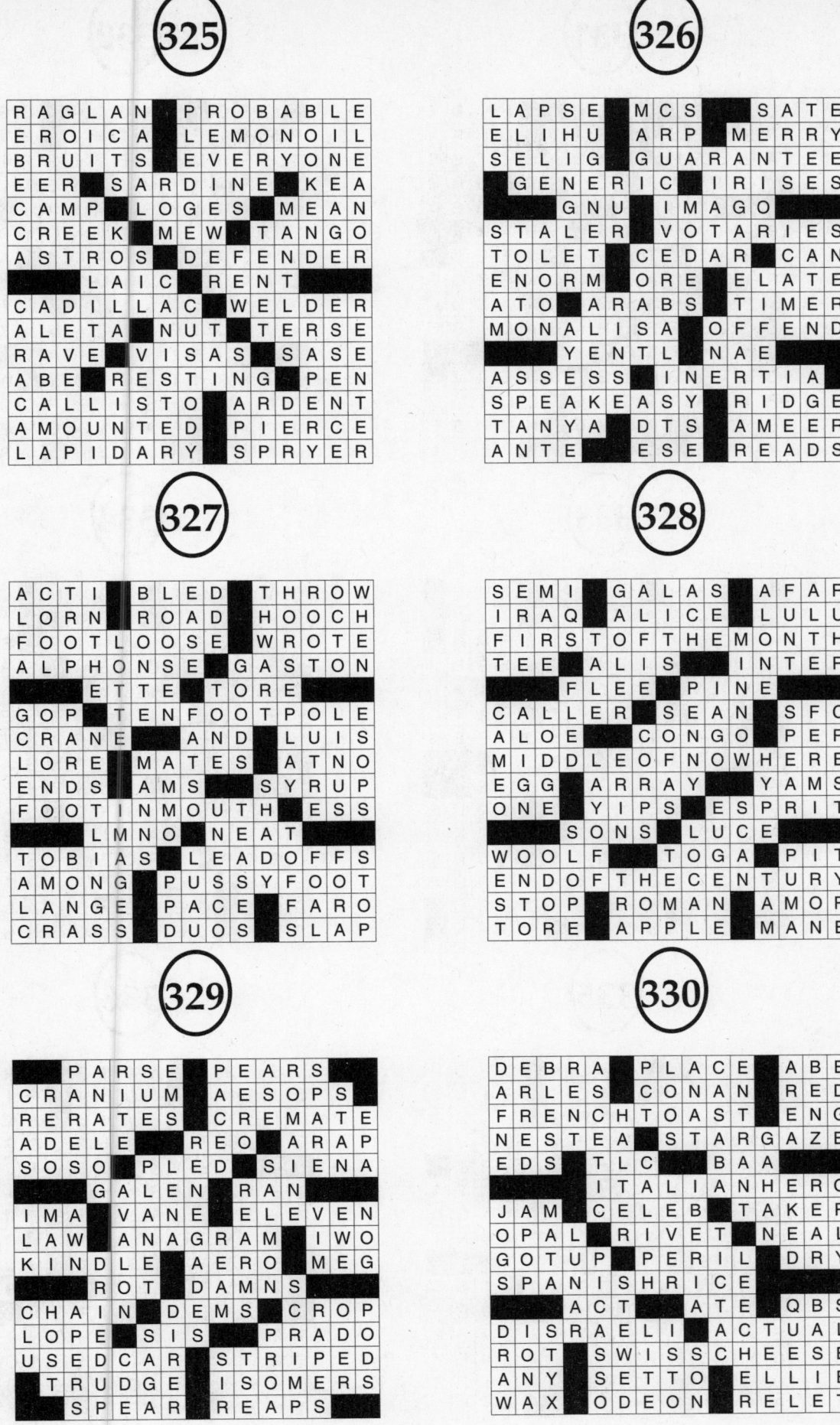

325

```
R A G L A N ■ P R O B A B L E
E R O I C A ■ L E M O N O I L
B R U I T S ■ E V E R Y O N E
E E R ■ S A R D I N E ■ K E A
C A M P ■ L O G E S ■ M E A N
C R E E K ■ M E W ■ T A N G O
A S T R O S ■ D E F E N D E R
■ ■ L A I C ■ R E N T ■ ■
C A D I L L A C ■ W E L D E R
A L E T A ■ N U T ■ T E R S E
R A V E ■ V I S A S ■ S A S E
A B E ■ R E S T I N G ■ P E N
C A L L I S T O ■ A R D E N T
A M O U N T E D ■ P I E R C E
L A P I D A R Y ■ S P R Y E R
```

326

```
L A P S E ■ M C S ■ S A T E
E L I H U ■ A R P ■ M E R R Y
S E L I G ■ G U A R A N T E E
■ G E N E R I C ■ I R I S E S
■ ■ G N U ■ I M A G O ■ ■
S T A L E R ■ V O T A R I E S
T O L E T ■ C E D A R ■ C A N
E N O R M ■ O R E ■ E L A T E
A T O ■ A R A B S ■ T I M E R
M O N A L I S A ■ O F F E N D
■ ■ Y E N T L ■ N A E ■ ■
A S S E S S ■ I N E R T I A
S P E A K E A S Y ■ R I D G E
T A N Y A ■ D T S ■ A M E E R
A N T E ■ E S E ■ R E A D S
```

327

```
A C T I ■ B L E D ■ T H R O W
L O R N ■ R O A D ■ H O O C H
F O O T L O O S E ■ W R O T E
A L P H O N S E ■ G A S T O N
■ ■ E T T E ■ T O R E ■ ■
G O P ■ T E N F O O T P O L E
C R A N E ■ A N D ■ L U I S
L O R E ■ M A T E S ■ A T N O
E N D S ■ A M S ■ S Y R U P
F O O T I N M O U T H ■ E S S
■ ■ L M N O ■ N E A T ■ ■
T O B I A S ■ L E A D O F F S
A M O N G ■ P U S S Y F O O T
L A N G E ■ P A C E ■ F A R O
C R A S S ■ D U O S ■ S L A P
```

328

```
S E M I ■ G A L A S ■ A F A R
I R A Q ■ A L I C E ■ L U L U
F I R S T O F T H E M O N T H
T E E ■ A L I S ■ I N T E R
■ ■ F L E E ■ P I N E ■ ■
C A L L E R ■ S E A N ■ S F C
A L O E ■ C O N G O ■ P E R
M I D D L E O F N O W H E R E
E G G ■ A R R A Y ■ Y A M S
O N E ■ Y I P S ■ E S P R I T
■ ■ S O N S ■ L U C E ■ ■
W O O L F ■ T O G A ■ P I T
E N D O F T H E C E N T U R Y
S T O P ■ R O M A N ■ A M O R
T O R E ■ A P P L E ■ M A N E
```

329

```
■ P A R S E ■ P E A R S ■
C R A N I U M ■ A E S O P S
R E R A T E S ■ C R E M A T E
A D E L E ■ R E O ■ A R A P
S O S O ■ P L E D ■ S I E N A
■ G A L E N ■ R A N ■
I M A ■ V A N E ■ E L E V E N
L A W ■ A N A G R A M ■ I W O
K I N D L E ■ A E R O ■ M E G
■ R O T ■ D A M N S ■
C H A I N ■ D E M S ■ C R O P
L O P E ■ S I S ■ P R A D O
U S E D C A R ■ S T R I P E D
■ T R U D G E ■ I S O M E R S
■ S P E A R ■ R E A P S ■
```

330

```
D E B R A ■ P L A C E ■ A B E
A R L E S ■ C O N A N ■ R E D
F R E N C H T O A S T ■ E N G
N E S T E A ■ S T A R G A Z E
E D S ■ T L C ■ B A A ■
■ I T A L I A N H E R O
J A M ■ C E L E B ■ T A K E R
O P A L ■ R I V E T ■ N E A L
G O T U P ■ P E R I L ■ D R Y
S P A N I S H R I C E ■
■ A C T ■ A T E ■ Q B S
D I S R A E L I ■ A C T U A L
R O T ■ S W I S S C H E E S E
A N Y ■ S E T T O ■ E L L I E
W A X ■ O D E O N ■ R E L E T
```

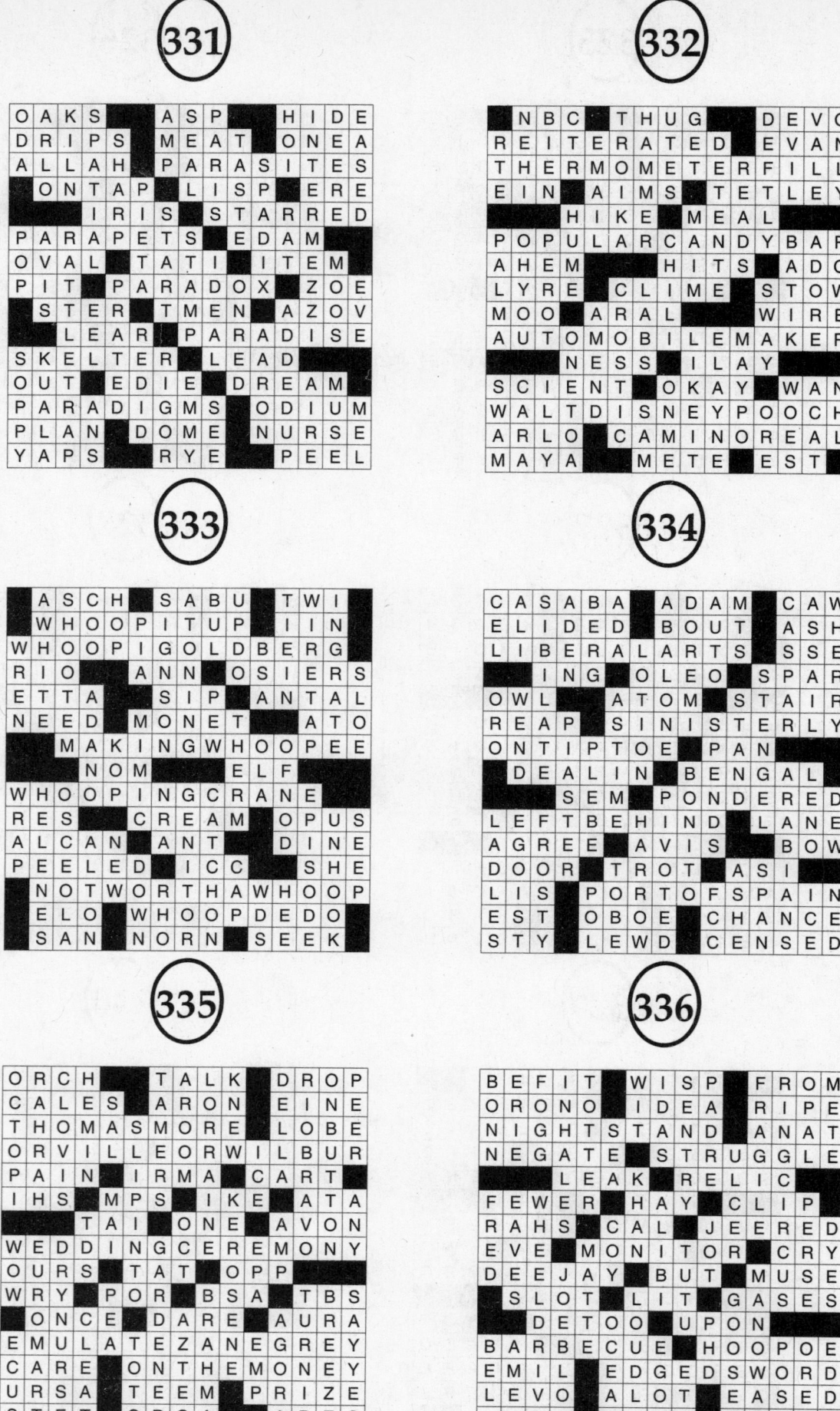

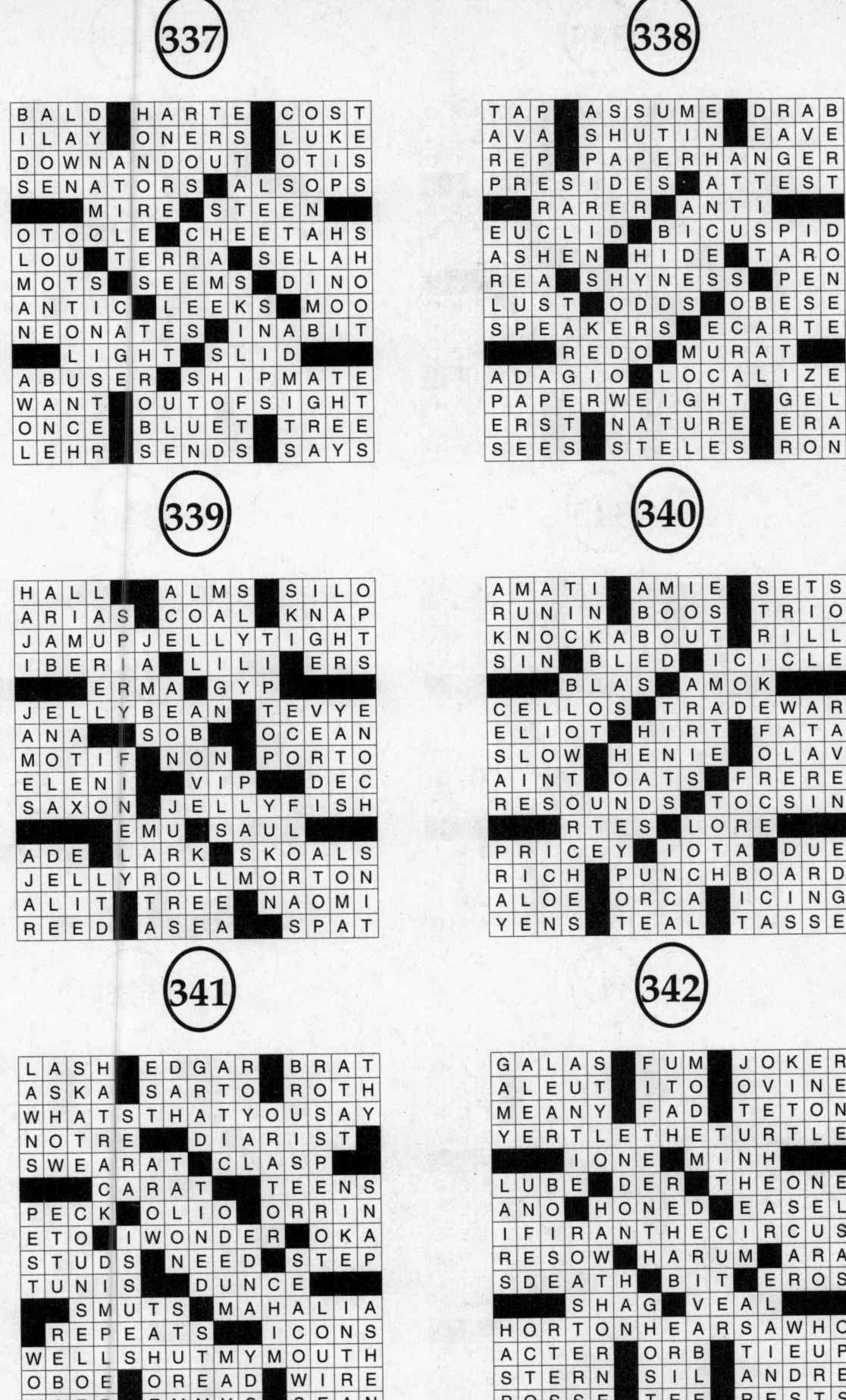

337

BALD · HARTE · COST
ILAY · ONERS · LUKE
DOWNANDOUT · OTIS
SENATORS · ALSOPS
· · MIRE · STEEN ·
OTOOLE · CHEETAHS
LOU · TERRA · SELAH
MOTS · SEEMS · DINO
ANTIC · LEEKS · MOO
NEONATES · INABIT
· LIGHT · SLID · ·
ABUSER · SHIPMATE
WANT · OUTOFSIGHT
ONCE · BLUET · TREE
LEHR · SENDS · SAYS

338

TAP · ASSUME · DRAB
AVA · SHUTIN · EAVE
REP · PAPERHANGER
PRESIDES · ATTEST
· RARER · ANTI · ·
EUCLID · BICUSPID
ASHEN · HIDE · TARO
REA · SHYNESS · PEN
LUST · ODDS · OBESE
SPEAKERS · ECARTE
· REDO · MURAT · ·
ADAGIO · LOCALIZE
PAPERWEIGHT · GEL
ERST · NATURE · ERA
SEES · STELES · RON

339

HALL · ALMS · SILO
ARIAS · COAL · KNAP
JAMUPJELLYTIGHT
IBERIA · LILI · ERS
· ERMA · GYP · ·
JELLYBEAN · TEVYE
ANA · SOB · OCEAN
MOTIF · NON · PORTO
ELENI · VIP · DEC
SAXON · JELLYFISH
· EMU · SAUL · ·
ADE · LARK · SKOALS
JELLYROLLMORTON
ALIT · TREE · NAOMI
REED · ASEA · SPAT

340

AMATI · AMIE · SETS
RUNIN · BOOS · TRIO
KNOCKABOUT · RILL
SIN · BLED · ICICLE
· BLAS · AMOK ·
CELLOS · TRADEWAR
ELIOT · HIRT · FATA
SLOW · HENIE · OLAV
AINT · OATS · FRERE
RESOUNDS · TOCSIN
· RTES · LORE · ·
PRICEY · IOTA · DUE
RICH · PUNCHBOARD
ALOE · ORCA · ICING
YENS · TEAL · TASSE

341

LASH · EDGAR · BRAT
ASKA · SARTO · ROTH
WHATSTHATYOUSAY
NOTRE · DIARIST ·
SWEARAT · CLASP ·
· CARAT · TEENS
PECK · OLIO · ORRIN
ETO · IWONDER · OKA
STUDS · NEED · STEP
TUNIS · DUNCE ·
· SMUTS · MAHALIA
· REPEATS · ICONS
WELLSHUTMYMOUTH
OBOE · OREAD · WIRE
WARD · EMMYS · SEAN

342

GALAS · FUM · JOKER
ALEUT · ITO · OVINE
MEANY · FAD · TETON
YERTLETHETURTLE
· IONE · MINH · ·
LUBE · DER · THEONE
ANO · HONED · EASEL
IFIRANTHECIRCUS
RESOW · HARUM · ARA
SDEATH · BIT · EROS
· SHAG · VEAL ·
HORTONHEARSAWHO
ACTER · ORB · TIEUP
STERN · SIL · ANDRE
POSSE · TEE · RESTS

343

```
B A N D B   L S U   T O R S O
A L I A R   I N N   A P E A R
N A C I O   N A B   C E L L O
    K N U T E R O C K N E
D E A T H V A L L E Y D A Y S
T A N Y A S   E S E   A S E A
S U D   H E A R T   T E S T
      N A T L   E C C E
C A P E   C O R A L   P R O
U T E S   U H F   P U R E E D
B E D T I M E F O R B O N Z O
    A L L A M E R I C A N
B E L I E   I R A   A D A I R
O N E N D   S E L   R I N G O
W E D G E   T D S   S E T O N
```

344

```
R E T I R E   W A D   C S T
E V E N E R   R O M E   R H O
N E A T E R   E R I K   Y O O
    R O S   P A S S E D O U T
S H S   E R O D E S   A F T S
P O O L S I D E   A N T S Y
O M N I   G U M S   U G H
    Y E P   K N E W   E B A N
R E P R O   D R E S S A G E
E L I A   P A W N E E   N E E
P I L L B O X E S   N O S
I S L   A L E E   M A C H O S
N E O   K E L P   A T H E N A
S S W   E R S   D E S E E D
```

345

```
S C A T   A L I A   Y P R E S
H U G O   C O A X   E L E C T
A J A X   C O M E   S A M O A
H O S I E R S B L E S S I N G
    C L U E   A I M
I M B I B E   D E T R A C T S
M O L T O   M I C A   L E I
P L A Y W R I G H T S F E A R
E L I   E L I O   E R A S E
L Y R I C I S T   J E E R E D
      R A G   K I D S
A C C O U N T A N T S H O P E
R O A N S   O V E N   M I L K
T O S E E   N I L E   A L O E
S T A R S   I D L Y   N Y P D
```

346

```
A L D A   B M I   W I L E
O V E R S E E R   S T A D I A
K I N D E R G A R T E N E R S
    O R E   Q U A N D A R Y
  M E R I T   G I D E
B A S S E T   O R D E R E R
A L T   S A L S A   R E N E S
U T A H   S U I T S   R A F T
R E T O P   G E S T E   M I A
  D E M U R E R   E X C E L S
    E R E I   A T O L L
R O E B L I N G   L O R
I M G O I N G A M I L K I N G
G O O D E S   N O N S E N S E
S O N Y   G I G   R A C E
```

347

```
R A I S E   P A C A   R F D
E S S E X   B A Y O U   E A U
A I R A P P A R E N T   I C E
    S O I R   F O R G E T
H O H O   A N G L I C A N
O N A N   R E D R Y D E R
S E R A L   T I N E A   A X E
T I T L E   I L O   T O N E S
E N A   T O L L S   S U C R E
L A T I T U D E   T E T E
    T E E T E R E D   S S S S
S T A R R S   L O O M
H I C   M I S S M A N A G E S
I N K   A D I O S   T R E V I
P A S   N E X T   O T O E S
```

348

```
H U T S   L I S A   R I C H
O L E O   M U S H Y   E V I E
P U R L   O I L E R   M A N X
E L M   J O S E   F O N D A
F A I R A S A S T A R W H E N
O T T E R   H R E   O R E
R E E D   A T R A I N   E S S
    O N L Y O N E I S
B M T   A L I C E S   A M A S
O A R   Z E N   A M I S H
S H I N I N G I N T H E S K Y
W A L E S   L I R A   L A S
E L L E   Q U I T O   P A N T
L I E D   U S U R Y   R I C E
L A D Y   A C M E   O D E R
```

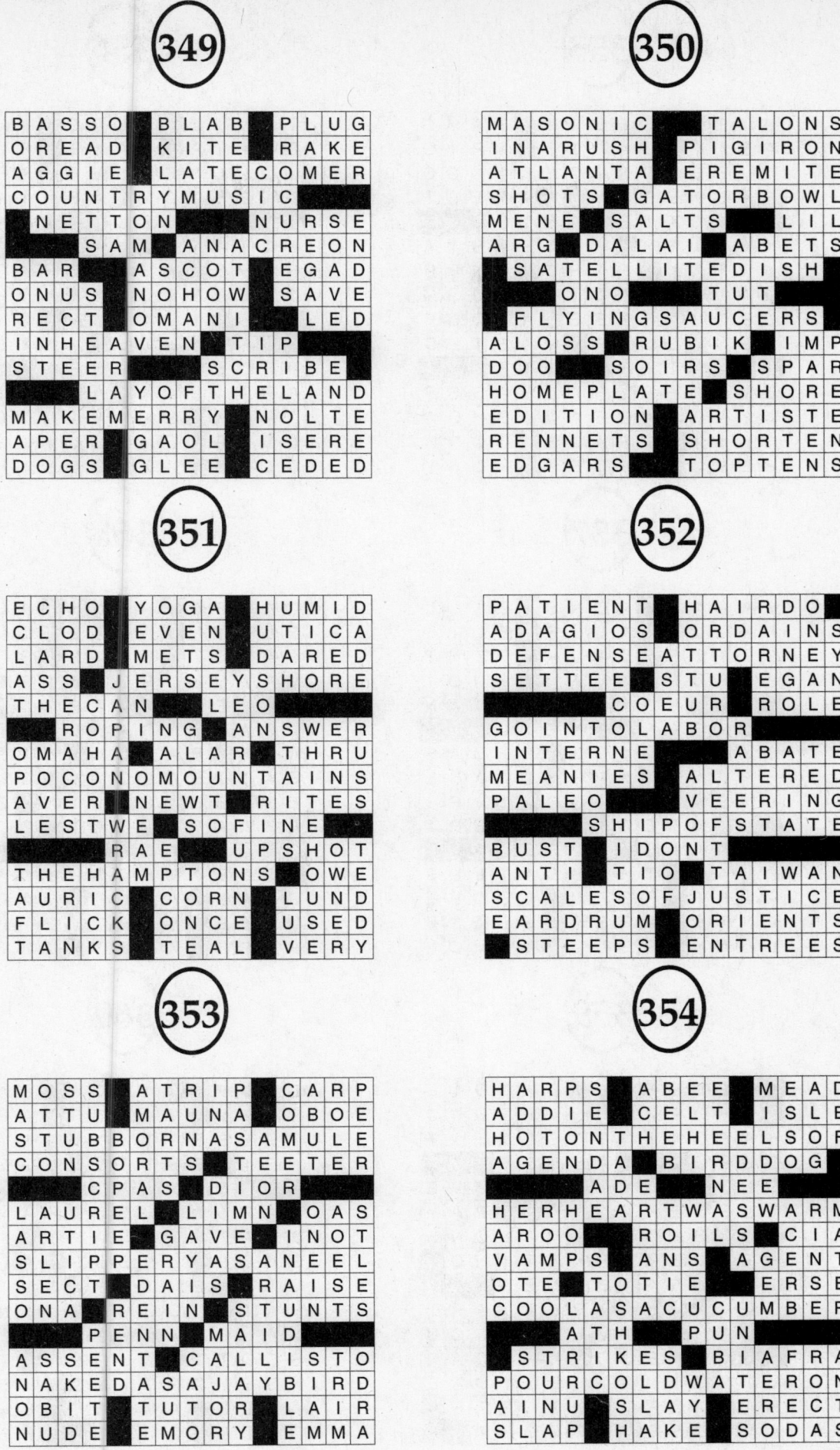

349

B	A	S	S	O	■	B	L	A	B	■	P	L	U	G
O	R	E	A	D	■	K	I	T	E	■	R	A	K	E
A	G	G	I	E	■	L	A	T	E	C	O	M	E	R
C	O	U	N	T	R	Y	M	U	S	I	C	■		
■	N	E	T	T	O	N	■		N	U	R	S	E	
			S	A	M	■	A	N	A	C	R	E	O	N
B	A	R	■	A	S	C	O	T	■	E	G	A	D	
O	N	U	S	■	N	O	H	O	W	■	S	A	V	E
R	E	C	T	■	O	M	A	N	I	■	L	E	D	
I	N	H	E	A	V	E	N	■	T	I	P			
S	T	E	E	R	■		S	C	R	I	B	E		
■		L	A	Y	O	F	T	H	E	L	A	N	D	
M	A	K	E	M	E	R	R	Y	■	N	O	L	T	E
A	P	E	R	■	G	A	O	L	■	I	S	E	R	E
D	O	G	S	■	G	L	E	E	■	C	E	D	E	D

350

M	A	S	O	N	I	C	■	T	A	L	O	N	S	
I	N	A	R	U	S	H	■	P	I	G	I	R	O	N
A	T	L	A	N	T	A	■	E	R	E	M	I	T	E
S	H	O	T	S	■	G	A	T	O	R	B	O	W	L
M	E	N	E	■	S	A	L	T	S	■	L	I	L	
A	R	G	■	D	A	L	A	I	■	A	B	E	T	S
■	S	A	T	E	L	L	I	T	E	D	I	S	H	
		O	N	O	■		T	U	T	■				
F	L	Y	I	N	G	S	A	U	C	E	R	S		
A	L	O	S	S	■	R	U	B	I	K	■	I	M	P
D	O	O	■	S	O	I	R	S	■	S	P	A	R	
H	O	M	E	P	L	A	T	E	■	S	H	O	R	E
E	D	I	T	I	O	N	■	A	R	T	I	S	T	E
R	E	N	N	E	T	S	■	S	H	O	R	T	E	N
E	D	G	A	R	S	■	T	O	P	T	E	N	S	

351

E	C	H	O	■	Y	O	G	A	■	H	U	M	I	D
C	L	O	D	■	E	V	E	N	■	U	T	I	C	A
L	A	R	D	■	M	E	T	S	■	D	A	R	E	D
A	S	S	■	J	E	R	S	E	Y	S	H	O	R	E
T	H	E	C	A	N	■	L	E	O	■				
■		R	O	P	I	N	G	■	A	N	S	W	E	R
O	M	A	H	A	■	A	L	A	R	■	T	H	R	U
P	O	C	O	N	O	M	O	U	N	T	A	I	N	S
A	V	E	R	■	N	E	W	T	■	R	I	T	E	S
L	E	S	T	W	E	■	S	O	F	I	N	E	■	
■			R	A	E	■		U	P	S	H	O	T	
T	H	E	H	A	M	P	T	O	N	S	■	O	W	E
A	U	R	I	C	■	C	O	R	N	■	L	U	N	D
F	L	I	C	K	■	O	N	C	E	■	U	S	E	D
T	A	N	K	S	■	T	E	A	L	■	V	E	R	Y

352

P	A	T	I	E	N	T	■	H	A	I	R	D	O	■
A	D	A	G	I	O	S	■	O	R	D	A	I	N	S
D	E	F	E	N	S	E	A	T	T	O	R	N	E	Y
S	E	T	T	E	E	■	S	T	U	■	E	G	A	N
■				C	O	E	U	R	■	R	O	L	E	
G	O	I	N	T	O	L	A	B	O	R	■			
I	N	T	E	R	N	E	■		A	B	A	T	E	
M	E	A	N	I	E	S	■	A	L	T	E	R	E	D
P	A	L	E	O	■		V	E	E	R	I	N	G	
■		S	H	I	P	O	F	S	T	A	T	E		
B	U	S	T	■	I	D	O	N	T	■				
A	N	T	I	■	T	I	O	■	T	A	I	W	A	N
S	C	A	L	E	S	O	F	J	U	S	T	I	C	E
E	A	R	D	R	U	M	■	O	R	I	E	N	T	S
■	S	T	E	E	P	S	■	E	N	T	R	E	E	S

353

M	O	S	S	■	A	T	R	I	P	■	C	A	R	P
A	T	T	U	■	M	A	U	N	A	■	O	B	O	E
S	T	U	B	B	O	R	N	A	S	A	M	U	L	E
C	O	N	S	O	R	T	S	■	T	E	E	T	E	R
■		C	P	A	S	■	D	I	O	R	■			
L	A	U	R	E	L	■	L	I	M	N	■	O	A	S
A	R	T	I	E	■	G	A	V	E	■	I	N	O	T
S	L	I	P	P	E	R	Y	A	S	A	N	E	E	L
S	E	C	T	■	D	A	I	S	■	R	A	I	S	E
O	N	A	■	R	E	I	N	■	S	T	U	N	T	S
■			P	E	N	N	■	M	A	I	D			
A	S	S	E	N	T	■	C	A	L	L	I	S	T	O
N	A	K	E	D	A	S	A	J	A	Y	B	I	R	D
O	B	I	T	■	T	U	T	O	R	■	L	A	I	R
N	U	D	E	■	E	M	O	R	Y	■	E	M	M	A

354

H	A	R	P	S	■	A	B	E	E	■	M	E	A	D
A	D	D	I	E	■	C	E	L	T	■	I	S	L	E
H	O	T	O	N	T	H	E	H	E	E	L	S	O	F
A	G	E	N	D	A	■	B	I	R	D	D	O	G	■
■			A	D	E	■		N	E	E	■			
H	E	R	H	E	A	R	T	W	A	S	W	A	R	M
A	R	O	O	■	R	O	I	L	S	■	C	I	A	
V	A	M	P	S	■	A	N	S	■	A	G	E	N	T
O	T	E	■	T	O	T	I	E	■	E	R	S	E	
C	O	O	L	A	S	A	C	U	C	U	M	B	E	R
■		A	T	H	■		P	U	N	■				
■	S	T	R	I	K	E	S	■	B	I	A	F	R	A
P	O	U	R	C	O	L	D	W	A	T	E	R	O	N
A	I	N	U	■	S	L	A	Y	■	E	R	E	C	T
S	L	A	P	■	H	A	K	E	■	S	O	D	A	S

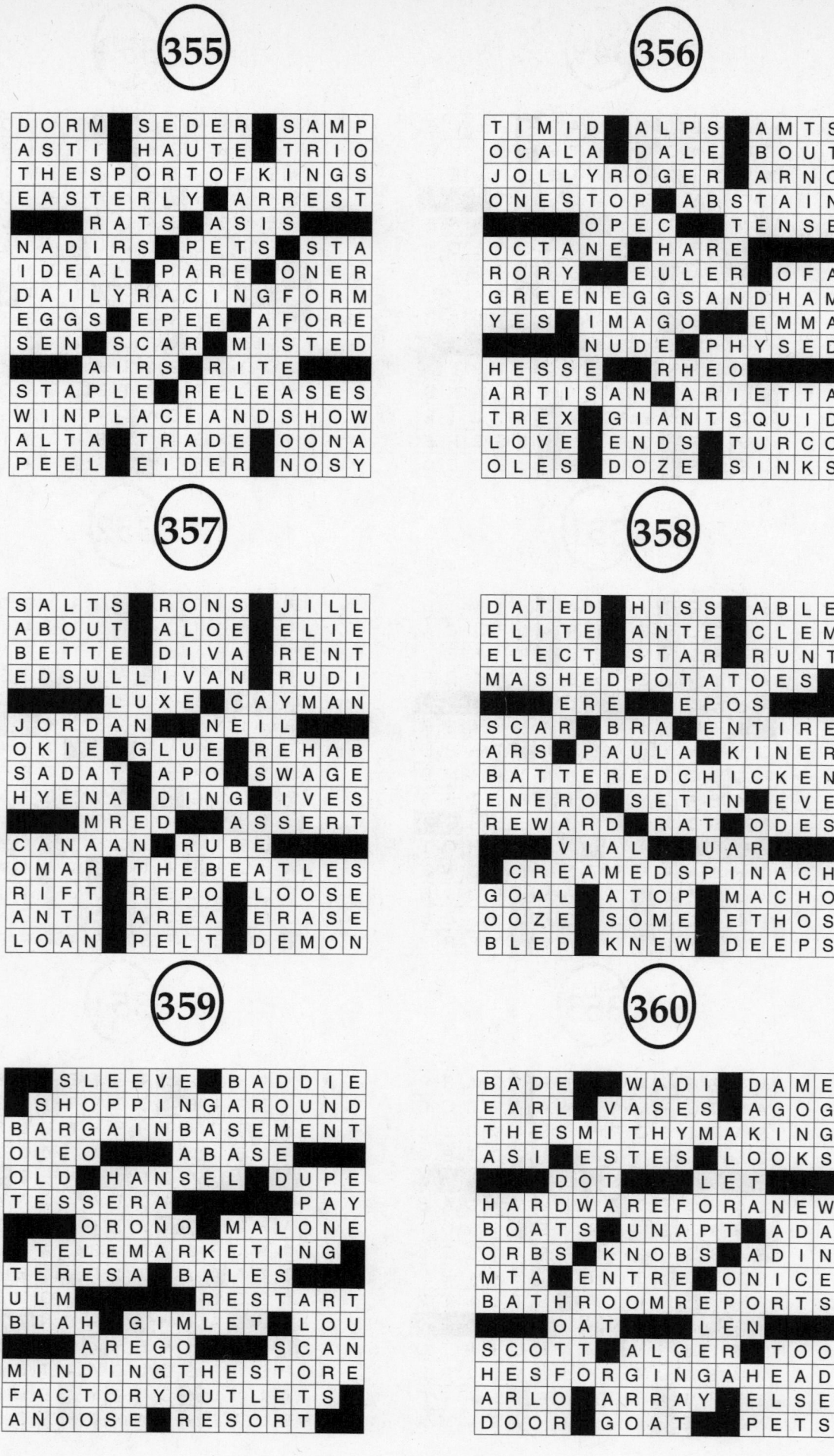

355

```
DORM  SEDER  SAMP
ASTI  HAUTE  TRIO
THESPORTOFKINGS
EASTERLY  ARREST
    RATS  ASIS
NADIRS  PETS  STA
IDEAL  PARE  ONER
DAILYRACINGFORM
EGGS  EPEE  AFORE
SEN  SCAR  MISTED
    AIRS  RITE
STAPLE  RELEASES
WINPLACEANDSHOW
ALTA  TRADE  OONA
PEEL  EIDER  NOSY
```

356

```
TIMID  ALPS  AMTS
OCALA  DALE  BOUT
JOLLYROGER  ARNO
ONESTOP  ABSTAIN
    OPEC  TENSE
OCTANE  HARE
RORY  EULER  OFA
GREENEGGSANDHAM
YES  IMAGO  EMMA
    NUDE  PHYSED
HESSE  RHEO
ARTISAN  ARIETTA
TREX  GIANTSQUID
LOVE  ENDS  TURCO
OLES  DOZE  SINKS
```

357

```
SALTS  RONS  JILL
ABOUT  ALOE  ELIE
BETTE  DIVA  RENT
EDSULLIVAN  RUDI
    LUXE  CAYMAN
JORDAN  NEIL
OKIE  GLUE  REHAB
SADAT  APO  SWAGE
HYENA  DING  IVES
    MRED  ASSERT
CANAAN  RUBE
OMAR  THEBEATLES
RIFT  REPO  LOOSE
ANTI  AREA  ERASE
LOAN  PELT  DEMON
```

358

```
DATED  HISS  ABLE
ELITE  ANTE  CLEM
ELECT  STAR  RUNT
MASHEDPOTATOES
    ERE  EPOS
SCAR  BRA  ENTIRE
ARS  PAULA  KINER
BATTEREDCHICKEN
ENERO  SETIN  EVE
REWARD  RAT  ODES
    VIAL  UAR
CREAMEDSPINACH
GOAL  ATOP  MACHO
OOZE  SOME  ETHOS
BLED  KNEW  DEEPS
```

359

```
  SLEEVE  BADDIE
  SHOPPINGAROUND
BARGAINBASEMENT
OLEO  ABASE
OLD  HANSEL  DUPE
TESSERA  PAY
  ORONO  MALONE
  TELEMARKETING
TERESA  BALES
ULM  RESTART
BLAH  GIMLET  LOU
  AREGO  SCAN
MINDINGTHESTORE
FACTORYOUTLETS
ANOOSE  RESORT
```

360

```
BADE  WADI  DAME
EARL  VASES  AGOG
THESMITHYMAKING
ASI  ESTES  LOOKS
    DOT  LET
HARDWAREFORANEW
BOATS  UNAPT  ADA
ORBS  KNOBS  ADIN
MTA  ENTRE  ONICE
BATHROOMREPORTS
    OAT  LEN
SCOTT  ALGER  TOO
HESFORGINGAHEAD
ARLO  ARRAY  ELSE
DOOR  GOAT  PETS
```

361 · 362 · 363 · 364 · 365 · 366

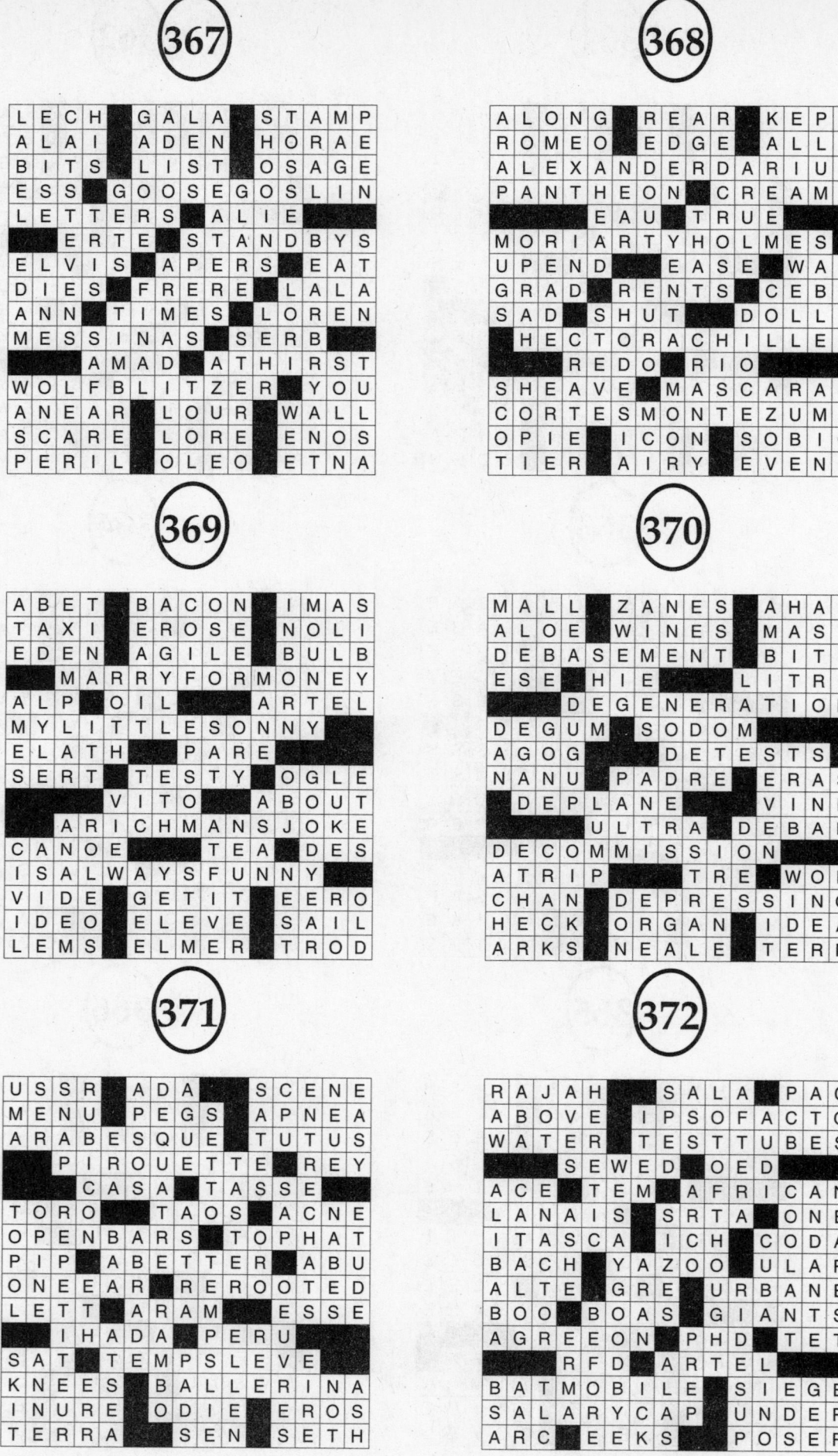

367

L	E	C	H		G	A	L	A			S	T	A	M	P
A	L	A	I		A	D	E	N			H	O	R	A	E
B	I	T	S		L	I	S	T			O	S	A	G	E
E	S	S		G	O	O	S	E		G	O	S	L	I	N
L	E	T	T	E	R	S		A	L	I	E				
		E	R	T	E		S	T	A	N	D	B	Y	S	
E	L	V	I	S		A	P	E	R	S		E	A	T	
D	I	E	S		F	R	E	R	E		L	A	L	A	
A	N	N		T	I	M	E	S		L	O	R	E	N	
M	E	S	S	I	N	A	S		S	E	R	B			
		A	M	A	D		A	T	H	I	R	S	T		
W	O	L	F	B	L	I	T	Z	E	R		Y	O	U	
A	N	E	A	R		L	O	U	R		W	A	L	L	
S	C	A	R	E		L	O	R	E		E	N	O	S	
P	E	R	I	L		O	L	E	O		E	T	N	A	

368

A	L	O	N	G		R	E	A	R		K	E	P	T
R	O	M	E	O		E	D	G	E		A	L	L	A
A	L	E	X	A	N	D	E	R	D	A	R	I	U	S
P	A	N	T	H	E	O	N		C	R	E	A	M	S
			E	A	U		T	R	U	E				
M	O	R	I	A	R	T	Y	H	O	L	M	E	S	
U	P	E	N	D		E	A	S	E		W	A	G	
G	R	A	D		R	E	N	T	S		C	E	B	U
S	A	D		S	H	U	T		D	O	L	L	Y	
	H	E	C	T	O	R	A	C	H	I	L	L	E	S
	R	E	D	O		R	I	O						
S	H	E	A	V	E		M	A	S	C	A	R	A	S
C	O	R	T	E	S	M	O	N	T	E	Z	U	M	A
O	P	I	E		I	C	O	N		S	O	B	I	G
T	I	E	R		A	I	R	Y		E	V	E	N	S

369

A	B	E	T		B	A	C	O	N		I	M	A	S
T	A	X	I		E	R	O	S	E		N	O	L	I
E	D	E	N		A	G	I	L	E		B	U	L	B
	M	A	R	R	Y	F	O	R	M	O	N	E	Y	
A	L	P		O	I	L			A	R	T	E	L	
M	Y	L	I	T	T	L	E	S	O	N	N	Y		
E	L	A	T	H		P	A	R	E					
S	E	R	T		T	E	S	T	Y		O	G	L	E
		V	I	T	O		A	B	O	U	T			
	A	R	I	C	H	M	A	N	S	J	O	K	E	
C	A	N	O	E		T	E	A		D	E	S		
I	S	A	L	W	A	Y	S	F	U	N	N	Y		
V	I	D	E		G	E	T	I	T		E	E	R	O
I	D	E	O		E	L	E	V	E		S	A	I	L
L	E	M	S		E	L	M	E	R		T	R	O	D

370

M	A	L	L		Z	A	N	E	S		A	H	A	S
A	L	O	E		W	I	N	E	S		M	A	S	T
D	E	B	A	S	E	M	E	N	T		B	I	T	E
E	S	E		H	I	E			L	I	T	R	E	
			D	E	G	E	N	E	R	A	T	I	O	N
D	E	G	U	M		S	O	D	O	M				
A	G	O	G		D	E	T	E	S	T	S			
N	A	N	U		P	A	D	R	E		E	R	A	S
	D	E	P	L	A	N	E			V	I	N	E	
		U	L	T	R	A		D	E	B	A	R		
D	E	C	O	M	M	I	S	S	I	O	N			
A	T	R	I	P		T	R	E		W	O	E		
C	H	A	N		D	E	P	R	E	S	S	I	N	G
H	E	C	K		O	R	G	A	N		I	D	E	A
A	R	K	S		N	E	A	L	E		T	E	R	N

371

U	S	S	R		A	D	A		S	C	E	N	E
M	E	N	U		P	E	G	S		A	P	N	E	A
A	R	A	B	E	S	Q	U	E		T	U	T	U	S
	P	I	R	O	U	E	T	T	E		R	E	Y	
	C	A	S	A		T	A	S	S	E				
T	O	R	O		T	A	O	S		A	C	N	E	
O	P	E	N	B	A	R	S		T	O	P	H	A	T
P	I	P		A	B	E	T	T	E	R		A	B	U
O	N	E	E	A	R		R	E	R	O	O	T	E	D
L	E	T	T		A	R	A	M		E	S	S	E	
	I	H	A	D	A		P	E	R	U				
S	A	T		T	E	M	P	S	L	E	V	E		
K	N	E	E	S		B	A	L	L	E	R	I	N	A
I	N	U	R	E		O	D	I	E		E	R	O	S
T	E	R	R	A		S	E	N		S	E	T	H	

372

R	A	J	A	H		S	A	L	A		P	A	C
A	B	O	V	E		I	P	S	O	F	A	C	T	O
W	A	T	E	R		T	E	S	T	T	U	B	E	S
		S	E	W	E	D		O	E	D				
A	C	E		T	E	M		A	F	R	I	C	A	N
L	A	N	A	I	S		S	R	T	A		O	N	E
I	T	A	S	C	A		I	C	H		C	O	D	A
B	A	C	H		Y	A	Z	O	O		U	L	A	R
A	L	T	E		G	R	E		U	R	B	A	N	E
B	O	O		B	O	A	S		G	I	A	N	T	S
A	G	R	E	E	O	N		P	H	D		T	E	T
	R	F	D		A	R	T	E	L					
B	A	T	M	O	B	I	L	E		S	I	E	G	E
S	A	L	A	R	Y	C	A	P		U	N	D	E	R
A	R	C		E	E	K	S			P	O	S	E	R

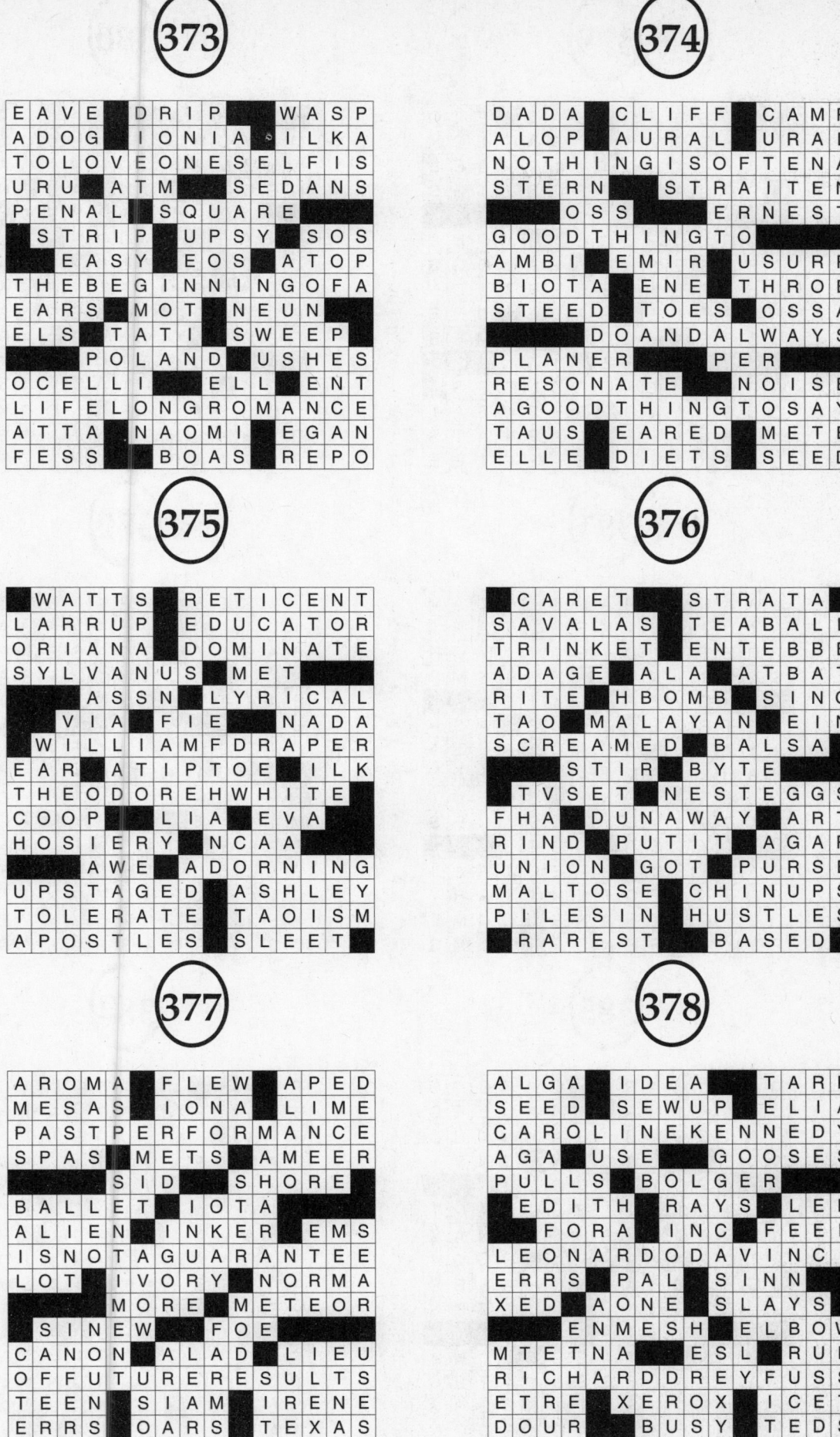

373

```
EAVE DRIP  WASP
ADOG IONIA ILKA
TOLOVEONESELFIS
URU ATM  SEDANS
PENAL SQUARE
 STRIP UPSY SOS
  EASY EOS ATOP
THEBEGINNINGOFA
EARS MOT NEUN
ELS TATI SWEEP
  POLAND USHES
OCELLI ELL ENT
LIFELONGROMANCE
ATTA NAOMI EGAN
FESS BOAS REPO
```

374

```
DADA CLIFF CAMP
ALOP AURAL URAL
NOTHINGISOFTENA
STERN STRAITEN
  OSS ERNEST
GOODTHINGTO
AMBI EMIR USURP
BIOTA ENE THROE
STEED TOES OSSA
  DOANDALWAYS
PLANER PER
RESONATE NOISE
AGOODTHINGTOSAY
TAUS EARED METE
ELLE DIETS SEED
```

375

```
 WATTS RETICENT
LARRUP EDUCATOR
ORIANA DOMINATE
SYLVANUS MET
  ASSN LYRICAL
 VIA FIE NADA
 WILLIAMFDRAPER
EAR ATIPTOE ILK
THEODOREHWHITE
COOP LIA EVA
HOSIERY NCAA
  AWE ADORNING
UPSTAGED ASHLEY
TOLERATE TAOISM
APOSTLES SLEET
```

376

```
 CARET STRATA
SAVALAS TEABALL
TRINKET ENTEBBE
ADAGE ALA ATBAT
RITE HBOMB SINO
TAO MALAYAN EIN
SCREAMED BALSA
  STIR BYTE
 TVSET NESTEGGS
FHA DUNAWAY ART
RIND PUTIT AGAR
UNION GOT PURSE
MALTOSE CHINUPS
PILESIN HUSTLES
RAREST BASED
```

377

```
AROMA FLEW APED
MESAS IONA LIME
PASTPERFORMANCE
SPAS METS AMEER
  SID SHORE
BALLET IOTA
ALIEN INKER EMS
ISNOTAGUARANTEE
LOT IVORY NORMA
  MORE METEOR
 SINEW FOE
CANON ALAD LIEU
OFFUTURERESULTS
TEEN SIAM IRENE
ERRS OARS TEXAS
```

378

```
ALGA IDEA TARP
SEED SEWUP ELIA
CAROLINEKENNEDY
AGA USE GOOSES
PULLS BOLGER
 EDITH RAYS LEE
 FORA INC FEEL
LEONARDODAVINCI
ERRS PAL SINN
XED AONE SLAYS
 ENMESH ELBOW
MTETNA ESL RUE
RICHARDDREYFUSS
ETRE XEROX ICET
DOUR BUSY TEDS
```

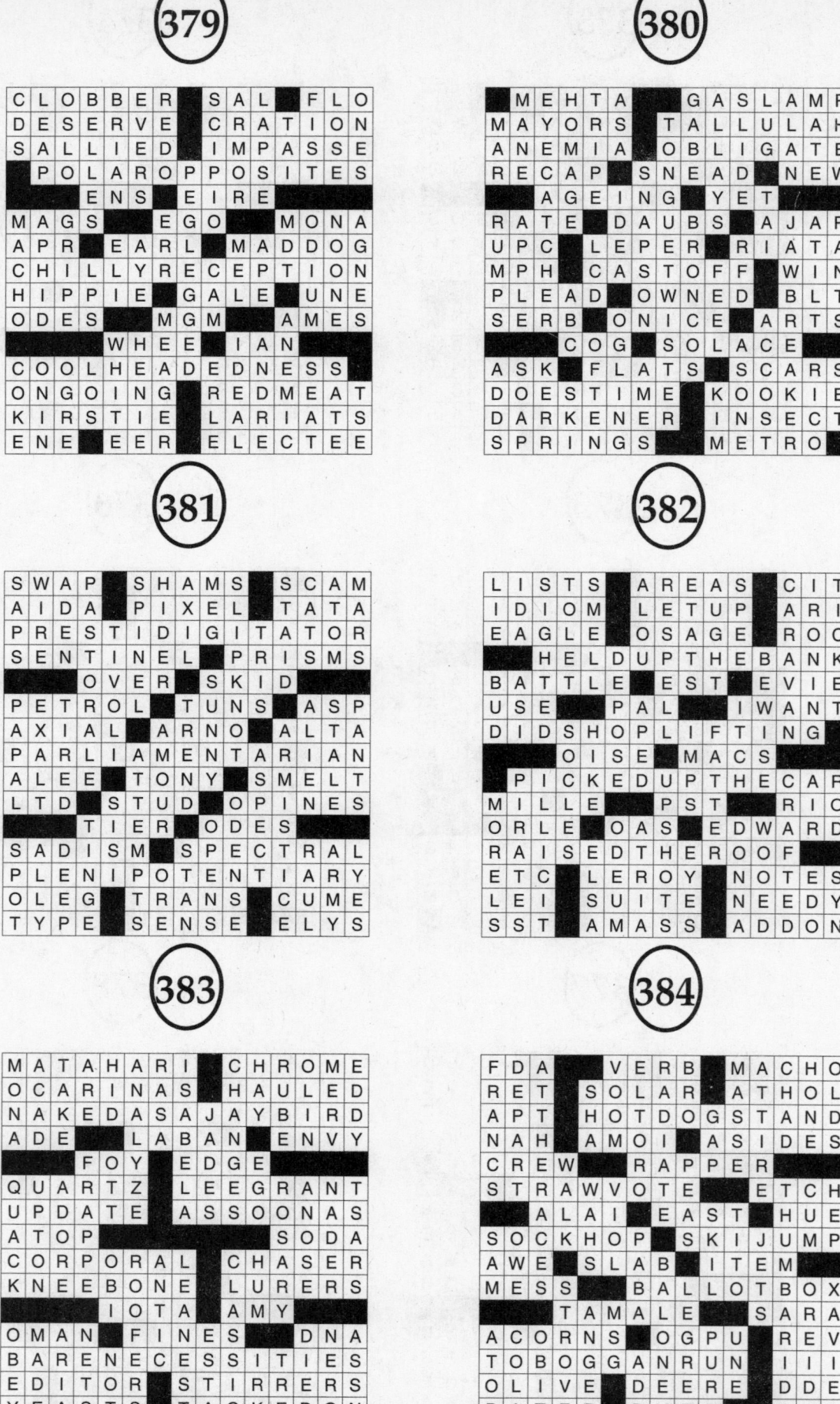

379

```
CLOBBER SAL FLO
DESERVE CRATION
SALLIED IMPASSE
 POLAROPPOSITES
   ENS EIRE
MAGS EGO MONA
APR EARL MADDOG
CHILLYRECEPTION
HIPPIE GALE UNE
ODES MGM AMES
  WHEE IAN
COOLHEADEDNESS
ONGOING REDMEAT
KIRSTIE LARIATS
ENE EER ELECTEE
```

380

```
 MEHTA GASLAMP
MAYORS TALLULAH
ANEMIA OBLIGATE
RECAP SNEAD NEW
 AGEING YET
RATE DAUBS AJAR
UPC LEPER RIATA
MPH CASTOFF WIN
PLEAD OWNED BLT
SERB ONICE ARTS
  COG SOLACE
ASK FLATS SCARS
DOESTIME KOOKIE
DARKENER INSECT
SPRINGS METRO
```

381

```
SWAP SHAMS SCAM
AIDA PIXEL TATA
PRESTIDIGITATOR
SENTINEL PRISMS
  OVER SKID
PETROL TUNS ASP
AXIAL ARNO ALTA
PARLIAMENTARIAN
ALEE TONY SMELT
LTD STUD OPINES
  TIER ODES
SADISM SPECTRAL
PLENIPOTENTIARY
OLEG TRANS CUME
TYPE SENSE ELYS
```

382

```
LISTS AREAS CIT
IDIOM LETUP ARI
EAGLE OSAGE ROC
 HELDUPTHEBANK
BATTLE EST EVIE
USE PAL IWANT
DIDSHOPLIFTING
 OISE MACS
 PICKEDUPTHECAR
MILLE PST RIO
ORLE OAS EDWARD
RAISEDTHEROOF
ETC LEROY NOTES
LEI SUITE NEEDY
SST AMASS ADDON
```

383

```
MATAHARI CHROME
OCARINAS HAULED
NAKEDASAJAYBIRD
ADE LABAN ENVY
 FOY EDGE
QUARTZ LEEGRANT
UPDATE ASSOONAS
ATOP SODA
CORPORAL CHASER
KNEEBONE LURERS
 IOTA AMY
OMAN FINES DNA
BARENECESSITIES
EDITOR STIRRERS
YEASTS TACKEDON
```

384

```
FDA VERB MACHO
RET SOLAR ATHOL
APT HOTDOGSTAND
NAH AMOI ASIDES
CREW RAPPER
STRAWVOTE ETCH
 ALAI EAST HUE
SOCKHOP SKIJUMP
AWE SLAB ITEM
MESS BALLOTBOX
 TAMALE SARA
ACORNS OGPU REV
TOBOGGANRUN III
OLIVE DEERE DDE
PATER DYER EAR
```

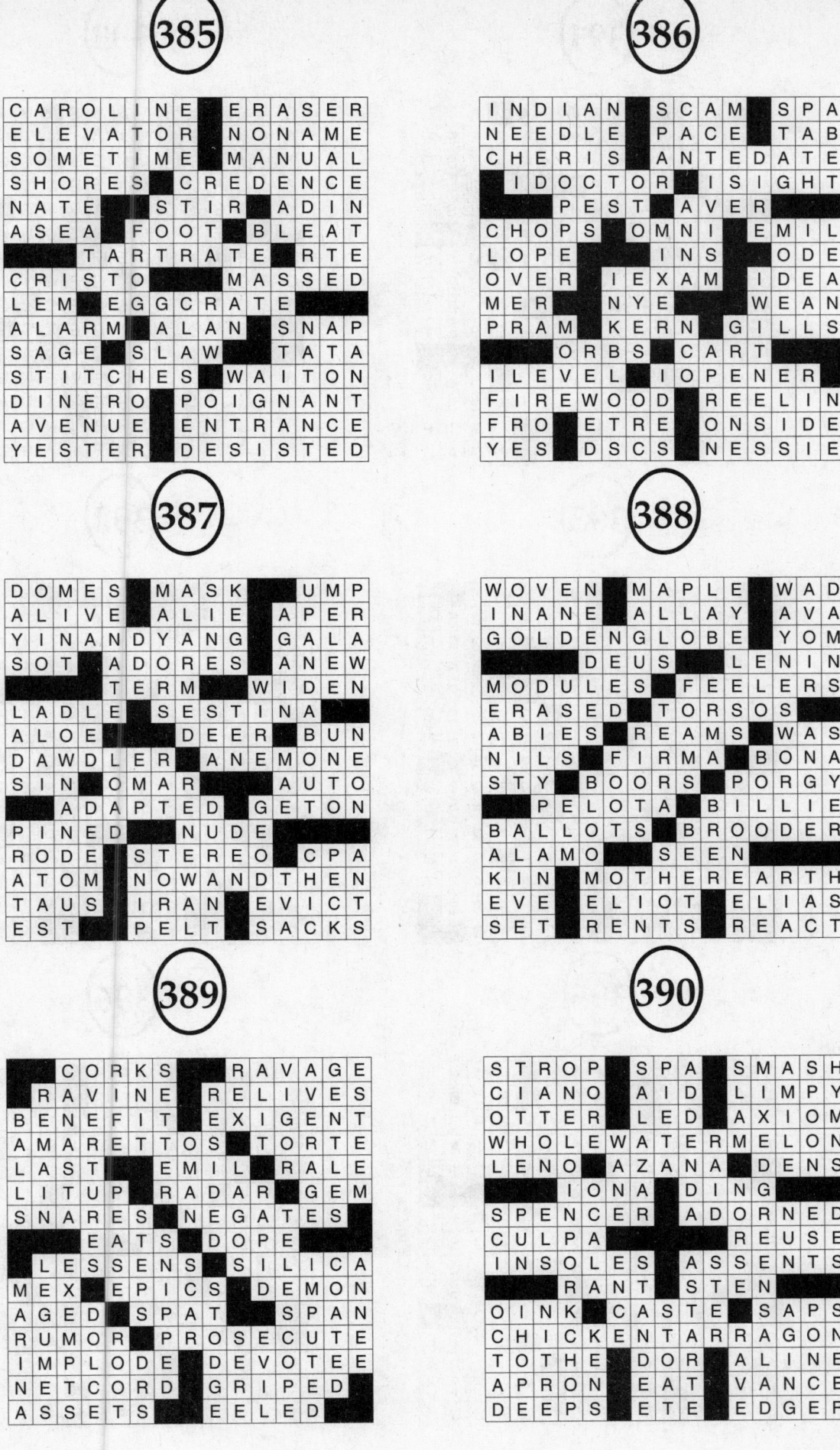

385

```
CAROLINE ERASER
ELEVATOR NONAME
SOMETIME MANUAL
SHORES CREDENCE
NATE STIR ADIN
ASEA FOOT BLEAT
TARTRATE RTE
CRISTO MASSED
LEM EGGCRATE
ALARM ALAN SNAP
SAGE SLAW TATA
STITCHES WAITON
DINERO POIGNANT
AVENUE ENTRANCE
YESTER DESISTED
```

386

```
INDIAN SCAM SPA
NEEDLE PACE TAB
CHERIS ANTEDATE
IDOCTOR ISIGHT
PEST AVER
CHOPS OMNI EMIL
LOPE INS ODE
OVER IEXAM IDEA
MER NYE WEAN
PRAM KERN GILLS
ORBS CART
ILEVEL IOPENER
FIREWOOD REELIN
FRO ETRE ONSIDE
YES DSCS NESSIE
```

387

```
DOMES MASK UMP
ALIVE ALIE APER
YINANDYANG GALA
SOT ADORES ANEW
TERM WIDEN
LADLE SESTINA
ALOE DEER BUN
DAWDLER ANEMONE
SIN OMAR AUTO
ADAPTED GETON
PINED NUDE
RODE STEREO CPA
ATOM NOWANDTHEN
TAUS IRAN EVICT
EST PELT SACKS
```

388

```
WOVEN MAPLE WAD
INANE ALLAY AVA
GOLDENGLOBE YOM
DEUS LENIN
MODULES FEELERS
ERASED TORSOS
ABIES REAMS WAS
NILS FIRMA BONA
STY BOORS PORGY
PELOTA BILLIE
BALLOTS BROODER
ALAMO SEEN
KIN MOTHEREARTH
EVE ELIOT ELIAS
SET RENTS REACT
```

389

```
CORKS RAVAGE
RAVINE RELIVES
BENEFIT EXIGENT
AMARETTOS TORTE
LAST EMIL RALE
LITUP RADAR GEM
SNARES NEGATES
EATS DOPE
LESSENS SILICA
MEX EPICS DEMON
AGED SPAT SPAN
RUMOR PROSECUTE
IMPLODE DEVOTEE
NETCORD GRIPED
ASSETS EELED
```

390

```
STROP SPA SMASH
CIANO AID LIMPY
OTTER LED AXIOM
WHOLEWATERMELON
LENO AZANA DENS
IONA DING
SPENCER ADORNED
CULPA REUSE
INSOLES ASSENTS
RANT STEN
OINK CASTE SAPS
CHICKENTARRAGON
TOTHE DOR ALINE
APRON EAT VANCE
DEEPS ETE EDGER
```

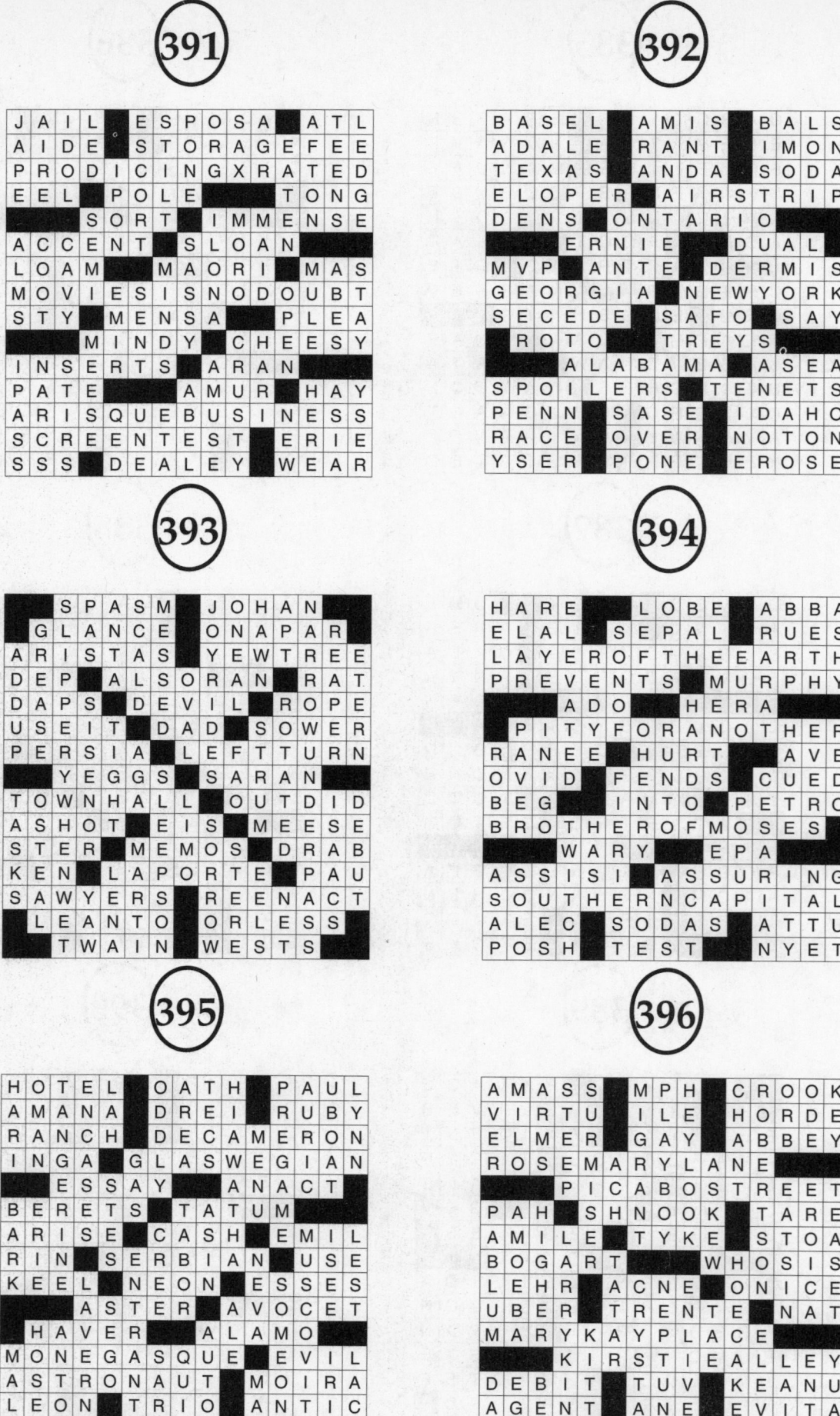

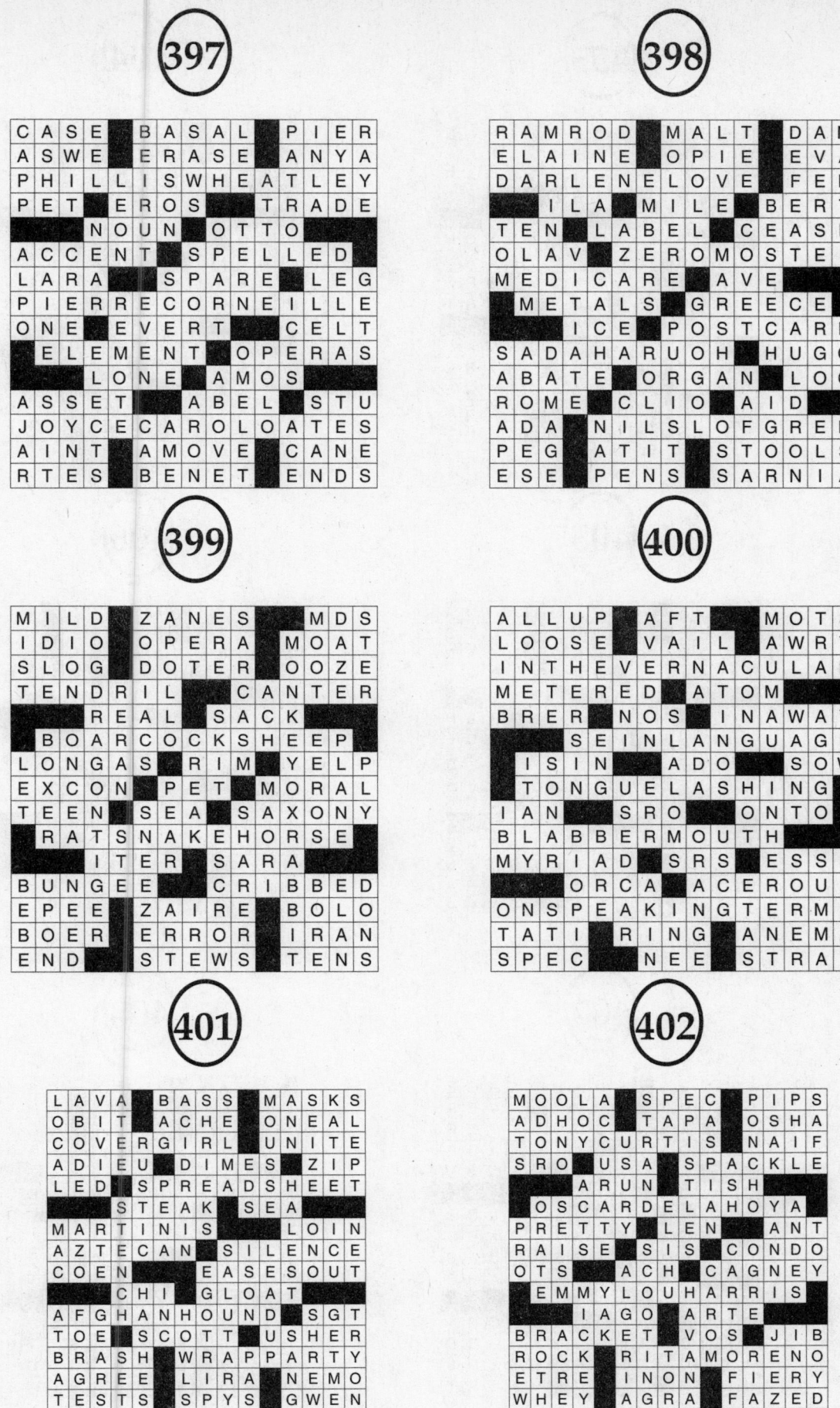

397

```
CASE ▪ BASAL ▪ PIER
ASWE ▪ ERASE ▪ ANYA
PHILLISWHEATLEY
PET ▪ EROS ▪ ▪ TRADE
▪ ▪ NOUN ▪ OTTO
ACCENT ▪ SPELLED
LARA ▪ SPARE ▪ LEG
PIERRECORNEILLE
ONE ▪ EVERT ▪ CELT
▪ ELEMENT ▪ OPERAS
▪ LONE ▪ AMOS
ASSET ▪ ABEL ▪ STU
JOYCECAROLOATES
AINT ▪ AMOVE ▪ CANE
RTES ▪ BENET ▪ ENDS
```

398

```
RAMROD ▪ MALT ▪ DAM
ELAINE ▪ OPIE ▪ EVA
DARLENELOVE ▪ FEN
▪ ILA ▪ MILE ▪ BERT
TEN ▪ LABEL ▪ CEASE
OLAV ▪ ZEROMOSTEL
MEDICARE ▪ AVE
▪ METALS ▪ GREECE
▪ ICE ▪ POSTCARD
SADAHARUOH ▪ HUGO
ABATE ▪ ORGAN ▪ LOG
ROME ▪ CLIO ▪ AID
ADA ▪ NILSLOFGREN
PEG ▪ ATIT ▪ STOOLS
ESE ▪ PENS ▪ SARNIA
```

399

```
MILD ▪ ZANES ▪ MDS
IDIO ▪ OPERA ▪ MOAT
SLOG ▪ DOTER ▪ OOZE
TENDRIL ▪ CANTER
▪ REAL ▪ SACK
BOARCOCKSHEEP
LONGAS ▪ RIM ▪ YELP
EXCON ▪ PET ▪ MORAL
TEEN ▪ SEA ▪ SAXONY
RATSNAKEHORSE
▪ ITER ▪ SARA
BUNGEE ▪ CRIBBED
EPEE ▪ ZAIRE ▪ BOLO
BOER ▪ ERROR ▪ IRAN
END ▪ STEWS ▪ TENS
```

400

```
ALLUP ▪ AFT ▪ MOTS
LOOSE ▪ VAIL ▪ AWRY
INTHEVERNACULAR
METERED ▪ ATOM
BRER ▪ NOS ▪ INAWAY
▪ SEINLANGUAGE
ISIN ▪ ADO ▪ SOW
TONGUELASHING
IAN ▪ SRO ▪ ONTO
BLABBERMOUTH
MYRIAD ▪ SRS ▪ ESSE
▪ ORCA ▪ ACEROUS
ONSPEAKINGTERMS
TATI ▪ RING ▪ ANEMA
SPEC ▪ NEE ▪ STRAY
```

401

```
LAVA ▪ BASS ▪ MASKS
OBIT ▪ ACHE ▪ ONEAL
COVERGIRL ▪ UNITE
ADIEU ▪ DIMES ▪ ZIP
LED ▪ SPREADSHEET
▪ STEAK ▪ SEA
MARTINIS ▪ LOIN
AZTECAN ▪ SILENCE
COEN ▪ EASESOUT
▪ CHI ▪ GLOAT
AFGHANHOUND ▪ SGT
TOE ▪ SCOTT ▪ USHER
BRASH ▪ WRAPPARTY
AGREE ▪ LIRA ▪ NEMO
TESTS ▪ SPYS ▪ GWEN
```

402

```
MOOLA ▪ SPEC ▪ PIPS
ADHOC ▪ TAPA ▪ OSHA
TONYCURTIS ▪ NAIF
SRO ▪ USA ▪ SPACKLE
▪ ARUN ▪ TISH
OSCARDELAHOYA
PRETTY ▪ LEN ▪ ANT
RAISE ▪ SIS ▪ CONDO
OTS ▪ ACH ▪ CAGNEY
▪ EMMYLOUHARRIS
▪ IAGO ▪ ARTE
BRACKET ▪ VOS ▪ JIB
ROCK ▪ RITAMORENO
ETRE ▪ INON ▪ FIERY
WHEY ▪ AGRA ▪ FAZED
```

403

```
A S S N   A D D U P   I S L E
T U N E   M O O L A   N L E R
B R O W N B E T T Y   S O A R
A L O H A   S E R E   T P K S
T Y P I N G   A E S O P
      R O U N D S   T R Y O N
S A V E   L O U   D E E J A Y
P I E   S L I M J I M   O R E
A D A P T S   B O X   B E S T
M E L E E   C O Y O T E
      O S T E R   N O R M A L
P O S T   A I R S   A R I S E
O N C E   S T E A K D I A N E
O M A R   T I B I A   E M E R
H E R S   S C A L Y   S I R S
```

404

```
B E A M   M T G   R E D A T E
A B B A   I W O   E R I C H S
J A C K A R O O   M A D M E N
A N D O R R A   C A T S E Y E
          C O C K A T O O
M S G   A R T I S T   A L B
A C H E D   P E E K A B O O
C R A N I A   D I A L I N
K A N G A R O O   N A U R U
S P A   T A R I F F   E E S
      B U C K A R O O
T O T A L L Y   A R L B E R G
A F R I C A   K I C K A P O O
G L A Z E S   A L E   L I M A
S A Y E R S   L S D   I C E D
```

405

```
R O S S   H I R A M   A Q U A
A S H E   A L O N E   P U T S
P L U M I S L A N D   R E A P
T O N I C S   M E S S I A H S
      S E L A     A L S
S I L   M E M P H I S   I A N
A D O B E   P A I R   O N C E
L A V E N D E R S A C H E T S
T H E E   O R E S   A S S E T
S O P   S T E R E O S   S D S
      O R S     R U S E
E N T H R O N E   T I A R A S
V I I I   P U R P L E R A I N
I T O N   E L I T E   E Z R A
L E N O   C L E A T   D E E P
```

406

```
B A M B I   A N A I S   I T O
A R E A S   R E L E T   N I N
M A R K M C G W I R E   L A S
A B E E   O O H   F L A R E
      S U L T A N O F S W A T
A B O A R D   R I G I D
B O I L S   S T E R   C O D
U N L E A S H   C E N S U R E
T D S   P O S E   O T T E R
      S H A R I   B O R E O N
I T S O U T T A H E R E
V A M P S   M I A   A R I A
A L A   H O M E R U N K I N G
N O R   E R A S E   B E L I E
A N T   D A T E S   C R E T E
```

407

```
L I N U S   S H A H   W A G E
A D O P T   A M M O   A V E R
F E E L I N G S U P E R I O R
F E L O N Y   L I L   A D E
      A T E A S E   P I N E D
G I L D S   K I T B A G
A D O   P I N   I S O L D E
T O U C H I N G S T O R I E S
O L D H A T   L O S   S A S
      A N S W E R   C H A R O
C E L T S   A T T I R E
O L E   E A R   S E N O R A
H A N D L I N G C H A R G E S
A T T U   N E E R   K I L N S
N E O N   T R O Y   S K E E T
```

408

```
  A L A E   I L S A   C A S H
G L E N N   D O W N   A R T E
M E A N T   E X I T   R E A L
S C H I R R A   S H E P A R D
      E E E   S H E R E
M A T   E T N A   M I N D E D
O S H A   A I L S   E T U D E
T H E M E R C U R Y S E V E N
H O T E L   E T T A   R E N T
S T A T I C   E A S E   T S E
      H O O K S   I D A
S L A Y T O N   G R I S S O M
H I P S   P A L E   S I T U P
E A S T   E V E N   O D O R S
A R E S   R E N E   N E W S
```

409

```
HEAP  PAPER  SLED
OLLA  IDAHO  MADE
DAVY  NOISE  EMIR
SNAP  URN  ELITE
    HOPELESSTASK
ACTOR  SEGOS
CRANES  SOP  SILO
HOMELESSSHELTER
EWES  LAD  STEEVE
    ELMER  CURIO
  ENDLESSNIGHT
PERIL  TAR  HOWE
ERAS  AGILE  INON
EVIL  BASTE  NERD
SYNE  SITON  GAMS
```

410

```
OHGOD  SITS  HALT
DEUCE  EDIT  ABIE
AWFUL  ROTE  MONA
  FLIPFLOPSIDES
  ALAS  SELENE
FARRAR  SPURT
ENA  HIPHOPBOOTS
ATMS  EAR  NORA
TIPTOPSHEET  ZEN
  ODETS  RIBEYE
MAGPIE  AGRA
CLIPCLOPBOARD
COVE  ELAN  DRIPS
ONER  RIPE  EERIE
YENS  SOAR  SLEPT
```

411

```
WAGED  MOTO  GLUM
ALONE  ASAP  LINE
SLAVS  CLUE  OBIS
  LOCKHORNSWITH
PAPYRI  USE  DEE
AGO  YOWLS  PLODS
MESS  SEA  STY
  STOCKEXCHANGE
  AHS  LOU  NULL
KAFKA  LYONS  ALI
ODE  SAY  TEHRAN
BARRELCHESTED
OGRE  PEAR  TWILL
LIEN  HULA  LEAVE
DOTE  AMES  ERNIE
```

412

```
SRS  CZAR  HILTON
TEC  RATE  AMOEBA
ISH  ANTS  UBOATS
GOODBYECOLUMBUS
MULES  NURSE  ASE
ARAB  IDES  AGER
SCRAMMED  CPR
  ESCAPE  FROMLA
  LPS  TOAPOINT
POME  DENY  ITTO
UNE  FAULT  ARIEL
LEAVINGLASVEGAS
SIDING  SITE  ATT
ADONIS  ONOR  NEO
RAWEST  NEWT  TRY
```

413

```
ALPS  PETS  PANEL
MORT  IRAE  ADORE
BOOR  NAUT  SENSE
ITMARKSTHESPOT
  SOPHIE  DOT
  PIE  ERIN  WIG
SITIN  ISON  SHOW
UNKNOWNQUANTITY
MOOG  AGUE  ORGAN
ONS  THEE  PRE
  SAO  ROMANO
  SYMBOLFORAKISS
SNAIL  EAST  ECHO
MAPLE  AMIE  RHEA
UPSET  PEER  SEAR
```

414

```
ODRA  SUSAN  BRA
PIES  CHOKE  REN
WEARYWILLIE  OPA
ARGALI  AIM  RILL
BARNUMANDBAILEY
ETA  MPS  SORBETS
EMS  LIZ  CADET
  THEFATMAN
MAGEE  PGA  DOM
ADELINA  ILL  ROE
SARASOTAFLORIDA
SPAR  ROB  ECHOES
ATL  EMMETTKELLY
GOD  MAILS  IMET
ERO  UNCLE  NESS
```

415

```
WEED  AMASS  KAY
ABLER ROBOT  IVE
NEWBORNBABY  LET
TRAINEES   MAORI
STY  ANS  KEITH
   BLESSEDEVENT
SHARD  ONES  RIO
POLO CANON  ITLL
AYE AUDI  FAZED
TAXDEDUCTION
   HORSE ISR ASK
ALAMO  ELEGANCE
GAL BUNDLEOFJOY
EVE  IMAGE  TOONE
DAY  CAGED  RUED
```

416

```
CHIC  GLEAM  ZAPS
ZORA  RANDI  ADUE
AMINOACIDS  GAZA
RESTATED  MORMON
   ISIS  HANES
SPACES  DATABASE
WELLS  GIVEN  PTA
EAVE  SEARS  APER
ALI ATONE  ISLET
RENEGADE  JOSEPH
  ALENE  BENE
GRIPED  MARIMBAS
LOLA  ADDISABABA
USES  ROLLE  LEEK
MAYO  DAISY  ERTE
```

417

```
AMMO  ABET  SCAR
PIANO MONO  TADA
ERROR BRIO  AVIS
  GRILLEDSHRIMP
SMA GEE  MOTLEY
CURRIEDCRAB
ORION  HALOGEN
TATI STAHL  PNOM
 LASSOES  MAGOO
  CLAMSCASINO
ARTAUD  HOS  NET
LOBSTERBISQUE
EGOS  RAIN  USERS
RUNE  EVEN  ENROL
TEES  DENY  ASTO
```

418

```
BOFF  BLAST  LOPE
RULE  RALLY  AVIV
AGER  ONAIR  VANE
THEREWARDOFA
STREWN  END  OPE
  RICOH  EARWAX
SSS NORAS  ANTI
THINGWELLDONEIS
AURA  STARR  DOT
STENOS  SWATH
HEN RAT  GHOSTS
  TOHAVEDONEIT
THAW AMIGO  CORA
KIWI RENEW  HUEY
OMEN ADORN  OLDS
```

419

```
JEST  SATAN  SWAG
OREO  EDICT  KENO
SILO  NORTH  ULNA
HELLFIRE  ALLOT
  AEON  SULKS
COSTAR  CREEPUP
OTHER FLAG  DRNO
STE SPEARED  ITS
MELD  EASY  ERNIE
ORLEANS  SIEGES
 STINT  POST
ACHED  ILLTREAT
NOON  GOBAD  AXLE
TACT  ALICE  CAVE
ELKE  LASER  TMAN
```

420

```
WADE  ECOLE  AFAR
ALEE  GOMER  BOCA
IFCLEOPATRASAID
FAO LIENS  GELDS
   ITS  CON
YESTOMARCANTONY
OAKEN  BOOBY  RIA
GRAM  FOULS  MACH
ATT BLINI  LITHO
SHEWOULDCEASETO
  AWE  VIC
AMATI  AVIAN  FAS
BEQUEENOFDENILE
ECUS  ANISE  AJAX
THAI  TODOS  TINY
```

421

```
SPOT  STASH  BIT
USUAL SOLTI  ATE
BITTERSWEET   YEP
  LEAH INE   SOME
BAA PORTERHOUSE
IRS SNO   SAG
MITT DAHS  SOFAR
BEERBARRELPOLKA
OLDIE SHOO  DART
  PEA  UMS   MOO
STOUTFELLOW  INN
HELP FRI  NOON
ALI DRAFTDODGER
REV EASED  PEONS
EXE MYERS  SSGT
```

422

```
LAST  ASAP  CAPOS
ALAI  SURE  OVATE
WEST  HEMP  PASTA
SCHULTZ  PRESTON
    SIR  BEAST
LSD NAPERY   MAI
OPENEYED  SPIES
FAMOUSSERGEANTS
TROMP  VIETMINH
YES  SCIONS  MAE
   TOTAL  ETC
STRYKER  OROURKE
TIARA  TATA  PAAR
ENVOY  EMIL  ITEM
PEELS  ROSS  DELA
```

423

```
BARB  SABOTS  TAB
OTOE  TREBEK  HUE
ROMA  ILLINI  ERA
EMPTYNETS  BABAR
  SIGNS  LOSE
ATEIN   DIOPTER
THAT  SWAINS  SLY
SOT  THICKET  MAD
ERS SALTED  GATE
ANOMALY   BONER
  FIRE  SCABS
SNEAK  GOLDCOATS
NOD  ISOPOD  UHOH
APE  SPOUSE  TODO
PEN  TAPPED  HYDE
```

424

```
TERPS  VINE  SPOT
ADORE  IBEG  OSLO
NUYORKCITY  FILE
    VIES  PATOIS
PERMITS  STRIFE
EXHALE  WAITER
SCORE  HALAS  ECO
TOYS  SAXON  CLAP
ONO  LOREN  FLIRT
  USURPS  SLEEVE
CRATES  STUFFED
RABIES  PEAS
IRON  PIINTHESKY
FLAT  ODES  EERIE
FATS  TORE  SLITS
```

425

```
WAGE  LOPPED  TLC
EBON  OUIOUI  RIO
FLYSWATTERS  ISR
TEA OTO   AMAZE
  JOHNTRAVOLTA
AMPULE  RUNON
ROOMY  OLDWORLD
CULP ALLEY  LIAR
HEARTFUL  GILDA
  OHARE  DETEST
TAMPEREDWITH
ARIES  ISU  SPA
POX HIDDENPOWER
EMU ORIOLE  WARM
RAP WEIRDY  EMMY
```

426

```
KCJONES  PER  KIL
IRONONS  ALAMEDA
DOGTROT  TOWERED
   AMS  JCPENNEY
SOAP  BEHEST
ECBENTLEY  TONIC
NUB COUP   RONA
ELO OWE  SPA STR
CUTS  SKID  IOU
ASSET VCANDREWS
  RESEAT  ARNO
MCHAMMER  BAT
CROPPER MANIPLE
AIRHOLE ONEFOOT
NBA STD NCWYETH
```

427

```
AGO  MESSES  ABED
CAR  ATTIRE  BALI
CRAZYHORSE  SLOE
ONCE  OLSEN  CANT
RELEASE    INGE
DRESS  SUP  SCAR
   ELAINE  SETS
 MADCOWDISEASE
RAVE  COLSON
EGIS  OLE  CARTS
ANAS   PREHEAT
LUTE  GLARE  ABBA
EMIR  RAGINGBULL
SPOT  OPENER  FEE
TINS  TSETSE  FDR
```

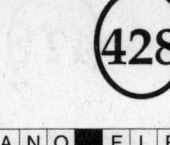

428

```
BEANO  FLEE  COST
LASER  RUBY  OBIE
OCEAN  ALOE  NICE
CHATEAULAFEET
   ORB   TUMS
POL  YEAR  LOTSA
AMOI  ABEL  TOADS
PATTYDEFOIEGRAS
ARTIE  DELL  AINT
 SONNY  RAGS  SOS
  ETAL  WIS
 GRAPESSUZETTE
EZRA  PALO  ZOOEY
WEAR  EVEN  LUNAR
EDDY  DEWY  ELISE
```

429

```
HUAC  TEMPO  RIMS
USSR  ONTAP  EROO
BEHINDBARS  HORN
   TOOL   TANGO
INSET  ONTHEBEAM
NOURI  CURED  DNA
RUNINS  MOA
ENGAGEMENTRINGS
   PER  HADDIE
AKA  TINAS  HEAVE
BANKVAULT  ROKER
ARENA   ARAL
CAME  HOBBYHORSE
UTIL  ADELA  GELT
SECT  HELEN  YOYO
```

430

```
SPACE  BACH  EGGO
POPPY  OBOE  GOAD
APPLE  NEVERGOTO
RTE  WASTE  EIDER
TOA  ANA  ROANS
APLASTICSURGEON
  OHS  HUTS  ADO
RISK  NAP   STEW
ASH  BEEP  RNA
WHOLOVESTHEWORK
  OARED  HEW  NEE
MITZI  ARRAY  ESE
OFPICASSO  OFTEN
ASAN  LAVA  ROWEL
BORG  APPT  KOOKY
```

431

```
BAWL  SALEM  BRIM
ALIA  OLIVA  LAZE
SONYRCAMAGNAVOX
STOLE  ENLACED
  AMES  SICK
TIC  IDLE  ELEVEN
IDA  SNORE  YALE
MARSSATURNVENUS
IHOP  SPREE  EDT
DOLLOP  TERR  DES
  IRAQ  DOSE
 GENERAL  UTICA
LITTLETINYSHORT
OGRE  NAMED  INON
PIER  TROTS  CAPO
```

432

```
DISKS  REACT  PHD
ETHIC  EERIE  LOU
CLOTHESLINE  ASS
ALDENTE  DENTIST
  OONA  EON
 SECONDSTORYJOB
TICK  PAR  AWE
RESISTS  RIPENED
ONE  RUG  OVEN
MONKEYBUSINESS
  HID  MALT
TROPICS  CLIPPER
RAW  BAKERSFIELD
AGE  LAINE  FELLA
PER  ENDED  SRTAS
```

433

```
MATT METZ DICE
AUER ASHE ATOZ
CRAY STRAWVOTE
ROB STEELIE TKO
ARAMIS EON BAIT
MAGES BLT ROGET
ELSA JAI MORELS
THESTICKS
ZAPPED TVS TULE
AMAIN BLY EATIN
NAVE FEE ILLINI
ELL AIRPACK LEG
GOLDBRICK LIAM
AVID AGUE EZRA
MAPS SSTS DEBS
```

434

```
LADS MOPSY NEWS
ECOL IRAQI ECHO
GRUELANDUNUSUAL
SEGUE ASI STATE
TEAM ROSE
ITCH HERMITGRAB
DOA NANA LEGATO
TERRE TDS ESSEX
ARTHUR ITAL TIE
GRAFTUNION HAND
AREA PYRE
AMOCO RES ABHOR
PARTNERSINGRIME
ARCO HOAGY ELAN
TSAR SWINE WONT
```

435

```
SITU BASH ECLAT
ATAN INCA NOONE
TALI GNAT TEVYE
ELISABETHSHUE
SOAPBOX ERRANT
HEY ISLA PER
FADE SHOOFLYPIE
ISERE UNO LALLY
SHOESTRING CELS
TED TALC EDH
SNORRI TROTSKY
REALLYBIGSHEW
ORANG SUIT MARC
PINTO ARLO ANNA
SATAN TILL NESS
```

436

```
BALM PLEA AZOV
OLIO HELDA DEKE
LAMS IDEAL SNAG
DREADLOCKES OPA
IDONT PIPPIN
UNICEF RAHRAH
ROK AMAT ERODE
ATARAXY OMNIBUS
LINED RENA IST
TARTAN ROTATE
OILRUB CLXVI
ZOE MOORETOCOME
ANTE NOURI KHAN
RIGS EPSOM ENID
KAOS STYE DONS
```

437

```
CHASE ADAS AZIZ
HOSEA GIST MORE
ASTER ESTE ENID
STOPTHEPRESSES
MARSHA LOVE
ARTA EPILOG
GIGS SKYE ALOHA
LOOKWHOSTALKING
ALLEY SCAM ANOS
DEFEAT ALBA
THOU ELNINO
LISTENTOREASON
BITE MIII PULSE
AMEX ECOL PREEN
GAMY DENY OUTED
```

438

```
GENIE AWOL FILM
ARENA KIWI ASIA
PORCUPINEQUILLS
SOO INK UVRAYS
MIX SEEP
PREMIUMQUALITY
RIO REPOUR AWEE
ANGIE SLA DYING
STEN THAWER LEG
PATCHWORKQUILT
LOOT UMA
INSULT IOU MEA
MINDYOURPSANDQS
ALOE NAME ROGUE
NEWS ELAN STEAM
```

439

```
E U R E K A C A   A M U S E D
T H E M A T I C   N O N U S E
E U G E N E O R   E R I E P A
S H O E       E M M A   S Y N
      R A N G   D I N K
M I A   E A U C L A I R E W I
A B N O R M A L     S A L E M
Y S E R   E M A I L   F L E A
B E G A N     R O A S T I N G
E N G L E W O O D C O   E Y E
      S W A N   E T U I
M A W   B L O C       C O S A
E N I D O K   E D I S O N N J
G A L O R E   D E M E N T I A
A T T E N D   E L P A S O T X
```

440

```
B E A D S   S L A M   B A L S
A V I E W   R E P O   E M I T
B A R B A R A A N N   R A M A
A N S A T E   S E A S I D E R
      T H E B E A C H B O Y S
  G R E E C E   O R E
M O O   H A U L   U R G E S
C A L I F O R N I A G I R L S
S T E N O   D O N T   U S E
      S A N   G O A T E E
H E L P M E R H O N D A
E N L I S T E E   A R N E S S
A J A R   C A R O L I N E N O
R O M E   O D O R   F E R A L
D Y A D   M Y N A   T R O P E
```

441

```
S P A R   H I T M E   S K E W
C O L A   E R R O R   T A P E
A D O G   F R I N G E A R E A
R I N G S   I S T   T Y L E R
P A G E A N T   H A H
      D R E A M   R E P U T E
T A K E I T T O   C R A N I A
I B I D   T E A C H   C U T S
M O N G O L   T H E L I M I T
E U G E N E   S E R I F
      I D A   S Y R I A N S
A Z T E C   D D T   A C T U P
B O R D E R L I N E   R O D E
L O A D   O A K U M   I N G A
E M M Y   D I E T S   M E E K
```

442

```
C O A T   S P A T   E C L A T
A B B A   K O C H   T I A R A
P I C K E I T H E R E T H E R
E S S E X   T I A   A R A P
      S I C K   S T U D
T H O U T H O U M A K E S T
H A R P   A N N   E L I H U
E R A   K R A M E R S   N O T
A S T O N   E T A   S A N A
  H E R E I S T H Y T H I G H
      D E C I   N E R O
F R E E   E L S   I R O N S
R E W R I T E T H E O T H E O
I D O L S   N O M O   L I E D
T O K Y O   T W O S   Y O D A
```

443

```
S O F T B O I L E D   A M A D
I F Y O U C H O K E   B A L E
P L O W S H A R E S   A N T E
P A D S   E V E   K A T I E
E T O   A R E N A   R E A R S
R E R A N   T I E   C E E
      B A A   E T N A   A G E
A S M U R F W H A T C O L O R
R H O   C A Y S   L O U
F O R   H R E   D R A W N
S W A M I   S L O P E   V I E
  B L O C S   A B A   P E P E
F O I L   U N D E R M I N E D
L A Z E   D O E S I T T U R N
U T E S   S T R E S S T E S T
```

444

```
S E T T L E   T A R T A R E
E N R O U T E   A R E A R U G
A M A L G A M   C R E P I N G
V I L L A G E V O I C E
E T E   R E N I   V E R N O N
R Y E S   D C I I   O X O
      E A R   E N S L A V E D
V I E T N A M V E T E R A N S
O N T H E I C E   E T C
L O T   S I R S   H A U S
S N E E Z E   S E E P   U N E
      V E S T A L V I R G I N
A N T E N N A   L I Q U I D S
L E A N D E R   S C U T T L E
P E N T A D S   T E H E E D
```

445

```
BOW ■ RAVER ■ AFACE
IRA ■ ELOPE ■ BRUIT
GEL ■ MORON ■ AETNA
WITHOU[TEX]CEPTION ■
IDEO ■ ■ HERE ■ GAB
GARGLED ■ ■ ESKIMO
■ WAXERS ■ EROS
GREA[TEX]PECTATIONS
LEGS ■ DAEDAL ■
AFGHAN ■ MADLIBS
DIS ■ DOWD ■ OBIE
■ THEORIEN[TEX]PRESS
STERN ■ DREAR ■ RET
CELLI ■ TRACE ■ ICE
IDLES ■ HYPOS ■ ATT
```

446

```
ANTS ■ APEG ■ SEPIA
GORE ■ MANE ■ ORINS
LEIA ■ ACTORFINCH
EXPLORERDRAKE ■
TILERY ■ YES ■ CBS
STERILE ■ CNOTE
■ LAX ■ SOONER
ARCHITECTWREN
SCOPES ■ DEE ■
UNBOX ■ ONADIME
PEI ■ SAD ■ ORATOR
■ NOVELISTCRANE
JUSTICEJAY ■ ELAN
INOIL ■ COMP ■ RICO
MINCE ■ KNEE ■ SCOW
```

447

```
HUGO ■ JEDI ■ SPAM
ALAN ■ VOTES ■ ARNO
WEVEBEENLETDOWN
KEENAN ■ AVER ■ MAD
■ DYES ■ EYESORE
ATM ■ OEIL ■ OWL ■
SHETURNEDUSOUT
HARE ■ COO ■ PLOT
■ IVEBEENTAKENIN
■ MIR ■ SEGA ■ ALT
AMISTAD ■ DESK ■
RAD ■ ESOS ■ NELLIE
SHEBRUSHEDMEOFF
ORAL ■ REINA ■ PEST
NEST ■ ESPO ■ TWOS
```

448

```
BULB ■ REO ■ BEV ■
UNEASIER ■ IRAQI
SIXPACKBEZIQUE
■ TWOS ■ REQUIRE
AHSIN ■ SIT ■ EXES
FAQS ■ EDEN ■ TROIS
ALUM ■ REX ■ ZOOT
ROE ■ BRIQUET ■ IDO
■ EVES ■ UNS ■ EZRA
FAZED ■ FIAT ■ REAR
UBER ■ SEZ ■ RUSTS
RUBDOWN ■ TEED ■
■ SOIXANTEQUINZE
EXCEL ■ ERUPTION
■ TSE ■ XII ■ ENOS
```

449

```
IFAT ■ JOEFRI ■ BAH
NINE ■ EXILES ■ ITO
SATMATINEES ■ GAL
ENLACED ■ ALOOFLY
ACE ■ TRIB ■ HOOT
MERLE ■ CLOD ■ MOSH
■ ADD ■ URAL ■ TSU
■ SHORTERDAYS ■
ROC ■ NOAM ■ OME
UNUM ■ PROF ■ PARER
BERI ■ NATO ■ ENE
YARDAGE ■ CROSSED
TRI ■ SUNPAINTERS
UTE ■ INVADE ■ EDGE
EHS ■ ANYWED ■ MAYA
```

450

```
ABCS ■ EGGO ■ ADAMS
SNAP ■ LOOM ■ LENIN
HALO ■ ETUI ■ LATTE
■ IFORGOTTOWRITE
■ LEI ■ TED ■
ABS ■ GAB ■ PITIFUL
SANTACLAUS ■ ALPO
CLEAN ■ AWN ■ CRAFT
ALEX ■ THENWHYNOT
PYRITES ■ YOU ■ SRO
■ MER ■ ERA ■
GIVEHIMAJINGLE ■
UNITE ■ USES ■ LOAN
MUSEE ■ ITEM ■ OGRE
SPARS ■ ROPE ■ WEPT
```

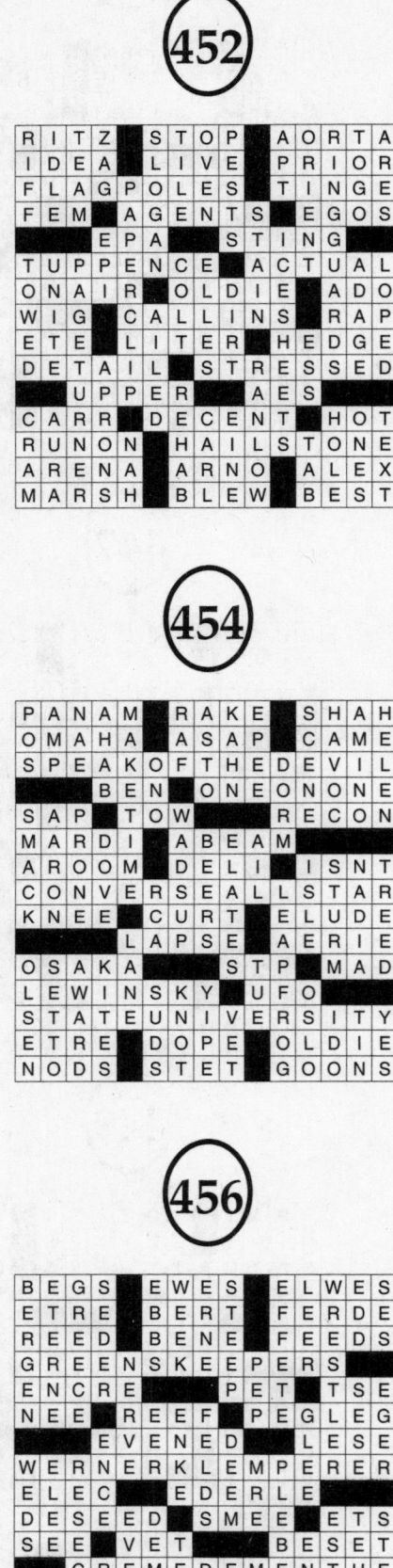

451

```
MAME  DEGAS  OWLS
ALEX  ABASE  OREO
CASTIRONSTOMACH
SWARMING    SAPPHO
    OPUS  ESTH
GRAVES  BAAS  SHA
EATEN  TORI  SPAN
SWORDSWALLOWING
TENT  CITY  FERNS
ERE  BANS  AFLOAT
   WAVE  WRIT
CREOLE  PRESELLS
LUMPINTHETHROAT
ASIA  GOOSE  ERMA
MELT  EASTS  DDAY
```

452

```
RITZ  STOP  AORTA
IDEA  LIVE  PRIOR
FLAGPOLES  TINGE
FEM  AGENTS  EGOS
    EPA  STING
TUPPENCE  ACTUAL
ONAIR  OLDIE  ADO
WIG  CALLINS  RAP
ETE  LITER  HEDGE
DETAIL  STRESSED
  UPPER  AES
CARR  DECENT  HOT
RUNON  HAILSTONE
ARENA  ARNO  ALEX
MARSH  BLEW  BEST
```

453

```
BROKE  ZAPPA  FDA
MARIS  SNERT  AER
WHENTHATEEL  MAI
   GEEZER  MIRE
GASSERS  PSALMS
ONIT  BATSANEYE
PESOS  OHNO
WINKRIGHTBACK
   IOTA  SLOES
DONTBESHY  CODE
GROUSE  IMPASSE
LILT  WASHUP
AVA  THATSAMORAY
DEL  OAKIE  ANODE
ERA  WHETS  SEWON
```

454

```
PANAM  RAKE  SHAH
OMAHA  ASAP  CAME
SPEAKOFTHEDEVIL
   BEN  ONEONONE
SAP  TOW  RECON
MARDI  ABEAM
AROOM  DELI  ISNT
CONVERSEALLSTAR
KNEE  CURT  ELUDE
   LAPSE  AERIE
OSAKA  STP  MAD
LEWINSKY  UFO
STATEUNIVERSITY
ETRE  DOPE  OLDIE
NODS  STET  GOONS
```

455

```
SCAM  RATED  AFRO
NORM  EVOKE  PLEA
OKEEFFEMEABREAK
RIN  LURED  LOADS
TEABAGS   HON
   IKE  THOUSAND
ABAT  SHOOS  LAY
HALSOFMONTEZUMA
ACT  NOOSE  AMEN
SHORTAGE  WAN
   OIL  BRIEFED
SCRAM  BRAID  OVA
QUESEURATSEURAT
FEAT  RIGHT  SADE
TSPS  NOSES  EYED
```

456

```
BEGS  EWES  ELWES
ETRE  BERT  FERDE
REED  BENE  FEEDS
GREENSKEEPERS
ENCRE   PET  TSE
NEE  REEF  PEGLEG
  EVENED  LESE
WERNERKLEMPERER
ELEC  EDERLE
DESEED  SMEE  ETS
SEE  VET  BESET
  CREMEDEMENTHE
DETER  NEVE  THEE
EVENT  SLEW  REEL
CEDES  ELLS  ERSE
```

457

```
SHEAR  TATI   BABA
LENTO  OPUS   APER
AROOM  NATO   SOFT
GOSPELTRUTH   GOI
      RIO   OATERS
GECKOS  RAPSHEET
ALAI  ABILENE
SODOM  OAF  TIGER
     SURINAM  SORE
ROCKSALT  OSMOND
ICESIN   AOK
VEL  COUNTRYROAD
ALES  VEAL  WORRY
LORE  ELIA  ALETA
STYX  RELS  YEMEN
```

458

```
TRAP  DUETS  OHOH
HUGH  APNEA  DATA
USAF  PSILOVEYOU
STRAPPED   ASSET
  CELT  OILS
CASTLE  PTBOATS
ASCOT  RATER  SUP
SCAR  LATEX  PASO
HAL  LIVER  MARIO
 PDJAMES  GASSER
  ONAN  TINY
RAISA   TRANSFER
PGTHIRTEEN  TALE
MUTE  AIMAT  ERSE
SAYS  DEPTS  MEAL
```

459

```
JUMP  TOGA  EMOTE
ASEA  IMAS  RABAT
WEAR  RIFT  ALERT
  IFATFIRSTYOU
SASSED  ERIE
HUP  EEE  CRITIC
ARIEL  CASH  NOGO
DONTSUCCEEDDONT
ERAT  NEUT  ROBOT
SALAMI  SAO  ARE
  ITEM  SWEDEN
TRYSKYDIVING
RIATA  GLAD  YALE
ASKED  ELIE  PRAY
PESTO  DENS  TIME
```

460

```
LEAPT  MASH  TGIF
IGLOO  INTO  IAMA
BALLPLAYER  ASPS
RDA  KIM  STREET
ASH  NEIGH  RANDB
 JON  LARA  GAR
SPRAT  PARTYLINE
PREY  MANSE  INCA
HOPSCOTCH  GREEK
EVE  ANTE  TOE
ROAMS  IDAHO  WAY
ILLUSE  GOD  ATA
COIL  RAVEREVIEW
ANNE  IVAN  GAVIN
LEGS  KENT  GLENS
```

461

```
TRAP  PATON  POOR
RIGA  RHODA  ERMA
ICESQUARES  GRIN
MARAUD  TRAWLING
  DIEM  RENEE
METED  AIRBAG
EARN  ALLOUT  APO
TRIANGLESCHEMES
ASP  ARENAS  REAL
 GRATER  SANTO
STOIC  YVES
LACROSSE  AMUSES
USED  ATMOCIRCLE
ETAL  NAURU  EASE
SYNE  ATSEA  STAR
```

462

```
SHAHS  DRAW  GOSH
COBRA  IAGO  ONTO
AKLEPTOMANIACIS
TEE  PONDS  STERE
 PHONO  ICE
SOMEONEWHOHELPS
AMOR  NOTI  ERA
RAD  SKA  BAA  KEY
ANE  PARC  DESI
HIMSELFASHEJUST
 WEB  LIENS
STOIC  SIGMA  SCI
CANTHELPHIMSELF
ALEC  SUET  OUTOF
MESH  ERRS  READY
```

463

```
WACS  SMART ACTS
OPAL  TORAH PYRE
KEMO  ELENA EBAN
  REMOTECONTROLS
PILOT  ANKA  REO
ATL  ODE   LIGER
XIII  EDGESIN
 FARAWAYPLACES
  OLYMPIA  ANON
PIANO   CYD  GAY
EDS  HESS  TRIPE
 DISTANTCOUSINS
ADUE  LEAPS FEUD
LIMA  ARNIE LEDA
STEM  INTER ERST
```

464

```
DOGS  MAO   ARTIS
ERIE  HERA  CEASE
NELL  EACH  RHONE
GOLFENTHUSIASTS
   MGRS   ADS
ROSARY  FAN  HECK
EVADE  CELTS  DRE
HAVETHATFAIRWAY
ATE  SEPIA  SEIZE
BEDE  RED  ATONED
   SHO   PREP
LOOKINTHEIREYES
ALVIN  WARS  NORA
BEAME  AIRE  ERIN
SOLOS  SLY   DECK
```

465

```
LIARS  RAPS  ROSA
ANGEL  ISEE  OWES
SCAPE  CART  UNIT
THROUGHPUT  GENE
   TOE   LEHRER
PONCHO  CLEAR
ONEO  NEHI  SIENA
SCRUB  AIM  EDGED
HEDGE  SLAB  EGAD
   HAITI  ERRORS
VERDUN   ATE
EMIR  DOUGHFACES
NOGO  OGRE  ORATE
UTEP  OLIN  RENTA
EELS  REST  MATER
```

466

```
GARB  AWES  YALTA
AGAR  DOLT  EMAIL
FORYEARSI  SIDLE
FREAK  MARGARET
EARNER   SEN
   DABS  ODDMAN
SPAS  NEMO  NOONE
WANTEDTOBEOLDER
ABOUT  SCOT  LEWD
BANNED  KENO
   RES   ATWOOD
SHANGHAI  TORRE
HAITI  ANDNOWIAM
ALLOT  ROLE  INNO
PEONY  ISEE  EGGS
```

467

```
MOLAR  FEUD  SAAR
ADOBE  AMMO  UNDO
ROUNDTRIPTICKET
ERTE  OER  ETCHES
   RAT   ALSO
ABE  CIRCULARSAW
LUX  REELS  ELLA
TRACE  COT  BRAIN
ARCH  ATRIA  IVE
ROTARYPHONE  NED
   RIAS   TRW
BOTTOM  ORE  AFAR
ORBITALVELOCITY
SCAN  HEED  AKRON
SARG  ANNO  SOMME
```

468

```
ELLS  ADAIR  OMAR
LUAU  MERCI  HALO
GRILLONESFAMILY
AIRFARE  LLAMAS
REDUB  BADEGG
   REB  PAS  EPIC
REFILL  PICA  OBE
SPACEONADOGSLED
TOR  ROAR  PETITE
USMC  DNA  ELI
   ANSATE  ELOPE
STEPUP  ARSENAL
AUTOBODYRUSTING
KNOT  ROONE  TODI
SANE  TRUSS  ONAN
```

469

```
TAKEI   RAGU  SHAM
AMISS   IRAN  HEXA
MOSTOFFALL    ALLY
ESS   BALL   OODLES
      RAVE  FORE
SAHARA  HISTORIC
CLAYS   SOLE  FORA
ALTO   CARED  FRAN
REEF   OUST  CRETE
PERFORCE   THEMED
      LURE  VOID
WAPITI  LITE   LEE
OLEG   DAYSOFFOLD
RASH   OMNI  LEASE
KNOT   RANT  YEMEN
```

470

```
CATO   ELISE   BOAT
AMIS   ALLYE   ENDO
TINKERBELL   LIZA
ONCALL   VISITED
NOTRE   APIECE
      MEDGAREVERS
SOY   TEA   NEATH
APE  JAN  PUT  SEA
KELSO   NEZ    ESQ
ILLCHANCEIT
      INDOOR  OPCIT
LOSESIT   APIANO
AVON   DOUBLEPLAY
ZINC   ANSEL  PYNE
EDGE   SEEDY  AXED
```

471

```
AJAR   TIARA   ACDC
LONE   UNTIL   UHOH
FETA   CLONE   RACE
LEWISANDCLARK
   ARON     ELI
DICKANDJANE    OSS
ALOES   USER    TWO
NOUN   DANKE   DEER
CNN   AUNT   DREAR
EAT   BENANDJERRY
      EYE     ARID
FREDANDGINGER
SLAM   RERAN   IRON
PACE   CRANK   NILE
ATTN   HOBOS   GELT
```

472

```
AGAPE   SNAP   NEST
SIDED   POLE   ASEA
KRONA   ATAN   STAG
ADRAMACRITICIS
NEE   SEEN   MAMIE
TREBEK   PRADO
      SEESTO   TEN
AMANWHOLEAVES
FLO   HEARSE
ELVES   NEXTTO
WIEST   ALOE   OER
NOTURNUNSTONED
SANE   ONCE   RHINE
ALTE   WEIR   INTER
GLOM   EXES   GOERS
```

473

```
HARES   TADA   SLAB
AGENT   EDEN   HELL
SINCEIDONTHAVEU
ALA   ADDS   ONICE
TELLMEY   LOOK
      ASS   BUMPSOFF
ALAN   AURAL   REL
SINGINGSCRABBLE
AMA   NORTH   ESTA
POTATOES   ODE
      LUKE   TFORTWO
EPSON   BRIT   AYS
BYTHEBEAUTIFULC
AREA   ELKS   MANIA
NETS   DIET   ENTER
```

474

```
OTIS   DFLAT   GASP
DENT   IRAQI   ITTO
ELSA   PINUP   ZEAL
LORDPLEASEMAKE
HAL   OYL   LOSER
ALEUT   PHIL   EDS
RING   STOOGES
METHEPERSONTHAT
      SWELTER   YOUR
SEM   IDES   BETTE
YEARN   EAU   WOE
MYDOGTHINKSIAM
BOMB   HINDI   STAT
OREO   INFUN   NETS
LENT   STOPS   TREK
```

475

```
LARD  PROMO  AMMO
ETUI  OATER  RAID
GONG  EDAMSAPPLE
OPTIC  RBIS  LET
   THEMUENSTERS
PEPSICO  ROTH
ICE  CROW   UFOS
THEGOUDABYEGIRL
YOKE   NEON  SEA
   EWEN  EYESHOT
JIMROQUEFORT
ANE  OUTS  ORLOP
CHEDDARBOX  OAHU
KITE  LIANE  BROZ
OSSA  SATED  ESSO
```

476

```
CROC  AFAR   SCAB
HILO  LOLA  SHALL
ELAINEMAY  TRITE
REFLEXES  ARENAS
   WIN  EVADERS
APRILSTEVENS
PRIVY  NERD  FED
EATS  RETRY  TAXI
XYZ  GENE   ARIES
   FREDRICMARCH
SHRIEKS  ROI
WEAVES  DOGSLEDS
INKED  JUNEHAVOC
PIETY  AKIN  REDO
EERO   RECT  KNOW
```

477

```
BOAR  ABBAS  JOSH
ABLE  FRANC  ALIT
HITBELOWTHEBELT
STOOD  SLIER  GOP
   RIB   MIR
DOWNFORTHECOUNT
ERA  YOURE  ABNER
IAGO  SNEAK  ESAI
SCENT  OATES  ELL
THROWINTHETOWEL
   RON   PEN
SSS  ODETO  ALIAS
HOPEFORAREMATCH
ALAS  OTTER  NOTO
WERE  REELS  DOIT
```

478

```
BERG  STAMP  BIRD
ABEL  HOMER  YOYO
NATEBITATIBETAN
ENDEARED  CABANA
   CHEM  VERY
CALLAS  POW  EBBS
ODIUM  ILIAC  ARA
BOMBARDADRABMOB
ORB  SUITS  TABOR
LESS  TOE  LADIDA
   HELM  BALD
OBLATE  TENPENCE
TOOBADIHIDABOOT
TOMB  GAUGE  TROT
OBEY  ENDED  SAKE
```

479

```
COAT  EPIC  RATON
ABLE  NADA  EVADE
WISEACRES  VEXES
STOOL  APIE  IST
   FOLD  EDNA
 COFFEEGROUNDS
JEU  TMEN  LEERED
ACTS  OMAHA  WEAR
GIDEON  TOTS  AMY
 LOWFATSPREADS
   SADE  EYED
BRO  SEAT  DUBAI
RAMBO  SORRYLOTS
ICIER  ERIE  TARA
GETAT  DODO  STAY
```

480

```
SNAG  ABODE  PAUL
TOFU  NODAL  EDNA
EARN  KNOCKKNOCK
WHOSTHERE  APPLE
   MAS  NEATER
FLUID  SCROLL
EAST  SALAMI  JAB
THEHANDYMANYOUR
ERR  VOIDED  ANNA
   TUREEN  EMITS
SIMILE   IBM
KNITS  DOORBELLS
ONTHEBLINK  RAIL
AIRE  VINCE  ECRU
LEES  DIKED  DEAR
```

481

```
WASP  SCAMP  ALTO
ARTE  YODEL  PEER
SCORESBELOWPAAR
HAP  MORN  WELD
UNI  EPA  DEUCE
PETER  OTB  SPRY
  LAUNCHES  TAE
PULLSACAANJOB
ELM  DEBUNKED
BABA  SSR  ESTOP
BYRDS  ADZ  RUR
  EDIT  SMEE  ITA
TELLSASAABSTORY
OGLE  GINZA  ADUE
GOAD  STEER  MEND
```

482

```
ETAL  INDIA  KEDS
SIVA  SAUCE  EXIT
SLOWLERNER  WHEE
EDIFIER  COT  IMP
SERUM  ORA  HUB
  LOEWEPROFILE
HOD  SLEW  EROTIC
ALEC  DRAGS  SOSO
DEFAME  ROTC  RAN
JOLLYRODGERS
  AFT  USE  OPERA
WET  HUT  TRAILER
AXIS  HARTATTACK
SPOT  OGDEN  ETUI
PONY  HEART  DERN
```

483

```
AGAS  AID  [BUCK]SAW
INRE  UGLY  APACE
RAIN  NILE  URGED
SWASH[BUCK]LER  DIAS
  OILER  LIV
STARVE  [BUCK]BOARDS
ORR  ESTERS  TOAT
WAR[BUCK]S  BEA  AETNA
EDAM  TARMAC  HER
DESIRER  CROSS[BUCK]
  NAT  FACET
  MISC  [BUCK]EYESTATE
EMOTE  EARS  AHAB
FETES  TRES  WACO
TSAR  SSS  ASON
```

484

```
MITZI  HASTA  SSS
ARSON  OPART  APE
SEEYENWAVER  YEA
  SVELTE  ANWAR
SOVIETS  SNEERS
CLEARS  READER
HORS  ZORRO  EST
WRY  ANAGRAM  EAU
ADS  LINES  BVDS
  ARMLET  STREAK
SUNDAE  PARENTS
CLEAN  HARLOW
ACE  ANYWEEVERSE
MEW  CAPES  ERODE
PRE  SHEDS  SYBIL
```

485

```
SSTS  DORIC  UN[BLOCK]
UNIT  EBOLI  ASEA
NINE  CONAN  SARG
[BLOCK]PARTIES  DATIVE
  NOBS  RETIRES
EXHUME  ARON
STUMBLING[BLOCK]  ACE
TRESS  CUE  KARAT
HAD  [BLOCK]ANDTACKLE
  PALM  SPASMS
REFUGEE  THUD
OMELET  WRITERS[BLOCK]
ACME  TRIER  MILA
DEUS  EATAT  ICED
[BLOCK]ER  RESTS  CODE
```

486

```
WEPT  STASI  JETS
OVER  TIMER  OCHO
RITA  ALAMO  CLAN
MARIPYTHONJUANA
SNIPE  ELL  ALTER
  SPED  IRMA
BICEPS  SNEERERS
BSA  ENWRAPS  LIE
SOMBRERO  ATAMAN
  ROSA  LYON
ASWAN  TSE  WAIST
SPILIGHTNINGDER
PINE  AFOOT  RAGE
ERGS  MUNRO  AHOY
NESS  SLYER  MOSS
```

487

```
AGER  MEDAL  PETS
SOLO  ANITA  ATOE
PASSOUTFAILSAFE
STEEPLE  DUSTUP
    BEER  KANE
  RUNDOWNWALKUP
WOODS  HOAR  APE
AMOS  MEATY  CROC
RNS  AUNT  CRANK
SITINSTANDOUT
    STIR  IRAS
EROTIC  GOCARTS
COOLCATSHOTDOGS
HAZE  LAPEL  EMIT
ODES  SPARS  REFS
```

488

```
SWAMP  AHMED  MAY
PIXIE  VIOLA  A&E
OPENACANOFWORMS
TEST  HIT  EPI
    WIL  JUSTONE
CAVORT  MAT  ENOS
ANISE  ACME  DENS
NOTONESCUPOFTEA
ORAL  ATOP  POTTY
NAME  SOY  CARESS
SKIMMER  MAL
  NIA  FOP  ARLO
99BOTTLESOFBEER
101  ZAIRE  ELSIE
102  OWENS  ZETAS
```

489

```
BAD  SAD  SPRAY
OPES  MOLE  ALONE
ROVE  AFOG  VANNA
SLICEDTURKEY
CLASSES  EIDETIC
HOT  TIERED  DODO
TSE  ELLA  GUTSY
  BELLYFLOP
BEDIM  OBIS  ASS
AGOG  BANISH  ETA
ROASTER  ATECROW
  HYDROGENBOMB
AESOP  OVEN  ESAU
RANTO  YENS  ROTC
CROSS  ORT  LAK
```

490

```
RAPT  CORGI  ZOLA
EIRE  ATURN  ENOS
DROPALOTOFBUCKS
DEMILLES  LOSEIT
  DODOS  JON
  PUTDOWNCASH
BLOW  POURS  OREO
RABI  TED  DOLE
EVEN  SETAT  AWAD
LAYOUTMONEY
  PES  NAMED
ADESTE  ABALONES
FORKOVERABUNDLE
ANTI  EXCEL  DOVE
REED  SPORE  EWES
```

491

```
STARR  POOL  ALMA
NOVAE  ERTE  GOES
CROSSCROSS  EDNA
COWPEAS  BONEUP
  TRIEDOUT
ASE  TAKESTAKES
CLEARINGS  AGILE
HUNGON  AGENDA
ALALA  DISSENTER
DATESDATES  TER
  ETAGERES
THEASP  ATALOSS
HONG  PUMPSPUMPS
EMIL  LACE  PLAIT
MODE  ERAS  YURTS
```

492

```
MEDAL  SPIC  HAD
ALIBI  HESA  LAME
BLAC[KK]NIGHT  UNAS
EIN  EONS  SOLUTE
LONGRUN  CHU[KK]ER
STER  NYALAS  AUT
  ASS  MENU  HRS
STUN  ATE  ROSS
CPR  INTO  DEA
ORI  DEMOTE  TAPS
RECHEW  RUSHDIE
BA[KK]ERS  SECT  DEN
EDNA  BOO[KK]EEPERS
TEED  OKIE  PONCE
TRE  YSER  SIDES
```

493

```
C A R V E   L A I C   S H A M
A L I E N   O R E O   T A D A
S T A N D S F I R M   I N E Z
H A L O   A T E   E U R O P E
      M O D E L O U T F I T S
S T A   B E D   S P A R
H A R P O   E L O   I D E A
E X P R E S S C O N C E R N S
L I S I   M O O   A D A N O
    N E A L   S P A   Y E N
P A R T S C O M P A N Y
U N H O O K   A R T   A L I T
L I E U   D O B U S I N E S S
E T A T   A L E C   S C A L A
S A S S   B A L E   H Y P E R
```

494

```
  K L A T C H   N A B O B S
B E E F A L O   U P A T R E E
R E S T F U L   M I N C I N G
O P S   F E E D B A G   G A R
T O T S Y   I N E   S P A T E
H U A C   S N A R E   A D O S
S T R I K E 1   1 L I N E R S
      E N E       I R A
T W E N T Y 1   1 O R M O R E
W A A C   A H O O T   A C E S
A S T E P   I N C   E S T E S
N T H   L E T S L I P   U N A
G R E Y E S T   O N E M P T Y
S E R I A T E   C R E O L E S
  L E N D E R   K I S S E R
```

495

```
C H E D D A R   A T T I R E D
G E N O E S E   F U R N A C E
S W A G M A N   E C U A D O R
    O M B   R A K E   A L E
P R E F E C T U R E   T R E K
L A D     A N D R E I
O B I S   B R A   B A M B I S
W A L T Z I N G M A T I L D A
S T E R O L   A U G   D E L L
    A G L E T S     N E V
S W A Y   A L E S S A N D R O
T A X   R B I S   A D O
A L I Q U O T   J U M B U C K
G E N U I N E   A D E L P H I
E D G I N G S   W I N E S A P
```

496

```
O C T   A M P S   P A N T S
A L E   D I E T S   A L A M O
K A N   E X T R A   C O Z E N
L I A B L E   A N Y T H I N G
E M C E E D   I T I S A
Y S E R   B E G A N   P E Z
    L E A S H   N I E C E
A N N I E G E T Y O U R G U N
D O I N G   S E E T V
D R X   E T H A N   I M A M
    S E R I O   O R N A T E
Y O U C A N D O   L O G G E R
M O T E S   A T O O T   N A M
C H A N T   L E D G E   U S A
A S H E S   R E Y S   M E N
```

497

```
J E A N S   H A H A   G E M S
A R I E L   I C O N   O V E N
B E R R A   L E O N   L I R A
  R O Y A L S D O A F L I P
S K I   T I E     C E L T S
O A F P O L L S D A I R Y
A L L E N   A U L D
K E E N   W A Y N E   T U T U
    O H M S     O W N E R
  A D R Y P O O L F A I L S
C A P R A   H E F   F L A
A P R I L F O O L S D A Y
S L O E   A L P O   A R I A S
T E N S   C L E O   Y E N T A
E A S T   T A N K   S A G A N
```

498

```
L O G E   I P A S S   T W O S
O B I T   N O R T E   O A T H
E E R O   M O B I L   M U S E
S Y D N E Y P O L L A C K
S E L I G   E R E   G A E L S
  R E A R E D   T O O T S I E
    N E V   C T R   H O T
  D U S T I N H O F F M A N
B E N   T I E   E E O
R A I N M A N   T O R M E S
A R M E E   N A H   M E N L O
  B A R R Y L E V I N S O N
S L U R   B I O T A   T I G E
L O E B   I S N O T   U L A N
R U D Y   S H E P S   M E N D
```

499

```
D I S C S ■ D R O S S ■ I M P
O N E U P ■ D E P O T ■ N O R
S C A R L E T F A C E ■ D O E
T A T T E D ■ S L I P P E R Y
■ ■ I N I T ■ A P E X E S
R O U N D T R I P L E T ■
A R P ■ I S A L L ■ R E P O
S C O L D ■ V E E ■ N I X E D
P A N E ■ E N A T E ■ I T O
■ T A B L E T H U N T E R
S T O G I E ■ S I T E ■
T O M O R R O W ■ G R I E G S
U T A ■ B A K E D H A M L E T
D U H ■ A T R I A ■ L A I N E
S P A ■ G E A R S ■ S N E E R
```

500

```
A B E T ■ M S S ■ O S S O
M U L E ■ S T O K E ■ A H A B
B L U E H A W A I I ■ R I I S
L O T ■ A G O N I Z E ■ I L E
E V E N B E T ■ N E G A T E S
R A D I I ■ O R G ■ G R A D S
■ A T O N E ■ R O C K I E
T A P ■ R E I N A ■ E N D
E N A M O R ■ C U G A T ■
A T R A P ■ S E N ■ G E N I I
M I S W I S H ■ H E R D I N G
M L I ■ E P I S O D E ■ G L O
A L I I ■ I I T O G E T H E R
T E S T ■ E T U D E ■ I T T O
E S M E ■ L E D ■ C Y S T
```